Pitt Press Mathematical Series

THE ELEMENTS

OF

STATICS AND DYNAMICS.

PART I. ELEMENTS OF STATICS.
PART II. ELEMENTS OF DYNAMICS.

CAMBRIDGE UNIVERSITY PRESS
C. F. CLAY, Manager
LONDON: Fetter Lane, E.C. 4

NEW YORK: G. P. PUTNAM'S SONS
BOMBAY, CALCUTTA, MADRAS: MACMILLAN AND CO., Ltd.
TORONTO: J. M. DENT AND SONS, Ltd.
TOKYO: THE MARUZEN-KABUSHIKI-KAISHA

THE ELEMENTS

OF

STATICS AND DYNAMICS

BY

S. L. LONEY, M.A.

PROFESSOR OF MATHEMATICS AT THE ROYAL HOLLOWAY COLLEGE
(UNIVERSITY OF LONDON),
SOMETIME FELLOW OF SIDNEY SUSSEX COLLEGE, CAMBRIDGE.

CAMBRIDGE
AT THE UNIVERSITY PRESS
1919

Pitt Press Mathematical Series

THE ELEMENTS

OF

STATICS AND DYNAMICS.

PART I. ELEMENTS OF STATICS.

CAMBRIDGE UNIVERSITY PRESS

C. F. CLAY, Manager

LONDON: Fetter Lane, E.C. 4

NEW YORK: G. P. PUTNAM'S SONS

BOMBAY, CALCUTTA, MADRAS: MACMILLAN AND CO., Ltd.

TORONTO: J. M. DENT AND SONS, Ltd.

TOKYO: THE MARUZEN-KABUSHIKI-KAISHA

THE ELEMENTS

OF

STATICS AND DYNAMICS

BY

S. L. LONEY, M.A.

PROFESSOR OF MATHEMATICS AT THE ROYAL HOLLOWAY COLLEGE
(UNIVERSITY OF LONDON),
SOMETIME FELLOW OF SIDNEY SUSSEX COLLEGE, CAMBRIDGE.

PART I. STATICS.

FIFTEENTH EDITION.

CAMBRIDGE:
AT THE UNIVERSITY PRESS
1920

First Edition, Dec. 1890.
Second Edition, Sept. 1892.
Third Edition, June, 1893.
Fourth Edition, enlarged, Jan. 1895.
Reprinted 1897, 1899, 1900, 1902, 1904.
New Edition (revised and enlarged), July, 1906.
Reprinted 1907, 1908, 1911, 1914, 1918, 1920.

PREFACE TO PART I.

IN the following work I have aimed at writing a working text-book on Statics for the use of Junior Students.

Throughout the book will be found a large number of examples; most of them, with the exception of many of those at the end of the Chapter on Friction and the Miscellaneous Examples at the end of the volume, are of an easy type.

I have tried to make the book complete as far as it goes; it is suggested, however, that the student should, on the first reading of the subject, omit everything marked with an asterisk.

I must express my obligations to my friend Mr H. C. Robson, M.A., Fellow and Lecturer of Sidney Sussex College, Cambridge, for his kindness in reading through the proof-sheets, and for many suggestions that he has made to me.

Any corrections of errors, or hints for improvement will be thankfully received.

S. L. LONEY.

BARNES, S.W.
December, 1890.

PREFACE TO THE TENTH EDITION.

THE book has been somewhat altered, and I hope improved, for this edition, and the type entirely re-set. Graphic solutions have been introduced much earlier, and more use has been made of graphic methods throughout the book. More experimental work has also been introduced.

The chapter on Work has been placed earlier, and much greater stress has been laid upon the Principle of Work.

Sundry somewhat long analytical proofs have been relegated to the last chapter, and here I have not scrupled to introduce alternative proofs involving the use of the Differential Calculus.

For ten of the new figures in this book I am much indebted to the kindness and courtesy of Dr R. T. Glazebrook, who allowed me to use the blocks prepared for his Statics. Most of these figures have the additional merit of having been drawn from actual apparatus in use at the Cavendish Laboratory at Cambridge.

S. L. LONEY.

ROYAL HOLLOWAY COLLEGE
    ENGLEFIELD GREEN, SURREY.
        July 23rd, 1906.

CONTENTS.

STATICS.

STATICS.

CHAPTER I.

INTRODUCTION.

1. A **Body** is a portion of matter limited in every direction.

2. **Force** is anything which changes, or tends to change, the state of rest, or uniform motion, of a body.

3. **Rest.** A body is said to be at rest when it does not change its position with respect to surrounding objects.

4. **Statics** is the science which treats of the action of forces on bodies, the forces being so arranged that the bodies are at rest.

The science which treats of the action of force on bodies in motion is called **Dynamics.**

In the more modern system of nomenclature which is gradually gaining general acceptance, the science which treats of the action of force on bodies is called Dynamics, and it has two subdivisions, Statics and Kinetics, treating of the action of forces on bodies which are at rest and in motion respectively.

5. A **Particle** is a portion of matter which is indefinitely small in size, or which, for the purpose of our investigations, is so small that the distances between its different parts may be neglected.

A body may be regarded as an indefinitely large number of indefinitely small portions, or as a conglomeration of particles.

6. A **Rigid Body** is a body whose parts always preserve an invariable position with respect to one another.

This conception, like that of a particle, is idealistic. In nature no body is perfectly rigid. Every body yields, perhaps only very slightly, if force be applied to it. If a rod, made of wood, have one end firmly fixed and the other end be pulled, the wood stretches slightly; if the rod be made of iron the deformation is very much less.

To simplify our enquiry we shall assume that all the bodies with which we have to deal are perfectly rigid.

7. Equal Forces. Two forces are said to be equal when, if they act on a particle in opposite directions, the particle remains at rest.

8. Mass. The mass of a body is the quantity of matter in the body. The unit of mass used in England is a pound and is defined to be the mass of a certain piece of platinum kept in the Exchequer Office.

Hence the mass of a body is two, three, four... lbs., when it contains two, three, four... times as much matter as the standard lump of platinum.

In France, and other foreign countries, the theoretical unit of mass used is a gramme, which is equal to about 15·432 grains. The practical unit is a kilogramme (1000 grammes), which is equal to about 2·2046 lbs.

9. Weight. The idea of weight is one with which everyone is familiar. We all know that a certain amount of exertion is required to prevent any body from falling to the ground. The earth attracts every body to itself with a force which, as we shall see in Dynamics, is proportional to the mass of the body.

The force with which the earth attracts any body to itself is called the weight of the body.

10. *Measurement of Force.* We shall choose, as our unit of force in Statics, the weight of one pound. The unit of force is therefore equal to the force which would just support a mass of one pound when hanging freely.

We shall find in Dynamics that the weight of one pound is not quite the same at different points of the earth's surface.

In Statics, however, we shall not have to compare forces at different points of the earth's surface, so that this variation in the weight of a pound is of no practical importance; we shall therefore neglect this variation and assume the weight of a pound to be constant.

11. In practice the expression " weight of one pound " is, in Statics, often shortened into " one pound." The student will therefore understand that " a force of 10 lbs." means " a force equal to the weight of 10 lbs."

12. *Forces represented by straight lines.* A force will be completely known when we know (i) its magnitude, (ii) its direction, and (iii) its point of application, *i.e.* the point of the body at which the force acts.

Hence we can conveniently represent a force by a straight line drawn through its point of application; for a straight line has both magnitude and direction.

Thus suppose a straight line *OA* represents a force, equal to 10 lbs. weight, acting at a point *O*. A force of 5 lbs. weight acting in the same direction would be represented by *OB*, where *B* bisects the distance *OA*, whilst a force, equal to 20 lbs. weight, would be represented by OC, where OA is produced till AC equals OA.

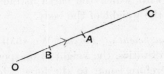

An arrowhead is often used to denote the direction in which a force acts.

13. *Subdivisions of Force.* There are three different forms under which a force may appear when applied to a mass, *viz.* as (i) an attraction, (ii) a tension, and (iii) a reaction.

14. *Attraction.* An attraction is a force exerted by one body on another without the intervention of any visible instrument and without the bodies being necessarily in contact. The only example we shall have in this book is the attraction which the earth has for every body; this attraction is (Art. 9) called its weight.

15. *Tension.* If we tie one end of a string to any point of a body and pull at the other end of the string, we exert a force on the body; such a force, exerted by means of a string or rod, is called a **tension.**

If the string be light [*i.e.* one whose weight is so small that it may be neglected] the force exerted by the string is the same throughout its length.

For example, if a weight W be supported by means of a light string passing over the smooth edge of a table it is found that the same force must be applied to the

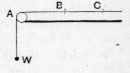

string whatever be the point, *A*, *B*, or *C* of the string at which the force is applied.

Now the force at *A* required to support the weight is the same in each case; hence it is clear that the effect at *A* is the same whatever be the point of the string to which the tension is applied and that the tension of the string is therefore the same throughout its length.

Again, if the weight *W* be supported by a light string passing round a smooth peg *A*, it is found that the same force must be exerted at the other end of the string whatever be the direction (*AB*, *AC*, or *AD*) in which the string is pulled and that this force is equal to the weight *W*.

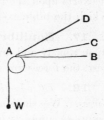

[These forces may be measured by attaching the free end of the string to a spring-balance.]

Hence *the tension of a light string passing round a smooth peg is the same throughout its length.*

If two or more strings be knotted together the tensions are not necessarily the same in each string.

The student must carefully notice that the tension of a string is not proportional to its length. It is a common error to suppose that the longer a string the greater is its tension; it is true that we can often apply our force more advantageously if we use a longer piece of string, and hence a beginner often assumes that, other things being equal, the longer string has the greater tension.

16. *Reaction.* If one body lean, or be pressed, against another body, each body experiences a force at the point of contact; such a force is called a reaction.

The force, or action, that one body exerts on a second body is equal and opposite to the force, or reaction, that the second body exerts on the first.

This statement will be found to be included in Newton's Third Law of Motion [Part II., Art. 73].

Examples. If a ladder lean against a wall the force exerted by the end of the ladder upon the wall is equal and opposite to that exerted by the wall upon the end of the ladder.

If a cube of wood is placed upon a table the force which it exerts upon the table is equal and opposite to the force which the table exerts on it.

17. Equilibrium. When two or more forces act upon a body and are so arranged that the body remains at rest, the forces are said to be in equilibrium.

18. *Introduction, or removal, of equal and opposite forces.* We shall assume that if at any point of a rigid body we apply two equal and opposite forces, they will have no effect on the equilibrium of the body; similarly, that if at any point of a body two equal and opposite forces are acting they may be removed.

19. *Principle of the Transmissibility of Force. If a force act at any point of a rigid body, it may be considered to act at any other point in its line of action provided that this latter point be rigidly connected with the body.*

Let a force F act at a point A of a body in a direction AX. Take any point B in AX and at B introduce two

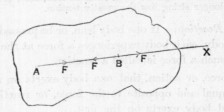

equal and opposite forces, each equal to F, acting in the directions BA and BX; these will have no effect on the equilibrium of the body.

The forces F acting at A in the direction AB, and F at B in the direction BA are equal and opposite; we shall assume that they neutralise one another and hence that they may be removed.

We have thus left the force F at B acting in the direction BX and its effect is the same as that of the original force F at A.

The internal forces in the above body would be different according as the force F is supposed applied at A or B; of the internal forces, however, we do not treat in the present book.

20. *Smooth bodies.* If we place a piece of smooth polished wood, having a plane face, upon a table whose top is made as smooth as possible we shall find that, if we attempt to move the block along the surface of the table, some resistance is experienced. There is always some force, however small, between the wood and the surface of the table.

If the bodies were perfectly smooth there would be no force, parallel to the surface of the table, between the block and the table; the only force between them would be perpendicular to the table.

Def. When two bodies, which are in contact, are perfectly smooth the force, or reaction, between them is perpendicular to their common surface at the point of contact.

CHAPTER II.

COMPOSITION AND RESOLUTION OF FORCES.

21. Suppose a flat piece of wood is resting on a smooth table and that it is pulled by means of three strings attached to three of its corners, the forces exerted by the strings being horizontal; if the tensions of the strings be so adjusted that the wood remains at rest it follows that the three forces are in equilibrium.

Hence two of the forces must together exert a force equal and opposite to the third. This force, equal and opposite to the third, is called the resultant of the first two.

22. Resultant. Def. *If two or more forces P, Q, S... act upon a rigid body and if a single force, R, can be found whose effect upon the body is the same as that of the forces P, Q, S... this single force R is called the resultant of the other forces and the forces P, Q, S... are called the components of R.*

It follows from the definition that if a force be applied to the body equal and opposite to the force R, then the forces acting on the body will balance and the body be in equilibrium; conversely, if the forces acting on a body balance then either of them is equal and opposite to the resultant of the others.

23. *Resultant of forces acting in the same straight line.*

If two forces act on a body in the same direction their resultant is clearly equal to their sum; thus two forces acting in the same direction, equal to 5 and 7 lbs. weight respectively, are equivalent to a force of 12 lbs. weight acting in the same direction as the two forces.

If two forces act on a body in opposite directions their resultant is equal to their difference and acts in the direction of the greater; thus two forces acting in opposite directions and equal to 9 and 4 lbs. weight respectively are equivalent to a force of 5 lbs. weight acting in the direction of the first of the two forces.

24. When two forces act at a point of a rigid body in different directions their resultant may be obtained by means of the following

Theorem. Parallelogram of Forces. *If two forces, acting at a point, be represented in magnitude and direction by the two sides of a parallelogram drawn from one of its angular points, their resultant is represented both in magnitude and direction by the diagonal of the parallelogram passing through that angular point.*

This fundamental theorem of Statics, or rather another form of it, *viz.* the Triangle of Forces (Art. 36), was first enunciated by Stevinus of Bruges in the year 1586. Before his time the science of Statics rested on the Principle of the Lever as its basis.

In the following article we shall give an experimental proof; a more formal proof will be found in the last chapter.

In Art. 72 of Part II. of this book will be found a proof founded on Newton's Laws of Motion.

25. Experimental proof. Let F and G be two light pulleys attached to a fixed support; over them let there pass two light strings tied together at O, and carrying scale-pans L and M at their other ends.

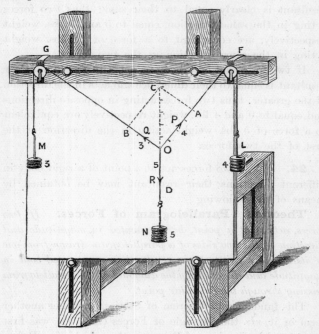

A second string is knotted at O and carries a third scale-pan N.

Into these scale-pans are placed known weights, and the whole system is allowed to take up a position of equilibrium. Let the weights in the scale-pans, together with the weights of the scale-pans themselves, be P, Q and R lbs. respectively.

On a blackboard, or a piece of paper, conveniently placed behind the system draw the lines OF, OG, ON as in the figure.

Taking some convenient scale (say three inches, or less, per one lb.) mark off OA, OB, and OD to represent P, Q, and R lbs. Complete the parallelogram $OACB$. Then OC will be found to be equal in length, and opposite in direction, to OD.

But, since P, Q, and R balance, therefore R must be equal and opposite to the resultant of P and Q.

Therefore the resultant of P and Q is represented by OC, *i.e.* by the diagonal of the parallelogram whose sides represent P and Q.

This will be found to be true whatever be the relative magnitudes of P, Q, and R, provided only that one of them is not greater than the sum of the other two.

In the figure P, Q, and R are taken respectively to be 4, 3, and 5 lbs. In this case, since $5^2 = 4^2 + 3^2$, the angle AOB is a right angle.

When the experiment is performed, it will probably be found that the point O may be moved into one of several positions close to one another. The reason for this is that we cannot wholly get rid of the friction on the pivots of the pulleys. The effect of this friction will be minimised, in this and similar statical experiments, if the pulleys are of fairly large diameter; aluminium pulleys are suitable because they can be made of comparatively large size and yet be of small weight.

Apparatus of the solid type shewn in the above figure is not necessary for a rough experiment. The pulleys F and G may have holes bored through them through which bradawls can be put; these bradawls may then be pushed into a vertical blackboard.

The pulleys and weights of the foregoing experiment may be replaced by three Salter's Spring Balances. Each of these balances shews, by a pointer which travels up and down a graduated face, what force is applied to the hook at its end.

Three light strings are knotted at O and attached to the ends of the spring balances. The three balances are then drawn out to shew any convenient tensions, and laid on a horizontal table and fixed to it by hooks or nails as shewn. The readings of the balances then give the tensions P, Q, and R of the three strings. Just as in the

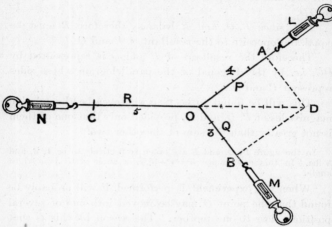

preceding experiment we draw lines OA, OB, and OC to represent P, Q, and R on any scale that is convenient, and then verify that OC is equal in magnitude and exactly opposite in direction to OD, the diagonal of the parallelogram of which OA and OB are adjacent sides.

26. To find the direction and magnitude of the resultant of two forces, we have to find the direction and magnitude of the diagonal of a parallelogram of which the two sides represent the forces.

Ex. 1. *Find the resultant of forces equal to 12 and 5 lbs. weight respectively acting at right angles.*

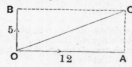

Let OA and OB represent the forces so that OA is 12 units of length and OB is 5 units of length; complete the rectangle $OACB$.

Then $\qquad OC^2 = OA^2 + AC^2 = 12^2 + 5^2 = 169. \quad \therefore \quad OC = 13.$

Also $\qquad\qquad\qquad \tan COA = \dfrac{AC}{OA} = \dfrac{5}{12}.$

Hence the resultant is a force equal to 13 lbs. weight making with the first force an angle whose tangent is $\frac{5}{12}$, *i.e.* about 22° 37′.

Ex. 2. *Find the resultant of forces equal to the weights of 5 and 3 lbs. respectively acting at an angle of* 60°.

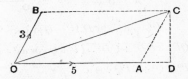

Let OA and OB represent the forces, so that OA is 5 units and OB 3 units of length; also let the angle AOB be 60°.

Complete the parallelogram $OACB$ and draw CD perpendicular to OA. Then OC represents the required resultant.

Now $\qquad AD = AC \cos CAD = 3 \cos 60° = \frac{3}{2}; \quad \therefore \quad OD = \frac{13}{2}.$

Also $\qquad\qquad\qquad DC = AC \sin 60° = 3\dfrac{\sqrt{3}}{2}.$

$$\therefore \quad OC = \sqrt{OD^2 + DC^2} = \sqrt{\frac{169}{4} + \frac{27}{4}} = \sqrt{49} = 7,$$

and $\qquad\qquad\qquad \tan COD = \dfrac{DC}{OD} = \dfrac{3\sqrt{3}}{13} = \cdot3997.$

Hence the resultant is a force equal to 7 lbs. weight in a direction making with OD an angle whose tangent is ·3997.

On reference to a table of natural tangents this angle is easily seen to be about 21° 47′.

27. The resultant, R, of two forces P and Q acting at an angle a may be easily obtained by Trigonometry.

For let OA and OB represent the forces P and Q acting at an angle a. Complete the parallelogram $OACB$ and draw CD perpendicular to OA, produced if necessary.

Let R denote the magnitude of the resultant.

Then $OD = OA + AD = OA + AC \cos DAC$

$$= P + Q \cos BOD = P + Q \cos \alpha.$$

[If D fall between O and A, as in the second figure, we have
$OD = OA - DA = OA - AC \cos DAC = P - Q \cos (180° - \alpha) = P + Q \cos \alpha.$]

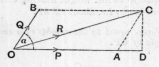 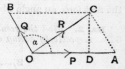

Also $\qquad DC = AC \sin DAC = Q \sin \alpha.$

$\therefore R^2 = OC^2 = OD^2 + CD^2 = (P + Q \cos \alpha)^2 + (Q \sin \alpha)^2$

$$= P^2 + Q^2 + 2PQ \cos \alpha.$$

$$\therefore \mathbf{R} = \sqrt{\mathbf{P^2 + Q^2 + 2PQ \cos \alpha}} \quad\text{.................(i)}.$$

Also $\qquad \tan COD = \dfrac{DC}{OD} = \dfrac{Q \sin \alpha}{P + Q \cos \alpha} \quad\text{...........(ii)}.$

These two equations give the required magnitude and direction of the resultant.

Cor. 1. If the forces be at right angles, we have $\alpha = 90°$, so that $R = \sqrt{P^2 + Q^2}$, and $\tan COA = \dfrac{Q}{P}$.

Cor. 2. If the forces be each equal to P, we have

$$R = \sqrt{P^2 (1 + 1 + 2 \cos \alpha)} = P \sqrt{2 (1 + \cos \alpha)}$$

$$= P \sqrt{2 \cdot 2 \cos^2 \dfrac{\alpha}{2}} = 2P \cos \dfrac{\alpha}{2},$$

and $\qquad \tan COA = \dfrac{P \sin \alpha}{P + P \cos \alpha} = \dfrac{2 \sin \dfrac{\alpha}{2} \cos \dfrac{\alpha}{2}}{2 \cos^2 \dfrac{\alpha}{2}} = \tan \dfrac{\alpha}{2},$

so that the resultant of two equal forces bisects the angle between them; this is obvious also from first principles.

EXAMPLES. I.

1. In the following seven examples P and Q denote two component forces acting at an angle a and R denotes their resultant. [The results should also be verified by a graph and measurement.]

    (i). If $P = 24$; $Q = 7$; $a = 90°$; find R.

    (ii). If $P = 13$; $R = 14$; $a = 90°$; find Q.

    (iii). If $P = 7$; $Q = 8$; $a = 60°$; find R.

    (iv). If $P = 5$; $Q = 9$; $a = 120°$; find R.

    (v). If $P = 3$; $Q = 5$; $R = 7$; find a.

    (vi). If $P = 13$; $Q = 14$; $a = \sin^{-1}\frac{12}{13}$; find R.

    (vii). If $P = 5$; $R = 7$; $a = 60°$; find Q.

2. Find the greatest and least resultants of two forces whose magnitudes are 12 and 8 lbs. weight respectively.

3. Forces equal respectively to 3, 4, 5, and 6 lbs. weight act on a particle in directions respectively north, south, east, and west; find the direction and magnitude of their resultant.

4. Forces of 84 and 187 lbs. weight act at right angles; find their resultant.

5. Two forces whose magnitudes are P and $P\sqrt{2}$ lbs. weight act on a particle in directions inclined at an angle of 135° to each other; find the magnitude and direction of the resultant.

6. Two forces acting at an angle of 60° have a resultant equal to $2\sqrt{3}$ lbs. weight; if one of the forces be 2 lbs. weight, find the other force.

7. Find the resultant of two forces equal to the weights of 13 and 11 lbs. respectively acting at an angle whose tangent is $\frac{12}{5}$. Verify by a drawing.

8. Find the resultant of two forces equal to the weights of 10 and 9 lbs. respectively acting at an angle whose tangent is $\frac{4}{3}$. Verify by a drawing.

9. Two equal forces act on a particle; find the angle between them when the square of their resultant is equal to three times their product.

10. Find the magnitude of two forces such that, if they act at right angles, their resultant is $\sqrt{10}$ lbs. weight, whilst when they act at an angle of 60° their resultant is $\sqrt{13}$ lbs. weight.

11. Find the angle between two equal forces P when their resultant is (1) equal to P, (2) equal to $\dfrac{P}{2}$.

12. At what angle do forces, equal to $(A + B)$ and $(A - B)$, act so that the resultant may be $\sqrt{A^2 + B^2}$?

13. Two given forces act on a particle; find in what direction a third force of given magnitude must act so that the resultant of the three may be as great as possible.

14. By drawing alone solve the following:
   (i). If $P=10$; $Q=15$; $\alpha=37°$; find R.
   (ii). If $P= 9$; $Q= 7$; $\alpha=133°$; find R.
   (iii). If $P= 7$; $Q= 5$; $R=10$; find α.
   (iv). If $P=7·3$; $R=8·7$; $\alpha= 65°$; find Q.

28. Two forces, given in magnitude and direction, have only one resultant; for only one parallelogram can be constructed having two lines OA and OB (Fig. Art. 27) as adjacent sides.

29. A force may be resolved into two components in an infinite number of ways; for an infinite number of parallelograms can be constructed having OC as a diagonal and each of these parallelograms would give a pair of such components.

30. The most important case of the resolution of forces occurs when we resolve a force into two components **at right angles** to one another.

Suppose we wish to resolve a force F, represented by OC, into two components, one of which is in the direction OA and the other is perpendicular to OA.

Draw CM perpendicular to OA and complete the parallelogram $OMCN$. The forces represented by OM and ON have as their resultant the force OC, so that OM and ON are the required components.

Let the angle AOC be a.

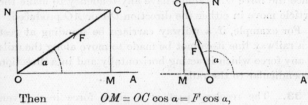

Then $\qquad OM = OC \cos a = F \cos a$,

and $\qquad ON = MC = OC \sin a = F \sin a$.

[If the point M lie in OA produced backwards, as in the second figure, the component of F in the direction OA

$= -OM = -OC \cos COM = -OC \cos (180^\circ - a) = OC \cos a = F \cos a$.

Also the component perpendicular to OA

$$= ON = MC = OC \sin COM = F \sin a.]$$

Hence, in each case, the required components are

$$F \cos a \text{ and } F \sin a.$$

Thus a force equal to 10 lbs. weight acting at an angle of 60° with the horizontal is equivalent to $10 \cos 60^\circ \ (= 10 \times \frac{1}{2} = 5$ lbs. weight) in a horizontal direction, and $10 \sin 60^\circ \ (= 10 \times \frac{\sqrt{3}}{2} = 5 \times 1\cdot732 = 8\cdot66$ lbs. weight) in a vertical direction.

31. Def. The Resolved Part of a given force in a given direction is the component in the given direction which, with a component in a direction perpendicular to the given direction, is equivalent to the given force.

Thus in the previous article the resolved part of the force F in the direction OA is $F \cos a$. Hence

The Resolved Part of a given force in a given direction is obtained by multiplying the given force by the cosine of the angle between the given force and the given direction.

32. A force cannot produce any effect in a direction perpendicular to its own line of action. For (Fig. Art. 30) there is no reason why the force ON should have any tendency to make a particle at O move in the direction OA

rather than to make it move in the direction AO produced; hence the force ON cannot have any tendency to make the particle move in either the direction OA or AO produced.

For example, if a railway carriage be standing at rest on a railway line it cannot be made to move along the rails by any force which is acting horizontally and in a direction perpendicular to the rails.

33. The resolved part of a given force in a given direction represents the *whole effect* of the force in the given direction. For (Fig. Art. 30) the force OC is completely represented by the forces ON and OM. But the force ON has no effect in the direction OA. Hence the whole effect of the force F in the direction OA is represented by OM, *i.e.* by the resolved part of the force in the direction OA.

34. A force may be resolved into two components in any two assigned directions.

Let the components of a force F, represented by OC, in the

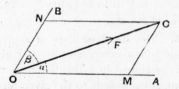

directions OA and OB be required and let the angles AOC and COB be α and β respectively.

Draw CM parallel to OB to meet OA in M and complete the parallelogram $OMCN$.

Then OM and ON are the required components.

Since MC and ON are parallel, we have

$$OCM = \beta; \text{ also } OMC = 180° - CMA = 180° - (\alpha + \beta).$$

Since the sides of the triangle OMC are proportional to the sines of the opposite angles, we have

$$\frac{OM}{\sin OCM} = \frac{MC}{\sin MOC} = \frac{OC}{\sin OMC}.$$

$$\therefore \quad \frac{OM}{\sin \beta} = \frac{MC}{\sin \alpha} = \frac{F}{\sin (\alpha + \beta)}.$$

Hence the required components are

$$F \frac{\sin \beta}{\sin (\alpha + \beta)} \text{ and } F \frac{\sin \alpha}{\sin (\alpha + \beta)}.$$

35. The student must carefully notice that the components of a force in two assigned directions are not the same as the resolved parts of the forces in these directions. For example, the resolved part of F in the direction OA is, by Art. 30, $F \cos \alpha$.

EXAMPLES. II.

1. A force equal to 10 lbs. weight is inclined at an angle of 30° to the horizontal; find its resolved parts in a horizontal and vertical direction respectively.

2. Find the resolved part of a force P in a direction making (1) an angle of 45°, (2) an angle equal to $\cos^{-1}\left(\frac{12}{13}\right)$ with its direction.

3. A truck is at rest on a railway line and is pulled by a horizontal force equal to the weight of 100 lbs. in a direction making an angle of 60° with the direction of the rails; what is the force tending to urge the truck forwards?

4. Resolve a force of 100 lbs. weight into two equal forces acting at an angle of 60° to each other. Verify by a graph and measurement.

5. Resolve a force of 50 lbs. weight into two forces making angles of 60° and 45° with it on opposite sides. Verify by a graph and measurement.

6. Find the components of a force P along two directions making angles of 30° and 45° with P on opposite sides.

7. If a force P be resolved into two forces making angles of 45° and 15° with its direction, shew that the latter force is $\frac{\sqrt{6}}{3}P$.

8. Find a horizontal force and a force inclined at an angle of 60° with the vertical whose resultant shall be a given vertical force F.

9. If a force be resolved into two component forces and if one component be at right angles to the force and equal to it in magnitude, find the direction and magnitude of the other component.

10. A force equal to the weight of 20 lbs. acting vertically upwards is resolved into two forces, one being horizontal and equal to the weight of 10 lbs.; what is the magnitude and direction of the other force?

11. By a graphic construction and measurement resolve a force equal to 35 lbs. wt. into components making angles of 98° and 40° with it on opposite sides.

36. Triangle of Forces. *If three forces, acting at a point, be represented in magnitude and direction by the sides of a triangle, taken in order, they will be in equilibrium.*

Let the forces P, Q, and R acting at the point O be represented in magnitude and direction by the sides AB,

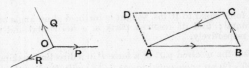

BC, and CA of the triangle ABC; they shall be in equilibrium.

Complete the parallelogram $ABCD$.

The forces represented by BC and AD are the same, since BC and AD are equal and parallel.

Now the resultant of the forces AB and AD, is, by the parallelogram of forces, represented by AC.

Hence the resultant of AB, BC, and CA is equal to the resultant of forces AC and CA, and is therefore zero.

Hence the three forces P, Q, and R are in equilibrium.

Cor. Since forces represented by AB, BC, and CA are in equilibrium, and since, when three forces are in equilibrium, each is equal and opposite to the resultant of the other two, it follows that the resultant of AB and BC is equal and opposite to CA, *i.e.* their resultant is represented by AC.

Hence the resultant of two forces, acting at a point and represented by the sides AB and BC of a triangle, is represented by the third side AC.

37. In the Triangle of Forces the student must carefully note that the forces must be parallel to the sides of a triangle *taken in order*, *i.e. taken the same way round*.

For example, if the first force act in the direction AB, the second must act in the direction BC, and the third in the direction CA; if the second force were in the direction CB, instead of BC, the forces would not be in equilibrium.

The three forces must also act *at a point*; if the lines of action of the forces were BC, CA, and AB they would not be in equilibrium; for the forces AB and BC would have a resultant, acting at B, equal and parallel to AC. The system of forces would then reduce to two equal and parallel forces acting in opposite directions, and, as we shall see in a later chapter, such a pair of forces could not be in equilibrium.

38. The converse of the Triangle of Forces is also true, *viz.* that *If three forces acting at a point be in equilibrium they can be represented in magnitude and direction by the sides of any triangle which is drawn so as to have its sides respectively parallel to the directions of the forces.*

Let the three forces P, Q, and R, acting at a point O, be in equilibrium. Measure off lengths OL and OM along the directions of P and Q to represent these forces respectively.

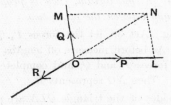

Complete the parallelogram $OLNM$ and join ON.

Since the three forces P, Q, and R are in equilibrium, each must be equal and opposite to the resultant of the other two. Hence R must be equal and opposite to the resultant of P and Q, and must therefore be represented by NO. Also LN is equal and parallel to OM.

Hence the three forces P, Q, and R are parallel and proportional to the sides OL, LN, and NO of the triangle OLN.

Any other triangle, whose sides are parallel to those of the triangle OLN, will have its sides proportional to those of OLN and therefore proportional to the forces.

Again, any triangle, whose sides are respectively perpendicular to those of the triangle OLN, will have its sides proportional to the sides of OLN and therefore proportional to the forces.

39. The proposition of the last article gives an easy graphical method of determining the relative directions of three forces which are in equilibrium and whose magnitudes are known. We have to construct a triangle whose sides are proportional to the forces, and this, by Euc. I. 22, can always be done unless two of the forces added together are less than the third.

40. Lami's Theorem. *If three forces acting on a particle keep it in equilibrium, each is proportional to the sine of the angle between the other two.*

Taking Fig., Art 38, let the forces P, Q, and R be in equilibrium. As before, measure off lengths OL and OM to represent the forces P and Q, and complete the parallelogram $OLNM$. Then NO represents R.

Since the sides of the triangle OLN are proportional to the sines of the opposite angles, we have

$$\frac{OL}{\sin LNO} = \frac{LN}{\sin LON} = \frac{NO}{\sin OLN}.$$

But
$$\sin LNO = \sin NOM = \sin (180° - QOR) = \sin QOR,$$
$$\sin LON = \sin (180° - LOR) = \sin ROP,$$

and
$$\sin OLN = \sin (180° - POQ) = \sin POQ.$$

Also
$$LN = OM.$$

Hence
$$\frac{OL}{\sin QOR} = \frac{OM}{\sin ROP} = \frac{NO}{\sin POQ},$$

i.e.
$$\frac{P}{\sin QOR} = \frac{Q}{\sin ROP} = \frac{R}{\sin POQ}.$$

41. Polygon of Forces. *If any number of forces, acting on a particle, be represented, in magnitude and direction, by the sides of a polygon, taken in order, the forces shall be in equilibrium.*

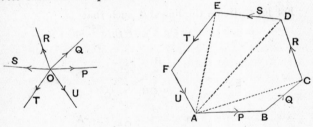

Let the sides AB, BC, CD, DE, EF and FA of the polygon $ABCDEF$ represent the forces acting on a particle O. Join AC, AD and AE.

By the corollary to Art. 36, the resultant of forces AB and BC is represented by AC.

Similarly the resultant of forces AC and CD is represented by AD; the resultant of forces AD and DE by AE; and the resultant of forces AE and EF by AF.

Hence the resultant of all the forces is equal to the resultant of AF and FA, *i.e.* the resultant vanishes.

Hence the forces are in equilibrium.

A similar method of proof will apply whatever be the number of forces. It is also clear from the proof that the sides of the polygon need not be in the same plane.

The converse of the Polygon of Forces is not true; for the ratios of the sides of a polygon are not known when the directions of the sides are known. For example, in the above figure, we might take any point A' on AB and draw $A'F'$ parallel to AF to meet EF in F'; the new polygon $A'BCDEF'$ has its sides respectively parallel to those of the polygon $ABCDEF$ but the corresponding sides are clearly not proportional.

42. *The resultant of two forces, acting at a point O in directions OA and OB and represented in magnitude by $\lambda . OA$ and $\mu . OB$, is represented by $(\lambda + \mu) . OC$, where C is a point in AB such that $\lambda . CA = \mu . CB$.*

For let C divide the line AB, such that

$$\lambda . CA = \mu . CB.$$

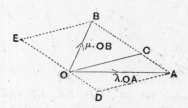

Complete the parallelograms $OCAD$ and $OCBE$.

By the parallelogram of forces the force $\lambda . OA$ is equivalent to forces represented by $\lambda . OC$ and $\lambda . OD$.

Also the force $\mu . OB$ is equivalent to forces represented by $\mu . OC$ and $\mu . OE$.

Hence the forces $\lambda . OA$ and $\mu . OB$ are together equivalent to a force $(\lambda + \mu) OC$ together with forces $\lambda . OD$ and $\mu . OE$.

But, (since $\lambda \cdot OD = \lambda \cdot CA = \mu \cdot CB = \mu \cdot OE$) these two latter forces are equal and opposite and therefore are in equilibrium.

Hence the resultant is $(\lambda + \mu) \cdot OC$.

Cor. The resultant of forces represented by OA and OB is $2OC$, where C is the middle point of AB.

This is also clear from the fact that OC is half the diagonal OD of the parallelogram of which OA and OB are adjacent sides.

EXAMPLES. III.

1. Three forces acting at a point are in equilibrium; if they make angles of 120° with one another, shew that they are equal.

If the angles are 60°, 150°, and 150°, in what proportions are the forces?

2. Three forces acting on a particle are in equilibrium; the angle between the first and second is 90° and that between the second and third is 120°; find the ratios of the forces.

3. Forces equal to $7P$, $5P$, and $8P$ acting on a particle are in equilibrium; find, by geometric construction and by calculation, the angle between the latter pair of forces.

4. Forces equal to $5P$, $12P$, and $13P$ acting on a particle are in equilibrium; find by geometric construction and by calculation the angles between their directions.

5. Construct geometrically the directions of two forces $2P$ and $3P$ which make equilibrium with a force of $4P$ whose direction is given.

6. The sides AB and AC of a triangle ABC are bisected in D and E; shew that the resultant of forces represented by BE and DC is represented in magnitude and direction by $\frac{3}{2}BC$.

7. P is a particle acted on by forces represented by $\lambda \cdot AP$ and $\lambda \cdot PB$ where A and B are two fixed points; shew that their resultant is constant in magnitude and direction wherever the point P may be.

8. $ABCD$ is a parallelogram; a particle P is attracted towards A and C by forces which are proportional to PA and PC respectively and repelled from B and D by forces proportional to PB and PD; shew that P is in equilibrium wherever it is situated.

The following are to be solved by **geometric construction.** In each case P and Q are two forces inclined at an angle α and R is their resultant making an angle θ with P.

9. $P = 25$ lbs. wt., $Q = 20$ lbs. wt. and $\theta = 35°$; find R and α.

10. $P = 50$ kilog., $Q = 60$ kilog. and $R = 70$ kilog.; find α and θ.

11. $P = 30$, $R = 40$ and $\alpha = 130°$; find Q and θ.

12. $P = 60$, $\alpha = 75°$ and $\theta = 40°$; find Q and R.

13. $P = 60$, $R = 40$ and $\theta = 50°$; find Q and α.

14. $P = 80$, $\alpha = 55°$ and $R = 100$; find Q and θ.

15. A boat is being towed by means of a rope which makes an angle of 20° with the boat's length; assuming that the resultant reaction R of the water on the boat is inclined at 40° to the boat's length and that the tension of the rope is equal to 5 cwt., find, by drawing, the resultant force on the boat, supposing it to be in the direction of the boat's length.

EXAMPLES. IV.

1. Two forces act at an angle of 120°. The greater is represented by 80 and the resultant is at right angles to the less. Find the latter.

2. If one of two forces be double the other and the resultant be equal to the greater force, find the angle between the forces.

3. Two forces acting on a particle are at right angles and are balanced by a third force making an angle of 150° with one of them. The greater of the two forces being 3 lbs. weight, what must be the values of the other two?

4. The resultant of two forces acting at an angle equal to $\frac{5}{3}$ds of a right angle is perpendicular to the smaller component. The greater being equal to 30 lbs. weight, find the other component and the resultant.

5. The magnitudes of two forces are as 3 : 5, and the direction of the resultant is at right angles to that of the smaller force; compare the magnitudes of the larger force and of the resultant.

6. The sum of two forces is 18, and the resultant, whose direction is perpendicular to the lesser of the two forces, is 12; find the magnitude of the forces.

7. If two forces P and Q act at such an angle that $R = P$, shew that, if P be doubled, the new resultant is at right angles to Q.

8. The resultant of two forces P and Q is equal to $\sqrt{3}Q$ and makes an angle of 30° with the direction of P; shew that P is either equal to, or is double of, Q.

9. Two forces equal to $2P$ and P respectively act on a particle; if the first be doubled and the second increased by 12 lbs. weight the direction of the resultant is unaltered; find the value of P.

10. The resultant of two forces P and Q acting at an angle θ is equal to $(2m+1)\sqrt{P^2+Q^2}$; when they act at an angle $90° - \theta$, the resultant is $(2m-1)\sqrt{P^2+Q^2}$; prove that

$$\tan \theta = \frac{m-1}{m+1}.$$

11. The resultant of forces P and Q is R; if Q be doubled R is doubled, whilst, if Q be reversed, R is again doubled; shew that

$$P : Q : R :: \sqrt{2} : \sqrt{3} : \sqrt{2}.$$

12. If the resultant, R, of two forces P and Q, inclined to one another at any given angle, make an angle θ with the direction of P, shew that the resultant of forces $(P+R)$ and Q, acting at the same given angle, will make an angle $\dfrac{\theta}{2}$ with the direction of $(P+R)$.

13. Three given forces acting at a point are in equilibrium. If one of them be turned about its point of application through a given angle, find by a simple construction the resultant of the three, and, if the inclination of the force continue to alter, shew that the inclination of the resultant alters by half the amount.

14. Decompose a force, whose magnitude and line of action are given, into two equal forces passing through two given points, giving a geometrical construction, (1) when the two points are on the same side of the force, (2) when they are on opposite sides.

15. Two given forces act at two given points of a body; if they are turned round those points in the same direction through any two equal angles, shew that their resultant will always pass through a fixed point.

16. A, B, and C are three fixed points, and P is a point such that the resultant of forces PA and PB always passes through C; shew that the locus of P is a straight line.

17. A given force acting at a given point in a given direction is resolved into two components. If for all directions of the components one remains of invariable magnitude, shew that the extremity of the line representing the other lies on a definite circle.

18. Shew that the system of forces represented by the lines joining any point to the angular points of a triangle is equivalent to the system represented by straight lines drawn from the same point to the middle points of the sides of the triangle.

19. Find a point within a quadrilateral such that, if it be acted on by forces represented by the lines joining it to the angular points of the quadrilateral, it will be in equilibrium.

20. Four forces act along and are proportional to the sides of the quadrilateral $ABCD$; three act in the directions AB, BC, and CD and the fourth acts from A to D; find the magnitude and direction of their resultant, and determine the point in which it meets CD.

21. The sides BC and DA of a quadrilateral $ABCD$ are bisected in F and H respectively; shew that if two forces parallel and equal to AB and DC act on a particle, then the resultant is parallel to HF and equal to $2 . HF$.

22. The sides AB, BC, CD, and DA of a quadrilateral $ABCD$ are bisected at E, F, G, and H respectively. Shew that the resultant of the forces acting at a point which are represented in magnitude and direction by EG and HF is represented in magnitude and direction by AC.

23. From a point, P, within a circle whose centre is fixed, straight lines PA_1, PA_2, PA_3, and PA_4 are drawn to meet the circumference, all being equally inclined to the radius through P; shew that, if these lines represent forces radiating from P, their resultant is independent of the magnitude of the radius of the circle.

CHAPTER III.

COMPOSITION AND RESOLUTION OF FORCES (*continued*).

43. *The sum of the resolved parts of two forces in a given direction is equal to the resolved part of their resultant in the same direction.*

Let OA and OB represent the two forces P and Q, and OC their resultant R, so that $OACB$ is a parallelogram.

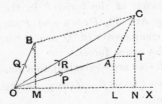

Let OX be the given direction; draw AL, BM, and CN perpendicular to OX and AT perpendicular to CN.

The sides of the two triangles OBM, ACT are respectively parallel, and OB is equal to AC in magnitude;

$$\therefore \quad OM = AT = LN.$$

Hence $\qquad ON = OL + LN = OL + OM.$

But OL, OM, and ON represent respectively the resolved parts of P, Q, and R in the direction OX.

Hence the theorem is proved.

The theorem may easily be extended to the resultant of any number of forces acting at a point.

44. *To find the resultant of any number of forces in one plane acting upon a particle.*

Let the forces P, Q, R... act upon a particle at O.

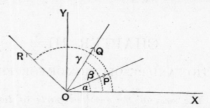

Through O draw a fixed line OX and a line OY at right angles to OX.

Let the forces P, Q, R, ... make angles a, β, γ... with OX.

The components of the force P in the directions OX and OY are, by Art. 30, $P \cos a$ and $P \sin a$ respectively; similarly, the components of Q are $Q \cos \beta$ and $Q \sin \beta$; similarly for the other forces.

Hence the forces are equivalent to a component,

$$P \cos a + Q \cos \beta + R \cos \gamma \dots \text{ along } OX,$$

and a component,

$$P \sin a + Q \sin \beta + R \sin \gamma \dots \text{ along } OY.$$

Let these components be X and Y respectively, and let F be their resultant inclined at an angle θ to OX.

Since F is equivalent to $F \cos \theta$ along OX, and $F \sin \theta$ along OY, we have, by the previous article,

$$F \cos \theta = X \dots\dots\dots\dots\dots(1),$$

and $$F \sin \theta = Y \dots\dots\dots\dots\dots(2).$$

Hence, by squaring and adding,

$$F^2 = X^2 + Y^2.$$

Also, by division, $$\tan \theta = \frac{Y}{X}.$$

These two equations give F and θ, *i.e.*, the magnitude and direction of the required resultant.

Ex. 1. *A particle is acted upon by three forces, in one plane, equal to* 2, 2√2, *and* 1 *lbs. weight respectively; the first is horizontal, the second acts at* 45° *to the horizon, and the third is vertical; find their resultant.*

Here
$$X = 2 + 2\sqrt{2}\cos 45° + 0 = 2 + 2\sqrt{2} \cdot \frac{1}{\sqrt{2}} = 4,$$

$$Y = 0 + 2\sqrt{2}\sin 45° + 1 = 2\sqrt{2} \cdot \frac{1}{\sqrt{2}} + 1 = 3.$$

Hence
$$F\cos\theta = 4; \quad F\sin\theta = 3;$$
$$\therefore \ F = \sqrt{4^2 + 3^2} = 5, \text{ and } \tan\theta = \tfrac{3}{4}.$$

The resultant is therefore a force equal to 5 lbs. weight acting at an angle with the horizontal whose tangent is $\tfrac{3}{4}$, *i.e.* 36° 52′.

Ex. 2. *A particle is acted upon by forces represented by* P, $2P$, $3\sqrt{3}P$, *and* $4P$; *the angles between the first and second, the second and third, and the third and fourth are* 60°, 90°, *and* 150° *respectively. Shew that the resultant is a force* P *in a direction inclined at an angle of* 120° *to that of the first force.*

In this example it will be a simplification if we take the fixed line

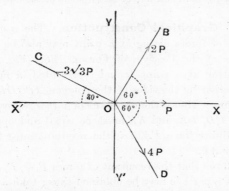

OX to coincide with the direction of the first force P; let XOX' and YOY' be the two fixed lines at right angles.

The second, third, and fourth forces are respectively in the first, second, and fourth quadrants, and we have clearly

$$BOX = 60°; \quad COX' = 30°; \text{ and } DOX = 60°.$$

The first force has no component along OY.

The second force is equivalent to components $2P\cos 60°$ and $2P\sin 60°$ along OX and OY respectively.

The third force is equivalent to forces

$$3\sqrt{3}P\cos 30° \quad \text{and} \quad 3\sqrt{3}P\sin 30°$$

along OX' and OY respectively,

i.e. to forces $-3\sqrt{3}P\cos 30°$ and $3\sqrt{3}P\sin 30°$ along OX and OY.

So the fourth force is equivalent to $4P\cos 60°$ and $4P\sin 60°$ along OX and OY', i.e. to $4P\cos 60°$ and $-4P\sin 60°$ along OX and OY.

Hence
$$X = P + 2P\cos 60° - 3\sqrt{3}P\cos 30° + 4P\cos 60°$$

$$= P + P - \frac{9P}{2} + 2P = -\frac{P}{2},$$

and
$$Y = 0 + 2P\sin 60° + 3\sqrt{3}P\sin 30° - 4P\sin 60°$$

$$= P\sqrt{3} + \frac{3\sqrt{3}}{2}P - 4P \cdot \frac{\sqrt{3}}{2} = \frac{\sqrt{3}}{2}P.$$

Hence, if F be the resultant at an angle θ with OX, we have

$$F = \sqrt{X^2 + Y^2} = P,$$

and
$$\tan\theta = \frac{Y}{X} = -\sqrt{3} = \tan 120°,$$

so that the resultant is a force P at an angle of 120° with the first force.

45. Graphical Construction. The resultant of a system of forces acting at a point may also be obtained by means of the Polygon of Forces. For, (Fig. Art. 41,) forces acting at a point O and represented in magnitude and direction by the sides of the polygon $ABCDEF$ are in equilibrium. Hence the resultant of forces represented by AB, BC, CD, DE, and EF must be equal and opposite to the remaining force FA, i.e., the resultant must be represented by AF.

It follows that the resultant of forces P, Q, R, S, and T acting on a particle may be obtained thus; take a point A and draw AB parallel and proportional to P, and in succession BC, CD, DE, and EF parallel and proportional respectively to Q, R, S, and T; the required resultant will be represented in magnitude and direction by the line AF.

The same construction would clearly apply for any number of forces.

Ex. *Four forces equal to 2, 2½, 1 and 3 kilogrammes wt. act along straight lines OP, OQ, OR and OS, such that ∠ POQ = 40°, ∠ QOR = 100°, and ∠ ROS = 125°; find their resultant in magnitude and direction.*

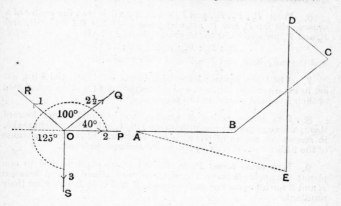

Draw *AB* parallel to *OP* and equal to 2 inches; through *B* draw *BC* parallel to *OQ* and equal to 2·5 inches, and then *CD* parallel to *OR* and equal to 1 inch, and finally *DE* parallel to *OS* and equal to 3 inches. On measurement we have *AE* equal to 2·99 inches and ∠ *BAE* equal to a little over 14°.

Hence the resultant is 2·95 kilogrammes wt. acting at 14° to *OP*.

EXAMPLES. V.

[Questions 2, 3, 4, 5, and 8 are suitable for graphic solutions.]

1. Forces of 1, 2, and √3 lbs. weight act at a point *A* in directions *AP*, *AQ*, and *AR*, the angle *PAQ* being 60° and *PAR* a right angle; find their resultant.

2. A particle is acted on by forces of 5 and 3 lbs. weight which are at right angles and by a force of 4 lbs. weight bisecting the angle between them; find the force that will keep it at rest.

3. Three equal forces, *P*, diverge from a point, the middle one being inclined at an angle of 60° to each of the others. Find the resultant of the three.

4. Three forces $5P$, $10P$, and $13P$ act in one plane on a particle, the angle between any two of their directions being $120°$. Find the magnitude and direction of their resultant.

5. Forces $2P$, $3P$, and $4P$ act at a point in directions parallel to the sides of an equilateral triangle taken in order; find the magnitude and line of action of the resultant.

6. Forces P_1, P_2, P_3, and P_4 act on a particle O at the centre of a square $ABCD$; P_1 and P_2 act along the diagonals OA and OB, and P_3 and P_4 perpendicular to the sides AB and BC. If

$$P_1 : P_2 : P_3 : P_4 :: 4 : 6 : 5 : 1,$$

find the magnitude and direction of their resultant.

7. $ABCD$ is a square; forces of 1 lb. wt., 6 lbs. wt., and 9 lbs. wt. act in the directions AB, AC, and AD respectively; find the magnitude of their resultant correct to two places of decimals.

8. Five forces, acting at a point, are in equilibrium; four of them, whose respective magnitudes are 4, 4, 1, and 3 lbs. weight make, in succession, angles of $60°$ with one another. Find the magnitude of the fifth force. Verify by a drawing and measurement.

9. Four equal forces P, Q, R, and S act on a particle in one plane; the angles between P and Q, between Q and R, and between R and S are all equal and that between P and S is $108°$. Find their resultant.

10. Forces of 2, $\sqrt{3}$, 5, $\sqrt{3}$, and 2 lbs. wt. respectively act at one of the angular points of a regular hexagon towards the five other angular points; find the direction and magnitude of the resultant.

11. Forces of 2, 3, 4, 5, and 6 lbs. wt. respectively act at an angular point of a regular hexagon towards the other angular points taken in order; find their resultant.

12. Shew that the resultant of forces equal to 7, 1, 1, and 3 lbs. wt. respectively acting at an angular point of a regular pentagon towards the other angular points, taken in order, is $\sqrt{71}$ lbs. wt. Verify by a drawing and measurement.

13. Equal forces P act on an angular point of an octagon towards each of the other angular points; find their resultant.

By the use of trigonometrical Tables, or by a graphic construction find the magnitude (to two places of decimals) and the direction (to the nearest minute by calculation, and to the nearest degree by drawing) of the resultant of

14. three forces equal to 11, 7, and 8 lbs. weight, making angles of $18°18'$, $74°50'$, and $130°20'$ with a fixed line,

15. four forces equal to 4, 3, 2, and 1 lb. weight, making angles of 20°, 40°, 60°, and 80° with a fixed line,

16. four forces equal to 8, 12, 15, and 20 lbs. weight, making angles of 30°, 70°, 120° 15', and 155° with a fixed line,

17. three forces equal to 85, 47, and 63 kilog. wt. acting along lines OA, OB, and OC, where $\angle AOB = 78°$ and $\angle BOC = 125°$.

46. *To find the conditions of equilibrium of any number of forces acting upon a particle.*

Let the forces act upon a particle O as in Art. 44.

If the forces balance one another the resultant must vanish, *i.e.* F must be zero.

Hence $\qquad X^2 + Y^2 = 0.$

Now the sum of the squares of two real quantities cannot be zero unless each quantity is separately zero;

$$\therefore\ X = 0, \text{ and } Y = 0.$$

Hence, if the forces acting on a particle be in equilibrium, the algebraic sum of their resolved parts in two directions at right angles are separately zero.

Conversely, if the sum of their resolved parts in two directions at right angles separately vanish, the forces are in equilibrium.

For, in this case, both X and Y are zero, and therefore F is zero also.

Hence, since the resultant of the forces vanishes, the forces are in equilibrium.

47. When there are only three forces acting on a particle the conditions of equilibrium are often most easily found by applying Lami's Theorem (Art. 40).

48. Ex. 1. *A body of 65 lbs. weight is suspended by two strings of lengths 5 and 12 feet attached to two points in the same horizontal line whose distance apart is 13 feet; find the tensions of the strings.*

Let AC and BC be the two strings, so that

$$AC = 5 \text{ ft.}, \quad BC = 12 \text{ ft.}, \text{ and } AB = 13 \text{ ft.}$$

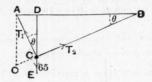

Since $13^2 = 12^2 + 5^2$, the angle ACB is a right angle.

Let the direction CE of the weight be produced to meet AB in D; also let the angle CBA be θ, so that

$$\angle ACD = 90° - \angle BCD = \angle CBD = \theta.$$

Let T_1 and T_2 be the tensions of the strings. By Lami's theorem we have

$$\frac{T_1}{\sin ECB} = \frac{T_2}{\sin ECA} = \frac{65}{\sin ACB};$$

$$\therefore \quad \frac{T_1}{\sin BCD} = \frac{T_2}{\sin \theta} = \frac{65}{\sin 90°};$$

$$\therefore \quad T_1 = 65 \cos \theta, \text{ and } T_2 = 65 \sin \theta.$$

But $\qquad \cos \theta = \dfrac{BC}{BA} = \dfrac{12}{13}, \text{ and } \sin \theta = \dfrac{AC}{AB} = \dfrac{5}{13};$

$$\therefore \quad T_1 = 60, \text{ and } T_2 = 25 \text{ lbs. wt.}$$

Otherwise thus; The triangle ACB has its sides respectively perpendicular to the directions of the forces T_1, T_2, and 65;

$$\therefore \quad \frac{T_1}{BC} = \frac{T_2}{CA} = \frac{65}{AB};$$

$$\therefore \quad T_1 = 65 \frac{BC}{AB} = 60, \text{ and } T_2 = 65 \frac{AC}{AB} = 25.$$

Graphically; produce BC to meet a vertical line through A in O. Then ACO is a triangle having its sides parallel to the three forces T_1, T_2, and W. Hence it is the triangle of forces, and

$$\therefore \quad \frac{T_1}{AC} = \frac{T_2}{CO} = \frac{W}{OA}.$$

Ex. 2. *A string ABCD, attached to two fixed points A and D, has two equal weights, W, knotted to it at B and C and rests with the portions AB and CD inclined at angles of 30° and 60° respectively to the vertical. Find the tensions of the portions of the string and the inclination of BC to the vertical.*

Let the tensions in the strings be T_1, T_2, and T_3 respectively and let BC be inclined at an angle θ to the vertical.

[N.B. The string BC pulls B towards C and pulls C towards B, the tension being the same throughout its length.]

Since B is in equilibrium the vertical components and the horizontal components of the forces acting on it must both vanish (Art. 46).

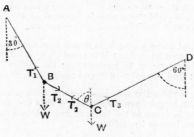

Hence
$$T_1 \cos 30° - T_2 \cos \theta = W \dots\dots\dots\dots\dots\dots(1),$$
and
$$T_1 \sin 30° - T_2 \sin \theta = 0 \dots\dots\dots\dots\dots(2).$$
Similarly, since C is in equilibrium,
$$T_3 \cos 60° + T_2 \cos \theta = W \dots\dots\dots\dots\dots(3),$$
and
$$T_3 \sin 60° - T_2 \sin \theta = 0 \dots\dots\dots\dots\dots(4).$$
From (1) and (2), substituting for T_1, we have
$$W = T_2[\cot 30° \sin \theta - \cos \theta] = T_2[\sqrt{3} \sin \theta - \cos \theta]\dots\dots(5).$$
So from (3) and (4), substituting for T_3, we have
$$W = T_2[\cot 60° \sin \theta + \cos \theta] = T_2\left[\frac{1}{\sqrt{3}} \sin \theta + \cos \theta\right] \dots\dots(6);$$
therefore from (5) and (6),
$$\sqrt{3} \sin \theta - \cos \theta = \frac{1}{\sqrt{3}} \sin \theta + \cos \theta ;$$
$$\therefore 2 \sin \theta = 2\sqrt{3} \cos \theta ;$$
$$\therefore \tan \theta = \sqrt{3}, \text{ and hence } \theta = 60°.$$
Substituting this value in (5), we have
$$W = T_2\left[\sqrt{3} \cdot \frac{\sqrt{3}}{2} - \frac{1}{2}\right] = T_2.$$

Hence from (2), we have

$$T_1 = T_2 \frac{\sin 60°}{\sin 30°} = W \cdot \sqrt{3},$$

and from (4)

$$T_3 = T_2 \frac{\sin \theta}{\sin 60°} = T_2 = W.$$

Hence the inclination of BC to the vertical is 60°, and the tensions of the portions AB, BC, and CD are $W\sqrt{3}$, W, and W respectively.

EXAMPLES. VI.

1. Two men carry a weight W between them by means of two ropes fixed to the weight; one rope is inclined at 45° to the vertical and the other at 30°; find the tension of each rope.

2. A body, of mass 2 lbs., is fastened to a fixed point by means of a string of length 25 inches; it is acted on by a horizontal force F and rests at a distance of 20 inches from the vertical line through the fixed point; find the value of F and the tension of the string.

3. A body, of mass 130 lbs., is suspended from a horizontal beam by strings, whose lengths are respectively 1 ft. 4 ins. and 5 ft. 3 ins., the strings being fastened to the beam at two points 5 ft. 5 ins. apart. What are the tensions of the strings?

4. A body, of mass 70 lbs., is suspended by strings, whose lengths are 6 and 8 feet respectively, from two points in a horizontal line whose distance apart is 10 feet; find the tensions of the strings.

5. A mass of 60 lbs. is suspended by two strings of lengths 9 and 12 feet respectively, the other ends of the strings being attached to two points in a horizontal line at a distance of 15 feet apart; find the tensions of the strings.

6. A string suspended from a ceiling supports three bodies, each of mass 4 lbs., one at its lowest point and each of the others at equal distances from its extremities; find the tensions of the parts into which the string is divided.

7. Two equal masses, of weight W, are attached to the extremities of a thin string which passes over 3 tacks in a wall arranged in the form of an isosceles triangle, with the base horizontal and with a vertical angle of 120°; find the pressure on each tack.

8. A stream is 96 feet wide and a boat is dragged down the middle of the stream by two men on opposite banks, each of whom pulls with a force equal to 100 lbs. wt.; if the ropes be attached to the same point of the boat and each be of length 60 feet, find the resultant force on the boat.

9. A string passing over two smooth parallel bars in the same horizontal plane has two equal weights fastened to its ends and another equal weight is fastened to a point of the string between the bars; find the position of equilibrium of the system and the thrust upon each bar.

10. A string is tied to two points in a horizontal plane; a ring of weight 27 lbs. can slide freely along the string and is pulled by a horizontal force equal to the weight of P lbs. If in the position of equilibrium the portions of the string be inclined at angles of 45° and 75° to the vertical, find the value of P.

11. Two weightless rings slide on a smooth vertical circle and through the rings passes a string which carries weights at the two ends and at a point between the rings. If equilibrium exist when the rings are at points distant 30° from the highest point of the circle, find the relation between the three weights.

12. Two masses, each equal to 112 lbs., are joined by a string which passes over two small smooth pegs, A and B, in the same horizontal plane; if a mass of 5 lbs. be attached to the string halfway between A and B, find in inches the depth to which it will descend below the level of AB, supposing AB to be 10 feet.

What would happen if the small mass were attached to any other point of the string?

13. A body, of mass 10 lbs., is suspended by two strings, 7 and 24 inches long, their other ends being fastened to the extremities of a rod of length 25 inches. If the rod be so held that the body hangs immediately below its middle point, find the tensions of the string.

14. A heavy chain has weights of 10 and 16 lbs. attached to its ends and hangs in equilibrium over a smooth pulley; if the greatest tension of the chain be 20 lbs. wt., find the weight of the chain.

15. A heavy chain, of length 8 ft. 9 ins. and weighing 15 lbs., has a weight of 7 lbs. attached to one end and is in equilibrium hanging over a smooth peg. What length of the chain is on each side?

16. A body is free to slide on a smooth vertical circular wire and is connected by a string, equal in length to the radius of the circle, to the highest point of the circle; find the tension of the string and the reaction of the circle.

17. A uniform plane lamina in the form of a rhombus, one of whose angles is 120°, is supported by two forces applied at the centre in the directions of the diagonals so that one side of the rhombus is horizontal; shew that, if P and Q be the forces and P be the greater, then

$$P^2 = 3Q^2.$$

18. The ends of a driving rein are passed through two smooth rings which are fastened, one to each side of the bit. They are then doubled back and tied to fixed points in the headpiece one on each side of the horse's head. Find the pressure produced by the bit on the horse's tongue by a given pull P of the driver.

19. Three equal strings, of no sensible weight, are knotted together to form an equilateral triangle ABC and a weight W is suspended from A. If the triangle and weight be supported, with BC horizontal, by means of two strings at B and C, each at the angle of 135° with BC, shew that the tension in BC is

$$\frac{W}{6}(3 - \sqrt{3}).$$

20. Three weightless strings AC, BC, and AB are knotted together to form an isosceles triangle whose vertex is C. If a weight W be suspended from C and the whole be supported, with AB horizontal, by two forces bisecting the angles at A and B, find the tension of the string AB.

21. A weightless string is suspended from two points not in the same horizontal line and passes through a small smooth heavy ring which is free to slide on the string; find the position of equilibrium of the ring.

If the ring, instead of being free to move on the string, be tied to a given point of it, find equations to give the ratio of the tensions of the two portions of the string.

22. Four pegs are fixed in a wall at the four highest points of a regular hexagon (the two lowest points of the hexagon being in a horizontal straight line) and over these is thrown a loop supporting a weight W; the loop is of such a length that the angles formed by it at the lowest pegs are right angles. Find the tension of the string and the pressures on the pegs.

23. Explain how the force of the current may be used to urge a ferry-boat across the river, assuming that the centre of the boat is attached by a long rope to a fixed point in the middle of the stream.

24. *Explain how a vessel is enabled to sail in a direction nearly opposite to that of the wind.*

Shew also that the sails of the vessel should be set so as to bisect the angle between the keel and the apparent direction of the wind in order that the force to urge the vessel forward may be as great as possible.

[Let AB be the direction of the keel and therefore that of the ship's motion, and OA the apparent direction of the wind, the angle OAB being acute and equal to α. Let AC be the direction of the sail, AC being between OA and AB and the angle BAC being θ.

Let P be the force of the wind on the sail; resolve it in directions along and perpendicular to the sail. The component $(KA =) P\cos(\alpha - \theta)$ along the sail has no effect. The component $(LA =) P\sin(\alpha - \theta)$ perpendicular to the sail may again be resolved into two, *viz.* $(NA =) P\sin(\alpha - \theta)\cos\theta$ perpendicular to AB and $(MA =) P\sin(\alpha - \theta)\sin\theta$ along AB.

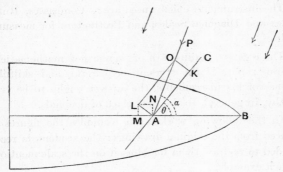

The former component produces motion sideways, *i.e.* in a direction perpendicular to the length of the ship. This is called lee-way and is considerably lessened by the shape of the keel which is so designed as to give the greatest possible resistance to this motion.

The latter component, $P\sin(\alpha - \theta)\sin\theta$, along AB is never zero unless the sail is set in either the direction of the keel or of the wind, or unless α is zero in which case the wind is directly opposite to the direction of the ship.

Thus there is always a force to make the ship move forward; but the rudder has to be continually applied to counteract the tendency of the wind to turn the boat about.

This force $= \frac{1}{2}P[\cos(\alpha - 2\theta) - \cos\alpha]$ and it is therefore greatest when $\cos(\alpha - 2\theta)$ is greatest, *i.e.* when $\alpha - 2\theta = 0$, *i.e.* when $\theta = \dfrac{\alpha}{2}$, *i.e.* when the direction of the sail bisects the angle between the keel and the apparent direction of the wind.]

49. Examples of graphical solution. Many problems which would be difficult or, at any rate, very laborious, to solve by analytical methods are comparatively easy to solve graphically.

These questions are of common occurrence in engineering and other practical work. There is generally little else involved besides the use of the Triangle of Forces and Polygon of Forces.

The instruments chiefly used are:—Compasses, Rulers, Scales and Diagonal Scales, and Protractors for measuring angles.

The results obtained are of course not mathematically accurate; but, if the student be careful, and skilful in the use of his instruments, the answer ought to be trustworthy, in general, to the first place of decimals.

In the following worked out examples the figures are reduced from the original drawings; the student is recommended to re-draw them for himself on the scale mentioned in each example.

50. Ex. 1. *ACDB is a string whose ends are attached to two points, A and B, which are in a horizontal line and are seven feet*

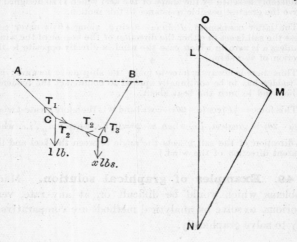

apart. The lengths of AC, CD, and DB are $3\frac{1}{2}$, 3, and 4 feet respectively, and at C is attached a one-pound weight. An unknown weight is attached to D of such a magnitude that, in the position of equilibrium, CDB is a right angle. Find the magnitude of this weight and the tensions of the strings.

Let T_1, T_2, and T_3 be the required tensions and let x lbs. be the weight at D.

Take a vertical line OL, one inch in length, to represent the weight, one pound, at C. Through O draw OM parallel to AC, and through L draw LM parallel to CD.

By the triangle of forces OM represents T_1, and LM represents T_2.

Produce OL vertically downwards and through M draw MN parallel to BD.

Then, since LM represents T_2, it follows that T_3 is represented by MN, and x by LN.

By actual measurement, we have

$$OM=3\cdot05 \text{ ins.}, \quad LM=2\cdot49 \text{ ins.}, \quad MN=5\cdot1 \text{ ins.},$$

and

$$NL=5\cdot63 \text{ ins.}$$

Hence the weight at D is $5\cdot63$ lbs. and the tensions are respectively $3\cdot05$, $2\cdot49$, and $5\cdot1$ lbs. wt.

Ex. 2. *A and B are two points in a horizontal line at a distance of 16 feet apart; AO and OB are two strings of lengths 6 and 12 feet*

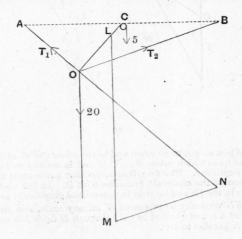

carrying, at O, a body of weight 20 lbs.; a third string, attached to the body at O, passes over a small smooth pulley at the middle point, C, of AB and is attached to a body of weight 5 lbs.; find the tensions of the strings AO and OB.

Let T_1 and T_2 be the required tensions. On OC mark off OL, equal to one inch, to represent the tension, 5 lbs. wt., of the string OC. Draw LM vertical and equal to 4 inches. Through M draw MN, parallel to OB, to meet AO produced in N.

Then, by the Polygon of Forces, the lines ON and NM will represent the tensions T_1 and T_2.

On measurement, ON and NM are found to be respectively 3·9 and 2·45 inches.

Hence　　　　　　　　$T_1 = 5 \times 3 \cdot 9 = 19 \cdot 5$ lbs. wt.,

and　　　　　　　　　$T_2 = 5 \times 2 \cdot 45 = 12 \cdot 25$ lbs. wt.

Ex. 3. The Crane. The essentials of a Crane are represented in the annexed figure. AB is a vertical post; AC a beam, called the jib, capable of turning about its end A; it is supported by a wooden bar, or chain, CD, called the tie, which is attached to a point D of the post AB. At C is a pulley, over which passes a chain one end of which

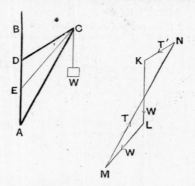

is attached to a weight to be lifted and to the other end of which, E, is applied the force which raises W. This end is usually wound round a drum or cylinder. The tie CD is sometimes horizontal, and often the direction of the chain CE coincides with it. In the above crane the actions in the jib and tie may be determined graphically as follows.

Draw KL vertically to represent W on any scale, and then draw LM equal to KL and parallel to CE; through M draw MN parallel to AC and KN parallel to DC.

Then *KLMN* is a polygon of forces for the equilibrium of *C*; for we assume the tension of the chain to be unaltered in passing over the pulley *C*, and hence that the tension of *CE* is equal to *W*. Hence, if *T* be the thrust of *AC* and *T′* the pull of *CD*, we have

$$\frac{T}{MN} = \frac{T'}{NK} = \frac{W}{KL}.$$

Hence *T* and *T′* are represented by *MN* and *NK* on the same scale that *KL* represents *W*.

EXAMPLES. VII.

[*The following examples are to be solved by geometric construction.*]

1. A boat is towed along a river by means of two ropes, attached to the same point, which are pulled by two men who keep at opposite points of the bank 50 feet apart; one rope is 30 feet long and is pulled with a force equal to the weight of 35 lbs., and the other rope is 45 feet long; the boat is in this way made to move uniformly in a straight line; find the resistance offered to the boat by the stream and the tension of the second rope.

2. The jib of a crane is 10 feet long, and the tie-rod is horizontal and attached to a point 6 feet vertically above the foot of the jib; find the tension of the tie-rod, and the thrust on the jib, when the crane supports a mass of 1 ton.

3. *A* and *B* are two fixed points, *B* being below *A*, and the horizontal and vertical distances between them are 4 feet and 1 foot respectively; *AC* and *BC* are strings of length 5 and 3 feet respectively, and at *C* is tied a body of weight 1 cwt.; find the tensions of the strings.

4. *ABCD* is a light string attached to two points, *A* and *D*, in the same horizontal line, and at the points *B* and *C* are attached weights. In the position of equilibrium the distances of the points *B* and *C* below the line *AD* are respectively 4 and 6 feet. If the lengths of *AB* and *CD* be respectively 6 and 8 feet and the distance *AD* be 14 feet, find the weight at *C*, the magnitude of the weight at *B* being 4 lbs.

5. A framework *ABC* is kept in a vertical plane with *AB* horizontal by supports at *A* and *B*; if the lengths *AB*, *BC*, and *CA* be 10, 7, and 9 feet respectively, and a weight of 10 cwt. be placed at *C*, find the reactions at *A* and *B* and the forces exerted by the different portions of the framework.

6. A framework *ABC* is supported at *A* and *B* so that it is in a vertical plane with *AB* horizontal, and a weight of 200 lbs. is hung on at *C*; if *AB*=5 feet, *BC*=4 feet, and *AC*=3 feet, find the tensions or thrusts in *AC* and *CB*, and the reactions at *A* and *B*.

7. The jib of a crane is 20 feet long, the tie 16 feet, and the post 10 feet. A load of 10 cwts. is hung at the end of a chain which passes over a pulley at the end of the jib and then along the tie. Find the thrust in the jib and the pull in the tie.

8. In the figure of Ex. 3, Art. 50, the tie DC is horizontal and the chain coincides with it; if $W = 500$ lbs., $AC = 11$ feet, and $DC = 5$ feet, find the actions along DC and AC.

9. In the figure of Ex. 3, Art. 50, the angle $CDB = 45°$, and the angle $ACD = 15°$; the chain EC coincides with DC; if W be one ton, find the forces exerted by the parts AC, CD.

10. In the figure of Ex. 3, Art. 50, $DA = 15$ feet, $DC = 20$ feet and $AC = 30$ feet, and a weight of one ton is suspended from C, find the thrusts or tensions produced in AC, CD, and DA when the chain coincides with

　　　　　　　(1)　the jib CA,
　　　　　　　(2)　the tie CD.

11. In the figure of Ex. 3, Art. 50, the jib AC is 25 feet long, the tie CD is 18 feet, $AD = 12$ feet and $AE = 8$ feet; find the tensions or thrusts in AC and CD, when a weight of 2 tons is suspended from the end of the chain.

12. $ABCD$ is a frame-work of four weightless rods, loosely jointed together, AB and AD being each of length 4 feet and BC and CD of length 2 feet. The hinge C is connected with A by means of a fine string of length 5 feet. Weights of 100 lbs. each are attached to B and D and the whole is suspended from A. Shew that the tension in AC is 52 lbs. weight.

13. In the preceding question, instead of the string AC a weightless rod BD of length 3 feet is used to stiffen the frame; a weight of 100 lbs. is attached to C and nothing at B and D. Shew that the thrust in the rod BD is about 77 lbs. weight.

14. In question 12 there are no weights attached to B and D and the whole framework is placed on a smooth horizontal table; the hinges B and D are pressed toward one another by two forces each equal to the weight of 25 lbs. in the straight line BD. Shew that the tension of the string is about 31·6 lbs. weight.

15. $ABCD$ is a rhombus formed by four weightless rods loosely jointed together, and the figure is stiffened by a weightless rod, of one half the length of each of the four rods, joined to the middle points of AB and AD. If this frame be suspended from A and a weight of 100 lbs. be attached to it at C, shew that the thrust of the cross rod is about 115·5 lbs. weight.

CHAPTER IV.

PARALLEL FORCES.

51. In Chapters II. and III. we have shewn how to find the resultant of forces which meet in a point. In the present chapter we shall consider the composition of parallel forces.

In the ordinary statical problems of every-day life parallel forces are of constant occurrence.

Two parallel forces are said to be **like** when they act in the same direction; when they act in opposite parallel directions they are said to be **unlike**.

52. *To find the resultant of two parallel forces acting upon a rigid body.*

Case I. *Let the forces be* **like**.

Let P and Q be the forces acting at points A and B of the body, and let them be represented by the lines AL and BM.

Join AB and at A and B apply two equal and opposite forces, each equal to S, and acting in the directions BA and AB respectively. Let these forces be represented by AD and BE. These two forces balance one another and have no effect upon the equilibrium of the body.

Complete the parallelograms $ALFD$ and $BMGE$; let the diagonals FA and GB be produced to meet in O. Draw OC parallel to AL or BM to meet AB in C.

The forces P and S at A have a resultant P_1, represented by AF. Let its point of application be removed to O.

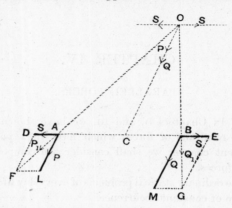

So the forces Q and S at B have a resultant Q_1 represented by BG. Let its point of application be transferred to O.

The force P_1 at O may be resolved into two forces, S parallel to AD, and P in the direction OC.

So the force Q_1 at O may be resolved into two forces, S parallel to BE, and Q in the direction OC.

Also these two forces S acting at O are in equilibrium.

Hence the original forces P and Q are equivalent to a force $(P + Q)$ acting along OC, *i.e.* acting at C parallel to the original directions of P and Q.

To determine the position of the point C. The triangle OCA is, by construction, similar to the triangle ALF;

$$\therefore \frac{OC}{CA} = \frac{AL}{LF} = \frac{P}{S},$$

so that $P \cdot CA = S \cdot OC$ ....(1).

So, since the triangles OCB and BMG are similar, we have

$$\frac{OC}{CB} = \frac{BM}{MG} = \frac{Q}{S},$$

so that

$$Q \cdot CB = S \cdot OC \ldots\ldots\ldots\ldots\ldots(2),$$

Hence, from (1) and (2), we have

$$P \cdot CA = Q \cdot CB,$$

so that

$$\frac{CA}{CB} = \frac{Q}{P},$$

i.e. C divides the line AB *internally* in the inverse ratio of the forces.

Case II.   *Let the forces be* **unlike.**

Let P, Q be the forces (P being the greater) acting at points A and B of the body, and let them be represented by the lines AL and BM.

Join AB, and at A and B apply two equal and opposite forces, each equal to S, and acting in the directions BA and AB respectively. Let these forces be represented by AD and BE respectively; they balance one another and have no effect on the equilibrium of the body.

Complete the parallelograms $ALFD$ and $BMGE$, and produce the diagonals AF and GB to meet in O.

[These diagonals will always meet unless they be parallel, in which case the forces P and Q will be equal.]

Draw OC parallel to AL or BM to meet AB in C.

The forces P and S acting at A have a resultant P_1 represented by AF. Let its point of application be transferred to O.

So the forces Q and S acting at B have a resultant Q_1 represented by BG. Let its point of application be transferred to O.

The force P_1 at O may be resolved into two forces, S parallel to AD, and P in the direction CO produced.

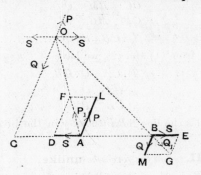

So the forces Q_1 at O may be resolved into two forces, S parallel to BE, and Q in the direction OC.

Also these two forces S acting at O are in equilibrium.

Hence the original forces P and Q are equivalent to a force $P - Q$ acting in the direction CO produced,
  i.e. acting at C in a direction parallel to that of P.

To determine the position of the point C. The triangle OCA is, by construction, similar to the triangle FDA;

$$\therefore \quad \frac{OC}{CA} = \frac{FD}{DA} = \frac{AL}{AD} = \frac{P}{S},$$

so that $\qquad\qquad P \cdot CA = S \cdot OC \dots\dots\dots\dots\dots(1),$

Also, since the triangles OCB and BMG are similar, we have

$$\frac{OC}{CB} = \frac{BM}{MG} = \frac{Q}{S},$$

so that $\qquad\qquad Q \cdot CB = S \cdot OC \dots\dots\dots\dots\dots(2).$

Hence, from (1) and (2), $P \cdot CA = Q \cdot CB.$

Hence $\dfrac{CA}{CB} = \dfrac{Q}{P}$, *i.e.* C divides the line AB *externally* in the inverse ratio of the forces.

To sum up; If two parallel forces, P and Q, act at points A and B of a rigid body,

(i)   their resultant is a force whose line of action is parallel to the lines of action of the component forces; also, when the component forces are like, its direction is the same as that of the two forces, and, when the forces are unlike, its direction is the same as that of the greater component.

(ii)   the point of application is a point C in AB such that

$$P \cdot AC = Q \cdot BC.$$

(iii)   the magnitude of the resultant is the sum of the two component forces when the forces are like, and the difference of the two component forces when they are unlike.

53.   *Case of failure of the preceding construction.*

In the second figure of the last article, if the forces P and Q be equal, the triangles FDA and GEB are equal in all respects, and hence the angles DAF and EBG will be equal.

In this case the lines AF and GB will be parallel and will not meet in any such point as O; hence the construction fails.

Hence there is no single force which is equivalent to two equal unlike parallel forces.

We shall return to the consideration of this case in Chapter VI.

4—2

54. If we have a number of like parallel forces acting on a rigid body we can find their resultant by successive applications of Art. 53. We must find the resultant of the first and second, and then the resultant of this resultant and the third, and so on.

The magnitude of the final resultant is the sum of the forces.

If the parallel forces be not all like, the magnitude of the resultant will be found to be the algebraic sum of the forces each with its proper sign prefixed.

Later on (see Art. 114) will be found formulae for calculating the centre of a system of parallel forces, *i.e.* the point at which the resultant of the system acts.

55. *Resultant of two parallel forces. Experimental verification.*

Take a uniform rectangular bar of wood about 3 feet long, whose cross-section is a square of side an inch or rather more. A face of this bar should be graduated, say in inches or half inches, as in the figure.

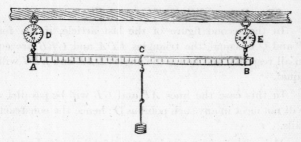

Let the ends *A* and *B* be supported by spring balances which are attached firmly to a support. For this purpose a Salter's circular balance is the more convenient form as it drops much less than the ordinary form when it is stretched. On the bar AB let there be a movable loop C carrying a hook from which weights can be suspended; this loop can be moved into any position along the bar.

Before putting on any weights, and when C is at the middle point of AB, let the readings of the balances D and E be taken. The bar being uniform, these readings should be the same and equal to R (say).

Now hang known weights, amounting in all to W, on to C, and move C into any position C_1 on the bar. Observe the new readings of the balances D and E, and let them be P and Q respectively.

Then $P - R\,(= P_1)$ and $Q - R\,(= Q_1)$ are the additional readings due to the weight W, and therefore P_1 and Q_1 are the forces at D and E which balance the force W at C_1.

It will be found that the sum of
$$P_1 \text{ and } Q_1 \text{ is equal to } W \dots\dots\dots\dots(1).$$

Again measure carefully the distances AC_1 and BC_1.

It will be found that
$$P_1 \times AC_1 = Q_1 \,.\, BC_1 \dots\dots\dots\dots\dots(2).$$

In other words *the resultant of forces P_1 and Q_1 at A and B is equal to $P_1 + Q_1$ acting at C_1, where*
$$P_1 \,.\, AC_1 = Q_1 \,.\, BC_1.$$
But this is the result given by the theoretical investigation of Art. 52 (Case I).

Perform the experiment again by shifting the position of C_1, keeping W the same; the values of P_1 and Q_1 will alter, but their sum will still be W, and the new value of $P_1 \,.\, AC_1$ will be found to be equal to the new value of $Q_1 \,.\, BC_1$.

Similarly the theorem of Art. 52 will be found to be true for any position of C_1 and any value of W.

Numerical illustration. Suppose the weight of the beam and the attached apparatus (without any weights) to be 2 lbs. Then the original reading, R, of the balances will be each 1 lb. Put on a weight of 4 lbs. at C and move C to C_1 until the readings of the balances A and B are respectively 4 and 2 lbs.

Then a force 4 lbs. at C_1 is balanced by a force 3 lbs. $(=4-1)$ at A and 1 lb. $(=2-1)$ at B.

Measure the distances AC_1 and BC_1; they will be found to be 9 inches and 27 inches respectively (assuming the length AB to be 3 feet, *i.e.* 36 inches).

We thus have $\qquad\qquad P_1 . AC_1 = 3 \times 9$,

and $\qquad\qquad\qquad Q_1 . BC_1 = 1 \times 27$,

and these are equal.

Hence the truth of Art. 52 (Case I) for this case.

Unlike parallel forces.

In the last experiment the forces P_1, W and Q_1 at A, C_1, and B are in equilibrium, so that the resultant of P_1 upwards and W downwards is equal and opposite to Q_1. Measure the distances AB and C_1B. Then it will be found that

$$Q_1 = W - P,$$

and $\qquad\qquad P_1 . AB = W . C_1 B.$

Hence the truth of Art. 52 (Case II) is verified.

56. Ex. *A horizontal rod, 6 feet long, whose weight may be neglected, rests on two supports at its extremities; a body, of weight 6 cwt., is suspended from the rod at a distance of $2\frac{1}{2}$ feet from one end; find the reaction at each point of support. If one support could only bear a thrust equal to the weight of 1 cwt., what is the greatest distance from the other support at which the body could be suspended?*

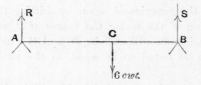

Let AB be the rod and R and S the reactions at the points of support. Let C be the point at which the body is suspended so that

$AC = 3\frac{1}{2}$ and $CB = 2\frac{1}{2}$ feet. For equilibrium the resultant of R and S must balance 6 cwt. Hence, by Art. 52,

$$R + S = 6 \dots\dots\dots\dots\dots\dots\dots\dots(1),$$

and

$$\frac{R}{S} = \frac{BC}{AC} = \frac{2\frac{1}{2}}{3\frac{1}{2}} = \frac{5}{7} \dots\dots\dots\dots\dots\dots(2).$$

Solving (1) and (2), we have $R = \frac{5}{2}$, and $S = \frac{7}{2}$. Hence the reactions are $2\frac{1}{2}$ and $3\frac{1}{2}$ cwt. respectively.

If the reaction at A can only be equal to 1 cwt., S must be 5 cwt. Hence, if AC be x, we have

$$\frac{1}{5} = \frac{BC}{AC} = \frac{6 - x}{x}.$$

$$\therefore \quad x = 5 \text{ feet.}$$

Hence BC is 1 foot.

EXAMPLES. VIII.

In the four following examples A and B denote the points of application of parallel forces P and Q, and C is the point in which their resultant R meets AB.

1. Find the magnitude and position of the resultant (the forces being like) when
   (i) $P = 4$; $Q = 7$; $AB = 11$ inches;
   (ii) $P = 11$; $Q = 19$; $AB = 2\frac{1}{2}$ feet;
   (iii) $P = 5$; $Q = 5$; $AB = 3$ feet.

2. Find the magnitude and position of the resultant (the forces being unlike) when
   (i) $P = 17$; $Q = 25$; $AB = 8$ inches;
   (ii) $P = 23$; $Q = 15$; $AB = 40$ inches;
   (iii) $P = 26$; $Q = 9$; $AB = 3$ feet.

3. The forces being like,
   (i) if $P = 8$; $R = 17$; $AC = 4\frac{1}{2}$ inches; find Q and AB;
   (ii) if $Q = 11$; $AC = 7$ inches; $AB = 8\frac{3}{4}$ inches; find P and R;
   (iii) if $P = 6$; $AC = 9$ inches; $CB = 8$ inches; find Q and R.

4. The forces being unlike,
   (i) if $P = 8$; $R = 17$; $AC = 4\frac{1}{2}$ inches; find Q and AB;
   (ii) if $Q = 11$; $AC = -7$ inches; $AB = 8\frac{3}{4}$ inches; find P and R;
   (iii) if $P = 6$; $AC = -9$ inches; $AB = 12$ inches; find Q and R.

5. Find two like parallel forces acting at a distance of 2 feet apart, which are equivalent to a given force of 20 lbs. wt., the line of action of one being at a distance of 6 inches from the given force.

6. Find two unlike parallel forces acting at a distance of 18 inches apart which are equivalent to a force of 30 lbs. wt., the greater of the two forces being at a distance of 8 inches from the given force.

7. Two parallel forces, P and Q, act at given points of a body; if Q be changed to $\dfrac{P^2}{Q}$, shew that the line of action of the resultant is the same as it would be if the forces were simply interchanged.

8. Two men carry a heavy cask of weight $1\frac{1}{2}$ cwt., which hangs from a light pole, of length 6 feet, each end of which rests on a shoulder of one of the men. The point from which the cask is hung is one foot nearer to one man than to the other. What is the pressure on each shoulder?

9. Two men, one stronger than the other, have to remove a block of stone weighing 270 lbs. by means of a light plank whose length is 6 feet; the stronger man is able to carry 180 lbs.; how must the block be placed so as to allow him that share of the weight?

10. A uniform rod, 12 feet long and weighing 17 lbs., can turn freely about a point in it and the rod is in equilibrium when a weight of 7 lbs. is hung at one end; how far from the end is the point about which it can turn?

N.B. *The weight of a uniform rod may be taken to act at its middle point.*

11. A straight uniform rod is 3 feet long; when a load of 5 lbs. is placed at one end it balances about a point 3 inches from that end; find the weight of the rod.

•12. A uniform bar, of weight 3 lbs. and length 4 feet, passes over a prop and is supported in a horizontal position by a force equal to 1 lb. wt. acting vertically upwards at the other end; find the distance of the prop from the centre of the beam.

13. A heavy uniform rod, 4 feet long, rests horizontally on two pegs which are one foot apart; a weight of 10 lbs. suspended from one end, or a weight of 4 lbs. suspended from the other end, will just tilt the rod up; find the weight of the rod and the distances of the pegs from the centre of the rod.

14. A uniform iron rod, $2\frac{1}{2}$ feet long and of weight 8 lbs., is placed on two rails fixed at two points, A and B, in a vertical wall. AB is horizontal and 5 inches long; find the distances at which the ends of the rod extend beyond the rails if the difference of the thrusts on the rails be 6 lbs. wt.

15. A uniform beam, 4 feet long, is supported in a horizontal position by two props, which are 3 feet apart, so that the beam projects one foot beyond one of the props; shew that the force on one prop is double that on the other.

16. A straight weightless rod, 2 feet in length, rests in a horizontal position between two pegs placed at a distance of 3 inches apart, one peg being at one end of the rod, and a weight of 5 lbs. is suspended from the other end; find the pressure on the pegs.

17. One end of a heavy uniform rod, of weight W, rests on a smooth horizontal plane, and a string tied to the other end of the rod is fastened to a fixed point above the plane; find the tension of the string.

18. A man carries a bundle at the end of a stick which is placed over his shoulder; if the distance between his hand and his shoulder be changed how does the pressure on his shoulder change?

19. A man carries a weight of 50 lbs. at the end of a stick, 3 feet long, resting on his shoulder. He regulates the stick so that the length between his shoulder and his hands is (i) 12, (ii) 18 and (iii) 24 inches; how great are the forces exerted by his hand and the pressures on his shoulder in each case?

20. Three parallel forces act on a horizontal bar. Each is equal to 1 lb. wt., the right-hand one acting vertically upward and the other two vertically down at distances of 2 ft. and 3 ft. respectively from the first; find the magnitude and position of their resultant.

21. A portmanteau, of length 3 feet and height 2 feet and whose centre of gravity is at its centre of figure, is carried upstairs by two men who hold it by the front and back edges of its lower face. If this be inclined at an angle of 30° to the horizontal, and the weight of the portmanteau be 1 cwt., find how much of the weight each supports.

CHAPTER V.

MOMENTS.

57. Def. *The moment of a force about a given point is the product of the force and the perpendicular drawn from the given point upon the line of action of the force.*

Thus the moment of a force F about a given point O is

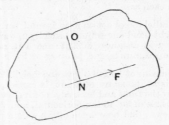

$F \times ON$, where ON is the perpendicular drawn from O upon the line of action of F.

It will be noted that the moment of a force F about a given point O never vanishes, unless either the force vanishes or the force passes through the point about which the moment is taken.

58. *Geometrical representation of a moment.*

Suppose the force F to be represented in magnitude, direction, and line of action by the line AB. Let O be any given point and ON the perpendicular from O upon AB or AB produced.

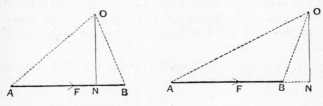

Join OA and OB.

By definition the moment of F about O is $F \times ON$, *i.e.* $AB \times ON$. But $AB \times ON$ is equal to twice the area of the triangle OAB [for it is equal to the area of a rectangle whose base is AB and whose height is ON]. Hence the moment of the force F about the point O is represented by twice the area of the triangle OAB, *i.e. by twice the area of the triangle whose base is the line representing the force and whose vertex is the point about which the moment is taken.*

59. *Physical meaning of the moment of a force about a point.*

Suppose the body in the figure of Art. 57 to be a plane lamina [*i.e.* a body of very small thickness, such as a piece of sheet-tin or a thin piece of board] resting on a smooth table and suppose the point O of the body to be fixed. The effect of a force F acting on the body would be to cause it to turn about the point O as a centre, and this effect would not be zero unless (1) the force F were zero, or (2) the force F passed through O, in which case the distance ON would vanish. Hence the product $F \times ON$ would seem to be a fitting measure of the tendency of F to turn the body about O. This may be experimentally verified as follows;

Let the lamina be at rest under the action of two strings whose tensions are F and F_1, which are tied to fixed points of the lamina and whose lines of action lie in the plane of the lamina. Let ON and ON_1 be the perpendiculars drawn from the fixed point O upon the lines of action of F and F_1.

If we measure the lengths ON and ON_1 and also the

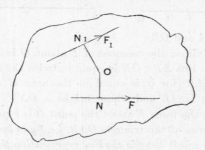

forces F and F_1, it will be found that the product $F \cdot ON$ is always equal to the product $F_1 \cdot ON_1$.

Hence the two forces, F and F_1, will have equal but opposite tendencies to turn the body about O if their moments about O have the same magnitude.

These forces F and F_1 may be measured by carrying the strings over light smooth pulleys and hanging weights at their ends sufficient to give equilibrium; or by tying the strings to the hooks of two spring balances and noting the readings of the balances, as in the cases of Art. 25.

60. Experiment. *To shew that if a body, having one point fixed, be acted upon by two forces and it be at rest, then the moments of the two forces about the fixed point are equal but opposite.*

Take the bar used in Art. 55 and suspend it at C so that it rests in a horizontal position; if the bar be uniform

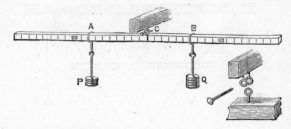

C will be its middle point; if it be not uniform, then C will be its centre of gravity [Chapter IX]. The beam must be so suspended that it turns easily and freely about C.

When the forces are parallel. From any two points A, B of the bar suspend carriers on which place weights until the beam again balances in a horizontal position.

Let P be the total weight, including that of the carrier, at A, and Q the total weight similarly at B. Measure carefully the distances AC and BC.

Then it will be found that the products $P \cdot AC$ and $Q \cdot BC$ are equal.

The theorem can be verified to be true for more than two forces by placing several such carriers on the bar and putting weights upon them of such an amount that equilibrium is secured.

In every such case it will be found that the sum of the moments of the weights on one side of C is equal to the sum of the moments of those on the other side.

When the forces are not parallel. Arrange the bar as before but let light strings be attached at A and B which after passing over light pulleys support carriers at their other ends. Let these carriers have weights put upon them until the beam balances in a horizontal position.

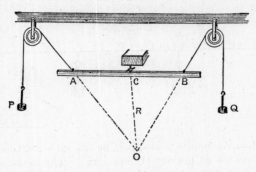

Let P and Q be the total weights on the carriers including the weights of the carriers themselves; these will be the tensions of the strings at A and B.

Measure the perpendicular distances, p and q, from C upon OA and OB respectively.

Then it will be found that

$$P \cdot p = Q \cdot q.$$

61. *Positive and negative moments.* In Art. 57 the force F would, if it were the only force acting on the lamina, make it turn in a direction opposite to that in which the hands of a watch move, when the watch is laid on the table with its face upwards.

The force F_1 would, if it were the only force acting on the lamina, make it turn in the same direction as that in which the hands of the watch move.

The moment of F about O, *i.e.* in a direction $\circlearrowleft$, is said to be *positive*, and the moment of F_1 about O, *i.e.* in a direction $\circlearrowright$, is said to be *negative*.

Algebraic sum of moments. The algebraic sum of the moments of a set of forces about a given point is the sum of the moments of the forces, each moment having its proper sign prefixed to it.

Ex. *ABCD is a square; along the sides AB, CB, DC, and DA forces act equal respectively to 6, 5, 8, and 12 lbs. wt. Find the algebraic sum of their moments about the centre, O, of the square, if the side of the square be 4 feet.*

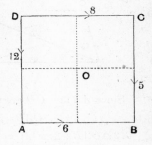

The forces along *DA* and *AB* tend to turn the square about *O* in the positive direction, whilst the forces along the sides *DC* and *CB* tend to turn it in the negative direction.

The perpendicular distance of *O* from each force is 2 feet.

Hence the moments of the forces are respectively

$$+6 \times 2, \quad -5 \times 2, \quad -8 \times 2, \quad \text{and} \quad +12 \times 2.$$

Their algebraic sum is therefore $2[6-5-8+12]$ or 10 units of moment, *i.e.* 10 times the moment of a force equal to 1 lb. wt. acting at the distance of 1 foot from *O*.

62. Theorem. *The algebraic sum of the moments of any two forces about any point in their plane is equal to the moment of their resultant about the same point.*

Case I. *Let the forces meet in a point.*

Let *P* and *Q* acting at the point *A* be the two forces and *O* the point about which the moments are taken. Draw *OC* parallel to the direction of *P* to meet the line of action of *Q* in the point *C*.

Let *AC* represent *Q* in magnitude and on the same scale let *AB* represent *P*; complete the parallelogram *ABDC*, and join *OA* and *OB*.

Then *AD* represents the resultant, *R*, of *P* and *Q*.

(α) If O be without the angle DAC, as in the first figure, we have to shew that

$$2\triangle OAB + 2\triangle OAC = 2\triangle OAD.$$

[For the moments of P and Q about O are in the same direction.]

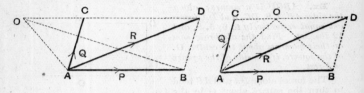

Since AB and OD are parallel, we have

$$\triangle OAB = \triangle DAB = \triangle ACD. \qquad \text{[Euc. I. 37]}$$
$$\therefore 2\triangle OAB + 2\triangle OAC = 2\triangle ACD + 2\triangle OAC = 2\triangle OAD.$$

(β) If O be within the angle CAD, as in the second figure, we have to shew that

$$2\triangle AOB - 2\triangle AOC = 2\triangle AOD.$$

[For the moments of P and Q about O are in opposite directions.]

As in (α), we have

$$\triangle AOB = \triangle DAB = \triangle ACD.$$
$$\therefore 2\triangle AOB - 2\triangle AOC = 2\triangle ACD - 2\triangle OAC = 2\triangle OAD.$$

Case II. *Let the forces be parallel.*

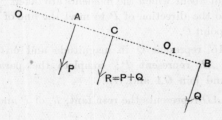

Let P and Q be two parallel forces and R $(= P + Q)$ their resultant.

From any point O in their plane draw $OACB$ perpendicular to the forces to meet them in A, C, and B respectively.

By Art. 52 we have $P \cdot AC = Q \cdot CB$ ....(1);

$\therefore$ the sum of the moments of P and Q about O

$$= Q \cdot OB + P \cdot OA$$
$$= Q (OC + CB) + P (OC - AC)$$
$$= (P + Q) OC + Q \cdot CB - P \cdot AC$$
$$= (P + Q) \cdot OC, \text{ by equation (1)},$$
$$= \text{moment of the resultant about } O.$$

If the point about which the moments are taken be between the forces, as O_1, the moments of P and Q have opposite signs.

In this case we have

Algebraic sum of moments of P and Q about O_1

$$= P \cdot O_1A - Q \cdot O_1B$$
$$= P (O_1C + CA) - Q (CB - O_1C)$$
$$= (P + Q) \cdot O_1C + P \cdot CA - Q \cdot CB$$
$$= (P + Q) \cdot O_1C, \text{ by equation (1)}.$$

The case when the point has any other position, as also the case when the forces have opposite parallel directions, are left for the student to prove for himself.

63. Case I of the preceding proposition may be otherwise proved in the following manner:

Let the two forces, P and Q, be represented by AB and AC respectively and let AD represent the resultant R so that $ABDC$ is a parallelogram.

Let O be any point in the plane of the forces. Join OA and draw BL and CM, parallel to OA, to meet AD in L and M respectively.

L. S.

5

Since the sides of the triangle ACM are respectively parallel to the sides of the triangle DBL, and since AC is equal to BD,

$$\therefore \quad AM = LD,$$

$$\therefore \quad \triangle OAM = \triangle OLD. \qquad \text{[Euc. i. 38]}$$

First, let O fall without the angle CAD, as in the first figure.

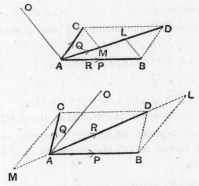

Then

$$2 \triangle OAB + 2 \triangle OAC$$
$$= 2 \triangle OAL + 2 \triangle OAM \qquad \text{[Euc. i. 37]}$$
$$= 2 \triangle OAL + 2 \triangle OLD$$
$$= 2 \triangle OAD.$$

Hence the sum of the moments of P and Q is equal to that of R.

Secondly, let O fall within the angle CAD, as in the second figure.

The algebraic sum of the moments of P and Q about O

$$= 2 \triangle OAB - 2 \triangle OAC$$
$$= 2 \triangle OAL - 2 \triangle OAM \qquad \text{[Euc. i. 37]}$$
$$= 2 \triangle OAL - 2 \triangle OLD$$
$$= 2 \triangle OAD$$
$$= \text{moment of } R \text{ about } O.$$

64. If the point O about which the moments are taken lie on the resultant, the moment of the resultant about the point vanishes. In this case the algebraic sum of the moments of the component forces about the given point vanishes, *i.e. The moments of two forces about any point on the line of action of their resultant are equal and of opposite sign.*

The student will easily be able to prove this theorem independently from a figure; for, in Art. 62, the point O will be found to coincide with the point D and we have only to shew that the triangles ACO and ABO are now equal, and this is obviously true.

65. Generalised theorem of moments. *If any number of forces in one plane acting on a rigid body have a resultant, the algebraic sum of their moments about any point in their plane is equal to the moment of their resultant.*

For let the forces be P, Q, R, S,... and let O be the point about which the moments are taken.

Let P_1 be the resultant of P and Q,

P_2 be the resultant of P_1 and R,

P_3 be the resultant of P_2 and S,

and so on till the final resultant is obtained.

Then the moment of P_1 about $O =$ sum of the moments of P and Q (Art. 62);

Also the moment of P_2 about $O =$ sum of the moments of P_1 and R

$=$ sum of the moments of P, Q, and R.

So the moment of P_3 about O

$=$ sum of the moments of P_2 and S

$=$ sum of the moments of P, Q, R, and S,

and so on until all the forces have been taken.

Hence the moment of the final resultant

$=$ algebraic sum of the moments of the component forces.

Cor. It follows, similarly as in Art. 64, that the algebraic sum of the moments of any number of forces about a point on the line of action of their resultant is zero; so, conversely, if the algebraic sum of the moments of any number of forces about any point in their plane vanishes, then, *either* their resultant is zero (in which case the forces are in equilibrium), *or* the resultant passes through the point about which the moments are taken.

66. The theorem of the previous article enables us to find points on the line of action of the resultant of a system of forces. For we have only to find a point about which the algebraic sum of the moments of the system of forces vanishes, and then the resultant must pass through that point. This principle is exemplified in Examples 2 and 3 of the following article.

If we have a system of parallel forces the resultant is known both in magnitude and direction when one such point is known.

67. Ex. 1. *A rod, 5 feet long, supported by two vertical strings attached to its ends, has weights of 4, 6, 8, and 10 lbs. hung from the rod at distances of 1, 2, 3, and 4 feet from one end. If the weight of the rod be 2 lbs., what are the tensions of the strings?*

Let AF be the rod, B, C, D, and E the points at which the weights

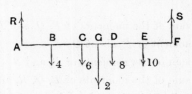

are hung; let G be the middle point; we shall assume that the weight of the rod acts here.

Let R and S be the tensions of the strings. Since the resultant of the forces is zero, its moment about A must be zero.

Hence, by Art. 65, the algebraic sum of the moments about A must vanish.

Therefore $4 \times 1 + 6 \times 2 + 2 \times 2\frac{1}{2} + 8 \times 3 + 10 \times 4 - S \times 5 = 0,$

$$\therefore \ 5S = 4 + 12 + 5 + 24 + 40 = 85,$$

$$\therefore \ S = 17.$$

Similarly, taking moments about F, we have

$$5R = 10 \times 1 + 8 \times 2 + 2 \times 2\frac{1}{2} + 6 \times 3 + 4 \times 4 = 65,$$

$$\therefore \ R = 13.$$

The tension R may be otherwise obtained. For the resultant of the weights is a weight equal to 30 lbs. and that of R and S is a force equal to $R + S$. But these resultants balance one another.

$$\therefore \ R + S = 30 ;$$

$$\therefore \ R = 30 - S = 30 - 17 = 13.$$

Ex. 2. *Forces equal to P, $2P$, $3P$, and $4P$ act along the sides of a square $ABCD$ taken in order; find the magnitude, direction, and line of action of the resultant.*

Let the side of the square be a.

The forces P and $3P$ are, by Art. 52, equal to a parallel force $2P$ acting at E, where DE is $\dfrac{a}{2}$.

The forces $4P$ and $2P$ are, similarly, equal to a force $2P$ acting at a point F on CD where DF is a.

Let the lines of action of these two components meet in O. Then the final resultant is equal to $2P\sqrt{2}$ acting in a direction parallel to CA.

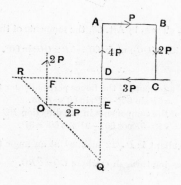

Otherwise thus; without making any geometric construction (which is often tedious) the line of action of the resultant force can be easily obtained by using the theorem of Art. 65.

Let the line of action meet AD and CD in Q and R.

Since Q is a point on the line of action of the resultant the algebraic sum of the moments of the four forces about Q must be zero;

$$\therefore\; P\,(DQ+a)+2P(a)=3P\,.\,DQ;$$

$$\therefore\; DQ=\frac{3a}{2}.$$

So for the point R we have

$$P\,.\,a+2P\,(RD+a)=4P\,.\,RD;$$

$$\therefore\; RD=\frac{3a}{2}.$$

Also the components of the forces perpendicular to CD are $4P-2P$, *i.e.* $2P$, and the components parallel to CD are $3P-P$, *i.e.* $2P$. Hence the magnitude of the resultant is $2\sqrt{2}P$.

Ex. 3. *Forces equal to* $3P$, $7P$, *and* $5P$ *act along the sides* AB, BC, *and* CA *of an equilateral triangle* ABC; *find the magnitude, direction, and line of action of the resultant.*

Let the side of the triangle be a, and let the resultant force meet

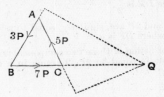

the side BC in Q. Then, by Art. 65, the moments of the forces about Q vanish.

$$\therefore\; 3P \times (QC+a) \sin 60° = 5P \times QC \sin 60°.$$

$$\therefore\; QC = \frac{3a}{2}.$$

The sum of the components of the forces perpendicular to BC

$$= 5P \sin 60° - 3P \sin 60° = P\sqrt{3}.$$

Also the sum of the components in the direction BC

$$= 7P - 5P \cos 60° - 3P \cos 60° = 3P.$$

Hence the resultant is $P\sqrt{12}$ inclined at an angle $\tan^{-1}\dfrac{\sqrt{3}}{3}$, *i.e.* $30°$, to BC and passing through Q where $CQ = \frac{3}{2}BC$.

EXAMPLES. IX.

1. The side of a square $ABCD$ is 4 feet; along the lines CB, BA, DA, and DB, respectively act forces equal to 4, 3, 2, and 5 lbs. weight; find, to the nearest decimal of a foot-pound, the algebraic sum of the moments of the forces about C.

2. The side of a regular hexagon $ABCDEF$ is 2 feet; along the sides AB, CB, DC, DE, EF, and FA act forces respectively equal to 1, 2, 3, 4, 5, and 6 lbs. wt.; find the algebraic sum of the moments of the forces about A.

3. A pole of 20 feet length is placed with its end on a horizontal plane and is pulled by a string, attached to its upper end and inclined at 30° to the horizon, whose tension is equal to 30 lbs. wt.; find the horizontal force which applied at a point 4 feet above the ground will keep the pole in a vertical position.

4. A uniform iron rod is of length 6 feet and mass 9 lbs., and from its extremities are suspended masses of 6 and 12 lbs. respectively; from what point must the rod be suspended so that it may remain in a horizontal position?

5. A uniform beam is of length 12 feet and weight 50 lbs., and from its ends are suspended bodies of weights 20 and 30 lbs. respectively; at what point must the beam be supported so that it may remain in equilibrium?

6. Masses of 1 lb., 2 lbs., 3 lbs., and 4 lbs. are suspended from a uniform rod, of length 5 ft., at distances of 1 ft., 2 ft., 3 ft., and 4 ft. respectively from one end. If the mass of the rod be 4 lbs., find the position of the point about which it will balance.

7. A uniform rod, 4 ft. in length and weighing 2 lbs., turns freely about a point distant one foot from one end and from that end a weight of 10 lbs. is suspended. What weight must be placed at the other end to produce equilibrium?

8. A heavy uniform beam, 10 feet long, whose mass is 10 lbs., is supported at a point 4 feet from one end; at this end a mass of 6 lbs. is placed; find the mass which, placed at the other end, would give equilibrium.

9. The horizontal roadway of a bridge is 30 feet long, weighs 6 tons, and rests on similar supports at its ends. What is the thrust borne by each support when a carriage, of weight 2 tons, is (1) half-way across, (2) two-thirds of the way across?

10. A light rod, AB, 20 inches long, rests on two pegs whose distance apart is 10 inches. How must it be placed so that the reactions of the pegs may be equal when weights of $2W$ and $3W$ respectively are suspended from A and B?

11. A light rod, of length 3 feet, has equal weights attached to it, one at 9 inches from one end and the other at 15 inches from the other end; if it be supported by two vertical strings attached to its ends and if the strings cannot support a tension greater than the weight of 1 cwt., what is the greatest magnitude of the equal weights?

12. A heavy uniform beam, whose mass is 40 lbs., is suspended in a horizontal position by two vertical strings each of which can sustain a tension of 35 lbs. weight. How far from the centre of the beam must a body, of mass 20 lbs., be placed so that one of the strings may just break?

13. A uniform bar, *AB*, 10 feet long and of mass 50 lbs., rests on the ground. If a mass of 100 lbs. be laid on it at a point, distant 3 feet from *B*, find what vertical force applied to the end *A* will just begin to lift that end.

14. A rod, 16 inches long, rests on two pegs, 9 inches apart, with its centre midway between them. The greatest masses that can be suspended in succession from the two ends without disturbing the equilibrium are 4 lbs. and 5 lbs. respectively. Find the weight of the rod and the position of the point at which its weight acts.

15. A straight rod, 2 feet long, is movable about a hinge at one end and is kept in a horizontal position by a thin vertical string attached to the rod at a distance of 8 inches from the hinge and fastened to a fixed point above the rod; if the string can just support a mass of 9 ozs. without breaking, find the greatest mass that can be suspended from the other end of the rod, neglecting the weight of the rod.

16. A tricycle, weighing 5 stone 4 lbs., has a small wheel symmetrically placed 3 feet behind two large wheels which are 3 feet apart; if the centre of gravity of the machine be at a horizontal distance of 9 inches behind the front wheels and that of the rider, whose weight is 9 stone, be 3 inches behind the front wheels, find the thrusts on the ground of the different wheels.

17. A tricycle, of weight 6 stone, has a small wheel symmetrically placed 3 ft. 6 ins. in front of the line joining the two large wheels which are 3 feet apart; if the centre of gravity of the machine be distant horizontally 1 foot in front of the hind wheels and that of the rider, whose weight is 11 stone, be 6 inches in front of the hind wheels, find how the weight is distributed on the different wheels.

18. A dog-cart, loaded with 4 cwt., exerts a force on the horse's back equal to 10 lbs. wt.; find the position of the centre of gravity of the load if the distance between the pad and the axle be 6 feet.

19. Forces of 3, 4, 5, and 6 lbs. wt. respectively act along the sides of a square *ABCD* taken in order; find the magnitude, direction, and line of action of their resultant.

20. $ABCD$ is a square; along AB, CB, AD, and DC equal forces, P, act; find their resultant.

21. $ABCD$ is a square the length of whose side is one foot; along AB, BC, DC, and AD act forces proportional to 1, 2, 4, and 3 respectively; shew that the resultant is parallel to a diagonal of the square and find where it cuts the sides of the square.

22. $ABCD$ is a rectangle of which adjacent sides AB and BC are equal to 3 and 4 feet respectively; along AB, BC, and CD forces of 30, 40, and 50 lbs. wt. act; find the resultant.

23. Three forces P, $2P$, and $3P$ act along the sides AB, BC, and CA of a given equilateral triangle ABC; find the magnitude and direction of their resultant, and find also the point in which its line of action meets the side BC.

24. ABC is an isosceles triangle whose angle A is $120°$ and forces of magnitude 1, 1, and $\sqrt{3}$ lbs. wt. act along AB, AC, and BC; shew that the resultant bisects BC and is parallel to one of the other sides of the triangle.

25. Forces proportional to AB, BC, and $2CA$ act along the sides of a triangle ABC taken in order; shew that the resultant is represented in magnitude and direction by CA and that its line of action meets BC at a point X where CX is equal to BC.

26. ABC is a triangle and D, E, and F are the middle points of the sides; forces represented by AD, $\frac{2}{3}BE$, and $\frac{1}{3}CF$ act on a particle at the point where AD and BE meet; shew that the resultant is represented in magnitude and direction by $\frac{1}{2}AC$ and that its line of action divides BC in the ratio $2 : 1$.

27. Three forces act along the sides of a triangle; shew that, if the sum of two of the forces be equal in magnitude but opposite in sense to the third force, then the resultant of the three forces passes through the centre of the inscribed circle of the triangle.

28. The wire passing round a telegraph pole is horizontal and the two portions attached to the pole are inclined at an angle of $60°$ to one another. The pole is supported by a wire attached to the middle point of the pole and inclined at $60°$ to the horizon; shew that the tension of this wire is $4\sqrt{3}$ times that of the telegraph wire.

29. At what height from the base of a pillar must the end of a rope of given length be fixed so that a man standing on the ground and pulling at its other end with a given force may have the greatest tendency to make the pillar overturn?

30. The magnitude of a force is known and also its moments about two given points A and B. Find, by a geometrical construction, its line of action.

31. Find the locus of all points in a plane such that two forces given in magnitude and position shall have equal moments, in the same sense, round any one of these points.

32. AB is a diameter of a circle and BP and BQ are chords at right angles to one another; shew that the moments of forces represented by BP and BQ about A are equal.

33. A cyclist, whose weight is 150 lbs., puts all his weight upon one pedal of his bicycle when the crank is horizontal and the bicycle is prevented from moving forwards. If the length of the crank is 6 inches and the radius of the chain-wheel is 4 inches, find the tension of the chain.

CHAPTER VI.

COUPLES.

68. Def. Two equal unlike parallel forces, whose lines of action are not the same, form a couple.

The Arm of a couple is the perpendicular distance between the lines of action of the two forces which form the couple, *i.e.* is the perpendicular drawn from any point lying on the line of action of one of the forces upon the line of action of the other. Thus the arm of the couple (P, P) is the length AB.

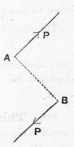

The Moment of a couple is the product of one of the forces forming the couple and the arm of the couple.

In the figure the moment of the couple is $P \times AB$.

Examples of a couple are the forces applied to the handle of a screw-press, or to the key of a clock in winding it up, or by the hands to the handle of a door in opening it.

A couple is by some writers called a Torque; by others the word Torque is used to denote the Moment of the Couple.

69.   Theorem. *The algebraic sum of the moments of the two forces forming a couple about any point in their plane is constant, and equal to the moment of the couple.*

Let the couple consist of two forces, each equal to P, and let O be any point in their plane.

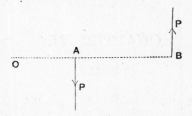

Draw OAB perpendicular to the lines of action of the forces to meet them in A and B respectively.

The algebraic sum of the moments of the forces about O

$$= P \cdot OB - P \cdot OA = P (OB - OA) = P \cdot AB$$

= the moment of the couple, and is therefore the same whatever be the point O about which the moments are taken.

70.   Theorem. *Two couples, acting in one plane upon a rigid body, whose moments are equal and opposite, balance one another.*

Let one couple consist of two forces (P, P), acting at the ends of an arm p, and let the other couple consist of two forces (Q, Q), acting at the ends of an arm q.

Case I. Let one of the forces P meet one of the forces Q in a point O, and let the other two forces meet in O'. From O' draw perpendiculars, $O'M$ and $O'N$, upon the forces which do not pass through O', so that the lengths of these perpendiculars are p and q respectively.

Since the moments of the couples are equal in magnitude, we have

$$P \cdot p = Q \cdot q,$$

i.e., $P \cdot O'M = Q \cdot O'N.$

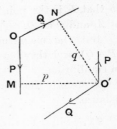

Hence, (Art. 64), O' is on the line of action of the resultant of P and Q acting at O, so that OO' is the direction of this resultant.

Similarly, the resultant of P and Q at O' is in the direction $O'O.$

Also these resultants are equal in magnitude; for the forces at O are respectively equal to, and act at the same angle as, the forces at $O'.$

Hence these two resultants destroy one another, and therefore the four forces composing the two couples are in equilibrium.

Case II. Let the forces composing the couples be all parallel, and let any straight line perpendicular to their directions meet them in the points A, B, C, and D, as in the figure, so that, since the moments are equal, we have

$$P \cdot AB = Q \cdot CD \dots\dots\dots\dots\dots(i).$$

Let L be the point of application of the resultant of Q at C and P at B, so that

$$P \cdot BL = Q \cdot CL \quad \text{(Art. 52)} \dots\dots(ii).$$

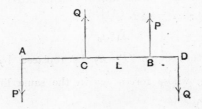

By subtracting (ii) from (i), we have
$$P \cdot AL = Q \cdot LD,$$
so that L is the point of application of the resultant of P at A, and Q at D.

But the magnitude of each of these resultants is $(P + Q)$, and they have opposite directions; hence they are in equilibrium.

Therefore the four forces composing the two couples balance.

71. Since two couples in the same plane, of equal but opposite moment, balance, it follows, by reversing the directions of the forces composing one of the couples, that

Any two couples of equal moment in the same plane are equivalent.

It follows also that two like couples of equal moment are equivalent to a couple of double the moment.

72. Theorem. *Any number of couples in the same plane acting on a rigid body are equivalent to a single couple, whose moment is equal to the algebraic sum of the moments of the couples.*

For let the couples consist of forces (P, P) whose arm is p, (Q, Q) whose arm is q, (R, R) whose arm is r, etc. Replace the couple (Q, Q) by a couple whose components have the same lines of action as the forces (P, P). The magnitude of each of the forces of this latter couple will be X, where $X \cdot p = Q \cdot q$, (Art. 71),

so that
$$X = Q\frac{q}{p}.$$

So let the couple (R, R) be replaced by a couple $\left(R\frac{r}{p}, R\frac{r}{p} \right)$, whose forces act in the same lines as the forces (P, P).

Similarly for the other couples.

Hence all the couples are equivalent to a couple, each of whose forces is $P + Q\dfrac{q}{p} + R\dfrac{r}{p} + \ldots$ acting at an arm p.

The moment of this couple is

$$\left(P + Q\,\frac{q}{p} + R\,\frac{r}{p} + \ldots \right) \cdot p,$$

$$i.e.,\ \ P\,.\,p + Q\,.\,q + R\,.\,r + \ldots.$$

Hence the original couples are equivalent to a single couple, whose moment is equal to the sum of their moments.

If all the component couples have not the same sign we must give to each moment its proper sign, and the same proof will apply.

EXAMPLES X.

1. *ABCD* is a square whose side is 2 feet; along *AB*, *BC*, *CD*, and *DA* act forces equal to 1, 2, 8, and 5 lbs. wt., and along *AC* and *DB* forces equal to $5\sqrt{2}$ and $2\sqrt{2}$ lbs. wt.; shew that they are equivalent to a couple whose moment is equal to 16 foot-pounds weight.

2. Along the sides *AB* and *CD* of a square *ABCD* act forces each equal to 2 lbs. weight, whilst along the sides *AD* and *CB* act forces each equal to 5 lbs. weight; if the side of the square be 3 feet, find the moment of the couple that will give equilibrium.

3. *ABCDEF* is a regular hexagon; along the sides *AB*, *CB*, *DE*, and *FE* act forces respectively equal to 5, 11, 5, and 11 lbs. weight, and along *CD* and *FA* act forces, each equal to x lbs. weight. Find x, if the forces be in equilibrium.

4. A horizontal bar *AB*, without weight, is acted upon by a vertical downward force of 1 lb. weight at *A*, a vertical upward force of 1 lb. weight at *B*, and a downward force of 5 lbs. weight at a given point *C* inclined to the bar at an angle of 30°. Find at what point of the bar a force must be applied to balance these, and find also its magnitude and direction.

73. Theorem. *The effect of a couple upon a rigid body is unaltered if it be transferred to any plane parallel to its own, the arm remaining parallel to its original position.*

Let the couple consist of two forces (P, P), whose arm is AB, and let their lines of action be AC and BD.

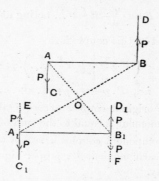

Let A_1B_1 be any line equal and parallel to AB.

Draw A_1C_1 and B_1D_1 parallel to AC and BD respectively.

At A_1 introduce two equal and opposite forces, each equal to P, acting in the direction A_1C_1 and the opposite direction A_1E.

At B_1 introduce, similarly, two equal and opposite forces, each equal to P, acting in the direction B_1D_1 and the opposite direction B_1F.

These forces will have no effect on the equilibrium of the body.

Join AB_1 and A_1B, and let them meet in O; then O is the middle point of both AB_1 and A_1B.

The forces P at B and P acting along A_1E have a resultant $2P$ acting at O parallel to BD.

The forces P at A and P acting along B_1F have a resultant $2P$ acting at O parallel to AC.

These two resultants are equal and opposite, and therefore balance. Hence we have left the two forces (P, P) at A_1 and B_1 acting in the directions A_1C_1 and B_1D_1, *i.e.*, parallel to the directions of the forces of the original couple.

Also the plane through A_1C_1 and B_1D_1 is parallel to the plane through AC and BD.

Hence the theorem is proved.

Cor. From this proposition and Art. 71 we conclude that *A couple may be replaced by any other couple acting in a parallel plane, provided that the moments of the two couples are the same.*

74. Theorem. *A single force and a couple acting in the same plane upon a rigid body cannot produce equilibrium, but are equivalent to the single force acting in a direction parallel to its original direction.*

Let the couple consist of two forces, each equal to P, their lines of action being OB and O_1C respectively.

Let the single force be Q.

Case I. If Q be not parallel to the forces of the couple, let it be produced to meet one of them in O.

Then P and Q, acting at O, are equivalent to some force R, acting in some direction OL which lies between OA and OB.

Let OL be produced (backwards if necessary) to meet the other force of the couple in O_1, and let the point of application of R be transferred to O_1.

Draw O_1A_1 parallel to OA.

Then the force R may be resolved into two forces Q and P, the former acting in the direction O_1A_1, and the latter in the direction opposite to O_1C.

This latter force P is balanced by the second force P of the couple acting in the direction O_1C.

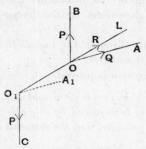

Hence we have left as the resultant of the system a force Q acting in the direction O_1A_1 parallel to its original direction OA.

Case II. Let the force Q be parallel to one of the forces of the couple.

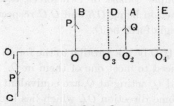

Let O_1O meet the force Q in O_2.

The parallel forces P at O and Q at O_2 are, by Art. 52, equivalent to a force $(P + Q)$ acting at some point O_3 in a direction parallel to OB. The unlike parallel forces $(P + Q)$ at O_3 and P at O_1 are, similarly, equivalent to a force Q acting at some point O_4 in a direction parallel to O_3D.

Hence the resultant of the system is equal to the single force Q acting in a direction parallel to its original direction.

75. *If three forces, acting upon a rigid body, be represented in magnitude, direction, and line of action by the sides
of a triangle taken in order, they are equivalent to a couple
whose moment is represented by twice the area of the triangle.*

Let ABC be the triangle and P, Q, and R the forces, so
that P, Q, and R are represented by the sides BC, CA, and
AB of the triangle.

Through B draw LBM parallel to the side AC, and introduce two equal and opposite
forces, equal to Q, at B, acting
in the directions BL and BM
respectively. By the triangle
of forces (Art. 36) the forces P,
R, and Q acting in the straight
line BL, are in equilibrium.

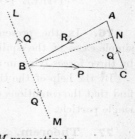

Hence we are left with the
two forces, each equal to Q,
acting in the directions CA and BM respectively.

These form a couple whose moment is $Q \times BN$, where
BN is drawn perpendicular to CA.

Also $Q \times BN = CA \times BN =$ twice the area of the triangle
ABC.

Cor. In a similar manner it may be shewn that if
a system of forces acting on one plane on a rigid body be
represented in magnitude, direction, and line of action by
the sides of the polygon, they are equivalent to a couple
whose moment is represented by twice the area of the
polygon.

CHAPTER VII.

EQUILIBRIUM OF A RIGID BODY ACTED ON BY THREE FORCES IN A PLANE.

76. In the present chapter we shall discuss some simple cases of the equilibrium of a rigid body acted upon by three forces lying in a plane.

By the help of the theorem of the next article we shall find that the conditions of equilibrium reduce to those of a single particle.

77. Theorem. *If three forces, acting in one plane upon a rigid body, keep it in equilibrium, they must either meet in a point or be parallel.*

If the forces be not all parallel, at least two of them must meet; let these two be P and Q, and let their directions meet in O.

The third force R shall then pass through the point O.

Since the algebraic sum of the moments of any number of forces about a point in their plane is equal to the moment of their resultant,

therefore the sum of the moments of P, Q, and R about O is equal to the moment of their resultant.

But this resultant vanishes since the forces are in equilibrium.

Hence the sum of the moments of P, Q, and R about O is zero.

But, since P and Q both pass through O, their moments about O vanish.

Hence the moment of R about O vanishes.

Hence by Art. 57, since R is not zero, its line of action must pass through O.

Hence the forces meet in a point.

Otherwise. The resultant of P and Q must be some force passing through O.

But, since the forces P, Q, and R are in equilibrium, this resultant must balance R.

But two forces cannot balance unless they have the same line of action.

Hence the line of action of R must pass through O.

78. By the preceding theorem we see that the conditions of equilibrium of three forces, acting in one plane, are easily obtained. For the three forces must meet in a point; and by using Lami's Theorem, (Art. 40), or by resolving the forces in two directions at right angles, (Art. 46), or by a graphic construction, we can obtain the required conditions.

Ex. 1. *A heavy uniform rod AB is hinged at A to a fixed point, and rests in a position inclined at 60°*
to the horizontal, being acted upon by
a horizontal force F applied at the
lower end B: find the action at the
hinge and the magnitude of F.

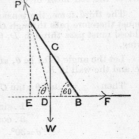

Let the vertical through C, the middle point of the rod, meet the horizontal line through B in the point D and let the weight of the rod be W.

There are only three forces acting on the rod, viz., the force F, the weight W, and the unknown reaction, P, of the hinge.

These three forces must therefore meet in a point.

Now F and W meet at D; hence the direction of the action at the hinge must be the line DA.

Draw AE perpendicular to EB, and let the angle ADE be θ.

Then
$$\tan \theta = \frac{AE}{ED} = \frac{2AE}{EB} = 2 \tan 60° = 2\sqrt{3}.$$

Also, by Lami's Theorem,

$$\frac{F}{\sin WDA} = \frac{W}{\sin ADB} = \frac{P}{\sin WDB},$$

i.e.,
$$\frac{F}{\sin (90° + \theta)} = \frac{W}{\sin (180° - \theta)} = \frac{P}{\sin 90°}.$$

$$\therefore F = W \frac{\cos \theta}{\sin \theta} = W \cot \theta = \frac{W}{2\sqrt{3}} = \frac{W}{6}\sqrt{3},$$

and
$$P = W \frac{1}{\sin \theta} = W \sqrt{1 + \cot^2 \theta} = W \sqrt{\frac{13}{12}}.$$

Otherwise; ADE is a triangle of forces, since its sides are parallel to the forces. Hence θ can be measured, and

$$\frac{P}{AD} = \frac{F}{ED} = \frac{W}{AE}.$$

Ex. 2. *A uniform rod, AB, is inclined at an angle of 60° to the vertical with one end A resting against a smooth vertical wall, being supported by a string attached to a point C of the rod, distant 1 foot from B, and also to a ring in the wall vertically above A; if the length of the rod be 4 feet, find the position of the ring and the inclination and tension of the string.*

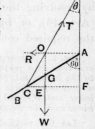

Let the perpendicular to the wall through A and the vertical line through the middle point, G, of the rod meet in O.

The third force, the tension T of the string, must therefore pass through O. Hence CO produced must pass through D, the position of the ring.

Let the angle CDA be θ, and draw CEF horizontal to meet OG in E and the wall in F.

Then
$$\tan \theta = \tan COE = \frac{CE}{OE} = \frac{CG \sin CGE}{AF}$$
$$= \frac{1 . \sin 60°}{3 . \cos 60°} = \frac{1}{\sqrt{3}}.$$

$$\therefore \theta = 30°.$$

$$\therefore ACD = 60° - \theta = 30°.$$

Hence $AD = AC = 3$ feet, giving the position of the ring.

If R be the reaction of the wall, and W be the weight of the beam, we have, since the forces are proportional to the sides of the triangle AOD,

$$\frac{T}{OD} = \frac{R}{AO} = \frac{W}{DA}.$$

$$\therefore T = W\frac{OD}{DA} = \frac{W}{\cos 30°} = W \cdot \frac{2}{\sqrt{3}},$$

and

$$R = W\frac{AO}{DA} = W\tan 30° = W \cdot \frac{1}{\sqrt{3}}.$$

Ex. 3. *A rod whose centre of gravity divides it into two portions, whose lengths are a and b, has a string, of length l, tied to its two ends and the string is slung over a small smooth peg; find the position of equilibrium of the rod, in which it is not vertical.*

[N.B. *The centre of gravity of a body is the point at which its weight may be assumed to act.*]

Let AB be the rod and C its centre of gravity; let O be the peg and let the lengths of the portions AO and OB of the string be x and y respectively.

Since there are only three forces acting on the body they must meet in a point.

But the two tensions pass through O; hence the line of action of the weight W must pass through O, and hence the line CO must be vertical.

Now the tension T of the string is not altered, since the string passes round a smooth peg; hence, since W balances the resultant of two *equal* forces, it must bisect the angle between them.

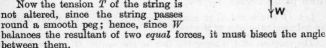

$$\therefore \angle AOC = \angle BOC = a \text{ (say)}.$$

Hence

$$\frac{x}{y} = \frac{AC}{CB} = \frac{a}{b}. \qquad \text{[Euc. vi. 3.]}$$

Also

$$x + y = l.$$

$\therefore$ solving these equations, we have

$$\frac{x}{a} = \frac{y}{b} = \frac{l}{a+b} \dots\dots\dots\dots\dots\dots(i).$$

Also, from the triangle AOB, we have

$$(a+b)^2 = x^2 + y^2 - 2xy \cos 2\alpha = (x+y)^2 - 2xy\,(1+\cos 2\alpha)$$
$$= (x+y)^2 - 4xy \cos^2\alpha = l^2 - 4\,\frac{l^2ab}{(a+b)^2}\cos^2\alpha.$$

$$\therefore \quad \cos^2\alpha = \frac{l^2 - (a+b)^2}{4l^2}\,\frac{(a+b)^2}{ab} \quad\dots\dots\dots\dots\dots(ii).$$

This equation gives α.

Let θ be the inclination of the rod to the horizon, so that

$$OCA = 90° + \theta.$$

From the triangle ACO we have

$$\frac{\sin (90° + \theta)}{\sin \alpha} = \frac{AO}{AC} = \frac{x}{a} = \frac{l}{a+b}\,, \text{ by (i).}$$

$$\therefore \quad \cos \theta = \frac{l \sin \alpha}{a+b}\,, \text{ giving } \theta.$$

Also, by resolving the forces vertically, we have $2T \cos \alpha = W$, giving T.

Numerical Example. If the length of the rod be 5 feet, the length of the string 7 feet, and if the centre of gravity of the rod divide it in the ratio $4:3$, shew that the portions of the string are at right angles, that the inclination of the rod to the horizon is $\tan^{-1}\frac{1}{7}$, and that the tension of the string is to the weight of the rod as $\sqrt{2}:2$.

Ex. 4. *A heavy uniform rod, of length $2a$, rests partly within and partly without a fixed smooth hemispherical bowl, of radius r; the rim of the bowl is horizontal, and one point of the rod is in contact with the rim; if θ be the inclination of the rod to the horizon, shew that*

$$2r \cos 2\theta = a \cos \theta.$$

Let the figure represent that vertical section of the hemisphere which passes through the rod.

Let AB be the rod, G its centre of gravity, and C the point where the rod meets the edge of the bowl.

The reaction at A is along the line to the centre, O, of the bowl; for AO is the only line through A which is perpendicular to the surface of the bowl at A.

Also the reaction at C is perpendicular to the rod; for this is the only direction that is perpendicular to both the rod and the rim of the bowl.

These two reactions meet in a point D; also, by Euc. III. 31, D must lie on the geometrical sphere of which the bowl is a portion.

Hence the vertical line through G, the middle point of the rod, must pass through D.

Through A draw AE horizontal to meet DG in E and join OC.

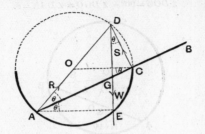

Since OC and AE are parallel,

$$\therefore \quad \angle OCA = \angle CAE = \theta.$$

Since $\qquad OC = OA, \quad \therefore \angle OAC = \angle OCA = \theta.$

Also $\qquad \angle GDC = 90° - \angle DGC = \theta.$

Now $\qquad AE = AG \cos \theta = a \cos \theta,$

and $\qquad AE = AD \cos 2\theta = 2r \cos 2\theta.$

$$\therefore \quad 2r \cos 2\theta = a \cos \theta, \text{ giving } \theta.$$

Also, by Lami's Theorem, if R and S be the reactions at A and C, we have

$$\frac{R}{\sin \theta} = \frac{S}{\sin ADG} = \frac{W}{\sin ADC},$$

$$i.e., \quad \frac{R}{\sin \theta} = \frac{S}{\cos 2\theta} = \frac{W}{\cos \theta}.$$

Numerical Example. If $r = \dfrac{\sqrt{3}}{2} a$, then we have $\theta = 30°$, and

$$R = S = W \frac{\sqrt{3}}{3}.$$

Ex. 5. *A beam whose centre of gravity divides it into two portions, a and b, is placed inside a smooth sphere; shew that, if θ be its inclination to the horizon in the position of equilibrium and 2α be the angle subtended by the beam at the centre of the sphere, then*

$$\tan \theta = \frac{b-a}{b+a} \tan \alpha.$$

In this case both the reactions, R and S, at the ends of the rod pass through the centre, O, of the sphere. Hence the centre of gravity, G, of the rod must be vertically below O.

Let OG meet the horizontal line through A in N.

Draw OD perpendicular to AB.

Then $\angle AOD = \angle BOD = a,$

and $\angle DOG = 90^\circ - \angle DGO = \angle DAN = \theta.$

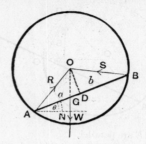

Hence

$$\frac{a}{b} = \frac{AG}{GB} = \frac{AD - GD}{BD + GD} = \frac{OD \tan AOD - OD \tan GOD}{OD \tan BOD + OD \tan GOD}$$

$$= \frac{\tan a - \tan \theta}{\tan a + \tan \theta}.$$

$$\therefore \ \tan \theta = \frac{b - a}{b + a} \tan a.$$

This equation gives θ.

Also, by Lami's Theorem,

$$\frac{R}{\sin BOG} = \frac{S}{\sin AOG} = \frac{W}{\sin AOB}.$$

$$\therefore \ \frac{R}{\sin (a + \theta)} = \frac{S}{\sin (a - \theta)} = \frac{W}{\sin 2a},$$

giving the reactions.

Numerical Example. If the rod be of weight 40 lbs., and subtend a right angle at the centre of the sphere, and if its centre of gravity divide it in the ratio 1 : 2, shew that its inclination to the horizon is $\tan^{-1}\frac{1}{3}$, and that the reactions are $8\sqrt{5}$ and $16\sqrt{5}$ lbs. weight respectively.

Ex. 6. *Shew how the forces which act on a kite maintain it in equilibrium, proving that the perpendicular to the kite must lie between the direction of the string and the vertical.*

Let AB be the middle line of the kite, B being the point at which the tail is attached; the plane of the kite is perpendicular to the plane of the paper. Let G be the centre of gravity of the kite including its tail.

The action of the wind may be resolved at each point of the kite into two components, one perpendicular to the kite and the other along its surface. The latter components have no effect on it and may be neglected. The former components compound into a single

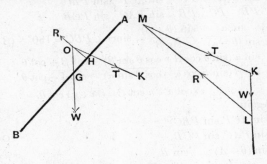

force *R* perpendicular to the kite which acts at a point *H* which is a short distance above *G*.

R and *W* meet at a point *O* and through it must pass the direction of the third force, *viz.* the tension *T* of the string.

Draw *KL* vertically to represent the weight *W*, and *LM* parallel to *HO* to represent *R*.

Then, by the triangle of forces, *MK* must represent the tension *T* of the string.

It is clear from the figure that the line *MK* must make a greater angle with the vertical *LK* than the line *LM*,

i.e. the perpendicular to the kite must lie between the vertical and the direction of the string.

From the triangle of forces it is clear that both *T* and *W* must be smaller than the force *R* exerted by the wind.

79. Trigonometrical Theorems.

There are two trigonometrical theorems which are useful in Statical Problems, *viz.* If *P* be any point in the base *AB* of a triangle *ABC*, and if *CP* divides *AB* into two parts *m* and *n*, and the angle *C* into two parts *a* and *β*, and if the angle *CPB* be *θ*, then

$$(m + n) \cot \theta = m \cot a - n \cot \beta \quad \dots \dots \dots (1),$$

and

$$(m + n) \cot \theta = n \cot A - m \cot B \quad \dots \dots (2).$$

For

$$\frac{m}{n} = \frac{AP}{PB} = \frac{AP}{PC} \cdot \frac{PC}{PB} = \frac{\sin ACP}{\sin PAC} \cdot \frac{\sin PBC}{\sin PCB}$$

$$= \frac{\sin \alpha}{\sin (\theta - \alpha)} \cdot \frac{\sin (\theta + \beta)}{\sin \beta}, \text{ since } \angle PBC = 180° - (\beta + \theta),$$

$$= \frac{\sin \alpha (\sin \theta \cos \beta + \cos \theta \sin \beta)}{\sin \beta (\sin \theta \cos \alpha - \cos \theta \sin \alpha)} = \frac{\cot \beta + \cot \theta}{\cot \alpha - \cot \theta},$$

$$\therefore \quad m \cot \alpha - n \cot \beta = (m + n) \cot \theta.$$

Again

$$\frac{m}{n} = \frac{\sin ACP}{\sin PAC} \frac{\sin PBC}{\sin PCB}$$

$$= \frac{\sin (\theta - A)}{\sin A} \cdot \frac{\sin B}{\sin (\theta + B)}$$

$$= \frac{(\sin \theta \cos A - \cos \theta \sin A) \sin B}{\sin A (\sin \theta \cos B + \cos \theta \sin B)}$$

$$= \frac{\cot A - \cot \theta}{\cot B + \cot \theta}.$$

$$\therefore \quad (m + n) \cot \theta = n \cot A - m \cot B.$$

As an illustration of the use of these formulæ take Ex. 5 of Art. 78. Here formula (2) gives

$$(a + b) \cot OGB = b \cot OAB - a \cot OBA,$$

i.e.,

$$(a + b) \tan \theta = b \tan \alpha - a \tan \alpha.$$

Other illustrations of their use will be found later on in this book.

EXAMPLES. XI.

1. A uniform rod, AB, of weight W, is movable in a vertical plane about a hinge at A, and is sustained in equilibrium by a weight P attached to a string BCP passing over a smooth peg C, AC being vertical; if AC be equal to AB, shew that $P = W \cos ACB$.

2. A uniform rod can turn freely about one of its ends, and is pulled aside from the vertical by a horizontal force acting at the other end of the rod and equal to half its weight; at what inclination to the vertical will the rod rest?

3. A rod AB, hinged at A, is supported in a horizontal position by a string BC, making an angle of $45°$ with the rod, and the rod has a mass of 10 lbs. suspended from B. Neglecting the weight of the rod, find the tension of the string and the action at the hinge.

4. A uniform heavy rod AB has the end A in contact with a smooth vertical wall, and one end of a string is fastened to the rod at a point C, such that $AC = \frac{1}{4}AB$, and the other end of the string is fastened to the wall; find the length of the string, if the rod rest in a position inclined at an angle to the vertical.

5. ACB is a uniform rod, of weight W; it is supported (B being uppermost) with its end A against a smooth vertical wall AD by means of a string CD, DB being horizontal and CD inclined to the wall at an angle of $30°$. Find the tension of the string and the reaction of the wall, and prove that $AC = \frac{1}{3}AB$.

6. A uniform rod, AB, resting with one end A against a smooth vertical wall is supported by a string BC which is tied to a point C vertically above A and to the other end B of the rod. Draw a diagram shewing the lines of action of the forces which keep the rod in equilibrium, and shew that the tension of the string is greater than the weight of the rod.

7. A uniform beam AB, of given length, is supported with its extremity, A, in contact with a smooth wall by means of a string CD fastened to a known point C of the beam and to a point D of the wall; if the inclination of the beam to the wall be given, shew how to find by geometrical construction the length of the string CD and the height of D above A.

For the problem to be possible, shew that the given angle BAD must be acute or obtuse according as AC is less or greater than $\frac{1}{2}AB$.

8. A uniform rod, of length a, hangs against a smooth vertical wall being supported by means of a string, of length l, tied to one end of the rod, the other end of the string being attached to a point in the wall; shew that the rod can rest inclined to the wall at an angle θ given by $\cos^2\theta = \dfrac{l^2 - a^2}{3a^2}$. What are the limits of the ratio of $a : l$ that equilibrium may be possible?

9. Equal weights P and P are attached to two strings ACP and BCP passing over a smooth peg C. AB is a heavy beam, of weight W, whose centre of gravity is a feet from A and b feet from B; shew that AB is inclined to the horizon at an angle

$$\tan^{-1}\left[\frac{a-b}{a+b}\tan\left(\sin^{-1}\frac{W}{2P}\right)\right].$$

10. A heavy uniform beam is hung from a fixed point by two strings attached to its extremities; if the lengths of the strings and beam be as $2:3:4$, shew that the tensions of the strings and the weight of the beam are as $2:3:\sqrt{10}$.

11. A heavy uniform rod, 15 inches long, is suspended from a fixed point by strings fastened to its ends, their lengths being 9 and 12 inches; if θ be the angle at which the rod is inclined to the vertical, shew that
$$25\sin\theta = 24.$$

12. A straight uniform rod, of weight 3 lbs., is suspended from a peg by two strings, attached at one end to the peg and at the other to the extremities of the rod; the angle between the strings is a right angle and one is twice as long as the other; find their tensions.

13. Two equal heavy spheres, of 1 inch radius, are in equilibrium within a smooth spherical cup of 3 inches radius. Shew that the action between the cup and one sphere is double that between the two spheres.

14. A sphere, of given weight W, rests between two smooth planes, one vertical and the other inclined at a given angle α to the vertical; find the reactions of the planes.

15. A solid sphere rests upon two parallel bars which are in the same horizontal plane, the distance between the bars being equal to the radius of the sphere; find the reaction of each bar.

16. A smooth sphere is supported in contact with a smooth vertical wall by a string fastened to a point on its surface, the other end being attached to a point in the wall; if the length of the string be equal to the radius of the sphere, find the inclination of the string to the vertical, the tension of the string, and the reaction of the wall.

17. A picture of given weight, hanging vertically against a smooth wall, is supported by a string passing over a smooth peg driven into the wall; the ends of the string are fastened to two points in the upper rim of the frame which are equidistant from the centre of the rim, and the angle at the peg is $60°$; compare the tension in this case with what it will be when the string is shortened to two-thirds of its length.

18. A picture, of 40 lbs. wt., is hung, with its upper and lower edges horizontal, by a cord fastened to the two upper corners and passing over a nail, so that the parts of the cord at the two sides of the nail are inclined to one another at an angle of $60°$. Find the tension of the cord in lbs. weight.

19. A picture hangs symmetrically by means of a string passing over a nail and attached to two rings in the picture; what is the tension of the string when the picture weighs 10 lbs., if the string be 4 feet long and the nail distant 1 ft. 6 inches from the horizontal line joining the rings?

20. A picture frame, rectangular in shape, rests against a smooth vertical wall, from two points in which it is suspended by parallel strings attached to two points in the upper edge of the back of the frame, the length of each string being equal to the height of the frame. Shew that, if the centre of gravity of the frame coincide with its centre of figure, the picture will hang against the wall at an angle $\tan^{-1}\dfrac{b}{3a}$ to the vertical, where a is the height and b the thickness of the picture.

21. It is required to hang a picture on a vertical wall so that it may rest at a given inclination, a, to the wall and be supported by a cord attached to a point in the wall at a given height h above the lowest edge of the picture; determine, by a geometrical construction, the point on the back of the picture to which the cord is to be attached and find the length of the cord that will be required.

22. A rod rests wholly within a smooth hemispherical bowl, of radius r, its centre of gravity dividing the rod into two portions of lengths a and b. Shew that, if θ be the inclination of the rod to the horizon in the position of equilibrium, then $\sin\theta = \dfrac{b-a}{2\sqrt{r^2-ab}}$, and find the reactions between the rod and the bowl.

23. In a smooth hemispherical cup is placed a heavy rod, equal in length to the radius of the cup, the centre of gravity of the rod being one-third of its length from one end; shew that the angle made by the rod with the vertical is $\tan^{-1}(3\sqrt{3})$.

24. A uniform rod, 4 inches in length, is placed with one end inside a smooth hemispherical bowl, of which the axis is vertical and the radius $\sqrt{3}$ inches; shew that a quarter of the rod will project over the edge of the bowl.

Prove also that the shortest rod that will thus rest is of length $2\sqrt{2}$ inches.

The following examples are to be solved graphically.

25. A heavy beam, AB, 10 feet long, is supported, A uppermost, by two ropes attached to it at A and B which are respectively inclined at $55°$ and $50°$ to the horizontal; if AB be inclined at $20°$ to the horizontal, find at what distance from A its centre of gravity is. Also, if its weight be 200 lbs., find the tensions of the two ropes.

26. A light rod AB, of length 2 feet, is smoothly jointed to a fixed support at A and rests horizontally; at D, where $AD=9$ inches, it carries a weight of 10 lbs., being supported by a light rod CB, where C is exactly underneath A and $AC=6$ inches; find the thrust in the rod CB.

27. *AB* is a uniform beam turning on a pivot at *C* and kept in equilibrium by a light string *AD* attached to the highest point *A* and to a point *D* vertically below *C*. If *AB*=3 ft., *AC*=1 ft., *CD*=2 ft., and *DA*=2·7 ft., and the weight of the beam be 10 lbs., find the tension of the string and the reaction of the pivot.

28. A cantilever consists of a horizontal rod *AB* hinged to a fixed support at *A*, and a rod *DC* hinged at a point *C* of *AB* and also hinged to a fixed point *D* vertically below *A*. A weight of 1 cwt. is attached at *B*; find the actions at *A* and *C*, given that *AB*=6 ft., *AC*=2 ft., and *AD*=3 ft., the weights of the rods being neglected.

29. The plane of a kite is inclined at 50° to the horizon, and its weight is 10 lbs. The resultant thrust of the air on it acts at a point 8 inches above its centre of gravity, and the string is tied at a point 10 inches above it. Find the tension of the string and the thrust of the air.

CHAPTER VIII.

GENERAL CONDITIONS OF EQUILIBRIUM OF A BODY ACTED ON BY FORCES IN ONE PLANE.

80. Theorem. *Any system of forces, acting in one plane upon a rigid body, can be reduced to either a single force or a single couple.*

By the parallelogram of forces any two forces, whose directions meet, can be compounded into one force; also, by Art. 52, two parallel forces can be compounded into one force provided they are not equal and unlike.

First compound together all the parallel forces, or sets of parallel forces, of the given system.

Of the resulting system take any two forces, not forming a couple, and find their resultant R_1; next find the resultant R_2 of R_1 and a suitable third force of the system; then determine the resultant of R_2 and a suitable fourth force of the system; and so on until all the forces have been exhausted.

Finally, we must either arrive at a single force, or we shall have two equal parallel unlike forces forming a couple.

81. Theorem. *If a system of forces act in one plane upon a rigid body, and if the algebraic sum of their moments about each of three points in the plane (not lying in the same straight line) vanish separately, the system of forces is in equilibrium.*

For any such system of forces, by the last article, reduces to either a single force or a single couple.

In our case they cannot reduce to a single couple; for, if they did, the sum of their moments about any point in their plane would, by Art. 69, be equal to a constant which is *not* zero, and this is contrary to our hypothesis.

Hence the system of forces cannot reduce to a single couple.

The system must therefore either be in equilibrium or reduce to a single force F.

Let the three points about which the moments are taken be A, B, and C.

Since the algebraic sum of the moments of a system of forces is equal to that of their resultant (Art. 62), therefore the moment of F about the point A must be zero.

Hence F is either zero, or passes through A.

Similarly, since the moment of F about B vanishes, F must be either zero or must pass through B,

i.e., F is either zero or acts in the line AB.

Finally, since the moment about C vanishes, F must be either zero or pass through C.

But (since the points A, B, C are *not* in the same straight line) the force cannot act along AB and also pass through C.

Hence the only admissible case is that F should be zero, *i.e.*, that the forces should be in equilibrium.

The system will also be in equilibrium if (1) the sum of the moments about each of two points, A and B, separately vanish, and if (2) the sum of the forces resolved along AB be zero. For, if (1) holds, the resultant, by the foregoing article, is either zero or acts along AB. Also, if (2) be true there is no resultant in the direction AB; hence the resultant force is zero. Also, as in the foregoing article, there is no resultant couple. Hence the system is in equilibrium.

82. Theorem. *A system of forces, acting in one plane upon a rigid body, is in equilibrium, if the sum of their components parallel to each of two lines in their plane be zero, and if the algebraic sum of their moments about any point be zero also.*

For any such system of forces, by Art. 80, can be reduced to either a single force or a single couple.

In our case they cannot reduce to a single force.

For, since the sums of the components of the forces parallel to two lines in their plane are separately zero, therefore the components of their resultant force parallel to these two lines are zero also, and therefore the resultant force vanishes.

Neither can the forces reduce to a single couple; for, if they did, the moment of this couple about any point in its plane would be equal to a constant which is *not* zero; this, however, is contrary to our hypothesis.

Hence the system of forces must be in equilibrium.

83. It will be noted that in the enunciation of the last article nothing is said about the directions in which we are to resolve. In practice, however, it is almost always desirable to resolve along two directions at right angles.

Hence the conditions of equilibrium of any system of forces, acting in one plane upon a rigid body, may be obtained as follows;

I. **Equate to zero the algebraic sum of the resolved parts of all the forces in some fixed direction.**

II. **Equate to zero the algebraic sum of the resolved parts of all the forces in a perpendicular direction.**

III. **Equate to zero the algebraic sum of the moments of the forces about any point in their plane.**

I and II ensure that there shall be no motion of the body as a whole; III ensures that there shall be no motion of rotation about any point.

The above three statical relations, together with the geometrical relations holding between the component portions of a system, will, in general, be sufficient to determine the equilibrium of any system acted on by forces which are in one plane.

In applying the preceding conditions of equilibrium to any particular case, great simplifications can often be introduced into the equations by properly choosing the directions along which we resolve. In general, the horizontal and vertical directions are the most suitable.

Again, the position of the point about which we take moments is important; it should be chosen so that as few of the forces as possible are introduced into the equation of moments.

84. We have shewn that the conditions given in the previous article are sufficient for the equilibrium of the system of forces; they are also necessary.

Suppose we knew only that the first two conditions were satisfied. The system of forces might then reduce to a single couple; for the forces of this couple, being equal and opposite, are such that their components in any direction would vanish. Hence, resolving in any third direction would give us no additional condition. In this case the forces would not be in equilibrium unless the third condition were satisfied.

Suppose, again, that we knew only that the components of the system along one given line vanished and that the moments about a given point vanished also; in this case the forces might reduce to a single force through the given point perpendicular to the given line; hence we see that it is necessary to have the sum of the components parallel to another line zero also.

85. We shall now give some examples of the application of the general conditions of equilibrium. In solving any statical problem the student should proceed as follows ;

(1) Draw the figure according to the conditions given.

(2) Mark all the forces acting on the body or bodies, taking care to assume an unknown reaction (to be determined) wherever one body presses against another, and to mark a tension along any supporting string, and to assume a reaction wherever the body is hinged to any other body or fixed point.

(3) For each body, or system of bodies, involved in the problem, equate to zero the forces acting on it resolved along two convenient perpendicular directions (generally horizontal and vertical).

(4) Also equate to zero the moments of the forces about any convenient point.

(5) Write down any geometrical relations connecting the lengths or angles involved in the figure.

Ex. 1. *A heavy uniform beam rests with one end upon a horizontal plane, and the other end upon a given inclined plane; it is kept in equilibrium by a string which is attached to the end resting on the horizontal plane and to the intersection of the inclined and horizontal planes; given that the inclination* (α) *of the beam to the horizontal is one-half that of the inclined plane, find the tension of the string and the reactions of the planes.*

Let *AB* be the beam, *AO* the horizontal, and *OB* the inclined plane.

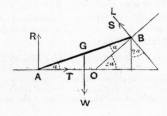

Let T be the tension of the string AO, W the weight of the body, R and S the reactions at A and B respectively vertical and perpendicular to OB.

Resolving horizontally and vertically we have

$$T = S \sin 2a \quad \dots\dots\dots\dots\dots\dots\dots(1),$$
$$W = R + S \cos 2a \quad \dots\dots\dots\dots\dots\dots(2).$$

Also, taking moments about A, we have

$$W \cdot a \cos a = S \cdot AB \sin ABL = S \cdot 2a \cos a \dots\dots\dots(3),$$

where $2a$ is the length of the beam.

These three equations give the circumstances of the equilibrium.

From (3), we have $\qquad S = \frac{1}{2} W$.

$\therefore$ from (2), $\qquad R = W - \frac{1}{2} W \cos 2a = W(1 - \frac{1}{2} \cos 2a)$.

Also, from (1),

$$T = \frac{W}{2} \sin 2a.$$

Hence the reactions and the tension of the string are determined.

Suppose that, instead of the inclination of the beam to the horizon being given, the length of the string were given ($= l$ say).

Let us assume the inclination of the beam to the horizon to be θ.

The equations (1) and (2) remain the same as before.

The equation of moments would be, however,

$$W \cdot a \cos \theta = S \cdot AB \sin ABL = S \cdot 2a \cos ABO$$
$$= S \cdot 2a \cos (2a - \theta) \quad \dots\dots\dots\dots\dots\dots(4).$$

We should have a geometrical equation to determine θ, viz.,

$$\frac{l}{2a} = \frac{OA}{AB} = \frac{\sin ABO}{\sin AOB} = \frac{\sin (2a - \theta)}{\sin 2a} \quad \dots\dots\dots\dots(5).$$

This latter equation determines θ, and then the equations (1), (2), and (4) would give T, R, and S.

This question might have been solved by resolving along and perpendicular to the beam; in each equation we should then have involved each of the quantities T, R, S, and W, so that the resulting equations would have been more complicated than those above.

It was also desirable to take moments about A; for this is the only convenient point in the figure through which pass two of the forces which act on the body.

Ex. 2. *A beam whose centre of gravity divides it into portions, of lengths a and b respectively, rests in equilibrium with its ends resting on two smooth planes inclined at angles a and β respectively to the horizon, the planes intersecting in a horizontal line; find the inclination of the beam to the horizon and the reactions of the planes.*

Let the planes be OA and OB, and let AB be the rod, whose centre of gravity is G, so that GA and GB are a and b respectively.

Let R and S be the reactions at A and B perpendicular to the inclined planes, and let θ be the inclination of the beam to the horizon.

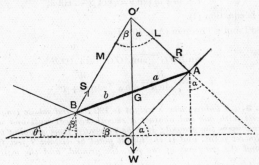

Resolving vertically and horizontally, we have

$$R\cos\alpha + S\cos\beta = W \quad\text{................(1)},$$
$$R\sin\alpha = S\sin\beta \quad\text{................(2)}.$$

Also, by taking moments about G, we have

$$R \cdot GA \sin GAL = S \cdot GB \sin GBM.$$

Now
$$\angle GAL = 90° - BAO = 90° - (\alpha - \theta),$$
and
$$\angle GBM = 90° - ABO = 90° - (\beta + \theta).$$

Hence the equation of moments becomes

$$R \cdot a \cos(\alpha - \theta) = S \cdot b \cos(\beta + \theta) \quad\text{................(3)}.$$

From (2), we have

$$\frac{R}{\sin\beta} = \frac{S}{\sin\alpha} = \frac{R\cos\alpha + S\cos\beta}{\sin\beta\cos\alpha + \sin\alpha\cos\beta} = \frac{W}{\sin(\alpha+\beta)}, \text{ by (1).}$$

These equations give R and S; also substituting for R and S in (3) we have

$$a\sin\beta\cos(\alpha - \theta) = b\sin\alpha\cos(\beta + \theta);$$
$$\therefore\ a\sin\beta(\cos\alpha\cos\theta + \sin\alpha\sin\theta) = b\sin\alpha(\cos\beta\cos\theta - \sin\beta\sin\theta);$$
$$\therefore\ (a+b)\sin\alpha\sin\beta\sin\theta = \cos\theta(b\sin\alpha\cos\beta - a\cos\alpha\sin\beta);$$
$$\therefore\ (a+b)\tan\theta = b\cot\beta - a\cot\alpha \quad\text{................(4)},$$

giving the value of θ.

Otherwise thus; Since there are only three forces acting on the body this question might have been solved by the methods of the last chapter.

For the three forces R, S, and W, must meet in a point O'.

The theorem of Art. 79 then gives

$$(a+b)\cot O'GA = b\cot\beta - a\cot\alpha,$$

$$i.e. \ (a+b)\tan\theta = b\cot\beta - a\cot\alpha,$$

which is equation (4).

Also Lami's Theorem (Art. 40) gives

$$\frac{R}{\sin BO'G} = \frac{S}{\sin AO'G} = \frac{W}{\sin AO'B},$$

$$i.e. \ \frac{R}{\sin\beta} = \frac{S}{\sin\alpha} = \frac{W}{\sin(\alpha+\beta)}.$$

Ex. 3. *A ladder, whose weight is* 192 *lbs. and whose length is* 25 *feet, rests with one end against a smooth vertical wall and with the other end upon the ground; if it be prevented from slipping by a peg at its lowest point, and if the lowest point be distant* 7 *feet from the wall, find the reactions of the peg, the ground, and the wall.*

Let AB be the rod and G its middle point; let R and R_1 be the reactions of the ground and wall, and S the horizontal reaction of the peg. Let the angle GAO be α, so that

$$\cos\alpha = \frac{AO}{AB} = \frac{7}{25},$$

and hence

$$\sin\alpha = \sqrt{1 - \frac{49}{625}} = \sqrt{\frac{576}{625}} = \frac{24}{25}.$$

Equating to zero the horizontal and vertical components of the forces acting on the rod, we have

$$R - 192 = 0 \dots\dots\dots\dots\dots(1),$$

and

$$R_1 - S = 0 \dots\dots\dots\dots\dots(2).$$

Also, taking moments about A, we have

$$192 \times AG\cos\alpha = R_1 \times AB\sin\alpha \dots\dots\dots\dots(3);$$

$$\therefore \ R_1 = 192 \times \tfrac{1}{2}\cot\alpha = 96 \times \frac{7}{24} = 28.$$

Hence, from (1) and (2),

$$R = 192 \ \text{and} \ S = 28.$$

The required reactions are therefore 28, 192, and 28 lbs. weight respectively.

The resultant of R and S must by the last chapter pass through O', the point of intersection of the weight and R_1.

Ex. 4. *One end of a uniform rod is attached to a hinge, and the other end is supported by a string attached to the extremity of the rod, and the rod and string are inclined at the same angle, θ, to the horizontal; if W be the weight of the rod, shew that the action at the hinge is* $\dfrac{W}{4}\sqrt{8+\operatorname{cosec}^2\theta}$.

Let AB be the rod, C its middle point, and BD the string meeting the horizontal line through A in D.

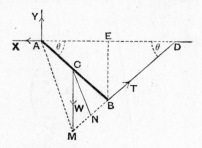

Let the tension of the string be T.

The action at the hinge is unknown both in magnitude and direction. Let the horizontal and vertical components of this action be X and Y, as marked in the figure. Draw BE perpendicular to AD. Then $AD = 2AE = 2AB\cos\theta$.

Resolving horizontally and vertically, we have

$$X = T\cos\theta \quad\dotfill (1),$$
$$Y + T\sin\theta = W \quad\dotfill (2).$$

Also, taking moments about A, we have

$$W\,.\,AC\cos\theta = T\,.\,AD\sin\theta = T\,.\,2AB\cos\theta\sin\theta \quad\dots(3).$$

From (3),
$$T = W\frac{AC}{2AB\sin\theta} = \frac{W}{4\sin\theta}.$$

Hence, by (1) and (2),
$$X = \frac{W}{4}\cot\theta, \quad\text{and}\quad Y = W - \frac{W}{4} = \frac{3W}{4}.$$

Therefore the action at the hinge $= \sqrt{X^2 + Y^2}$
$$= \frac{W}{4}\sqrt{9+\cot^2\theta} = \frac{W}{4}\sqrt{8+\operatorname{cosec}^2\theta}.$$

If DB meet the direction of W in M, then, by the last chapter, AM is the direction of the action at A. Hence, if CN be parallel to AM, then CMN is a triangle of forces.

Ex. 5. *A uniform heavy rod can turn freely about one end, which is fixed; to this end is attached a string which supports a sphere of radius a. If the length of the rod be 4a, the length of the string a, and the weights of the sphere and rod be each W, find the inclinations of the rod and string to the vertical and the tension of the string.*

Let *OA* be the rod, *OC* the string, *B* the centre of the sphere, and *D* the point in which the rod touches the sphere.

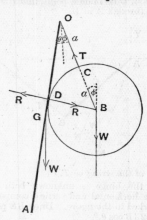

Between the sphere and the rod at *D* there is a reaction, *R*, perpendicular to *OD*, acting in opposite directions on the two bodies.

The forces which act on the sphere only must be in equilibrium; and so also must the forces which act on the rod.

Since there are only three forces acting on the sphere they must meet in a point, *viz.*, the centre of the sphere.

Hence *OCB* is a straight line.

Let θ and ϕ be the inclination of the rod and string to the vertical.

Then
$$\sin (\theta + \phi) = \frac{DB}{OB} = \frac{a}{2a} = \frac{1}{2},$$

so that
$$\theta + \phi = 30° \quad ....(1).$$

The forces acting on the rod are the reaction at *D*, the weight of the rod, and the action at the hinge *O*.

If we take moments about *O* we shall avoid this action, and we have

$$W \cdot 2a \sin \theta = R \cdot OD = R \cdot 2a \cos 30° \quad ....(2).$$

From the conditions of equilibrium of the sphere,

$$\frac{T}{\sin(\phi+60°)} = \frac{R}{\sin\phi} = \frac{W}{\sin 60°} \quad\ldots\ldots\ldots\ldots\ldots(3).$$

Therefore, from (2) and (3),

$$\frac{\sin\theta}{\cos 30°} = \frac{R}{W} = \frac{\sin\phi}{\sin 60°}.$$

$\therefore$ $\phi=\theta$, and hence, from (1),

$$\theta=\phi=15°.$$

Substituting in (3), we have

$$T=W\frac{\sin 75°}{\sin 60°} = W\frac{\sqrt{3}+1}{\sqrt{6}} = \frac{W}{6}(3\sqrt{2}+\sqrt{6}) = 1\cdot1153\times W,$$

and $\quad R=W\dfrac{\sin 15°}{\sin 60°} = W\dfrac{\sqrt{3}-1}{\sqrt{6}} = \dfrac{W}{6}(3\sqrt{2}-\sqrt{6}) = \cdot2988\times W.$

EXAMPLES. XII.

1. A uniform beam, AB, whose weight is W, rests with one end, A, on a smooth horizontal plane AC. The other end, B, rests on a plane CB inclined to the former at an angle of 60°. If a string CA, equal to CB, prevent motion, find its tension.

2. A ladder, of weight W, rests with one end against a smooth vertical wall and with the other resting on a smooth floor; if the inclination of the ladder to the horizon be 60°, find, by calculation and graphically, the horizontal force that must be applied to the lower end to prevent the ladder from sliding down.

3. A beam, of weight W, is divided by its centre of gravity C into two portions AC and BC, whose lengths are a and b respectively. The beam rests in a vertical plane on a smooth floor AD and against a smooth vertical wall DB. A string is attached to a hook at D and to the beam at a point P. If T be the tension of the string, and θ and ϕ be the inclinations of the beam and string respectively to the horizon,

shew that $\qquad T=W\dfrac{a\cos\theta}{(a+b)\sin(\theta-\phi)}.$

4. A ladder rests at an angle a to the horizon, with its ends resting on a smooth floor and against a smooth vertical wall, the lower end being attached by a string to the junction of the wall and floor; find the tension of the string.

Find also the tension of the string when a man, whose weight is one-half that of the ladder, has ascended the ladder two-thirds of its length.

5. One end of a uniform beam, of weight W, is placed on a smooth horizontal plane; the other end, to which a string is fastened, rests against another smooth plane inclined at an angle α to the horizon; the string, passing over a pulley at the top of the inclined plane, hangs vertically, and supports a weight P; shew that the beam will rest in all positions if $2P = W \sin \alpha$.

6. A heavy uniform beam rests with its extremities on two smooth inclined planes, which meet in a horizontal line, and whose inclinations to the horizon are α and β; find its inclination to the horizon in the position of equilibrium, and the reactions of the planes.

7. A uniform beam rests with a smooth end against the junction of the ground and a vertical wall, and is supported by a string fastened to the other end of the beam and to a staple in the wall. Find the tension of the string, and shew that it will be one-half the weight of the beam if the length of the string be equal to the height of the staple above the ground.

8. A uniform rod BC, of weight 2 lbs., can turn freely about B and is supported by a string AC, 8 inches long, attached to a point A in the same horizontal line as B, the distance AB being 10 inches. If the rod be 6 inches long, find the tension of the string. Verify by a drawing and measurement.

9. A uniform rod has its upper end fixed to a hinge and its other end attached by a string to a fixed point in the same horizontal plane as the hinge, the length of the string being equal to the distance between the fixed point and the hinge. If the tension of the string be equal to the weight W of the rod, shew that the rod is inclined to the horizon at an angle $\tan^{-1} \frac{1}{2}$, and that the action of the hinge is equal to a force $\frac{W}{5} \sqrt{10}$ inclined at an angle $\tan^{-1} \frac{1}{3}$ to the horizon.

10. A rod is movable in a vertical plane about a hinge at one end, and at the other end is fastened a weight equal to half the weight of the rod; this end is fastened by a string, of length l, to a point at a height c vertically over the hinge. Shew that the tension of the string is $\dfrac{lW}{c}$, where W is the weight of the rod.

11. AB is a uniform rod, of length $8a$, which can turn freely about the end A, which is fixed; C is a smooth ring, whose weight is twice that of the rod, which can slide on the rod, and is attached by a string CD to a point D in the same horizontal plane as the point A; if AD and CD be each of length a, find the position of the ring and the tension of the string when the system is in equilibrium.

Shew also that the action on the rod at the fixed end A is a horizontal force equal to $\sqrt{3}W$, where W is the weight of the rod.

12. A rigid wire, without weight, in the form of the arc of a circle subtending an angle a at its centre, and having two weights P and Q at its extremities, rests with its convexity downwards upon a horizontal plane; shew that, if θ be the inclination to the vertical of the radius to the end at which P is suspended, then

$$\tan \theta = \frac{Q \sin a}{P + Q \cos a}.$$

13. A smooth hemispherical bowl, of diameter a, is placed so that its edge touches a smooth vertical wall; a heavy uniform rod is in equilibrium, inclined at 60° to the horizon, with one end resting on the inner surface of the bowl, and the other end resting against the wall; shew that the length of the rod must be $a + \dfrac{a}{\sqrt{13}}$.

14. A cylindrical vessel, of height 4 inches and diameter 3 inches, stands upon a horizontal plane, and a smooth uniform rod, 9 inches long, is placed within it resting against the edge. Find the actions between the rod and the vessel, the weight of the former being 6 ounces.

15. A thin ring, of radius R and weight W, is placed round a vertical cylinder of radius r and prevented from falling by a nail projecting horizontally from the cylinder. Find the horizontal reactions between the cylinder and the ring.

16. A heavy carriage wheel, of weight W and radius r, is to be dragged over an obstacle, of height h, by a horizontal force F applied to the centre of the wheel; shew that F must be slightly greater than

$$W \frac{\sqrt{2rh - h^2}}{r - h}.$$

17. A uniform beam, of length $2a$, rests in equilibrium, with one end resting against a smooth vertical wall and with a point of its length resting upon a smooth horizontal rod, which is parallel to the wall and at a distance b from it; shew that the inclination of the beam to the vertical is

$$\sin^{-1} \left(\frac{b}{a} \right)^{\frac{1}{3}}.$$

18. A circular disc, BCD, of radius a and weight W, is supported by a smooth band, of inappreciable weight and thickness, which surrounds the disc along the arc BCD and is fastened at its extremities to the point A in a vertical wall, the portion AD touching the wall and the plane of the disc being at right angles to the wall. If the length of the band not in contact with the disc be $2b$, shew that the tension of the band is $\dfrac{W}{2} \dfrac{a^2 + b^2}{b^2}$, and find the reaction at D.

19. Two equal uniform heavy straight rods are connected at one extremity by a string and rest upon two smooth pegs in the same horizontal line, one rod upon one peg and the other upon the other; if the distance between the pegs be equal to the length of each rod and the length of the string be half the same, shew that the rods rest at an angle θ to the horizon given by $2 \cos^3 \theta = 1$.

20. A uniform rod, whose weight is W, is supported by two fine strings, one attached to each end, which, after passing over small fixed smooth pulleys, carry weights w_1 and w_2 respectively at the other ends. Shew that the rod is inclined to the horizon at an angle

$$\sin^{-1} \frac{w_1^2 - w_2^2}{W \sqrt{2 (w_1^2 + w_2^2) - W^2}}.$$

21. A uniform rod, of weight W, is supported in equilibrium by a string, of length $2l$, attached to its ends and passing over a smooth peg. If a weight W' be now attached to one end of the rod, shew that it can be placed in another position of equilibrium by sliding a length $\dfrac{lW'}{W + W'}$ of the string over the peg.

22. AB is a straight rod, of length $2a$ and weight λW, with the lower end A on the ground at the foot of a vertical wall AC, B and C being at the same vertical height $2b$ above A; a heavy ring, of weight W, is free to move along a string, of length $2l$, which joins B and C. If the system be in equilibrium with the ring at the middle point of the string, shew that

$$l^2 = a^2 - b^2 \frac{\lambda (\lambda + 2)}{(\lambda + 1)^2}.$$

23. A given square board $ABCD$, of side b, is supported horizontally by two given loops of string $OACO$ and $OBDO$ passing under opposite corners and hung over a fixed hook O; find the tensions of the strings, if the height of O above the board be b.

24. A gate weighing 100 lbs. is hung on two hinges, 3 feet apart, in a vertical line which is distant 4 feet from the centre of gravity of the gate. Find the magnitude of the reactions at each hinge on the assumption that the whole of the weight of the gate is borne by the lower hinge.

25. A triangle, formed of three rods, is fixed in a horizontal position and a homogeneous sphere rests on it; shew that the reaction on each rod is proportional to its length.

26. A light triangular frame ABC stands in a vertical plane, C being uppermost, on two supports, A and B, in the same horizontal line and a mass of 18 lbs. weight is suspended from C. If $AB = AC = 18$ feet, and $BC = 5$ feet, find the reactions of the supports.

27. The sides of a triangular framework are 13, 20, and 21 inches in length; the longest side rests on a horizontal smooth table and a weight of 63 lbs. is suspended from the opposite angle. Find the tension in the side on the table. Verify by a drawing and measurement.

28. A bowl is formed from a hollow sphere, of radius a, and is so placed that the radius of the sphere drawn to each point in the rim makes an angle a with the vertical, whilst the radius drawn to a point A of the bowl makes an angle β with the vertical; if a smooth uniform rod remain at rest with one end at A and a point of its length in contact with the rim, shew that the length of the rod is

$$4a \sin \beta \sec \frac{a-\beta}{2}.$$

86. In the following articles the conditions of equilibrium enunciated in Art. 83 will be obtained in a slightly different manner.

*87. Theorem. *Any system of forces, acting in one plane upon a rigid body, is equivalent to a force acting at an arbitrary point of the body together with a couple.*

Let P be any force of the system acting at a point A of the body, and let O be any arbitrary point. At O introduce

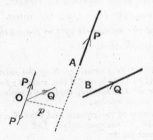

two equal and opposite forces, the magnitude of each being P, and let their line of action be parallel to that of P. These do not alter the state of equilibrium of the body.

The force P at A and the opposite parallel force P at O form a couple of moment $P \cdot p$, where p is the perpendicular from O upon the line of action of the original force P.

Hence the force P at A is equivalent to a parallel force P at O and a couple of moment $P \cdot p$.

So the force Q at B is equivalent to a parallel force Q at O and to a couple of moment $Q \cdot q$, where q is the perpendicular from O on the line of action of Q.

The same holds for each of the system of forces.

Hence the original system of forces is equivalent to forces P, Q, R... acting at O, parallel to their original directions, and a number of couples; these are equivalent to a single resultant force at O, and a single resultant couple of moment

$$P \cdot p + Q \cdot q + \ldots.$$

*88. By Art. 74 a force and a couple cannot balance unless each is zero.

Hence the resultant of P, Q, R,... at O must be zero, and therefore, by Art. 46, *the sum of their resolved parts in two directions must separately vanish.*

Also the moment $Pp + Qq + \ldots$ must be zero, *i.e., the algebraic sum of the moments of the forces about an arbitrary point O must vanish also.*

*89. Ex. *ABCD is a square; along the sides AB, BC, DC, and DA act forces equal to* 1, 9, 5, *and* 3 *lbs. weight; find the force, passing through the centre of the square, and the couple which are together equivalent to the given system.*

Let O be the centre of the square and let OX and OY be perpendicular to the sides BC, CD respectively.   Let the side of the square be $2a$.

The force 9 is equivalent to a force 9 along OY together with a couple of moment $9 \cdot a$.

The force 3 is equivalent to a force -3 along OY together with a couple of moment $3 \cdot a$.

The force 5 is equivalent to a force 5 along OX together with a couple of moment $-5 \cdot a$.

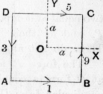

The force 1 is equivalent to a force 1 along OX together with a couple of moment $1 \cdot a$.

Hence the moment of the resultant couple is $9a + 3a - 5a + 1 \cdot a$, *i.e.*, $8 \cdot a$.

The component force along OX is 6 and the component along OY is 6.

Hence the resultant force is one of $6\sqrt{2}$ lbs. weight inclined at $45°$ to the side AB.

EXAMPLES. XIII.

1. A square is acted upon by forces equal to 2, 4, 6, and 8 lbs. weight along its sides taken in order; find the resultant force and the resultant couple of these forces, when the resultant force goes through the centre of the square.

2. $ABCD$ is a square; along DA, AB, BC, CD, and DB act forces equal to $P, 3P, 5P, 7P$, and $9\sqrt{2}P$; find the force, passing through A, and the couple, which are together equivalent to the system.

3. Forces equal to 1, 2, 3, 4, 5, and 6 lbs. weight respectively act along the sides AB, BC, CD, DE, EF, and FA of a regular hexagon; find the force, passing through A, and the couple, which are together equivalent to the system.

4. Given in position a force equal to 10 lbs. weight and a couple consisting of two forces, each equal to 4 lbs. weight, at a distance of 2 inches asunder, draw the equivalent single force.

Constrained body.

90. A body is said to be constrained when one or more points of the body are fixed. For example, a rod attached to a wall by a ball-socket has one point fixed and is constrained.

If a rigid body have two points A and B fixed, all the points of the body in the line AB are fixed, and the only way in which the body can move is by turning round AB as an axis. For example, a door attached to the door-post by two hinges can only turn about the line joining the hinges.

If a body have three points in it fixed, the three points not being in the same straight line, it is plainly immovable.

The only cases we shall consider are (1) when the body has one point fixed and is acted upon by a system of forces lying in a plane passing through the fixed point, and (2) when the body can only move about a fixed axis in it and is acted upon by a system of forces whose directions are perpendicular to the axis.

91. *When a rigid body has one point fixed, and is acted upon by a system of forces in a plane passing through the point, it will be in equilibrium if the algebraic sum of the moments of the forces about the fixed point vanishes.*

When a body has one point A fixed (as in the case of Ex. 4, Art. 85), there must be exerted at the point some force of constraint, F, which together with the given system of forces is in equilibrium. Hence the conditions of equilibrium of Art. 83 must apply.

If we resolve along two directions at right angles, we shall have two equations to determine the magnitude and direction of the force F.

If we take moments about A for all the forces, the force F (since it passes through A) does not appear in our equation, and hence the equation of moments of Art. 83 will become an equation expressing the fact that the algebraic sum of the moments of the given system of forces about A is zero.

Hence for the equilibrium of the body (unless we wish to find the force of constraint F) we have only to express that the algebraic sum of the moments of the forces about the fixed point A is zero.

92. Ex. *A rod AB has one end A fixed, and is kept in a horizontal position by a force equal to 10 lbs. weight acting at B in a direction inclined at 30° to the rod; if the rod be homogeneous, and of length 4 feet, find its weight.*

The moment of the weight about A must be equal to the moment of the force about A.

If W be the weight, the former moment is $W \times 2$, and the latter is $10 \times 4 \sin 30°$.

$$\therefore \quad 2W = 10 \times 4 \sin 30° = 20.$$
$$\therefore \quad W = 10 \text{ lbs. wt.}$$

93. *When a rigid body has an axis fixed, and is acted upon by forces, whose directions are perpendicular to this axis, it will be in equilibrium if the algebraic sum of the moments of the forces about the fixed axis vanishes.*

[If a force be perpendicular to a given axis and do not meet it, its moment about the axis is the product of the force and the perpendicular distance between the axis and the force.]

Suppose AB to be the fixed axis in the body, and let the body be acted on by forces P, Q... ; these forces need

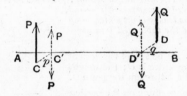

not be parallel but their directions must be perpendicular to the axis.

Draw CC' perpendicular to both the axis and P, and DD' perpendicular to the axis and Q; let their lengths be p and q.

At C' introduce two equal and opposite forces, each equal to P, one of these being parallel to the original force P.

The force P at C and the two forces (P, P) at C' are equivalent to a force P, parallel to the original P, and a couple of moment $P \cdot p$.

Similarly, the force Q at D is equivalent to a force Q at D' and a couple of moment $Q \cdot q$.

Similarly for the other forces.

The forces, since they intersect the axis, can have no effect in turning the body about the axis and are balanced by the forces of constraint applied to the axis.

The couples are, by Arts. 72 and 73, equivalent to a couple of moment $P \cdot p + Q \cdot q + \ldots$ in a plane perpendicular to the axis.

Hence the body will be in equilibrium if

$$P \cdot p + Q \cdot q + \ldots \text{ be zero};$$

also the latter expression is the algebraic sum of the moments of the forces about the axis.

Hence the theorem is true.

94. Ex. *A circular uniform table, of weight 80 lbs., rests on four equal legs placed symmetrically round its edge; find the least weight which hung upon the edge of the table will just over-turn it.*

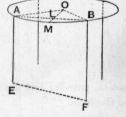

Let AE and BF be two of the legs of the table, whose centre is O; the weight of the table will act through the point O.

If the weight be hung on the portion of the table between A and B the table will, if it turn at all, turn about the line joining the points E and F. Also it will be just on the point of turning when the weight and the weight of the table have equal moments about EF.

Now the weight will clearly have the greatest effect when placed at M, the middle point of the arc AB.

Let OM meet AB in L, and let x be the required weight. Taking moments about EF, which is the same as taking moments about AB, we have

$$x \cdot LM = 80 \cdot OL.$$

But
$$LM = OM - OL = OA - OA \cos 45°$$

$$= OA \left(1 - \frac{1}{\sqrt{2}}\right).$$

$$\therefore x \left(1 - \frac{1}{\sqrt{2}}\right) OA = 80 \cdot OL = 80 \cdot \frac{1}{\sqrt{2}} \cdot OA,$$

and
$$x = \frac{80}{\sqrt{2} - 1} = 80 \left(\sqrt{2} + 1\right)$$

$$= 193 \cdot 1 \text{ lbs. wt.}$$

95. Theorem. *If three forces acting on a body keep it in equilibrium, they must lie in a plane.*

Let the three forces be P, Q, and R.

Let P_1 and Q_1 be *any* two points on the lines of action of P and Q respectively.

Since the forces are in equilibrium, they can, taken together, have no effect to turn the body about the line P_1Q_1. But the forces P and Q meet this line, and therefore separately have no effect to turn the body about P_1Q_1. Hence the third force R can have no effect to turn the body about P_1Q_1.

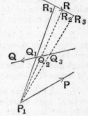

Therefore the line P_1Q_1 must meet R.

Similarly, if Q_2, Q_3,... be other points on the line of action of Q, the lines P_1Q_2, P_1Q_3,... must meet R.

Hence R must lie in the plane through P_1 and the line of action of Q, *i.e.*, the lines of action of Q and R must be in a plane which passes through P_1.

But P_1 is *any* point on the line of action of P; and hence the above plane passes through *any* point on the line of action of P,

   i.e., it contains the line of action of P.

Cor. From Art. 77 it now follows that the three forces must also meet in a point or be parallel.

EXAMPLES. XIV.

1. A square uniform plate is suspended at one of its vertices, and a weight, equal to half that of the plate, is suspended from the adjacent vertex of the square. Find the position of equilibrium of the plate.

2. A hollow vertical cylinder, of radius $2a$ and height $3a$, rests on a horizontal table, and a uniform rod is placed within it with its lower end resting on the circumference of the base; if the weight of the rod be equal to that of the cylinder, how long must the rod be so that it may just cause the cylinder to topple over?

3. A cylinder, whose length is b and the diameter of whose base is c, is open at the top and rests on a horizontal plane; a uniform rod rests partly within the cylinder and in contact with it at its upper and lower edges; supposing the weight of the cylinder to be n times that of the rod, find the length of the rod when the cylinder is on the point of falling over.

4. A square table stands on four legs placed respectively at the middle points of its sides; find the greatest weight that can be put at one of the corners without upsetting the table.

5. A round table stands upon three equidistant weightless legs at its edge, and a man sits upon its edge opposite a leg. It just upsets and falls upon its edge and two legs. He then sits upon its highest point and just tips it up again. Shew that the radius of the table is $\sqrt{2}$ times the length of a leg.

6. A circular table, whose weight is 10 lbs., is provided with three vertical legs attached to three points in the circumference equidistant from one another; find the least weight which hung from any point in the edge of the table will just cause it to overturn.

7. A square four-legged table has lost one leg; where on the table should a weight, equal to the weight of the table, be placed, so that the pressures on the three remaining legs of the table may be equal?

8. A square table, of weight 20 lbs., has legs at the middle points of its sides, and three equal weights, each equal to the weight of the table, are placed at three of the angular points. What is the greatest weight that can be placed at the fourth corner so that equilibrium may be preserved?

9. A circular metallic plate, of uniform thickness and of weight w, is hung from a point on its circumference. A string wound on its edge, carries a weight p. Find the angle which the diameter through the point of suspension makes with the vertical.

10. A uniform circular disc, of weight nW, has a particle, of weight W, attached to a point on its rim. If the disc be suspended from a point A on its rim, B is the lowest point; also, if suspended from B, A is the lowest point. Shew that the angle subtended by AB at the centre of the disc is $2 \sec^{-1} 2 (n+1)$.

11. A heavy horizontal circular ring rests on three supports at the points A, B, and C of its circumference. Given its weight and the sides and angles of the triangle ABC, find the reactions of the supports.

CHAPTER IX.

CENTRE OF GRAVITY.

96. Every particle of matter is attracted to the centre of the Earth, and the force with which the Earth attracts any particle to itself is, as we shall see in Dynamics, proportional to the mass of the particle.

Any body may be considered as an agglomeration of particles.

If the body be small, compared with the Earth, the lines joining its component particles to the centre of the Earth will be very approximately parallel, and, within the limits of this book, we shall consider them to be absolutely parallel.

On every particle, therefore, of a rigid body there is acting a force vertically downwards which we call its weight.

These forces may by the process of compounding parallel forces, Art. 52, be compounded into a single force, equal to the sum of the weights of the particles, acting at some definite point of the body. Such a point is called the centre of gravity of the body.

Centre of gravity. Def. *The centre of gravity of a body, or system of particles rigidly connected together, is that point through which the line of action of the weight of the body always passes in whatever position the body is placed.*

97. *Every body, or system of particles rigidly connected together, has a centre of gravity.*

Let *A, B, C, D*... be a system of particles whose weights are w_1, w_2, w_3....

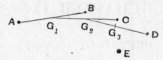

Join *AB*, and divide it at G_1 so that

$$AG_1 : G_1B :: w_2 : w_1.$$

Then parallel forces w_1 and w_2, acting at *A* and *B*, are, by Art. 52, equivalent to a force $(w_1 + w_2)$ acting at G_1.

Join G_1C, and divide it at G_2 so that

$$G_1G_2 : G_2C :: w_3 : w_1 + w_2.$$

Then parallel forces, $(w_1 + w_2)$ at G_1 and w_2 at *C*, are equivalent to a force $(w_1 + w_2 + w_3)$ at G_2.

Hence the forces w_1, w_2, and w_3 may be supposed to be applied at G_2 without altering their effect.

Similarly, dividing G_2D in G_3 so that

$$G_2G_3 : G_3D :: w_4 : w_1 + w_2 + w_3,$$

we see that the resultant of the four weights at *A, B, C,* and *D* is equivalent to a vertical force, $w_1 + w_2 + w_3 + w_4$, acting at G_3.

Proceeding in this way, we see that the weights of any number of particles composing any body may be supposed to be applied at some point of the body without altering their effect.

98. Since the construction for the position of the resultant of parallel forces depends *only* on the point of application and magnitude, and *not* on the direction of the forces, the point we finally arrive at is the same if the body be turned through any angle; for the weights of the portions of the body are still parallel, although they have not the same direction, relative to the body, in the two positions.

We can hence shew that a body can only have one centre of gravity. For, if possible, let it have two centres of gravity G and G_1. Let the body be turned, if necessary, until GG_1 be horizontal. We shall then have the resultant of a system of vertical forces acting both through G and through G_1. But the resultant force, being itself necessarily vertical, cannot act in the horizontal line GG_1.

Hence there can be only one centre of gravity.

99. If the body be not so small that the weights of its component parts may all be considered to be very approximately parallel, it has not necessarily a centre of gravity.

In any case, the point of the body at which we arrive by the construction of Art. 97, has, however, very important properties and is called its Centre of Mass, or Centre of Inertia. If the body be of uniform density its centre of mass coincides with its Centroid.

100. We shall now proceed to the determination of the centre of gravity of some bodies of simple forms.

I. A uniform rod.

Let AB be a uniform rod, and G its middle point.

Take any point P of the rod between G and A, and a point Q in GB, such that
$$GQ = GP.$$
The centre of gravity of equal particles at P and Q is clearly G; also, for every particle between G and A, there is an equal particle at an equal distance from G, lying between G and B.

The centre of gravity of each of these pairs of particles is at G; therefore the centre of gravity of the whole rod is at G.

101. II. A uniform parallelogram.

Let $ABCD$ be a parallelogram, and let E and F be the middle points of AD and BC.

Divide the parallelogram into a very large number of strips, by means of lines parallel to AD, of which PR and QS are any consecutive pair. Then

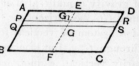

$PQSR$ may be considered to be a uniform straight line, whose centre of gravity is at its middle point G_1.

So the centre of gravity of all the other strips lies on EF, and hence the centre of gravity of the whole figure lies on EF.

So, by dividing the parallelogram by lines parallel to AB, we see that the centre of gravity lies on the line joining the middle points of the sides AB and CD.

Hence the centre of gravity is at G the point of intersection of these two lines.

G is clearly also the point of intersection of the diagonals of the parallelogram.

102. It is clear from the method of the two previous articles that, if in a uniform body we can find a point G such that the body can be divided into pairs of particles balancing about it, then G must be the centre of gravity of the body.

The centre of gravity of a uniform circle, or uniform sphere, is therefore its centre.

It is also clear that if we can divide a lamina into strips, the centre of gravity of which all lie on a straight line, then the centre of gravity of the lamina must lie on that line.

Similarly, if a body can be divided into portions, the centres of gravity of which lie in a plane, the centre of gravity of the whole must lie in that plane.

103. III. Uniform triangular lamina.

Let ABC be the triangular lamina and let D and E be the middle points of the sides BC
and CA. Join AD and BE, and
let them meet in G. Then G
shall be the centre of gravity of
the triangle.

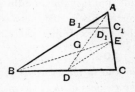

Let B_1C_1 be *any* line parallel
to the base BC meeting AD in D_1.

As in the case of the parallelogram, the triangle may be considered to be made up of a very large number of strips, such as B_1C_1, all parallel to the base BC.

Since B_1C_1 and BC are parallel, the triangles AB_1D_1 and ABD are similar; so also the triangles AD_1C_1 and ADC are similar.

Hence $$\frac{B_1D_1}{BD} = \frac{AD_1}{AD} = \frac{D_1C_1}{DC}.$$

But $BD = DC$; therefore $B_1D_1 = D_1C_1$. Hence the centre of gravity of the strip B_1C_1 lies on AD.

So the centres of gravity of all the other strips lie on AD, and hence the centre of gravity of the triangle lies on AD.

Join BE, and let it meet AD in G.

By dividing the triangle into strips parallel to AC we see, similarly, that the centre of gravity lies on BE.

Hence the required centre of gravity must be at G.

Since D is the middle point of BC and E is the middle point of CA, therefore DE is parallel to AB.

Hence the triangles GDE and GAB are similar,

$$\therefore \frac{GD}{GA} = \frac{DE}{AB} = \frac{CE}{CA} = \frac{1}{2},$$

so that $2GD = GA$, and $3GD = GA + GD = AD$.

$$\therefore \ GD = \tfrac{1}{3} AD.$$

Hence the centre of gravity of a triangle is on the line joining the middle point of any side to the opposite vertex at a distance equal to one-third the distance of the vertex from that side.

104. *The centre of gravity of any uniform triangular lamina is the same as that of three equal particles placed at the vertices of the triangle.*

Taking the figure of Art. 103, the centre of gravity of two equal particles, each equal to w, at B and C, is at D the middle point of BC; also the centre of gravity of $2w$ at D and w at A divides the line DA in the ratio of $1 : 2$. But G, the centre of gravity of the lamina, divides DA in the ratio of $1 : 2$.

Hence the centre of gravity of the three particles is the same as that of the lamina.

105. IV. Three rods forming a triangle.

Let BC, CA, and AB be the three rods, of the same thickness and material, forming the triangle, and let D, E, and F be the middle points of the rods. Join DE, EF, and FD. Clearly DE, EF, and FD are half of AB, BC, and CA respectively. The centres of gravity of the three rods are D, E, and F.

The centre of gravity of the rods AB and AC is therefore a point L on EF such that

$$EL : LF :: \text{weight at } F : \text{weight at } E$$
$$:: AB : AC$$
$$:: DE : DF,$$

so that DL bisects the angle FDE.

(Euc. vi. 3.)

Also the centre of gravity of the three rods must lie on DL.

Similarly the centre of gravity must lie on EM which bisects the angle DEF.

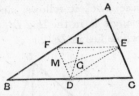

Hence the required point is the point at which EM and DL meet, and is therefore the centre of the circle inscribed in the triangle DEF,

i.e., the centre of the circle inscribed in the triangle formed by joining the middle points of the rods.

106. V. Tetrahedron.

Let $ABCD$ be the tetrahedron, E the middle point of AB, and G_1 the centre of gravity of the base ABC.

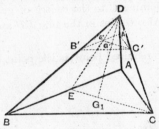

Take *any* section $A'B'C'$ of the tetrahedron which is parallel to ABC; let DE meet $A'B'$ in E' and let DG_1 meet $E'C'$ in G'.

Then

$$\frac{E'G'}{EG_1} = \frac{DG'}{DG_1}, \text{ by similar } \triangle\text{s } DE'G', DEG_1,$$

$$= \frac{C'G'}{CG_1}, \text{ by similar } \triangle\text{s } DG'C', DG_1C,$$

$$\therefore \frac{E'G'}{C'G'} = \frac{EG_1}{CG_1} = \frac{1}{2}.$$

Hence G' is the centre of gravity of the section $A'B'C'$.

By considering the tetrahedron as built up of triangles parallel to the base ABC, it follows, since the centre of gravity of each triangle is in the line DG_1, that the centre of gravity of the whole lies in DG_1.

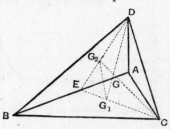

Similarly, it may be shewn that the centre of gravity lies on the line joining C to the centre of gravity G_2 of the opposite face. Also G_2 lies in the line ED and divides it in the ratio $1 : 2$.

Hence G, the required point, is the point of intersection of CG_2 and DG_1.

Join G_1G_2.

Then

$$\frac{G_2G}{GC} = \frac{G_2G_1}{DC}, \text{ by similar } \triangle s \ GG_2G_1 \text{ and } GCD,$$

$$= \frac{EG_1}{EC}, \text{ by similar } \triangle s \ EG_1G_2 \text{ and } ECD,$$

$$= \tfrac{1}{3}.$$

$$\therefore \ GC = 3 . G_2G,$$

$$\therefore \ G_2C = 4 . G_2G.$$

Similarly $\quad\quad G_1D = 4G_1G.$

Hence the centre of gravity of the pyramid lies on the line joining the centre of gravity of any face to the opposite angular point of the tetrahedron at a distance equal to one-quarter of the distance of the angular point from that face.

Cor. The centre of gravity of the tetrahedron is the same as that of equal particles placed at its vertices.

For equal weights w placed at the angular points ABC of a triangle are equivalent, by Art. 104, to a weight $3w$ placed at G_1, the centre of gravity of ABC. Also $3w$ at G_1 and w at D are equivalent to $4w$ at G, since G divides G_1D in the ratio $1 : 3$.

107. VI. Pyramid on any base. Solid Cone.

If the base of the pyramid in the previous article, instead of being a triangle, be any plane figure $ABCLMN...$ whose centre of gravity is G_1, it may be shewn, by a similar method of proof, that the centre of gravity must lie on the line joining D to G_1.

Also by drawing the planes DAG_1, DBG_1,... the whole pyramid may be split into a number of pyramids on triangular bases, the centres of gravity of which all lie on a plane parallel to $ABCL...$ and at a distance from D of three-quarters that of the latter plane.

Hence the centre of gravity of the whole lies on the line G_1D, and divides it in the ratio $1 : 3$.

Let now the sides of the plane base form a regular polygon, and let their number be indefinitely increased. Ultimately the plane base becomes a circle, and the pyramid becomes a solid cone having D as its vertex; also the point G_1 is now the centre of the circular base.

Hence the centre of gravity of a solid right circular cone is on the line joining the centre of the base to the vertex at a distance equal to one-quarter of the distance of the vertex from the base.

108. VII. Surface of a hollow cone.

Since the surface of a cone can be divided into an infinite number of triangular laminas, by joining the vertex of the cone to points on the circular base indefinitely close to one another, and since their centres of gravity all lie in a plane parallel to the base of the cone at a distance from the vertex equal to two-thirds of that of the base, the centre of gravity of the whole cone must lie in that plane.

But, by symmetry, the centre of gravity must lie on the axis of the cone.

Hence the required point is the point in which the above plane meets the axis, and therefore is on the axis at a point distant from the base one-third the height of the cone.

EXAMPLES. XV.

1. An isosceles triangular lamina has its equal sides of length 5 feet and its base of length 6 feet; find the distance of the centre of gravity from each of its sides.

2. The sides of a triangular lamina are 6, 8, and 10 feet in length; find the distance of the centre of gravity from each of the sides.

3. The base of an isosceles triangular lamina is 4 inches and the equal sides are each 7 inches in length; find the distances of its centre of gravity from the angular points of the triangle.

4. D is the middle point of the base BC of a triangle ABC; shew that the distance between the centres of gravity of the triangles ABD and ACD is $\frac{1}{3}BC$.

5. A heavy triangular plate ABC lies on the ground; if a vertical force applied at the point A be just great enough to begin to lift that vertex from the ground, shew that the same force will suffice, if applied at B or C.

6. Three men carry a weight, W, by putting it on a smooth triangular board, of weight w, and supporting the system on their shoulders placed respectively at the angular points; find the weight that each man supports.

7. The base of a triangle is fixed, and its vertex moves on a given straight line; shew that the centre of gravity also moves on a straight line.

8. The base of a triangle is fixed, and it has a given vertical angle; shew that the centre of gravity of the triangle moves on an arc of a certain circle.

9. A given weight is placed anywhere on a triangle; shew that the centre of gravity of the system lies within a certain triangle.

10. A uniform equilateral triangular plate is suspended by a string attached to a point in one of its sides, which divides the side in the ratio 2 : 1; find the inclination of this side to the vertical.

11. A uniform lamina in the shape of a right-angled triangle, and such that one of the sides containing the right angle is three times the other, is suspended by a string attached to the right angle; in the position of equilibrium, shew that the hypotenuse is inclined at an angle $\sin^{-1} \frac{3}{5}$ to the vertical.

12. A uniform triangular lamina, whose sides are 3, 4, and 5 inches, is suspended by a string from the middle point of the longest side; find the inclination of this side to the vertical.

109. General formulae for the determination of the centre of gravity.

In the following articles will be obtained formulae giving the position of the centre of gravity of any system of particles, whose position and weights are known.

Theorem. *If a system of particles whose weights are* $w_1, w_2, \ldots w_n$ *be on a straight line, and if their distances measured from a fixed point* O *in the line be*

$$x_1, x_2, \ldots x_n,$$

the distance, $\bar{x}$, *of their centre of gravity from the fixed point is given by*

$$\bar{x} = \frac{w_1 x_1 + w_2 x_2 + \ldots + w_n x_n}{w_1 + w_2 + \ldots + w_n}.$$

Let A, B, C, $D \ldots$ be the particles and let the centre of gravity of w_1 and w_2 at A and B be G_1; let the centre of gravity of $(w_1 + w_2)$ at G_1 and w_3 at C be G_2, and so for the other particles of the system.

By Art. 97, we have $w_1 \cdot AG_1 = w_2 \cdot G_1B$;

$$\therefore \ w_1(OG_1 - OA) = w_2(OB - OG_1).$$

Hence $\quad (w_1 + w_2) \cdot OG_1 = w_1 \cdot OA + w_2 \cdot OB,$

$$i.e., \quad OG_1 = \frac{w_1x_1 + w_2x_2}{w_1 + w_2} \quad \ldots\ldots\ldots\ldots(1).$$

Similarly, since G_2 is the centre of gravity of $(w_1 + w_2)$ at G_1 and w_3 at C, we have

$$OG_2 = \frac{(w_1 + w_2) \cdot OG_1 + w_3 \cdot OC}{(w_1 + w_2) + w_3}$$

$$= \frac{w_1x_1 + w_2x_2 + w_3x_3}{w_1 + w_2 + w_3}, \ \text{by (1).}$$

So $\quad OG_3 = \dfrac{(w_1 + w_2 + w_3) \cdot OG_2 + w_4 \cdot OD}{(w_1 + w_2 + w_3) + w_4}$

$$= \frac{w_1x_1 + w_2x_2 + w_3x_3 + w_4x_4}{w_1 + w_2 + w_3 + w_4}.$$

Proceeding in this manner we easily have

$$\bar{x} = \frac{w_1x_1 + w_2x_2 + \ldots + w_nx_n}{w_1 + w_2 + \ldots + w_n},$$

whatever be the number of the particles in the system.

Otherwise, The above formula may be obtained by the use of Article 65. For the weights of the particles form a system of parallel forces whose resultant is equal to their sum, $viz.$ $w_1 + w_2 + \ldots + w_n$. Also the sum of the moments of these forces about any point in their plane is the same as the moment of their resultant. But the sum of the moments of the forces about the fixed point O is

$$w_1x_1 + w_2x_2 + \ldots + w_nx_n.$$

Also, if $\bar{x}$ be the distance of the centre of gravity from O, the moment of the resultant is

$$(w_1 + w_2 + \ldots + w_n) \times \bar{x}.$$

Hence $\quad \bar{x}(w_1 + w_2 + \ldots + w_n) = w_1x_1 + w_2x_2 + \ldots + w_nx_n;$

$$i.e., \quad \bar{x} = \frac{w_1x_1 + w_2x_2 + \ldots + w_nx_n}{w_1 + w_2 + \ldots + w_n}.$$

110. Ex. 1. *A rod AB, 2 feet in length, and of weight 5 lbs., is trisected in the points C and D, and at the points A, C, D, and B are placed particles of 1, 2, 3, and 4 lbs. weight respectively; find what point of the rod must be supported so that the rod may rest in any position, i.e., find the centre of gravity of the system.*

Let G be the middle point of the rod and let the fixed point O of the previous article be taken to coincide with the end A of the rod. The quantities x_1, x_2, x_3, x_4, and x_5 are in this case 0, 8, 12, 16, and 24 inches respectively.

Hence, if X be the point required, we have

$$AX = \frac{1.0 + 2.8 + 5.12 + 3.16 + 4.24}{1 + 2 + 5 + 3 + 4}$$

$$= \frac{220}{15} = 14\frac{2}{3} \text{ inches.}$$

Ex. 2. *If, in the previous question, the body at B be removed and another body be substituted, find the weight of this unknown body so that the new centre of gravity may be at the middle point of the rod.*

Let λ lbs. be the required weight.

Since the distance of the new centre of gravity from A is to be 12 inches, we have

$$12 = \frac{1.0 + 2.8 + 5.12 + 3.16 + \lambda.24}{1 + 2 + 5 + 3 + \lambda} = \frac{124 + 24\lambda}{11 + \lambda}.$$

$$\therefore 132 + 12\lambda = 124 + 24\lambda.$$

$$\therefore \lambda = \frac{2}{3} \text{ lb.}$$

Ex. 3. *To the end of a rod, whose length is 2 feet and whose weight is 3 lbs., is attached a sphere, of radius 2 inches and weight 10 lbs.; find the position of the centre of gravity of the compound body.*

Let OA be the rod, G_1 its middle point, G_2 the centre of the sphere, and G the required point.

Then
$$OG = \frac{3 \cdot OG_1 + 10 \cdot OG_2}{3 + 10}.$$

But
$$OG_1 = 12 \text{ inches}; \quad OG_2 = 26 \text{ inches.}$$

$$\therefore OG = \frac{3.12 + 10.26}{3 + 10} = \frac{296}{13} = 22\frac{10}{13} \text{ inches.}$$

EXAMPLES. XVI.

1. A straight rod, 1 foot in length and of mass 1 ounce, has an ounce of lead fastened to it at one end, and another ounce fastened to it at a distance from the other end equal to one-third of its length; find the centre of gravity of the system.

2. A uniform bar, 3 feet in length and of mass 6 ounces, has 3 rings, each of mass 3 ounces, at distances 3, 15, and 21 inches from one end. About what point of the bar will the system balance?

3. A uniform rod AB is four feet long and weighs 3 lbs. One lb. is attached at A, 2 lbs. at a point distant 1 foot from A, 3 lbs. at 2 feet from A, 4 lbs. at 3 feet from A, and 5 lbs. at B. Find the distance from A of the centre of gravity of the system.

4. A telescope consists of 3 tubes, each 10 inches in length, one within the other, and of weights 8, 7, and 6 ounces. Find the position of the centre of gravity when the tubes are drawn out at full length.

5. Twelve heavy particles at equal intervals of one inch along a straight rod weigh 1, 2, 3,...12 grains respectively; find their centre of gravity, neglecting the weight of the rod.

6. Weights proportional to 1, 4, 9, and 16 are placed in a straight line so that the distances between them are equal; find the position of their centre of gravity.

7. A rod, of uniform thickness, has one-half of its length composed of one metal and the other half composed of a different metal, and the rod balances about a point distant one-third of its whole length from one end; compare the weight of equal quantities of the metal.

8. An inclined plane, with an angle of inclination of 60°, is 3 feet long; masses of 7, 5, 4, and 8 ounces are placed on the plane in order at distances of 1 foot, the latter being the highest; find the distance of their centre of gravity from the base of the inclined plane.

9. AB is a uniform rod, of length n inches and weight $(n+1)W$. To the rod masses of weight $W, 2W, 3W,...nW$ are attached at distances 1, 2, 3,...n inches respectively from A. Find the distance from A of the centre of gravity of the rod and weights.

10. A rod, 12 feet long, has a mass of 1 lb. suspended from one end, and, when 15 lbs. is suspended from the other end, it balances about a point distant 3 ft. from that end; if 8 lbs. be suspended there, it balances about a point 4 ft. from that end. Find the weight of the rod and the position of its centre of gravity.

111. Theorem. *If a system of particles, whose weights are* $w_1, w_2, \ldots w_n$, *lie in a plane, and if OX and OY be two fixed straight lines in the plane at right angles, and if the distances of the particles from OX be* $y_1, y_2, \ldots y_n$, *and the distance of their centre of gravity be* $\bar{y}$, *then*

$$\bar{y} = \frac{w_1 y_1 + w_2 y_2 + \ldots + w_n y_n}{w_1 + w_2 + \ldots + w_n}.$$

Similarly, if the distances of the particles from OY be
$x_1, x_2, \ldots x_n$ *and that of their centre of gravity be $\bar{x}$, then*

$$\bar{x} = \frac{w_1 x_1 + w_2 x_2 + \ldots + w_n x_n}{w_1 + w_2 + \ldots + w_n}.$$

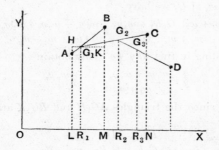

Let $A, B, C, \ldots$ be the particles, and $AL, BM, CN\ldots$ the
perpendiculars on OX.

Let G_1 be the centre of gravity of w_1 and w_2, G_2 the
centre of gravity of $(w_1 + w_2)$ at G_1 and w_3 at C, and so on.

Draw $G_1 R_1, G_2 R_2, \ldots$ perpendicular to OX, and through
G_1 draw HG_1K parallel to OX to meet AL and BM in H
and K.

Since G_1 is the centre of gravity of w_1 and w_2, we have

$$\frac{AG_1}{G_1 B} = \frac{w_2}{w_1}. \quad \text{(Art. 97.)}$$

Now $AG_1 H$ and $BG_1 K$ are similar triangles,

$$\therefore \frac{HA}{BK} = \frac{AG_1}{G_1 B} = \frac{w_2}{w_1}.$$

But $\qquad HA = HL - AL = G_1 R_1 - y_1,$

and $\qquad BK = BM - KM = y_2 - G_1 R_1;$

$$\therefore \frac{G_1 R_1 - y_1}{y_2 - G_1 R_1} = \frac{w_2}{w_1}.$$

Hence $\quad w_1(G_1R_1 - y_1) = w_2(y_2 - G_1R_1)$;

$$\therefore\ G_1R_1 = \frac{w_1y_1 + w_2y_2}{w_1 + w_2}\ \ldots\ldots\ldots\ldots(1).$$

Similarly, since G_2 is the centre of gravity of $(w_1 + w_2)$ at G_1 and w_3 at C, we have

$$G_2R_2 = \frac{(w_1 + w_2)\cdot G_1R_1 + w_3y_3}{w_1 + w_2 + w_3} = \frac{w_1y_1 + w_2y_2 + w_3y_3}{w_1 + w_2 + w_3},\ \text{by (1).}$$

Proceeding in this way we easily obtain

$$\bar{y} = \frac{w_1y_1 + w_2y_2 + \ldots + w_ny_n}{w_1 + w_2 + \ldots + w_n}.$$

Again, since the triangles AG_1H and BG_1K are similar, we have

$$\frac{HG_1}{G_1K} = \frac{AG_1}{G_1B} = \frac{w_2}{w_1}.$$

But $\quad HG_1 = LR_1 = OR_1 - OL = OR_1 - x_1,$

and $\quad G_1K = R_1M = OM - OR_1 = x_2 - OR_1.$

$$\therefore\ w_1(OR_1 - x_1) = w_2(x_2 - OR_1).$$

Hence $\quad OR_1 = \frac{w_1x_1 + w_2x_2}{w_1 + w_2}.$

Proceeding as before we finally have

$$\bar{x} = \frac{w_1x_1 + w_2x_2 + \ldots + w_nx_n}{w_1 + w_2 + \ldots + w_n}.$$

The theorem of this article may be put somewhat differently as follows;

The distance of the centre of gravity from **any** *line in the plane of the particles is equal to a fraction, whose numerator is the sum of the products of each weight into its distance from the given line, and whose denominator is the sum of the weights.*

In other words, the distance of the centre of gravity is equal to the **average** distance of the particles.

112. The formula of the preceding article may be deduced from Article 93. For, since the resultant weight $(w_1 + w_2 + ... + w_n)$ acting at G, where G is the centre of gravity of all the weights, is equivalent to the component weights w_1, w_2,... the resultant would, if the line OX be supposed to be a fixed axis, have the same moment about this fixed axis that the component weights have.

But the moment of the resultant is

$$(w_1 + w_2 + ... + w_n)\, \bar{y},$$

and the sum of the moments of the weights is

$$w_1 y_1 + w_2 y_2 + ... + w_n y_n.$$

Hence $$\bar{y} = \frac{w_1 y_1 + w_2 y_2 + ... + w_n y_n}{w_1 + w_2 + ... + w_n}.$$

In a similar manner we should have

$$\bar{x} = \frac{w_1 x_1 + w_2 x_2 + ... + w_n x_n}{w_1 + w_2 + ... + w_n}$$

113. Ex. 1. *A square lamina, whose weight is 10 lbs., has attached to its angular points particles whose weights, taken in order, are 3, 6, 5, and 1 lbs. respectively. Find the position of the centre of gravity of the system, if the side of the lamina be 25 inches.*

Let the particles be placed at the angular points O, A, B, and C. Let the two fixed lines from which the distances are measured be OA and OC.

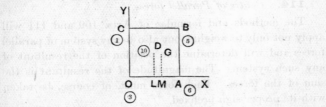

The weight of the lamina acts at its centre D. Let G be the required centre of gravity and draw DL and GM perpendicular to OX.

The distances of the points O, A, B, C, and D from OX are clearly 0, 0, 25, 25, and $12\frac{1}{2}$ inches respectively.

$$\therefore MG = \bar{y} = \frac{3 \cdot 0 + 6 \cdot 0 + 5 \cdot 25 + 1 \cdot 25 + 10 \cdot 12\frac{1}{2}}{3 + 6 + 5 + 1 + 10} = \frac{275}{25} = 11 \text{ ins.}$$

So the distances of the particles from OY are 0, 25, 25, 0, and $12\frac{1}{2}$ inches respectively.

$$\therefore OM = \bar{x} = \frac{3 \cdot 0 + 6 \cdot 25 + 5 \cdot 25 + 1 \cdot 0 + 10 \cdot 12\frac{1}{2}}{3 + 6 + 5 + 1 + 10} = \frac{400}{25} = 16 \text{ ins.}$$

Hence the required point may be obtained by measuring 16 inches from O along OA and then erecting a perpendicular of length 11 inches.

Ex. 2. *OAB is an isosceles weightless triangle, whose base OA is 6 inches and whose sides are each 5 inches; at the points O, A, and B are placed particles of weights 1, 2, and 3 lbs.; find their centre of gravity.*

Let the fixed line OX coincide with OA and let OY be a perpendicular to OA through the point O.

If BL be drawn perpendicular to OA, then $OL = 3$ ins., and

$$LB = \sqrt{5^2 - 3^2} = 4 \text{ ins.}$$

Hence, if G be the required centre of gravity and GM be drawn perpendicular to OX, we have

$$OM = \frac{1 \cdot 0 + 2 \cdot 6 + 3 \cdot 3}{1 + 2 + 3} = \frac{21}{6} = 3\frac{1}{2} \text{ inches,}$$

and

$$MG = \frac{1 \cdot 0 + 2 \cdot 0 + 3 \cdot 4}{1 + 2 + 3} = \frac{12}{6} = 2 \text{ inches.}$$

Hence the required point is obtained by measuring a distance $3\frac{1}{2}$ inches from O along OA and then erecting a perpendicular of length 2 inches.

114. *Centre of Parallel forces.*

The methods and formulae of Arts. 109 and 111 will apply not only to weights, but also to any system of parallel forces and will determine the position of the resultant of any such system. The magnitude of the resultant is the sum of the forces. Each force must, of course, be taken with its proper sign prefixed.

There is one case in which we obtain no satisfactory result; if the algebraic sum of the forces be zero, the resultant force is zero, and the formulae of Art. 111 give

$$\bar{x} = \infty , \text{ and } \bar{y} = \infty .$$

In this case the system of parallel forces is, as in Art. 53, equivalent to a couple.

EXAMPLES. XVII.

1. Particles of 1, 2, 3, and 4 lbs. weight are placed at the angular points of a square; find the distance of their c.g. from the centre of the square.

2. At two opposite corners A and C of a square $ABCD$ weights of 2 lbs. each are placed, and at B and D are placed 1 and 7 lbs. respectively; find their centre of gravity.

3. Particles of 5, 6, 9, and 7 lbs. respectively are placed at the corners A, B, C, and D of a horizontal square, the length of whose side is 27 inches; find where a single force must be applied to preserve equilibrium.

4. Five masses of 1, 2, 3, 4, and 5 ounces respectively are placed on a square table. The distances from one edge of the table are 2, 4, 6, 8, and 10 inches and from the adjacent edge 3, 5, 7, 9, and 11 inches respectively. Find the distance of the centre of gravity from the two edges.

5. Weights proportional to 1, 2, and 3 are placed at the corners of an equilateral triangle, whose side is of length a; find the distance of their centre of gravity from the first weight.

Find the distance also if the weights be proportional to 11, 13, and 6.

6. ABC is an equilateral triangle of side 2 feet. At A, B, and C are placed weights proportional to 5, 1, and 3, and at the middle points of the sides BC, CA, and AB weights proportional to 2, 4, and 6; shew that their centre of gravity is distant 16 inches from B.

7. Equal masses, each 1 oz., are placed at the angular points of a heavy triangular lamina, and also at the middle points of its sides; find the position of the centre of gravity of the masses.

8. ABC is a triangle right-angled at A, AB being 12 and AC 15 inches; weights proportional to 2, 3, and 4 respectively are placed at A, C, and B; find the distances of their centre of gravity from B and C.

9. Particles, of mass 4, 1, and 1 lbs., are placed at the angular points of a triangle; shew that the centre of gravity of the particles bisects the distance between the centre of gravity and one of the vertices of the triangle.

10. Three masses are placed at the angular points of a triangle ABC. Find their ratios if their centre of inertia be halfway between A and the middle point of BC.

11. Bodies of mass 2, 3, and 4 lbs. respectively are placed at the angular points A, B, and C of a triangle; find their centre of gravity G, and shew that forces $2GA$, $3GB$, and $4GC$ are in equilibrium.

12. ABC is a uniform triangular plate, of mass 3 lbs. Masses of 2, 3, and 5 lbs. respectively are placed at A, B, and C. Find the position of the centre of gravity of the whole system.

13. To the vertices A, B, and C of a uniform triangular plate, whose mass is 3 lbs. and whose centre of gravity is G, particles of masses 2 lbs., 2 lbs., and 11 lbs., are attached; shew that the centre of gravity of the system is the middle point of GC.

14. Masses of 2, 3, 2, 6, 9, and 6 lbs. are placed at the angular corners of a regular hexagon, taken in order; find their centre of gravity.

15. Weights proportional to 5, 4, 6, 2, 7, and 3 are placed at the angular points of a regular hexagon, taken in order; shew that their centre of gravity is the centre of the hexagon.

16. Weights proportional to 1, 5, 3, 4, 2, and 6 are placed at the angular points of a regular hexagon, taken in order; shew that their centre of gravity is the centre of the hexagon.

17. If weights proportional to the numbers 1, 2, 3, 4, 5, and 6 be placed at the angular points of a regular hexagon taken in order, shew that the distance of their centre of gravity from the centre of the circumscribing circle of the hexagon is $\frac{2}{7}$ ths of the radius of the circle.

18. At the angular points of a square, taken in order, there act parallel forces in the ratio $1 : 3 : 5 : 7$; find the distance from the centre of the square of the point at which their resultant acts.

19. A, B, C, and D are the angles of a parallelogram taken in order; like parallel forces proportional to 6, 10, 14, and 10 respectively act at A, B, C, and D; shew that the centre and resultant of these parallel forces remain the same, if, instead of these forces, parallel forces, proportional to 8, 12, 16, and 4, act at the points of bisection of the sides AB, BC, CD, and DA respectively.

20. Find the centre of parallel forces equal respectively to P, $2P$, $3P$, $4P$, $5P$, and $6P$, the points of application of the forces being at distances 1, 2, 3, 4, 5, and 6 inches respectively from a given point A measured along a given line AB.

21. Three parallel forces, P, Q, and R, act at the vertices A, B, and C, of a triangle and are proportional respectively to a, b, and c. Find the magnitude and position of their resultant.

115. *Given the centre of gravity of the two portions of a body, to find the centre of gravity of the whole body.*

Let the given centres of gravity be G_1 and G_2, and let the weights of the two portions be W_1 and W_2; the required point G, by Art. 97, divides G_1G_2 so that

$$G_1G : GG_2 :: W_2 : W_1.$$

The point G may also be obtained by the use of Art. 109.

Ex. *On the same base AB, and on opposite sides of it, isosceles triangles CAB and DAB are described whose altitudes are 12 inches and 6 inches respectively. Find the distance from AB of the centre of gravity of the quadrilateral CADB.*

Let CLD be the perpendicular to AB, meeting it in L, and let G_1 and G_2 be the centres of gravity of the two triangles CAB and DAB respectively. Hence

$$CG_1 = \tfrac{2}{3} \cdot CL = 8,$$

and $\qquad CG_2 = CL + LG_2 = 12 + 2 = 14.$

The weights of the triangles are proportional to their areas, *i.e.*, to $\tfrac{1}{2}AB \cdot 12$ and $\tfrac{1}{2}AB \cdot 6$.

If G be the centre of gravity of the whole figure, we have

$$CG = \frac{\triangle CAB \times CG_1 + \triangle DAB \times CG_2}{\triangle CAB + \triangle DAB}$$

$$= \frac{\tfrac{1}{2}AB \cdot 12 \times 8 + \tfrac{1}{2}AB \cdot 6 \times 14}{\tfrac{1}{2}AB \cdot 12 + \tfrac{1}{2}AB \cdot 6} = \frac{48 + 42}{6 + 3} = \frac{90}{9} = 10.$$

Hence $\qquad\qquad LG = CL - CG = 2$ inches.

This result may be verified experimentally by cutting the figure out of thin cardboard.

116. *Given the centre of gravity of the whole of a body and of a portion of the body, to find the centre of gravity of the remainder.*

Let G be the centre of gravity of a body $ABCD$, and G_1 that of the portion ADC.

Let W be the weight of the whole body and W_1 that of the portion ACD, so that $W_2 (= W - W_1)$ is the weight of the portion ABC.

Let G_2 be the centre of gravity of the portion ABC. Since the two portions of the body make up the whole, therefore W_1 at G_1 and W_2 at G_2 must have their centre of gravity at G.

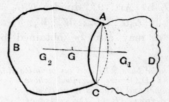

Hence G must lie on G_1G_2 and be such that

$$W_1 \cdot GG_1 = W_2 \cdot GG_2.$$

Hence, given G and G_1, we obtain G_2 by producing G_1G to G_2, so that

$$GG_2 = \frac{W_1}{W_2} \cdot GG_1$$

$$= \frac{W_1}{W - W_1} \cdot GG_1.$$

The required point may be also obtained by means of Art. 109.

Ex. 1. *From a circular disc, of radius r, is cut out a circle, whose diameter is a radius of the disc; find the centre of gravity of the remainder.*

Since the areas of circles are to one another as the squares of their radii,

∴ area of the portion cut out
: area of the whole circle

$$:: \left(\frac{r}{2}\right)^2 : r^2$$

$$:: 1 : 4.$$

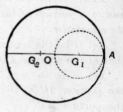

Hence the portion cut off is one-quarter, and the portion remaining is three-quarters, of the whole, so that $W_1 = \frac{1}{3} W_2$.

Now the portions W_1 and W_2 make up the whole disc, and therefore balance about O.

Hence $\qquad W_2 \cdot OG_2 = W_1 \cdot OG_1 = \frac{1}{3}W_2 \times \frac{1}{2}r.$

$$\therefore \quad OG_2 = \frac{1}{6}r.$$

This may be verified experimentally.

Ex. 2. *From a triangular lamina ABC is cut off, by a line parallel to its base BC, one-quarter of its area; find the centre of gravity of the remainder.*

Let AB_1C_1 be the portion cut off, so that

$$\triangle AB_1C_1 : \triangle ABC :: 1 : 4.$$

By Euc. vi. 19, since the triangles AB_1C_1 and ABC are similar, we have

$$\triangle AB_1C_1 : \triangle ABC :: AB_1{}^2 : AB^2.$$
$$\therefore \quad AB_1{}^2 : AB^2 :: 1 : 4,$$

and hence $\qquad AB_1 = \frac{1}{2}AB.$

The line B_1C_1 therefore bisects AB, AC, and AD.

Let G and G_1 be the centres of gravity of the triangles ABC and AB_1C_1 respectively; also let W_1 and W_2 be the respective weights of the portion cut off and the portion remaining, so that $W_2 = 3W_1$.

Since W_2 at G_2 and W_1 at G_1 balance about G, we have, by Art. 109,

$$DG = \frac{W_1 \cdot DG_1 + W_2 \cdot DG_2}{W_1 + W_2} = \frac{DG_1 + 3DG_2}{4} \quad \ldots\ldots\ldots\ldots(i).$$

But $\qquad DG = \frac{1}{3}DA = \frac{2}{3}DD_1,$

and $\qquad DG_1 = DD_1 + \frac{1}{3}D_1A = DD_1 + \frac{1}{3}DD_1 = \frac{4}{3}DD_1.$

Hence (i) is $\qquad 4 \times \frac{2}{3}DD_1 = \frac{4}{3}DD_1 + 3DG_2.$

$$\therefore \quad DG_2 = \frac{4}{9}DD_1.$$

This result can also be easily verified experimentally.

EXAMPLES. XVIII.

[*The student should verify some of the following questions experimentally; suitable ones for this purpose are Nos.* 1, 2, 4, 5, 8, 9, 10, 11, 17, 18, *and* 19.]

1. A uniform rod, 1 foot in length, is broken into two parts, of lengths 5 and 7 inches, which are placed so as to form the letter ⊤, the longer portion being vertical; find the centre of gravity of the system.

2. Two rectangular pieces of the same cardboard, of lengths 6 and 8 inches and breadths 2 and $2\frac{1}{2}$ inches respectively, are placed touching, but not overlapping, one another on a table so as to form a ⊤-shaped figure, the longer portion being vertical. Find the position of its centre of gravity.

3. A heavy beam consists of two portions, whose lengths are as 3 : 5, and whose weights are as 3 : 1; find the position of its centre of gravity.

4. Two sides of a rectangle are double of the other two, and on one of the longer sides an equilateral triangle is described; find the centre of gravity of the lamina made up of the rectangle and the triangle.

5. A piece of cardboard is in the shape of a square $ABCD$ with an isosceles triangle described on the side BC; if the side of the square be 12 inches and the height of the triangle be 6 inches, find the distance of the centre of gravity of the cardboard from the line AD.

6. An isosceles right-angled triangle has squares described externally on all its sides. Shew that the centre of gravity of the figure so formed is on the line, which bisects the hypotenuse and passes through the right angle, and divides it in the ratio 1 : 26.

7. Two uniform spheres, composed of the same materials, and whose diameters are 6 and 12 inches respectively, are firmly united; find the position of their centre of gravity.

8. From a parallelogram is cut one of the four portions into which it is divided by its diagonals; find the centre of gravity of the remainder.

9. A parallelogram is divided into four parts, by joining the middle points of opposite sides, and one part is cut away; find the centre of gravity of the remainder.

10. From a square a triangular portion is cut off, by cutting the square along a line joining the middle points of two adjacent sides; find the centre of gravity of the remainder.

11. From a triangle is cut off $\frac{1}{3}$th of its area by a straight line parallel to its base. Find the position of the centre of gravity of the remainder.

12. ABC is an equilateral triangle, of 6 inches side, of which O is the centre of gravity. If the triangle OBC be removed, find the centre of gravity of the remainder.

13. If from a triangle ABC three equal triangles ARQ, BPR, and CQP, be cut off, shew that the centres of inertia of the triangles ABC and PQR are coincident.

14. G is the centre of gravity of a given isosceles triangle, right-angled at A, and having BC equal to a. The portion GBC is cut away; find the distance of the centre of gravity of the remainder from A.

15. On the same base BC are two triangles, ABC and $A'BC$, the vertex A' falling within the former triangle. Find the position of A' when it is the centre of gravity of the area between the two triangles.

16. Two triangles, each $\frac{1}{m}$th of the whole, are cut off from a given triangle at two of its angular points, B and C, by straight lines parallel to the opposite sides; find the c.g. of remainder.

17. Out of a square plate shew how to cut a triangle, having one side of the square for base, so that the remainder may have its centre of gravity at the vertex of this triangle and therefore rest in any position if this point be supported.

18. A uniform plate of metal, 10 inches square, has a hole of area 3 square inches cut out of it, the centre of the hole being $2\frac{1}{2}$ inches from the centre of the plate; find the position of the centre of gravity of the remainder of the plate.

19. Where must a circular hole, of 1 foot radius, be punched out of a circular disc, of 3 feet radius, so that the centre of gravity of the remainder may be 2 inches from the centre of the disc?

20. Two spheres, of radii a and b, touch internally; find the centre of gravity of the solid included between them.

21. If a right cone be cut by a plane bisecting its axis at right angles, find the distance of the vertex of the cone from the centre of gravity of the frustum thus cut off.

22. A solid right circular cone of homogeneous iron, of height 64 inches and mass 8192 lbs., is cut by a plane perpendicular to its axis so that the mass of the small cone removed is 686 lbs. Find the height of the centre of gravity of the truncated portion above the base of the cone.

23. A solid right circular cone has its base scooped out, so that the hollow is a right cone on the same base; how much must be scooped out so that the centre of gravity of the remainder may coincide with the vertex of the hollow?

24. The mass of the moon is ·013 times that of the earth. Taking the earth's radius as 4000 miles and the distance of the moon's centre from the earth's centre as 60 times the earth's radius, find the distance of the c.g. of the earth and moon from the centre of the earth.

117.　Centre of gravity of a hemisphere.

If a hemisphere be of radius r, the centre of gravity lies on that radius which is perpendicular to its plane face, and is at a distance $\frac{3r}{8}$ from the centre of the plane face. If the hemisphere be hollow, the distance is $\frac{r}{2}$. The proofs of these statements are difficult by elementary methods; they will be found in the last chapter.

118.　*To find the centre of gravity of a quadrilateral lamina having two parallel sides.*

Let $ABCD$ be the quadrilateral, having the sides AB and CD parallel and equal to $2a$ and $2b$ respectively.

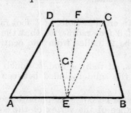

Let E and F be the middle points of AB and CD respectively. Join DE and EC; the areas of the triangles ADE, DEC, and BEC are proportional to their bases AE, DC, and EB, *i.e.*, are proportional to a, $2b$, and a.

Replace them by particles equal to one-third of their weight placed at their angular points (Art. 104).

We thus have weights proportional to

$$\frac{a}{3} + \frac{2b}{3} \text{ at each of } C \text{ and } D,$$

$$\frac{a}{3} \text{ at each of } A \text{ and } B,$$

and　　　$$\frac{2a}{3} + \frac{2b}{3} \text{ at } E.$$

Again, replace the equal weights at C and D by a weight proportional to $\dfrac{2a}{3} + \dfrac{4b}{3}$ at the middle point F of CD, and the equal weights at A and B by a weight proportional to $\dfrac{2a}{3}$ at E.

We thus have weights

$$\dfrac{2a}{3} + \dfrac{4b}{3} \text{ at } F,$$

and

$$\dfrac{4a}{3} + \dfrac{2b}{3} \text{ at } E.$$

Hence the required centre of gravity G is on the straight line EF, and is such that

$$\frac{EG}{GF} = \frac{\text{weight at } F}{\text{weight at } E} = \frac{a + 2b}{2a + b}.$$

EXAMPLES. XIX.

1. A triangular table rests on supports at its vertices; weights of 6, 8, and 10 lbs. are placed at the middle points of the sides. Find by how much the pressures on the legs are increased thereby.

2. A piece of thin uniform wire is bent into the form of a four-sided figure, $ABCD$, of which the sides AB and CD are parallel, and BC and DA are equally inclined to AB. If AB be 18 inches, CD 12 inches, and BC and DA each 5 inches, find the distance from AB of the centre of gravity of the wire.

3. AB, BC and CD are three equal uniform rods firmly joined, so as to form three successive sides of a regular hexagon, and are suspended from the point A; shew that CD is horizontal.

4. ABC is a piece of uniform wire; its two parts AB and BC are straight, and the angle ABC is 135°. It is suspended from a fixed point by a string attached to the wire at B, and the part AB is observed to be horizontal. Shew that BC is to AB as $\sqrt[4]{2}$ to 1.

5. A rod, of length $5a$, is bent so as to form five sides of a regular hexagon; shew that the distance of its centre of gravity from either end of the rod is

$$\frac{a}{10}\sqrt{133}.$$

6. The side CD of a uniform trapezoidal lamina $ABCD$ is twice as long as AB, to which it is opposite and parallel; compare the distances of the centre of gravity of $ABCD$ from AB and CD.

7. If the centre of gravity of a quadrilateral lamina $ABCD$ coincide with one of the angles A, shew that the distances of A and C from the line BD are as $1:2$.

8. A uniform quadrilateral $ABCD$ has the sides AB and AD, and the diagonal AC all equal, and the angles BAC and CAD are $30°$ and $60°$ respectively. If a weight, equal to two-thirds that of the triangle ABC, be attached at the point B, and the whole rest suspended from the point A, shew that the diagonal AC will be vertical.

9. Explain what will take place when 3 forces, represented by AB, BC, and CA respectively, act along the sides of a triangular board ABC which is supported on a smooth peg passing through its centre of gravity.

10. Three forces act at a point O in the plane of a triangle ABC, being represented by OA, OB and OC; where must be the point O so that the three forces may be in equilibrium?

11. A particle P is attracted to three points A, B, C by forces equal to $\mu . PA$, $\mu . PB$, and $\mu . PC$ respectively; shew that the resultant is $3\mu . PG$, where G is the centre of gravity of the triangle ABC.

12. A particle P is acted upon by forces towards the points A, B, C, ... which are represented by $\lambda . PA$, $\mu . PB$, $\nu . PC$, ...; shew that their resultant is represented by $(\lambda + \mu + \nu + ...)PG$, where G is the centre of gravity of weights placed at A, B, C, ... proportional to λ, μ, ν, ... respectively.

[This is the generalised form of Art. 42, and may be proved by successive applications of that article.]

13. A uniform rod is hung up by two strings attached to its ends, the other ends of the strings being attached to a fixed point; shew that the tensions of the strings are proportional to their lengths.

Prove that the same relation holds for a uniform triangular lamina hung up by three strings attached to its angular points.

14. Find the vertical angle of a cone in order that the centre of gravity of its whole surface, including its plane base, may coincide with the centre of gravity of its volume.

15. A cylinder and a cone have their bases joined together, the bases being of the same size; find the ratio of the height of the cone to the height of the cylinder so that the common centre of gravity may be at the centre of the common base.

16. Shew how to cut out of a uniform cylinder a cone, whose base coincides with that of the cylinder, so that the centre of gravity of the remaining solid may coincide with the vertex of the cone.

17. If the diameter of the base of a cone be to its altitude as $1 : \sqrt{2}$, shew that, when the greatest possible sphere has been cut out, the centre of gravity of the remainder coincides with that of the cone.

18. From a uniform right cone, whose vertical angle is 60°, is cut out the greatest possible sphere; shew that the centre of gravity of the remainder divides the axis in the ratio 11 : 49.

19. A solid in the form of a right circular cone has its base scooped out, so that the hollow so formed is a right circular cone on the same base and of half the height of the original cone; find the position of the centre of gravity of the cone so formed.

20. A uniform equilateral triangle ABC is supported with the angle A in contact with a smooth wall by means of a string BD, equal in length to a side of the triangle, which is fastened to a point D vertically above A. Shew that the distances of B and C from the wall are as 1 : 5.

21. A cone, whose height is equal to four times the radius of its base, is hung from a point in the circumference of its base; shew that it will rest with its base and axis equally inclined to the vertical.

22. Two right cones, consisting of the same material, have equal slant slides and vertical angles of 60° and 120° respectively, and are so joined that they have a slant side coincident. Shew that, if they be suspended from their common vertex, the line of contact will be inclined at 15° to the vertical.

23. A triangular piece of paper is folded across the line bisecting two sides, the vertex being thus brought to lie on the base of the triangle. Shew that the distance of the centre of inertia of the paper in this position from the base of the triangle is three-quarters that of the centre of inertia of the unfolded paper from the same line.

24. A rectangular sheet of stiff paper, whose length is to its breadth as $\sqrt{2}$ to 1, lies on a horizontal table with its longer sides perpendicular to the edge and projecting over it. The corners on the table are then doubled over symmetrically, so that the creases pass through the middle point of the side joining the corners and make angles of 45° with it. The paper is now on the point of falling over; shew that it had originally $\frac{25}{48}$ths of its length on the table.

25. At each of $n-1$ of the angular points of a regular polygon of n sides a particle is placed, the particles being equal; shew that the distance of their centre of gravity from the centre of the circle circumscribing the polygon is $\dfrac{r}{n-1}$, where r is the radius of the circle.

26. A square hole is punched out of a circular lamina, the diagonal of the square being a radius of the circle. Shew that the centre of gravity of the remainder is at a distance $\dfrac{a}{8\pi - 4}$ from the centre of the circle, where a is the diameter of the circle.

27. From a uniform triangular board a portion consisting of the area of the inscribed circle is removed; shew that the distance of the centre of gravity of the remainder from any side, a, is

$$\frac{S}{3as}\,\frac{2s^3 - 3\pi aS}{s^2 - \pi S},$$

where S is the area and s the semiperimeter of the board.

28. A circular hole of a given size is punched out of a uniform circular plate; shew that the centre of gravity lies within a certain circle.

29. *The distances of the angular points and intersection of the diagonals of a plane quadrilateral lamina from any line in its plane are a, b, c, d, and e; shew that the distance of the centre of inertia from the same line is $\frac{1}{3}\,(a + b + c + d - e)$.*

Let A, B, C, D be the angular points, and E the intersection of the diagonals. Then

$$\frac{\triangle ACD}{\triangle ACB} = \frac{\text{perpendicular from } D \text{ on } AC}{\text{perpendicular from } B \text{ on } AC} = \frac{DE}{EB} = \frac{d - e}{e - b}.$$

By Arts. 104 and 111 the distance of the centre of gravity of the $\triangle ACD$ from OX is $\dfrac{a + c + d}{3}$ and that of the $\triangle ACB$ is $\dfrac{a + c + b}{3}$.

Hence distance of required c.g. from OX

$$= \frac{\triangle ACD \times \frac{1}{3}\,(a + c + d) + \triangle ACB \times \frac{1}{3}\,(a + b + c)}{\triangle ACD + \triangle ACB}$$

$$= \frac{1}{3}\,\frac{(d - e)\,(a + c + d) + (e - b)\,(a + b + c)}{(d - e) + (e - b)}$$

$$= \frac{1}{3}\,(a + b + c + d - e), \text{ on reduction.}$$

30. If A and B be the positions of two masses, m and n, and if G be their centre of gravity, shew that, if P be any point, then

$$m \,.\, AP^2 + n \,.\, BP^2 = m \,.\, AG^2 + n \,.\, BG^2 + (m + n)\, PG^2.$$

Similarly, if there be any number of masses, m, n, p, ... at points A, B, C, ..., and G be their centre of gravity, shew that

$$m \,.\, AP^2 + n \,.\, BP^2 + p \,.\, CP^2 + ...$$
$$= m \,.\, AG^2 + n \,.\, BG^2 + p \,.\, CG^2 + ... + (m + n + p + ...)\, PG^2.$$

CHAPTER X.

CENTRE OF GRAVITY (*continued*).

119. *If a rigid body be in equilibrium, one point only of the body being fixed, the centre of gravity of the body will be in the vertical line passing through the fixed point of the body.*

Let O be the fixed point of the body, and G its centre of gravity.

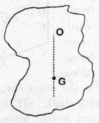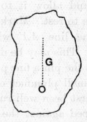

The forces acting on the body are the reaction at the fixed point of support of the body, and the weights of the component parts of the body.

The weights of these component parts are equivalent to a single vertical force through the centre of gravity of the body.

Also, when two forces keep a body in equilibrium, they must be equal and opposite and have the same line of action. But the lines of action cannot be the same unless the vertical line through G passes through the point O.

Two cases arise; the first, in which the centre of gravity G is below the point of suspension O, and the second, in which G is above O.

In the first case, the body, if slightly displaced from its position of equilibrium, will tend to return to this position; in the second case, the body will not tend to return to its position of equilibrium.

120. *To find, by experiment, the centre of gravity of a body of any shape.*

Take a flat piece of cardboard of any shape. Bore several small holes $A, B, C, D, \ldots$ in it of a size just large enough to freely admit of the insertion of a small pin.

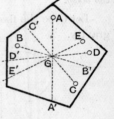

Hang up the cardboard by the hole A and allow it to hang freely and come to rest. Mark on the cardboard the line AA' which is now vertical. This may be done by hanging from the pin a fine piece of string with a small plummet of lead at the other end, the string having first been well rubbed with chalk. If the string be now flipped against the cardboard it will leave a chalked line, which is AA'. Now hang up the cardboard with the hole B on the pin, and mark in a similar manner the line BB' which is now vertical.

Perform the experiment again with the points C, D, E as the points through which the small pin passes, and obtain the corresponding vertical lines CC', DD', EE'.

These chalked lines AA', BB', CC', DD', EE' will all be found to pass through the same point G. If the thickness of the cardboard be neglected, this point G is its centre of gravity. If the pin be now passed through G, the cardboard will be found to rest in any position in which it is placed.

121. *If a body be placed with its base in contact with a horizontal plane, it will stand, or fall, according as the vertical line drawn through the centre of gravity of the body meets the plane within, or without, the base.*

The forces acting on the body are its weight, which acts at its centre of gravity G, and the reactions of the plane,

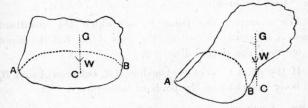

acting at different points of the base of the body. These reactions are all vertical, and hence they may be compounded into a single vertical force acting at some point of the base.

Since the resultant of two *like* parallel forces acts always at a point *between* the forces, it follows that the resultant of all the reactions on the base of the body cannot act through a point *outside* the base.

Hence, if the vertical line through the centre of gravity of the body meet the plane at a point outside the base, it cannot be balanced by the resultant reaction, and the body cannot therefore be in equilibrium, but must fall over.

If the base of the body be a figure having a re-entrant

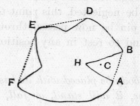

angle, as in the above figure, we must extend the meaning of the word "base" in the enunciation to mean the area included in the figure obtained by drawing a piece of thread tightly round the geometrical base. In the above figure the "base" therefore means the area $ABDEFA$.

For example, the point C, at which the resultant reaction acts, may lie within the area AHB, but it cannot lie without the dotted line AB.

If the point C were on the line AB, between A and B, the body would be on the point of falling over.

Ex. *A cylinder, of height h, and the radius of whose base is r, is placed on an inclined plane and prevented from sliding; if the inclination of the plane be gradually increased, find when the cylinder will topple.*

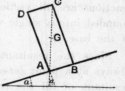

Let the figure represent the section of the cylinder when it is on the point of toppling over; the vertical line through the centre of gravity G of the body must therefore just pass through the end A of the base. Hence CAD must be equal to the angle of inclination, a, of the plane.

Hence
$$\frac{h}{2r} = \frac{CB}{AB} = \tan CAB = \cot a;$$

$$\therefore \tan a = \frac{2r}{h},$$

giving the required inclination of the plane.

Stable, unstable, and neutral equilibrium.

122. We have pointed out in Art. 119 that the body in the first figure of that article would, if slightly displaced, tend to return to its position of equilibrium, and that the body in the second figure would not tend to return to its original position of equilibrium, but would recede still further from that position.

These two bodies are said to be in stable and unstable equilibrium respectively.

Again, a cone, resting with its flat circular base in contact with a horizontal plane, would, if slightly displaced, return to its position of equilibrium; if resting with its vertex in contact with the plane it would, if slightly displaced, recede still further from its position of equilibrium; whilst, if placed with its slant side in contact with the plane, it will remain in equilibrium in any position. The equilibrium in the latter case is said to be neutral.

123. Consider, again, the case of a heavy sphere, resting on a horizontal plane, whose centre of gravity is not at its centre.

Let the first figure represent the position of equilibrium, the centre of gravity being either below the centre O, as G_1,

or above, as G_2. Let the second figure represent the sphere turned through a small angle, so that B is now the point of contact with the plane.

The reaction of the plane still acts through the centre of the sphere.

If the weight of the body act through G_1, it is clear that the body will return towards its original position of equilibrium, and therefore the body was originally in stable equilibrium.

If the weight act through G_2, the body will move still further from its original position of equilibrium, and therefore it was originally in unstable equilibrium.

If however the centre of gravity of the body had been at O, then, in the case of the second figure, the weight would still be balanced by the reaction of the plane; the body would thus remain in the new position, and the equilibrium would be called neutral.

124. Def. A body is said to be in **stable** equilibrium when, if it be slightly displaced from its position of equilibrium, the forces acting on the body tend to make it return towards its position of equilibrium; it is in **unstable** equilibrium when, if it be slightly displaced, the forces tend to move it still further from its position of equilibrium; it is in **neutral** equilibrium, if the forces acting on it in its displaced position are in equilibrium.

In general bodies which are " top-heavy," or which have small bases, are unstable.

Thus in theory a pin might be placed upright with its point on a horizontal table so as to be in equilibrium; in practice the " base " would be so small that the slightest displacement would bring the vertical through its centre of gravity outside its base and it would fall. So with a billiard cue placed vertically with its end on the table.

A body is, as a general principle, in a stable position of equilibrium when the centre of gravity is in the lowest position it can take up; examples are the case of the last article, and the pendulum of a clock; the latter when displaced always returns towards its position of rest.

Consider again the case of a man walking on a tight rope. He always carries a pole heavily weighted at one end, so that the centre of gravity of himself and the pole is always below his feet. When he feels himself falling in one direction, he shifts his pole so that this centre of gravity shall be on the other side of his feet, and then the resultant weight pulls him back again towards the upright position.

If a body has more than one theoretical position of equilibrium, the one in which its centre of gravity is lowest will in general be the stable position, and that in which the centre of gravity is highest will be the unstable one.

125. Ex. *A homogeneous body, consisting of a cylinder and a hemisphere joined at their bases, is placed with the hemispherical end on a horizontal table; is the equilibrium stable or unstable?*

Let G_1 and G_2 be the centres of gravity of the hemisphere and cylinder, and let A be the point of the body which is initially in contact with the table, and let O be the centre of the base of the hemisphere.

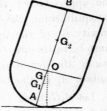

If h be the height of the cylinder, and r be the radius of the base, we have

$$OG_1 = \tfrac{3}{8}r, \text{ and } OG_2 = \frac{h}{2} \text{ (Art. 117).}$$

Also the weights of the hemisphere and cylinder are proportional to $\tfrac{2}{3}\pi r^3$ and $\pi \cdot r^2 h$.

The reaction of the plane, in the displaced position of the body, always passes through the centre O.

The equilibrium is stable or unstable according as G, the centre of gravity of the compound body, is below or above O,

i.e., according as

$$OG_1 \times \text{wt. of hemisphere is} \gtrless OG_2 \times \text{wt. of cylinder,}$$

i.e., according as $\qquad \frac{3}{8}r \times \frac{2}{3}\pi r^3$ is $\gtrless \frac{h}{2} \times \pi r^2 h$,

i.e., according as $\qquad \frac{r^2}{2}$ is $\gtrless h^2$,

i.e., according as $\qquad r$ is $\gtrless \sqrt{2h}$,

i.e., $\qquad\qquad\qquad\qquad \gtrless h \times 1\cdot42\ldots$

**126. Within the limits of this book we cannot enter into the general discussion of the equilibrium of one body resting on another; in the following article we shall discuss the case in which the portions of the two bodies in contact are spherical.

A body rests in equilibrium upon another fixed body, the portions of the two bodies in contact being spheres of radii r and R respectively; if the first body be slightly displaced, to find whether the equilibrium is stable or unstable, the bodies being rough enough to prevent sliding.

Let O be the centre of the spherical surface of the lower body, and O_1 that of the upper body; since there is equilibrium, the centre of gravity G_1 of the upper body must be in the line OO_1, which passes through the point of contact A_1 of the bodies.

Let A_1G_1 be h.

Let the upper body be slightly displaced, by rolling, so that the new position of the centre of the upper body is O_2, the new point of contact is A_2, the new position of the

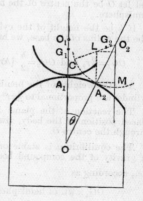

centre of gravity is G_2, and the new position of the point A_1 is C. Hence CG_2 is h.

Through A_2 draw A_2L vertically to meet O_2C in L, and draw O_2M vertically downwards to meet a horizontal line through A_2 in M.

Let the angle A_2OA_1 be θ, and let A_2O_2C be ϕ, so that the angle CO_2M is $(\theta + \phi)$.

Since the upper body has rolled into its new position, the arc A_1A_2 is equal to the arc CA_2.

Hence (*Elements of Trigonometry*, Art. 158) we have

$$R \cdot \theta = r \cdot \phi \dots\dots\dots\dots\dots(1),$$

where r and R are respectively the radii of the upper and lower surfaces.

The equilibrium is stable, or unstable, according as G_2 lies to the left, or right, of the line A_2L,
i.e., according as the distance of G_2 from O_2M is

$>$ or $<$ the distance of L from O_2M, *i.e.*, A_2M,

i.e., according as

$$O_2G_2 \sin(\theta + \phi) \text{ is } > \text{ or } < O_2A_2 \sin\theta,$$

i.e., according as

$$(r - h)\sin(\theta + \phi) \text{ is } > \text{ or } < r\sin\theta,$$

i.e., according as

$$\frac{r - h}{r} \text{ is } > \text{ or } < \frac{\sin\theta}{\sin(\theta + \phi)}.$$

But

$$\frac{\sin\theta}{\sin(\theta + \phi)} = \frac{\theta}{\theta + \phi},$$

since θ and ϕ are both very small,

$$= \frac{r}{r + R}, \text{ by equation (1).}$$

Hence the equilibrium is stable, or unstable, according as

$$\frac{r-h}{r} \text{ is} > \text{or} < \frac{r}{r+R},$$

i.e., according as $r - \dfrac{r^2}{r+R}$ is > or < h,

i.e., according as $\dfrac{Rr}{r+R}$ is > or < h,

i.e., according as

$$\frac{1}{h} \text{ is} > \text{or} < \frac{1}{r} + \frac{1}{R}.$$

If $\dfrac{1}{h} = \dfrac{1}{r} + \dfrac{1}{R}$, the equilibrium is sometimes said to be neutral; it is however really unstable, but the investigation is beyond the limits of this book.

Hence the equilibrium is stable only when

$$\frac{1}{h} \text{ is} > \frac{1}{r} + \frac{1}{R};$$

in all other cases it is unstable.

Cor. 1. If the surface of the lower body, instead of being convex, as in the above figure, be concave, as in the following figure, the above investigation will still apply provided we change the sign of R.

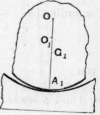

Hence the equilibrium is stable when

$$\frac{1}{h} \text{ is} > \frac{1}{r} - \frac{1}{R};$$

otherwise it is, in general, unstable.

Cor. 2. If the upper body have a plane face in contact with the lower body, as in the following figure, r is now infinite in value, and therefore $\frac{1}{r}$ is zero.

Hence the equilibrium is stable if

$$\frac{1}{h} \text{ be} > \frac{1}{R};$$

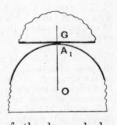

i.e., h be $< R.$

Hence the equilibrium is stable, if the distance of the centre of gravity of the upper body from its plane face be less than the radius of the lower body; otherwise the equilibrium is unstable.

Cor. 3. If the lower body be a plane, so that R is infinity, the equilibrium is stable if

$$\frac{1}{h} \text{ be} > \frac{1}{r}, \ i.e., \text{ if } h \text{ be} < r.$$

Hence, if a body of spherical base be placed on a horizontal table, it is in stable equilibrium, if the distance of its centre of gravity from the point of contact be less than the radius of the spherical surface.

EXAMPLES. XX.

1. A carpenter's rule, 2 feet in length, is bent into two parts at right angles to one another, the length of the shorter portion being 8 inches. If the shorter be placed on a smooth horizontal table, what is the length of the least portion on the table that there may be equilibrium?

2. A piece of metal, 18 cubic inches in volume, is made into a cylinder which rests with its base on an inclined plane, of 30° slope, and is prevented from slipping. How tall may the cylinder be made so that it may just not topple over?

3. If a triangular lamina ABC can just rest in a vertical plane with its edge AB in contact with a smooth table, prove that

$$BC^2 \sim AC^2 = 3AB^2.$$

4. The side CD of a uniform square plate $ABCD$, whose weight is W, is bisected at E and the triangle AED is cut off. The plate $ABCEA$ is placed in a vertical position with the side CE on a horizontal plane. What is the greatest weight that can be placed at A without upsetting the plate?

5. ABC is a flat board, A being a right angle and AC in contact with a flat table; D is the middle point of AC and the triangle ABD is cut away; shew that the triangle is just on the point of falling over.

6. A brick is laid with one-quarter of its length projecting over the edge of a wall; a brick and one-quarter of a brick are then laid on the first with one-quarter of a brick projecting over the edge of the first brick; a brick and a half are laid on this, and so on; shew that 4 courses of brick laid in the above manner will be in equilibrium without the aid of mortar, but that, if a fifth course be added, the structure will topple.

7. How many coins, of the same size and having their thicknesses equal to $\frac{1}{20}$th of their diameters, can stand in a cylindrical pile on an inclined plane, whose height is one-sixth of the base, assuming that there is no slipping?

If the edge of each coin overlap on one side that of the coin below, find by what fraction of the diameter each must overlap so that a pile of unlimited height may stand on the plane.

8. A number of bricks, each 9 inches long, 4 inches wide, and 3 inches thick, are placed one on another so that, whilst their narrowest surfaces, or thicknesses, are in the same vertical plane, each brick overlaps the one underneath it by half an inch; the lowest brick being placed on a table, how many bricks can be so placed without their falling over?

9. ABC is an isosceles triangle, of weight W, of which the angle A is 120°, and the side AB rests on a smooth horizontal table, the plane of the triangle being vertical; if a weight $\dfrac{W}{3}$ be hung on at C, shew that the triangle will just be on the point of toppling over.

10. The quadrilateral lamina $ABCD$ is formed of two uniform isosceles triangles ABC and ADC, whose vertices are B and D, on opposite sides of a common base AC, the angle ABC being a right angle. Shew that it will rest in a vertical plane with BC on a horizontal plane, provided the area of ADC be not greater than four times that of ABC.

11. A body, consisting of a cone and a hemisphere on the same base, rests on a rough horizontal table, the hemisphere being in contact with the table; find the greatest height of the cone so that the equilibrium may be stable.

12. A solid consists of a cylinder and a hemisphere of equal radius, fixed base to base; find the ratio of the height to the radius of the cylinder, so that the equilibrium may be neutral when the spherical surface rests on a horizontal plane.

13. A hemisphere rests in equilibrium on a sphere of equal radius; shew that the equilibrium is unstable when the curved, and stable when the flat, surface of the hemisphere rests on the sphere.

14. A heavy right cone rests with its base on a fixed rough sphere of given radius; find the greatest height of the cone if it be in stable equilibrium.

15. A uniform beam, of thickness $2b$, rests symmetrically on a perfectly rough horizontal cylinder of radius a; shew that the equilibrium of the beam will be stable or unstable according as b is less or greater than a.

16. A heavy uniform cube balances on the highest point of a sphere, whose radius is r. If the sphere be rough enough to prevent sliding, and if the side of the cube be $\dfrac{\pi r}{2}$, shew that the cube can rock through a right angle without falling.

17. A lamina in the form of an isosceles triangle, whose vertical angle is a, is placed on a sphere, of radius r, so that its plane is vertical and one of its equal sides is in contact with the sphere; shew that, if the triangle be slightly displaced in its own plane, the equilibrium is stable if $\sin a$ be less than $\dfrac{3r}{a}$, where a is one of the equal sides of the triangle.

18. A weight W is supported on a smooth inclined plane by a given weight P, connected with W by means of a string passing round a fixed pulley whose position is given. Find the position of W on the plane, and determine whether the position is stable or unstable.

19. A rough uniform circular disc, of radius r and weight p, is movable about a point distant c from its centre. A string, rough enough to prevent any slipping, hangs over the circumference and carries unequal weights W and w at its ends. Find the position of equilibrium, and determine whether it is stable or unstable.

20. A solid sphere rests inside a fixed rough hemispherical bowl of twice its radius. Shew that, however large a weight is attached to the highest point of the sphere, the equilibrium is stable.

21. A thin hemispherical bowl, of radius b and weight W, rests in equilibrium on the highest point of a fixed sphere, of radius a, which is rough enough to prevent any sliding. Inside the bowl is placed a small smooth sphere of weight w. Shew that the equilibrium is not stable unless

$$w < W \cdot \frac{a-b}{2b}.$$

CHAPTER XI.

WORK.

127. Work. Def. A force is said to do work when its point of application moves in the direction of the force.

The force exerted by a horse, in dragging a waggon, does work.

The force exerted by a man, in raising a weight, does work.

The pressure of the steam, in moving the piston of an engine, does work.

When a man winds up a watch or a clock he does work.

The measure of the work done by a force is the product of the force and the distance through which it moves its point of application in the direction of the force.

Suppose that a force acting at a point A of a body

moves the point A to D, then the work done by P is measured by the product of P and AD.

If the point D be on the side of A toward which the force acts, this work is positive; if D lie on the opposite side, the work is negative.

Next, suppose that the point of application of the force is moved to a point C, which does not lie on the line AB.

Draw *CD* perpendicular to *AB*, or *AB* produced. Then *AD* is the distance through which the point of application is moved in the direction of the force. Hence in the first figure the work done is $P \times AD$; in the second figure the

work done is $-P \times AD$. When the work done by the force is negative, this is sometimes expressed by saying that the force has work done against it.

In the case when *AC* is at right angles to *AB*, the points *A* and *D* coincide, and the work done by the force *P* vanishes.

As an example, if a body be moved about on a horizontal table the work done by its weight is zero. So, again, if a body be moved on an inclined plane, no work is done by the normal reaction of the plane.

128. The unit of work, used in Statics, is called a Foot-Pound, and is the work done by a force, equal to the weight of a pound, when it moves its point of application through one foot in its own direction. A better, though more clumsy, term than "Foot-Pound" would be Foot-Pound-weight.

Thus, the work done by the weight of a body of 10 pounds, whilst the body falls through a distance of 4 feet, is 10×4 foot-pounds.

The work done by the weight of the body, if it were raised through a vertical distance of 4 feet, would be -10×4 foot-pounds.

129. It will be noticed that the definition of work, given in Art. 127, necessarily implies motion. A man may use great exertion in *attempting* to move a body, and yet do no work on the body.

For example, suppose a man pulls at the shafts of a heavily-loaded van, which he cannot move. He may pull to the utmost of his power, but, since the force which he exerts does not move its point of application, he does no work (in the technical sense of the word).

130. Theorem. *To shew that the work done in raising a number of particles from one position to another is Wh, where W is the total weight of the particles, and h is the distance through which the centre of gravity of the particles has been raised.*

Let w_1, w_2, w_3, ... w_n be the weights of the particles; in the initial position let x_1, x_2, x_3, ... x_n be their heights above a horizontal plane, and $\bar{x}$ that of their centre of gravity, so that, as in Art. 111, we have

$$\bar{x} = \frac{w_1 x_1 + w_2 x_2 + \dots + w_n x_n}{w_1 + w_2 + \dots + w_n} \quad \dots\dots\dots\dots(1).$$

In the final position let x_1', x_2', ... x_n' be the heights of the different particles, and $\bar{x}'$ the height of the new centre of gravity, so that

$$\bar{x}' = \frac{w_1 x_1' + w_2 x_2' + \dots w_n x_n'}{w_1 + w_2 + \dots w_n} \quad \dots\dots\dots\dots(2).$$

But, since $w_1 + w_2 + \dots = W$, equations (1) and (2) give

$$w_1 x_1 + w_2 x_2 + \dots = W \cdot \bar{x},$$

and $$w_1 x_1' + w_2 x_2' + \dots = W \cdot \bar{x}'.$$

By subtraction we have

$$w_1 (x_1' - x_1) + w_2 (x_2' - x_2) + \dots = W (\bar{x}' - \bar{x}).$$

But the left-hand member of this equation gives the total work done in raising the different particles of the system from their initial position to their final position; also the right-hand side

$= W \times$ height through which the centre of gravity has been raised

$= W \cdot h.$

Hence the proposition is proved.

131. Power. Def. *The power of an agent is the amount of work that would be done by the agent if working uniformly for the unit of time.*

The unit of power used by engineers is called a **Horse-Power**. An agent is said to be working with one horse-power when it performs 33,000 foot-pounds in a minute, *i.e.*, when it would raise 33,000 lbs. through a foot in a minute, or when it would raise 330 lbs. through 100 feet in a minute, or 33 lbs. through 1000 feet in a minute.

This estimate of the power of a horse was made by Watt, but is above the capacity of ordinary horses. The word Horse-power is usually abbreviated into H.P.

132. It will be noted that the result of Art. 130 does not in any way depend on the initial or final arrangement of the particles amongst themselves, except in so far as the initial and final positions of the centre of gravity depend on these arrangements.

For example, a hole may be dug in the ground, the soil lifted out, and spread on the surface of the earth at the top of the hole. We only want the positions of the c.g. of the soil initially and finally, and then the work done is known. This work is quite independent of the path by which the soil went from its initial to its final position.

Ex. *A well, of which the section is a square whose side is 4 feet, and whose depth is 300 feet, is full of water; find the work done, in foot-pounds, in pumping the water to the level of the top of the well.*

Find also the H.P. of the engine which would just accomplish this work in one hour.

[N.B. A cubic foot of water weighs 1000 ounces.]

Initially the height of the centre of gravity of the water above the bottom of the well was 150 feet and finally it is 300 feet, so that the height through which the centre of gravity has been raised is 150 feet.

The volume of the water $= 4 \times 4 \times 300$ cubic feet.

Therefore its weight $= 4 \times 4 \times 300 \times \frac{1000}{16}$ lbs. $= 300,000$ lbs.

Hence the work done $= 300,000 \times 150$ ft.-lbs. $= 45,000,000$ ft.-lbs.

Let x be the required H.P. Then the work done by the engine in one hour
$$= x \times 60 \times 33,000.$$

Hence we have $x \times 60 \times 33,000 = 45,000,000;$

$$\therefore x = 22\tfrac{8}{11}.$$

133. *Graphical representation of the work done by a force.*

It is sometimes difficult to calculate directly the work done by a varying force, but it may be quite possible to obtain the result to a near degree of approximation.

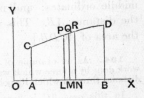

Suppose the force to always act in the straight line OX, and let us find the work done as its point of application moves from A to B. At A and B erect ordinates AC and DB to represent the value of the force for these two points of application. For any and every intermediate point of application L erect the ordinate LP to represent the corresponding value of the acting force; then the tops of these ordinates will clearly lie on some such curve as CPD.

Take M a very near point to L, so near that the force may be considered to have remained constant as its point of application moved through the small distance LM.

Then the work done by the force

= its magnitude × distance through which its

point of application has moved

$= LP \times LM = $ area PM very nearly.

Similarly whilst the point of application moves from M to N the work done

$=$ area QN very nearly, and so on.

Hence it follows that the work done as the point of application moves from A to B is, when the lengths LM, MN, ... are taken indefinitely small, equal more and more nearly to the area $ACDB$.

[Where the shape of the curve CPD is irregular a rough approximation to its area may be found as follows; divide AB into a number, say 10, of equal strips; take the middle ordinates of these strips and obtain the average of these middle ordinates; and multiply this average ordinate by the distance AB. This clearly gives an approximation to the area of $ACDB$.]

134. As an example of the above construction let us find the work done by a force which was initially zero and which varied as the distance through which its point of application was moved.

In this case AC is zero, and $NP = \lambda \cdot AN$, where λ is some constant.

$\therefore$ tan $PAN = \dfrac{PN}{AN} = \lambda$, so that P lies on a straight line passing through A. The work done $=$ area ABD $= \frac{1}{2}AB \cdot BD = \frac{1}{2} \cdot$ displacement of the point of application $\times$ the final value of the force.

EXAMPLES. XXI.

1. How much work is done by a man

(1) in climbing to the top of a mountain 2700 feet high, if his weight is 10 stone?

(2) in cycling 10 miles if the resistance to his motion be equal to 5 lbs. wt.?

2. A chain, whose mass is 8 lbs. per foot, is wound up from a shaft by the expenditure of four million units of work; find the length of the chain.

3. A shaft, whose horizontal section is a rectangle 10 ft. by 8 ft., is to be sunk 100 ft. into the earth. If the average weight of the soil is 150 lbs. per cubic foot, find the work done in bringing the soil to the surface.

4. How many cubic feet of water will an engine of 100 H.P. raise in one hour from a depth of 150 feet?

5. In how many hours would an engine of 18 H.P. empty a vertical shaft full of water if the diameter of the shaft be 9 feet, and the depth 420 feet?

6. Find the H.P. of an engine that would empty a cylindrical shaft full of water in 32 hours, if the diameter of the shaft be 8 feet and its depth 600 feet.

7. Find how long an engine of 20 H.P. would take to pump 5000 cubic feet of water to a height of 100 feet, one-third of the work being wasted by friction, etc.

8. A man whose weight is 10 stone climbs a rope at the rate of 18 inches per second. Prove that he is working at just under $\frac{2}{5}$ H.P.

9. A tower is to be built of brickwork, the base being a rectangle whose external measurements are 22 ft. by 9 ft., the height of the tower 66 feet, and the walls two feet thick; find the number of hours in which an engine of 3 H.P. would raise the bricks from the ground, the weight of a cubic foot of brickwork being 112 lbs.

10. At the bottom of a coal mine, 275 feet deep, there is an iron cage containing coal weighing 14 cwt., the cage itself weighing 4 cwt. 109 lbs., and the wire rope that raises it 6 lbs. per yard. Find the work done when the load has been lifted to the surface, and the H.P. of the engine that can do this work in 40 seconds.

11. A steamer is going at the rate of 15 miles per hour; if the effective H.P. of her engines be 10,000, what is the resistance to her motion?

12. A man is cycling at the rate of 6 miles per hour up a hill whose slope is 1 in 20; if the weight of the man and the machine be 200 lbs. prove that he must at the least be working at the rate of ·16 H.P.

13. A man rowing 40 strokes per minute propels a boat at the rate of 10 miles an hour, and the resistance to his motion is equal to 8 lbs. wt.; find the work he does in each stroke and the H.P. at which he is working.

14. A Venetian blind consists of 30 movable bars, the thickness of each bar being negligible, and, when it is hanging down, the distance between each pair of consecutive bars is $2\frac{1}{2}$ inches; if the weight of each bar be 4 ozs., find the work done in drawing up the blind.

If there were n such bars, what would be the corresponding work?

15. A Venetian blind consists of n thin bars, besides the top fixed bar, and the weight of the movable part is W. When let down the length of the blind is a, and when pulled up it is b; shew that the work done against gravity in drawing up the blind is

$$W \cdot \frac{n+1}{2n}(a-b).$$

16. A solid hemisphere of weight 12 lbs. and radius 1 foot rests with its flat face on a table. How many foot-lbs. of work are required to turn it over so that it may rest with its curved surface in contact with the table? [Use the result of Art. 130.]

17. A uniform log weighing half a ton is in the form of a triangular prism, the sides of whose cross section are $1\frac{1}{2}$ ft., 2 ft., and $2\frac{1}{2}$ ft. respectively, and the log is resting on the ground on its narrowest face. Prove that the work which must be done to raise it on its edge so that it may fall over on to its broadest face is approximately ·27 ft.-tons.

18. A force acts on a particle, its initial value being 20 lbs. wt. and its values being 25, 29, 32, 31, 27, and 24 lbs. wt. in the direction of the particle's motion when the latter has moved through 1, 2, 3, 4, 5, and 6 feet respectively; find, by means of a graph, the work done by the force, assuming that it varies uniformly during each foot of the motion.

CHAPTER XII.

MACHINES.

135. In the present chapter we shall explain and discuss the equilibrium of some of the simpler machines, viz., (1) The Lever, (2) The Pulley and Systems of Pulleys, (3) The Inclined Plane, (4) The Wheel and Axle, (5) The Common Balance, (6) The Steelyards, and (7) The Screw.

The Lever, The Wheel and Axle, The Balance, and the Steelyards are similar machines. In each we have either a point, or an axis, fixed about which the machine can revolve.

In the pulleys an essential part is a flexible string or strings.

We shall suppose the different portions of these machines to be smooth and rigid, that all cords or strings used are perfectly flexible, and that the forces acting on the machines always balance, so that they are at rest.

In actual practice these conditions are not even approximately satisfied in the cases of many machines.

136. When two external forces applied to a machine balance, one may be, and formerly always was, called the Power and the other may be called the Weight.

A machine is always used in practice to overcome some resistance; the force we exert on the machine is the power; the resistance to be overcome, in whatever form it may appear, is called the Weight.

Unfortunately the word Power is also used in a different sense with reference to a machine (Art. 131); of late years the word Effort has been used to denote what was formerly called the Power in the sense of this article. The word Resistance is also used instead of Weight; by some writers Load is substituted for Weight.

137. Mechanical Advantage.

If in any machine an effort P balance a resistance W, the ratio $W : P$ is called the mechanical advantage of the machine, so that

$$\frac{\text{Resistance}}{\text{Effort}} = \text{Mechanical Advantage},$$

and   Resistance = Effort × Mechanical Advantage.

Almost all machines are constructed so that the mechanical advantage is a ratio greater than unity.

If in any machine the mechanical advantage be less than unity, it may, with more accuracy, be called mechanical disadvantage.

The term Force-Ratio is sometimes used instead of Mechanical Advantage.

Velocity Ratio.

The velocity ratio of any machine is the ratio of the distance through which the point of application of the effort or "power" moves to the distance through which the point of application of the resistance, or "weight," moves in the same time; so that

$$\text{Velocity Ratio} = \frac{\text{Distance through which } P \text{ moves}}{\text{Distance through which } W \text{ moves}}.$$

If the machine be such that no work has to be done in lifting its component parts, and if it be perfectly smooth throughout, it will be found that the Mechanical Advantage and the Velocity Ratio are equal, so that in this case

$$\frac{W}{P} = \frac{\text{Distance through which } P \text{ moves}}{\text{Distance through which } W \text{ moves}},$$

and then

$P \times$ distance through which P moves

$\qquad = W \times$ distance through which W moves,

or, in other words,

work done by P will $= $ work done against W.

138. The following we shall thus find to be a universal principle, known as the **Principle of Work,** viz., *Whatever be the machine we use, provided that there be no friction and that the weight of the machine be neglected, the work done by the effort is always equivalent to the work done against the weight, or resistance.*

Assuming that the machine we are using gives mechanical advantage, so that the effort is less than the weight, the distance moved through by the effort is therefore greater than the distance moved through by the weight in the same proportion. This is sometimes expressed in popular language in the form; *What is gained in power is lost in speed.*

More accurate is the statement that mechanical advantage is always gained at a proportionate diminution of speed. No work is ever gained by the use of a machine though mechanical advantage is generally obtained.

139. It will be found in the next chapter that, as a matter of fact, some work, in practice, is always lost by the use of any machine.

The uses of a machine are

(1) to enable a man to lift weights or overcome

resistances much greater than he could deal with unaided, *e.g.*, by the use of a system of pulleys, or a wheel and axle, or a screw-jack, etc.,

(2) to cause a motion imparted to one point to be changed into a more rapid motion at some other point, *e.g.*, in the case of a bicycle,

(3) to enable a force to be applied at a more convenient point or in a more convenient manner, *e.g.*, in the use of a poker to stir the fire, or in the lifting of a bucket of mortar by means of a long rope passing over a pulley at the top of a building, the other end being pulled by a man standing on the ground.

I. The Lever.

140. The Lever consists essentially of a rigid bar, straight or bent, which has one point fixed about which the rest of the lever can turn. This fixed point is called the Fulcrum, and the perpendicular distances between the fulcrum and the lines of action of the effort and the weight are called the arms of the lever.

When the lever is straight, and the effort and weight act perpendicular to the lever, it is usual to distinguish three classes or orders.

Class I. Here the effort P and the weight W act on opposite sides of the fulcrum C.

Class II. Here the effort P and the weight W act on the same side of the fulcrum C, but the former acts at a greater distance than the latter from the fulcrum.

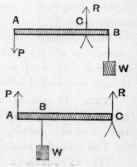

Class III. Here the effort
P and the weight W act on the
same side of the fulcrum C, but
the former acts at a less distance than the latter from the
fulcrum.

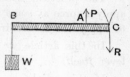

141. *Conditions of equilibrium of a straight lever.*

In each case we have three parallel forces acting on
the body, so that the reaction, R, at the fulcrum must
be equal and opposite to the resultant of P and W.

In the first class P and W are like parallel forces, so
that their resultant is $P + W$.   Hence

$$R = P + W.$$

In the second class P and W are unlike parallel forces,
so that

$$R = W - P.$$

So in the third class $R = P - W$.

In the first and third classes we see that R and P act
in opposite directions; in the second class they act in the
same direction.

In all three classes, since the resultant of P and W
passes through C, we have, as in Art. 52,

$$P \cdot AC = W \cdot BC,$$

i.e. $P \times$ the arm of $P = W \times$ the arm of W.

Since $\dfrac{W}{P} = \dfrac{\text{arm of } P}{\text{arm of } W}$, we observe that generally in
Class I., and always in Class II., there is mechanical
advantage, but that in Class III. there is mechanical
disadvantage.

The practical use of levers of the latter class is to apply a force at some point at which it is not convenient to apply the force directly.

In this article we have neglected the weight of the lever itself.

If this weight be taken into consideration we must, as in Art. 91, obtain the conditions of equilibrium by equating to zero the algebraic sum of the moments of the forces about the fulcrum C.

The principle of the lever was known to Archimedes who lived in the third century B.C.; until the discovery of the Parallelogram of Forces in the sixteenth century it was the fundamental principle of Statics.

142. Examples of the different classes of levers are;

Class I. A Poker (*when used to stir the fire, the bar of the grate being the fulcrum*); A Claw-hammer (*when used to extract nails*); A Crowbar (*when used with a point in it resting on a fixed support*); A Pair of Scales; The Brake of a Pump.

Double levers of this class are; A Pair of Scissors, A Pair of Pincers.

Class II. A Wheelbarrow; A Cork Squeezer; A Crowbar (*with one end in contact with the ground*); An Oar (*assuming the end of the oar in contact with the water to be at rest*).

A Pair of Nutcrackers is a double lever of this class.

Class III. The Treadle of a Lathe; The Human Forearm (*when the latter is used to support a weight placed on the palm of the hand. The Fulcrum is the elbow, and the tension exerted by the muscles is the effort*).

A Pair of Sugar-tongs is a double lever of this class.

143. *Bent Levers.*

Let AOB be a bent lever, of which O is the fulcrum, and let OL and OM be the perpendiculars from O upon the lines of action AC and BC of the effort P and resistance W.

The condition of equilibrium of Art. 91 again applies, and we have, by taking moments about O,

$$P \cdot OL = W \cdot OM \quad \text{............................}(1);$$
$$\therefore \frac{P}{W} = \frac{OM}{OL}$$

$$= \frac{\text{perpendicular from fulcrum on direction of resistance}}{\text{perpendicular from fulcrum on direction of effort}}.$$

To obtain the reaction at O let the directions of P and W meet in C. Since there are only three forces acting on the body, the direction of the reaction R at O must pass through C, and then, by Lami's Theorem, we have

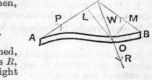

$$\frac{R}{\sin ACB} = \frac{P}{\sin BCO} = \frac{W}{\sin ACO}.$$

The reaction may also be obtained, as in Art. 46, by resolving the forces R, P, and W in two directions at right angles.

If the effort and resistance be parallel forces, the reaction R is parallel to either of them and equal to $(P+W)$, and, as before, we have
$$P \cdot OL = W \cdot OM,$$

where OL and OM are the perpendiculars from O upon the lines of action of the forces.

If the weight W' of the lever be not neglected, we have an additional term to introduce into our equation of moments.

144. *If two weights balance, about a fixed fulcrum, at the extremities of a straight lever, in any position inclined to the vertical, they will balance in any other position.*

Let AB be the lever, of weight W', and let its centre of gravity be G. Let the lever balance about a fulcrum O in any position inclined at an angle θ to the horizontal, the weights at A and B being P and W respectively.

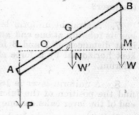

Through O draw a horizontal line $LONM$ to meet the lines of action of P, W', and W in L, N, and M respectively.

Since the forces balance about O, we have

$$P \cdot OL = W \cdot OM + W' \cdot ON.$$

$$\therefore P . OA \cos \theta = W . OB \cos \theta + W' . OG \cos \theta.$$

$$\therefore P . OA = W . OB + W' . OG.$$

This condition of equilibrium is independent of the inclination θ of the lever to the horizontal; hence in any other position of the lever the condition would be the same.

Hence, if the lever be in equilibrium in one position, it will be in equilibrium in all positions.

EXAMPLES. XXII.

1. In a weightless lever, if one of the forces be equal to 10 lbs. wt. and the thrust on the fulcrum be equal to 16 lbs. wt., and the length of the shorter arm be 3 feet, find the length of the longer arm.

2. Where must the fulcrum be so that a weight of 6 lbs. may balance a weight of 8 lbs. on a straight weightless lever, 7 feet long?

If each weight be increased by 1 lb., in what direction will the lever turn?

3. If two forces, applied to a weightless lever, balance, and if the thrust on the fulcrum be ten times the difference of the forces, find the ratio of the arms.

4. A lever, 1 yard long, has weights of 6 and 20 lbs. fastened to its ends, and balances about a point distant 9 inches from one end; find its weight.

5. A straight lever, AB, 12 feet long, balances about a point, 1 foot from A, when a weight of 13 lbs. is suspended from A. It will balance about a point, which is 1 foot from B, when a weight of 11 lbs. is suspended from B. Shew that the centre of gravity of the lever is 5 inches from the middle point of the lever.

6. A straight uniform lever is kept in equilibrium by weights of 12 and 5 lbs. respectively attached to the ends of its arms, and the length of one arm is double that of the other. What is the weight of the lever?

7. A straight uniform lever, of length 5 feet and weight 10 lbs., has its fulcrum at one end and weights of 3 and 6 lbs. are fastened to it at distances of 1 and 3 feet respectively from the fulcrum; it is kept horizontal by a force at its other end; find the thrust on the fulcrum.

8. A uniform lever is 18 inches long and is of weight 18 ounces; find the position of the fulcrum when a weight of 27 ounces at one end of the lever balances one of 9 ounces at the other.

If the lesser weight be doubled, by how much must the position of the fulcrum be shifted so as to preserve equilibrium?

9. Two weights, of 8 and 4 ounces, are in equilibrium when attached to the opposite ends of a rod of negligible weight; if 2 ounces be added to the greater, the fulcrum must be moved through $\frac{4}{7}$ths of an inch to preserve equilibrium; find the length of the lever.

10. The short arm of one lever is hinged to the long arm of a second lever, and the short arm of the latter is attached to a press; the long arms being each 3 feet in length, and the short arms 6 inches, find what thrust will be produced on the press by a force, equal to 10 stone weight, applied to the long end of the first lever.

11. A straight heavy uniform lever, 21 inches long, has a fulcrum at its end. A force, equal to the weight of 12 lbs., acting at a distance of 7 inches from the fulcrum, supports a weight of 3 lbs. hanging at the other end of the lever. If the weight be increased by 1 lb., what force at a distance of 5 inches from the fulcrum will support the lever?

12. On a lever, forces of 13 and 14 lbs. weight balance, and their directions meet at an angle whose cosine is $-\frac{5}{13}$; find the thrust on the fulcrum.

13. A straight lever is acted on, at its extremities, by forces in the ratio $\sqrt{3}+1 : \sqrt{3}-1$, and which are inclined at angles of 30° and 60° to its length. Find the magnitude of the thrust on the fulcrum, and the direction in which it acts.

14. The arms of a bent lever are at right angles to one another, and the arms are in the ratio of 5 to 1. The longer arm is inclined to the horizon at an angle of 45°, and carries at its end a weight of 10 lbs.; the end of the shorter arm presses against a horizontal plane; find the thrust on the plane.

15. The arms of a uniform heavy bent rod are inclined to one another at an angle of 120°, and their lengths are in the ratio of 2 : 1; if the rod be suspended from its angular point, find the position in which it will rest.

16. A uniform bar, of length $7\frac{1}{2}$ feet and weight 17 lbs., rests on a horizontal table with one end projecting $2\frac{1}{2}$ feet over the edge; find the greatest weight that can be attached to its end, without making the bar topple over.

17. A straight weightless lever has for its fulcrum a hinge at one end A, and from a point B is hung a body of weight W. If the strain at the hinge must not exceed $\frac{1}{2}W$ in either direction, upwards or downwards, shew that the effort must act somewhere within a space equal to $\frac{4}{3}AB$.

18. Shew that the propelling force on an eight-oared boat is 224 lbs. weight, supposing each man to pull his oar with a force of 56 lbs. weight, and that the length of the oar from the middle of the blade to the handle is three times that from the handle to the row-lock.

19. In a pair of nutcrackers, 5 inches long, if the nut be placed at a distance of $\frac{7}{8}$ inch from the hinge, a force equal to $3\frac{1}{2}$ lbs. wt. applied to the ends of the arms will crack the nut. What weight placed on the top of the nut will crack it?

20. A man raises a 3-foot cube of stone, weighing 2 tons, by means of a crowbar, 4 feet long, after having thrust one end of the bar under the stone to a distance of 6 inches; what force must be applied at the other end of the bar to raise the stone?

21. A cubical block, of edge a, is being turned over by a crowbar applied at the middle point of the edge in a plane through its centre of gravity; if the crowbar be held at rest when it is inclined at an angle of 60° to the horizon, the lower face of the block being then inclined at 30° to the horizon, and if the weight of the block be n times the force applied, find the length of the crowbar, the force being applied at right angles to the crowbar.

II. Pulleys.

145. A pulley is composed of a wheel of wood, or metal, grooved along its circumference to receive a string or rope; it can turn freely about an axle passing through its centre perpendicular to its plane, the ends of this axle being supported by a frame of wood called the block.

A pulley is said to be movable or fixed according as its block is movable or fixed.

The weight of the pulley is often so small, compared with the weights which it supports, that it may be neglected; such a pulley is called a weightless pulley.

We shall always neglect the weight of the string or rope which passes round the pulley.

We shall also in this chapter consider the pulley to be perfectly smooth, so that the tension of a string which passes round a pulley is constant throughout its length.

146. Single Pulley. The use of a single pulley is to apply an effort in a different direction from that in which it is convenient to us to apply the effort.

Thus, in the first figure, a man standing on the ground and pulling vertically at one end of the rope might support a weight W hanging at the other end; in the second figure the same man pulling sideways might support the weight.

In each case the tension of the string passing round the pulley is unaltered; the effort P is therefore equal to the weight W.

In the first figure the action on the fixed support to which the block is attached must balance the other forces on the pulley-block, and must therefore be equal to

$$W + P + w,$$

i.e., $2W + w$, where w is the weight of the pulley-block.

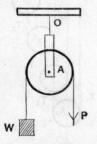
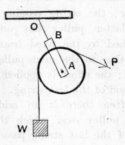

In the second figure, if the weight of the pulley be neglected, the effort P, and the weight W, being equal, must be equally inclined to the line OA.

Hence, if T be the tension of the supporting string OB and 2θ the angle between the directions of P and W, we have

$$T = P\cos\theta + W\cos\theta = 2W\cos\theta.$$

If w be the weight of the pulley, we should have,
$$T^2 = (W+w)^2 + P^2 + 2(W+w) \cdot P \cdot \cos 2\theta$$
$$= 2W^2 + 2Ww + w^2 + 2(W+w) \cdot W(2\cos^2\theta - 1), \text{ since } P \text{ and } W \text{ are equal,}$$
$$= w^2 + 4W(W+w)\cos^2\theta.$$

147. We shall discuss three systems of pulleys and shall follow the usual order; there is no particular reason for this order, but it is convenient to retain it for purposes of reference.

First system of Pulleys. *Each string attached to the supporting beam. To find the relation between the effort or "power" and the weight.*

In this system of pulleys the weight is attached to the lowest pulley, and the string passing round it has one end attached to the fixed beam, and the other end attached to the next highest pulley; the string passing round the latter pulley has one end attached to the fixed beam, and the other to the next pulley, and so on; the effort is applied to the free end of the last string.

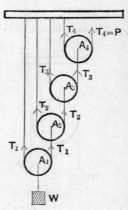

Often there is an additional fixed pulley over which the free end of the last string passes; the effort may then be applied as a downward force.

Let A_1, A_2, ... be the pulleys, beginning from the lowest, and let the tensions of the strings passing round them be T_1, T_2, ... Let W be the weight and P the power.

[N.B. The string passing round any pulley, A_2 say, pulls A_2 vertically *upwards*, and pulls A_3 *downwards*.]

I. *Let the weights of the pulleys be neglected.*

From the equilibrium of the pulleys A_1, A_2, ..., taken in order, we have

$$2T_1 = W; \quad \therefore \ T_1 = \tfrac{1}{2}W.$$

$$2T_2 = T_1; \quad \therefore \ T_2 = \tfrac{1}{2}T_1 = \frac{1}{2^2}\ W.$$

$$2T_3 = T_2; \quad \therefore \ T_3 = \tfrac{1}{2}T_2 = \frac{1}{2^3}\ W.$$

$$2T_4 = T_3; \quad \therefore \ T_4 = \tfrac{1}{2}T_3 = \frac{1}{2^4}\ W.$$

But, with our figure, $T_4 = P$.

$$\therefore \ P = \frac{1}{2^4}\ W.$$

Similarly, if there were n pulleys, we should have

$$P = \frac{1}{2^n}\ W.$$

Hence, in this system of pulleys, the mechanical advantage

$$= \frac{W}{P} = 2^n.$$

II. *Let the weights of the pulleys in succession, beginning from the lowest, be w_1, w_2, ...*

In this case we have an additional downward force on each pulley.

Resolving as before, we have

$$2T_1 = W + w_1,$$
$$2T_2 = T_1 + w_2,$$
$$2T_3 = T_2 + w_3,$$
$$2T_4 = T_3 + w_4.$$

$$\therefore \quad T_1 = \frac{W}{2} + \frac{w_1}{2},$$

$$T_2 = \tfrac{1}{2} T_1 + \frac{w_2}{2} = \frac{W}{2^2} + \frac{w_1}{2^2} + \frac{w_2}{2},$$

$$T_3 = \tfrac{1}{2} T_2 + \frac{w_3}{2} = \frac{W}{2^3} + \frac{w_1}{2^3} + \frac{w_2}{2^2} + \frac{w_3}{2},$$

and $\quad P = T_4 = \tfrac{1}{2} T_3 + \dfrac{w_4}{2} = \dfrac{W}{2^4} + \dfrac{w_1}{2^4} + \dfrac{w_2}{2^3} + \dfrac{w_3}{2^2} + \dfrac{w_4}{2}.$

Similarly, if there were n pulleys, we should have

$$P = \frac{W}{2^n} + \frac{w_1}{2^n} + \frac{w_2}{2^{n-1}} + \ldots + \frac{w_n}{2}.$$

$$\therefore \quad 2^n P = W + w_1 + 2 \,.\, w_2 + 2^2 w_3 + \ldots + 2^{n-1} w_n.$$

If the pulleys be all equal, we have

$$w_1 = w_2 = \ldots = w_n = w.$$

$$\therefore \quad 2^n P = W + w (1 + 2 + 2^2 + \ldots + 2^{n-1})$$

$$= W + w (2^n - 1),$$

by summing the geometrical progression.

It follows that the mechanical advantage, $\dfrac{W}{P}$, depends on the weight of the pulleys.

In this system of pulleys we observe that the greater the weight of the pulleys, the greater must P be to support a given weight W; the weights of the pulleys oppose the effort, and the pulleys should therefore be made as light as is consistent with the required strength.

Stress on the beam from which the pulleys are hung.

Let R be the stress on the beam. Since R, together with the force P, supports the system of pulleys, together with the weight W, we have

$$R + P = W + w_1 + w_2 + \ldots + w_n.$$

$$\therefore\ R = W + w_1 + w_2 + \ldots + w_n - \frac{W + w_1 + 2w_2 + 2^2 w_3 + \ldots + 2^{n-1} w_n}{2^n}$$

$$= W\left(1 - \frac{1}{2^n}\right) + w_1\left(1 - \frac{1}{2^n}\right) + w_2\left(1 - \frac{1}{2^{n-1}}\right)$$

$$+ w_3\left(1 - \frac{1}{2^{n-2}}\right) + \ldots + w_n\left(1 - \frac{1}{2}\right).$$

Ex. *If there be 4 movable pulleys, whose weights, commencing with the lowest, are 4, 5, 6, and 7 lbs., what effort will support a body of weight 1 cwt.?*

Using the notation of the previous article, we have

$$2T_1 = 112 + 4; \qquad \therefore\ T_1 = 58.$$

$$2T_2 = T_1 + 5 = 63; \qquad \therefore\ T_2 = 31\tfrac{1}{2}.$$

$$2T_3 = T_2 + 6 = 37\tfrac{1}{2}; \qquad \therefore\ T_2 = 18\tfrac{3}{4}.$$

$$2P = T_3 + 7 = 25\tfrac{3}{4}; \qquad \therefore\ P = 12\tfrac{7}{8} \text{ lbs. wt.}$$

148. Verification of the Principle of Work.

Neglecting the weights of the pulleys we have, if there be four pulleys,

$$P = \frac{1}{2^4}\,W.$$

If the weight W be raised through a distance x, the pulley A_2 would, if the distance $A_1 A_2$ remained unchanged, rise a distance x; but, at the same time, the length of the string joining A_1 to the beam is shortened by x, and a portion x of the string therefore slips round A_1; hence, altogether, the pulley A_2 rises through a distance $2x$.

Similarly, the pulley A_3 rises a distance $4x$, and the pulley A_4 a distance $8x$.

Since A_4 rises a distance $8x$, the strings joining it to the beam and to the point at which P is applied both shorten by $8x$.

Hence, since the slack string runs round the pulley A_4, the point of application of P rises through $16x$, *i.e.*, through sixteen times as far as the point of application of W.

Hence the velocity-ratio (Art. 137) $= 16$, so that it is equal to the mechanical advantage in this case.

Also

$$\frac{\text{work done by the effort}}{\text{work done against the weight}} = \frac{P \cdot 16x}{W \cdot x}$$

$$= \frac{\frac{1}{2^4} W \cdot 16x}{W \cdot x} = \frac{W \cdot x}{W \cdot x} = 1.$$

Hence the principle is verified.

Taking the weights of the pulleys into account, and taking the case of four pulleys, we have

$$P = \frac{W}{2^4} + \frac{w_1}{2^4} + \frac{w_2}{2^3} + \frac{w_3}{2^2} + \frac{w_4}{2}.$$

As before, if A_1 ascend a distance x, the other pulleys ascend distances $2x$, $4x$, and $8x$, respectively. Hence the work done on the weight and the weights of the pulleys

$$= W \cdot x + w_1 \cdot x + w_2 \cdot 2x + w_3 \cdot 4x + w_4 \cdot 8x$$

$$= 16x \left[\frac{W}{2^4} + \frac{w_1}{2^4} + \frac{w_2}{2^3} + \frac{w_3}{2^2} + \frac{w_4}{2} \right]$$

$$= 16x \times P = \text{work done by the effort.}$$

A similar method of proof would apply, whatever be the number of pulleys.

EXAMPLES. XXIII.

1. In the following cases, the movable pulleys are weightless, their number is n, the weight is W, and the " power " or effort is P;

    (1) If $n=4$ and $P=20$ lbs. wt., find W;

    (2) If $n=4$ and $W=1$ cwt., find P;

    (3) If $W=56$ lbs. wt. and $P=7$ lbs. wt., find n.

2. In the following cases, the movable pulleys are of equal weight w, and are n in number, P is the " power " or effort, and W is the weight;

    (1) If $n=4$, $w=1$ lb. wt., and $W=97$ lbs. wt., find P;

    (2) If $n=3$, $w=1\frac{1}{2}$ lbs. wt., and $P=7$ lbs. wt., find W;

    (3) If $n=5$, $W=775$ lbs. wt., and $P=31$ lbs. wt., find w;

    (4) If $W=107$ lbs. wt., $P=2$ lbs. wt., and $w=\frac{1}{3}$ lbs. wt., find n.

3. In the first system of pulleys, if there be 4 pulleys, each of weight 2 lbs., what weight can be raised by an effort equal to the weight of 20 lbs.?

4. If there be 3 movable pulleys, whose weights, commencing with the lowest, are 9, 2, and 1 lbs. respectively, what force will support a weight of 69 lbs.?

5. If there be 4 movable pulleys, whose weights commencing with the lowest, are 4, 3, 2, and 1 lbs. respectively, what force will support a weight of 54 lbs.?

6. If there be 4 movable pulleys, each of weight w, and the effort be P, shew that the stress on the beam is $15P - 11w$.

7. If there be 3 movable pulleys and their weights beginning from the lowest be 4, 2, and 1 lbs. respectively, what force will be required to support a weight of 28 lbs.?

8. Shew that, on the supposition that the pulleys are weightless, the mechanical advantage is greater than it actually is.

9. In the system of pulleys in which each hangs by a separate string, if there be 3 pulleys, it is found that a certain weight can be supported by an effort equal to 7 lbs. weight; but, if there be 4 pulleys, the same weight can be supported by an effort equal to 4 lbs. weight; find the weight supported and the weight of the pulleys, which are equal.

10. A system consists of 4 pulleys, arranged so that each hangs by a separate string, one end being fastened to the upper block, and all the free ends being vertical. If the weights of the pulleys, beginning at the lowest, be w, $2w$, $3w$, and $4w$, find the power necessary to support a weight of $15w$, and the magnitude of the single force necessary to support the beam to which the other ends of the string are attached.

11. In the system of 4 heavy pulleys, if P be the effort and W the weight, shew that the stress on the beam is intermediate between $\frac{15}{16}W$ and $15P$.

12. A man, of 12 stone weight, is suspended from the lowest of a system of 4 weightless pulleys, in which each hangs by a separate string, and supports himself by pulling at the end of the string which passes over a fixed pulley. Find the amount of his pull on this string.

13. A man, whose weight is 156 lbs., is suspended from the lowest of a system of 4 pulleys, each being of weight 10 lbs., and supports himself by pulling at the end of the string which passes over the fixed pulley. Find the force which he exerts on the string, supposing all the strings to be vertical.

149. Second system of pulleys. *The same string passing round all the pulleys. To find the relation between the effort and the weight.*

In this system there are two blocks, each containing pulleys, the upper block being fixed and the lower block movable. The same string passes round all the pulleys as in the figures.

If the number of pulleys in the upper block be the same as in the lower block (Fig. 1), one end of the string

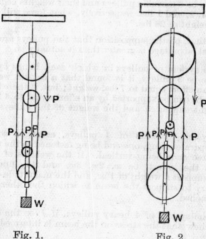

Fig. 1.   Fig. 2.

must be fastened to the upper block; if the number in the upper block be greater by one than the number in the lower block (Fig. 2), the end of the string must be attached to the lower block.

In the first case, the number of portions of string connecting the blocks is even; in the second case, the number is odd.

In either case, let n be the number of portions of string at the lower block. Since we have only one string passing over smooth pulleys, the tension of each of these portions is P, so that the total upward force at the lower block is $n \cdot P$.

Let W be the weight supported, and w the weight of the lower block.

Hence $W + w = nP$, giving the relation required.

In practice the pulleys of each block are often placed parallel to one another, so that the strings are not mathematically parallel; they are, however, very approximately parallel, so that the above relation is still very approximately true.

EXAMPLES. XXIV.

1. If a weight of 5 lbs. support a weight of 24 lbs., find the weight of the lower block, when there are 3 pulleys in each block.

2. If weights of 5 and 6 lbs. respectively at the free ends of the string support weights of 18 and 22 lbs. at the lower block, find the number of the strings and the weight of the lower block.

3. If weights of 4 lbs. and 5 lbs. support weights of 5 lbs. and 18 lbs. respectively, what is the weight of the lower block, and how many pulleys are there in it?

4. A weight of 6 lbs. just supports a weight of 28 lbs., and a weight of 8 lbs. just supports a weight of 42 lbs.; find the number of strings and the weight of the lower block.

5. In the second system of pulleys, if a basket be suspended from the lower block and a man in the basket support himself and the basket, by pulling at the free end of the rope, find the tension he exerts, neglecting the inclination of the rope to the vertical, and assuming the weight of the man and basket to be W.

If the free end of the rope pass round a pulley attached to the ground and then be held by the man, find the force he exerts.

6. A man, whose weight is 12 stone, raises 3 cwt. by means of a system of pulleys in which the same rope passes round all the pulleys, there being 4 in each block, and the rope being attached to the upper block; neglecting the weights of the pulleys, find what will be his thrust on the ground if he pull vertically downwards.

7. We are told that the cable by which "Great Paul," whose weight is 18 tons, was lifted into its place in the cathedral tower, passed four times through the two blocks of pulleys. From this statement give a description of the pulleys, and estimate the strength of the cable.

8. Prove the Principle of Work in this system of pulleys, and find the Velocity Ratio.

9. An ordinary block and tackle has two pulleys in the lower block and two in the upper. What force must be exerted to lift a load of 300 lbs.? If on account of friction a given force will only lift ·45 times as much as if the system were frictionless, find the force required.

10. In a block and tackle the velocity ratio is 8 : 1. The friction is such that only 55 % of the force applied can be usefully employed. Find what force will raise 5 cwt. by its use.

150.   Third system of pulleys. *All the strings attached to the weight. To find the relation between the effort and the weight.*

In this system the string passing round any pulley is attached at one end to a bar, from which the weight is suspended, and at the other end to the next lower pulley; the string round the lowest pulley is attached at one end to the bar, whilst at the other end of this string the power is applied. In this system the upper pulley is fixed.

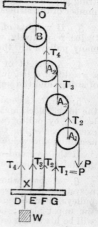

Let A_1, A_2, A_3, ... be the movable pulleys, beginning from the lowest, and let the tensions of the strings passing round these pulleys respectively be T_1, T_2, T_3, ...

If the power be P, we have clearly

$$T_1 = P.$$

I. *Let the weights of the pulleys be neglected.*

For the equilibrium of the pulleys, taken in order and commencing from the lowest, we have

$$T_2 = 2T_1 = 2P,$$
$$T_3 = 2T_2 = 2^2P,$$

and
$$T_4 = 2T_3 = 2^3P.$$

But, since the bar, from which W is suspended, is in equilibrium, we have

$$W = T_1 + T_2 + T_3 + T_4 = P + 2P + 2^2P + 2^3P$$

$$= P\frac{2^4 - 1}{2 - 1} = P(2^4 - 1) \quad \dots\dots\dots\dots\dots\dots(1).$$

If there were n pulleys, of which $(n-1)$ would be movable, we should have, similarly,

$$W = T_1 + T_2 + T_3 + \dots + T_n$$
$$= P + 2P + 2^2P + \dots + 2^{n-1}P$$
$$= P\left[\frac{2^n - 1}{2 - 1}\right],$$

by summing the geometrical progression,

$$= P(2^n - 1) \quad \dots\dots\dots\dots\dots\dots(2).$$

Hence the mechanical advantage is $2^n - 1$.

II. *Let the weights of the movable pulleys, taken in order and commencing with the lowest, be* $w_1, w_2, \dots$.

Considering the equilibrium of the pulleys in order, we have

$$T_2 = 2T_1 + w_1 = 2P + w_1,$$
$$T_3 = 2T_2 + w_2 = 2^2P + 2w_1 + w_2,$$
$$T_4 = 2T_3 + w_3 = 2^3P + 2^2w_1 + 2w_2 + w_3.$$

But, from the equilibrium of the bar,

$$W = T_4 + T_3 + T_2 + T_1$$
$$= (2^3 + 2^2 + 2 + 1) P + (2^2 + 2 + 1) w_1 + (2 + 1) w_2 + w_3$$
$$= \frac{2^4 - 1}{2 - 1} P + \frac{2^3 - 1}{2 - 1} w_1 + \frac{2^2 - 1}{2 - 1} w_2 + w_3$$
$$= (2^4 - 1) P + (2^3 - 1) w_1 + (2^2 - 1) w_2 + w_3 \quad \ldots\ldots(3).$$

If there were n pulleys, of which $(n-1)$ would be movable, we should have, similarly,

$$W = T_n + T_{n-1} + \ldots + T_2 + T_1$$
$$= (2^{n-1} + 2^{n-2} + \ldots + 1) P + (2^{n-2} + 2^{n-3} + \ldots + 1) w_1$$
$$+ (2^{n-3} + 2^{n-4} + \ldots + 1) w_2 + \ldots + (2 + 1) w_{n-2} + w_{n-1}$$
$$= \frac{2^n - 1}{2 - 1} P + \frac{2^{n-1} - 1}{2 - 1} w_1 + \frac{2^{n-2} - 1}{2 - 1} w_2$$
$$+ \ldots + \frac{2^2 - 1}{2 - 1} w_{n-2} + w_{n-1}$$
$$= (2^n - 1) P + (2^{n-1} - 1) w_1 + (2^{n-2} - 1) w_2 + \ldots$$
$$+ (2^2 - 1) w_{n-2} + (2 - 1) w_{n-1} \quad \ldots\ldots\ldots(4).$$

If the pulleys be all equal, so that

$$w_1 = w_2 = \ldots = w_{n-1} = w,$$

the relation (4) becomes

$$W = (2^n - 1) P + w \left[2^{n-1} + 2^{n-2} + \ldots + 2 - (n - 1) \right]$$
$$= (2^n - 1) P + w \left[2^n - n - 1 \right],$$

by summing the geometrical progression.

Stress on the supporting beam. This stress balances the effort, the weight, and the weight of the pulleys, and therefore equals

$$P + W + w_1 + w_2 + \ldots + w_n,$$

and hence is easily found.

Ex. *If there be 4 pulleys, whose weights, commencing with the lowest, are 4, 5, 6, and 7 lbs., what effort will support a body of weight 1 cwt.?*

Using the notation of the previous article, we have

$$T_2 = 2P + 4,$$
$$T_3 = 2T_2 + 5 = 4P + 13,$$
$$T_4 = 2T_3 + 6 = 8P + 32.$$

Also $\qquad 112 = T_4 + T_3 + T_2 + P = 15P + 49.$

$$\therefore P = \frac{63}{15} = 4\tfrac{1}{5} \text{ lbs. wt.}$$

151. In this system we observe that, the greater the weight of each pulley, the less is P required to be in order that it may support a given weight W. Hence the weights of the pulleys assist the effort. If the weights of the pulleys be properly chosen, the system will remain in equilibrium without the application of any effort whatever.

For example, suppose we have 3 movable pulleys, each of weight w, the relation (3) of the last article will become

$$W = 15P + 11w.$$

Hence, if $11w = W$, we have P zero, so that no power need be applied at the free end of the string to preserve equilibrium.

152. In the third system of pulleys, the bar supporting the weight W will not remain horizontal, unless the point at which the weight is attached be properly chosen. In any particular case the proper point of attachment can be easily found.

Taking the figure of Art. 146 let there be three movable pulleys, whose weights are negligible. Let the distances between the points D, E, F, and G at which the strings are attached, be successively a, and let the point at which the weight is attached be X.

The resultant of T_1, T_2, T_3, and T_4 must pass through X.

Hence by Art. 109,

$$DX = \frac{T_4 \times 0 + T_3 \times a + T_2 \times 2a + T_1 \times 3a}{T_4 + T_3 + T_2 + T_1}$$
$$= \frac{4P \cdot a + 2P \cdot 2a + P \cdot 3a}{8P + 4P + 2P + P} = \frac{11a}{15}.$$

$$\therefore DX = \tfrac{11}{15} DE, \text{ giving the position of } X.$$

153. This system of pulleys was not however designed in order to lift weights. If it be used for that purpose it is soon found to be unworkable. Its use is to give a short strong pull. For example it is used on board a yacht to set up the back stay.

In the figure of Art. 150, $DEFG$ is the deck of the yacht to which the strings are attached and there is no W.

The strings to the pulleys A_1, A_2, A_3, A_4 are inclined to the vertical and the point O is at the top of the mast which is to be kept erect. The resistance in this case is the force at O necessary to keep the mast up, and the effort is applied as in the figure.

154. Verification of the Principle of Work.

Suppose the weight W to ascend through a space x. The string joining B to the bar shortens by x, and hence the pulley A_3 descends a distance x. Since the pulley A_3 descends x and the bar rises x, the string joining A_3 to the bar shortens by $2x$, and this portion slides over A_3; hence the pulley A_2 descends a distance equal to $2x$ together with the distance through which A_3 descends, *i.e.*, A_2 descends a distance $2x + x$, or $3x$. Hence the string A_2F shortens by $4x$, which slips over the pulley A_2, so that the pulley A_1 descends a distance $4x$ together with the distance through which A_2 descends, *i.e.*, $4x + 3x$, or $7x$. Hence the string A_1G shortens by $8x$, and A_1 itself descends $7x$, so that the point of application of P descends $15x$.

Neglecting the weight of the pulleys, the work done by P therefore

$$= 15x \cdot P = x\left(2^4 - 1\right)P = x \cdot W \text{ by equation (1), Art. 150,}$$
$$= \text{work done on the weight } W.$$

Taking the weights of the pulleys into account, the work done by the effort and the weights of the pulleys [which in this case assist the power]

$$= P \cdot 15x + w_1 \cdot 7x + w_2 \cdot 3x + w_3 \cdot x$$
$$= x\left[P\left(2^4 - 1\right) + w_1\left(2^3 - 1\right) + w_2\left(2^2 - 1\right) + w_3\right]$$
$$= x \cdot W \text{ by equation (3), Art. 150,}$$
$$= \text{work done on the weight } W.$$

If there were n pulleys we should in a similar manner find the point of application of P moved through $(2^n - 1)$ times the distance moved through by W, so that the velocity ratio is $2^n - 1$.

EXAMPLES. XXV.

1. In the following cases, the pulleys are weightless and n in number, P is the "power" or effort and W the weight;

(1) If $n=4$ and $P=$ 2 lbs. wt., find W;

(2) If $n=5$ and $W=124$ lbs. wt., find P;

(3) If $W=105$ lbs. and $P=7$ lbs. wt., find n.

2. In the following cases, the pulleys are equal and each of weight w, P is the "power," and W is the weight;

(1) If $n=4$, $w=1$ lb. wt., and $P=$ 10 lbs. wt., find W;

(2) If $n=3$, $w=\frac{1}{2}$ lb. wt., and $W=114$ lbs. wt., find P;

(3) If $n=5$, $P=$ 3 lbs. wt., and $W=106$ lbs. wt., find w;

(4) If $P=4$ lbs. wt., $W=137$ lbs. wt., and $w=\frac{1}{2}$ lb. wt., find n.

3. If there be 5 pulleys, each of weight 1 lb., what effort is required to support 3 cwt.?

If the pulleys be of equal size, find to what point of the bar the weight must be attached, so that the beam may be always horizontal.

4. If the strings passing round a system of 4 weightless pulleys be fastened to a rod without weight at distances successively an inch apart, find to what point of the rod the weight must be attached, so that the rod may be horizontal.

5. Find the mechanical advantage, when the pulleys are 4 in number, and each is of weight $\frac{1}{64}$th that of the weight.

6. In a system of 3 weightless pulleys, in which each string is attached to a bar which carries the weight, if the diameter of each pulley be 2 inches, find to what point of the bar the weight should be attached so that the bar may be horizontal.

7. If the pulleys be equal, and the effort be equal to the weight of one of them, and the number of pulleys be 5, shew that the weight is 57 times the power.

8. In the third system of 3 pulleys, if the weights of the pulleys be all equal, find the relation of the effort to the weight when equilibrium is established. If each pulley weigh 2 ounces, what weight would be supported by the pulleys only?

If the weight supported be 25 lbs. wt., and the effort be 3 lbs. wt., find what must be the weight of each pulley.

9. In the third system of weightless pulleys, the weight is supported by an effort of 70 lbs. The hook by which one of the strings is attached to the weight breaks, and the string is then attached to the pulley which it passed over, and an effort of 150 lbs. is now required. Find the number of pulleys and the weight supported.

10. In the third system of weightless pulleys, if the string round the last pulley be tied to the weight, shew that the tension of the string is diminished in a ratio depending on the number of pulleys.

If the tension be decreased in the ratio 16 : 15, find the number of pulleys.

11. In the system of pulleys in which each string is attached to the weight, if each pulley have a weight w, and the sum of the weights of the pulleys be W', and P and W be the effort and weight in this case, shew that the effort $P + w$ would support the weight $W + W'$ in the same system if the pulleys had no weight.

12. If there be n weightless pulleys and if a string, whose ends are attached to the weights P and W, carry a pulley from which a weight W' is suspended, find the relation between P, W, and W'.

13. If there be n pulleys, each of diameter $2a$ and of negligible weight, shew that the distance of the point of application of the weight from the line of action of the effort should be $\dfrac{2^n}{2^n - 1}\, na$.

III. The Inclined Plane.

155. The Inclined Plane, considered as a mechanical power, is a rigid plane inclined at an angle to the horizon.

It is used to facilitate the raising of heavy bodies.

In the present chapter we shall only consider the case of a body resting on the plane, and acted upon by forces in a plane perpendicular to the intersection of the inclined plane and the horizontal, *i.e.*, in a vertical plane through the line of greatest slope.

The reader can picture to himself the line of greatest slope on an inclined plane in the following manner: take a rectangular sheet of cardboard $ABCD$, and place it at an angle to the horizontal, so that the line AB is in contact with a horizontal table: take any point P on the cardboard and draw PM perpendicular to the line AB; PM is the line of greatest slope passing through the point P.

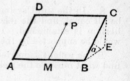

From C draw CE perpendicular to the horizontal plane through AB, and join BE. The lines BC, BE, and CE are called respectively the length, base, and height of the inclined plane; also the angle CBE is the inclination of the plane to the horizon.

In this chapter the inclined plane is supposed to be smooth, so that the only reaction between it and any body resting on it is perpendicular to the inclined plane.

Since the plane is rigid, it is capable of exerting any reaction, however great, that may be necessary to give equilibrium.

156. *A body, of given weight, rests on an inclined plane; to determine the relations between the effort, the weight, and the reaction of the plane.*

Let W be the weight of the body, P the effort, and R the reaction of the plane; also let a be the inclination of the plane to the horizon.

Case I. *Let the effort act up the plane along the line of greatest slope.*

Let AC be the inclined plane, AB the horizontal line through A, DE a vertical line, and let the perpendicular to the plane through D meet AB in F.

Then clearly

$$\angle FDE = 90° - \angle ADE$$

$$= \angle DAE = a.$$

By Lami's Theorem (Art. 40), since only three forces act on the body, each is proportional to the sine of the angle between the other two.

$$\therefore \frac{P}{\sin(R,\,W)} = \frac{R}{\sin(W,\,P)} = \frac{W}{\sin(P,\,R)},$$

$$i.e.,\quad \frac{P}{\sin(180° - a)} = \frac{R}{\sin(90° + a)} = \frac{W}{\sin 90°},$$

$$i.e.,\quad \frac{P}{\sin a} = \frac{R}{\cos a} = W \quad \ldots\ldots\ldots\ldots(1).$$

$$\therefore P = W \sin a, \text{ and } R = W \cos a.$$

The relation (1) may be written in the form

$$P : R : W$$

:: Height of plane : Base of plane : Length of plane.

Otherwise thus : Resolve W along and perpendicular to the plane; its components are

$$W \cos ADE, \ i.e., \ W \sin a, \ \text{along } DA,$$

and $W \sin ADE, \ i.e., \ W \cos a, \ \text{along } DF.$

Hence $P = W \sin a, \ \text{and } R = W \cos a.$

The work done by the force P in dragging the body from A to C is $P \times AC$.

But $P = W \sin a.$

Therefore the work done is $W \sin a \times AC$,

    $i.e., \ W \times AC \sin a, \ i.e., \ W \times BC.$

Hence the work done is the same as that which would be done in lifting the weight of the body through the same height without the intervention of the inclined plane. Hence the Principle of Work is true in this case.

Case II.   *Let the effort act horizontally.*

[In this case we must imagine a small hole in the plane at D through which a string is passed and attached to the body, or else that the body is *pushed* toward the plane by a horizontal force.]

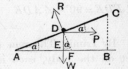

As in Case I., we have

$$\frac{P}{\sin (R, W)} = \frac{R}{\sin (W, P)} = \frac{W}{\sin (P, R)},$$

$i.e., \quad \dfrac{P}{\sin (180° - a)} = \dfrac{R}{\sin 90°} = \dfrac{W}{\sin (90° + a)},$

$i.e., \quad \dfrac{P}{\sin a} = \dfrac{R}{1} = \dfrac{W}{\cos a}$ ....(1).

$\therefore \ P = W \tan a, \ \text{and } R = W \sec a.$

The relation (1) may be written in the form
$$P : R : W$$
:: Height of Plane : Length of Plane : Base of Plane.

Otherwise thus: The components of W along and perpendicular to the plane are $W \sin \alpha$ and $W \cos \alpha$; the components of P, similarly, are $P \cos \alpha$ and $P \sin \alpha$.

$$\therefore P \cos \alpha = W \sin \alpha, \text{ and}$$

$$R = P \sin \alpha + W \cos \alpha = W \left[\frac{\sin^2 \alpha}{\cos \alpha} + \cos \alpha \right] = W \frac{\sin^2 \alpha + \cos^2 \alpha}{\cos \alpha} = W \sec \alpha.$$

$$\therefore P = W \tan \alpha, \text{ and } R = W \sec \alpha.$$

Case III. *Let the effort act at an angle θ with the inclined plane.*

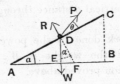

By Lami's Theorem we have
$$\frac{P}{\sin (R, W)} = \frac{R}{\sin (W, P)} = \frac{W}{\sin (P, R)},$$

$$i.e., \frac{P}{\sin (180^\circ - \alpha)} = \frac{R}{\sin (90^\circ + \theta + \alpha)} = \frac{W}{\sin (90^\circ - \theta)},$$

$$i.e., \frac{P}{\sin \alpha} = \frac{R}{\cos (\theta + \alpha)} = \frac{W}{\cos \theta}.$$

$$\therefore P = W \frac{\sin \alpha}{\cos \theta}, \text{ and } R = W \frac{\cos (\theta + \alpha)}{\cos \theta}.$$

Otherwise thus: Resolving along and perpendicular to the plane, we have
$$P \cos \theta = W \sin \alpha, \text{ and } R + P \sin \theta = W \cos \alpha.$$

$$\therefore P = W \frac{\sin \alpha}{\cos \theta},$$

$$\text{and } R = W \cos \alpha - P \sin \theta = W \left[\cos \alpha - \frac{\sin \alpha \sin \theta}{\cos \theta} \right]$$

$$= W \frac{\cos \alpha \cos \theta - \sin \alpha \sin \theta}{\cos \theta} = W \frac{\cos (\alpha + \theta)}{\cos \theta}.$$

If through E we draw EK parallel to P to meet DF in K, then DEK is a triangle of forces, and

$$\therefore P : R : W :: EK : KD : DE,$$

and thus we have a graphic construction for P and R.

It will be noted that Case III. includes both Cases I. and II.; if we make θ zero, we obtain Case I.; if we put θ equal to $(-\alpha)$, we have Case II.

Verification of the Principle of Work.

In Case III. let the body move a distance x along the plane; the distance through which the point of application of P moves, measured along its direction of application, is clearly $x \cos \theta$; also the vertical distance through which the weight moves is $x \sin \alpha$.

Hence the work done by the power is $P . x \cos \theta$, and that done against the weight is $W . x \sin \alpha$. These are equal by the relation proved above.

157. Experiment. *To find experimentally the relation between the effort and the weight in the case of an inclined plane.*

Take a wooden board AB, hinged at A to a second board, which can be clamped to a table; to the board AB let a sheet of glass be fixed in order to minimise the friction. At B is fixed a vertical graduated scale, so that the height of B above A can be easily read off.

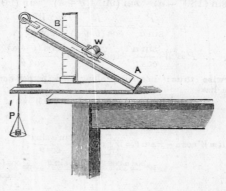

The weight consists of a heavy brass roller to which is attached a string which after passing over a pulley supports a scale-pan in which weights can be placed. These weights, together with the weight of the scale-pan, form the "effort" or "power" P.

The pulley is so arranged that the string between it and W is parallel to the plane.

Set the arm AB at any convenient angle; load the scale-pan so that W is just supported. [In actual practice it is better to take for P the mean of the values of the weights which will let W just run down and just drag it up respectively.]

Observe h the height of B above A, and l the length AB.

Then it will be found that $\dfrac{P}{W} = \dfrac{h}{l}$.

Now set the board at a different angle and determine P, h, l for this second experiment. The same relation will be found to be true.

If there be a slit along the length of the board through which the string can pass, then a pulley can be arranged in such a position that the string can be horizontal. In this case the effort, as in Case II. of Art. 156, will be horizontal and we shall find that

$$\frac{P}{W} = \frac{\text{Height of the plane}}{\text{Base of the plane}}.$$

158. If the power does not act in a vertical plane through the line of greatest slope there could not be equilibrium on a smooth inclined plane; in this case we could, however, have equilibrium if the inclined plane were rough. We shall return to this case in the next chapter.

EXAMPLES. XXVI.

1. What force, acting horizontally, could keep a mass of 16 lbs. at rest on a smooth inclined plane, whose height is 3 feet and length of base 4 feet, and what is the reaction of the plane?

2. A body rests on an inclined plane, being supported by a force acting up the plane equal to half its weight. Find the inclination of the plane to the horizon and the reaction of the plane.

3. A rope, whose inclination to the vertical is 30°, is just strong enough to support a weight of 180 lbs. on a smooth plane, whose inclination to the horizon is 30°. Find approximately the greatest tension that the rope could exert.

4. A body rests on a plane, inclined at an angle of 60° to the horizon, and is supported by a force inclined at an angle of 30° to the horizon; shew that the force and the reaction of the plane are each equal to the weight of the body.

5. A body, of weight $2P$, is kept in equilibrium on an inclined plane by a horizontal force P, together with a force P acting parallel to the plane; find the ratio of the base of the plane to the height and also the reaction of the plane.

6. A body rests on a plane, inclined to the horizon at an angle of 30°, being supported by a force inclined at 30° to the plane; find the ratio of the weight of the body to the force.

7. A weight is supported on an inclined plane by a force inclined to the plane; if the weight, the force, and the reaction be as the numbers 4, 3, and 2, find the inclination of the plane and the direction of the force.

8. A body, of 5 lbs. wt., is placed on a smooth plane inclined at 30° to the horizon, and is acted on by two forces, one equal to the weight of 2 lbs. and acting parallel to the plane and upwards, and the other equal to P and acting at an angle of 30° with the plane. Find P and the reaction of the plane.

9. Find the force which acting up an inclined plane will keep a body, of 10 lbs. weight, in equilibrium, it being given that the force, the reaction of the plane, and the weight of the body are in arithmetical progression.

10. If a force P, acting parallel to an inclined plane and supporting a mass of weight W, produces on the plane a thrust R, shew that the same power, acting horizontally and supporting a mass of weight R, will produce on the plane a thrust W.

11. Two boards, of lengths 11 and 8 feet, are fixed with their lower ends on a horizontal plane and their upper ends in contact; on these planes rest bodies of weights W and 12 lbs. respectively, which are connected by a string passing over the common vertex of the boards; find the value of W.

12. A number of loaded trucks, each containing 1 ton, on one part of a tramway inclined at an angle α to the horizon supports an equal number of empty trucks on another part whose inclination is β. Find the weight of a truck.

13. A body rests on a plane inclined to the horizon at an angle α; if the reaction of the plane be equal to the effort applied, shew that the inclination of the effort to the inclined plane is $90° - 2\alpha$.

14. A heavy string is placed with a portion of it resting on a given inclined plane, the remaining part hanging vertically over a small pulley at the top of the plane. Find what point of the string should be placed over the pulley for equilibrium.

15. On two inclined planes, of equal height, two weights are respectively supported, by means of a string passing over the common vertex and parallel to the planes; the length of one plane is double its height, and the length of the other plane is double its base; shew that the reaction of one plane is three times the reaction of the other.

16. A body, of weight 50 lbs., is in equilibrium on a smooth plane inclined at an angle of 20° 20′ to the horizon, being supported by a force acting up the plane; find, graphically or by use of trigonometrical tables, the force and the reaction of the plane.

17. A body, of weight 20 lbs., rests on a smooth plane inclined at an angle of 25° to the horizon, being supported by a force P acting at an angle of 35° with the plane; find, graphically or by use of trigonometrical tables, P and the reaction of the plane.

18. A body, of weight 30 lbs., rests on a smooth plane inclined at an angle of 28° 15′ to the horizon, being supported by a horizontal force P; find, graphically or by use of trigonometrical tables, P and the reaction of the plane.

IV. The Wheel and Axle.

159. This machine consists of a strong circular cylinder, or axle, terminating in two pivots, A and B,

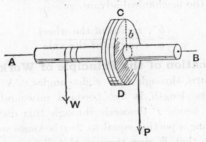

which can turn freely on fixed supports. To the cylinder is rigidly attached a wheel, CD, the plane of the wheel being perpendicular to the axle.

Round the axle is coiled a rope, one end of which is firmly attached to the axle, and the other end of which is attached to the weight.

Round the circumference of the wheel, in a direction opposite to that of the first rope, is coiled a second rope, having one end firmly attached to the wheel, and having the "power," or effort, applied at its other end. The circumference of the wheel is grooved to prevent the rope from slipping off.

160. *To find the relation between the effort and the weight.*

In Art. 93, we have shewn that a body, which can turn freely about a fixed axis, is in equilibrium if the algebraic sum of the moments of the forces about the axis vanishes. In this case, the only forces acting on the machine are the effort P and the weight W, which tend to turn the machine in opposite directions. Hence, if a be the radius of the axle, and b be the radius of the wheel, the condition of equilibrium is

$$P \cdot b = W \cdot a \dots\dots\dots\dots\dots\dots\dots(1).$$

Hence the mechanical advantage $= \dfrac{W}{P}$

$$= \frac{b}{a} = \frac{\text{radius of the wheel}}{\text{radius of the axle}}.$$

Verification of the Principle of Work. Let the machine turn through four right angles. A portion of string whose length is $2\pi b$ becomes unwound from the wheel, and hence P descends through this distance. At the same time a portion equal to $2\pi a$ becomes wound upon the axle, so that W rises through this distance. The work done by P is therefore $P \times 2\pi b$ and that done against W is $W \times 2\pi a$. These are equal by the relation (1).

Also the velocity-ratio (Art. 137)

$$= \frac{2\pi b}{2\pi a} = \frac{b}{a} = \text{the mechanical advantage.}$$

161. Theoretically, by making the quantity $\frac{b}{a}$ very large, we can make the mechanical advantage as great as we please; practically however there are limits. Since the pressure of the fixed supports on the axle must balance P and W, it follows that the thickness of the axle, *i.e.*, $2a$, must not be reduced unduly, for then the axle would break. Neither can the radius of the wheel in practice become very large, for then the machine would be unwieldy. Hence the possible values of the mechanical advantage are bounded, in one direction by the strength of our materials, and in the other direction by the necessity of keeping the size of the machine within reasonable limits.

162. In Art. 160 we have neglected the thicknesses of the ropes. If, however, they are too great to be neglected, compared with the radii of the wheel and axle, we may take them into consideration by supposing the tensions of the ropes to act along their middle threads.

Suppose the radii of the ropes which pass round the axle and wheel to be x and y respectively; the distances from the line joining the pivots at which the tensions now act are $(a+x)$ and $(b+y)$ respectively. Hence the condition of equilibrium is

$$P(b+y) = W(a+x),$$

so that $\quad \dfrac{P}{W} = \dfrac{\text{sum of the radii of the axle and its rope}}{\text{sum of the radii of the wheel and its rope}}.$

163. Other forms of the Wheel and Axle are the Windlass, used for drawing water from a well, and Capstan, used on board ship. In these machines the effort instead of being applied, as in Art. 159, by means of a rope passing round a cylinder, is applied at the ends of a spoke, or spokes, which are inserted in a plane perpendicular to the axle.

In the Windlass the axle is horizontal, and in the Capstan it is vertical.

In the latter case the resistance consists of the tension T of the rope round the axle, and the effort consists of the forces applied at the ends of bars inserted into sockets at the point A of the axle. The advantage of pairs of arms is that the strain on the bearings of the capstan is thereby much diminished or destroyed. The condition of equilibrium may be obtained as in Art. 160.

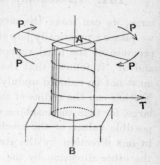

164. Differential Wheel and Axle. A slightly modified form of the ordinary wheel and axle is the differential wheel and axle. In this machine the axle consists of two cylinders, having a common axis, joined at their ends, the radii of the two cylinders being different. One end of the rope is wound round one of these cylinders, and its other end is wound in a contrary direction round the other cylinder. Upon the slack portion of the rope is slung a pulley to which the weight is attached. The part of the rope which passes round the smaller cylinder tends to turn the machine in the same direction as the effort.

As before, let b be the radius of the wheel and let a and c be the radii of the portion AC and CB of the axle, a being the smaller.

Since the pulley is smooth, the tension T of the string round it is the same throughout its length, and hence, for the equilibrium of the weight, we have $T = \frac{1}{2} W$.

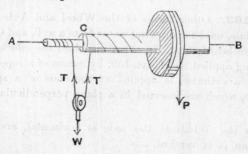

Taking moments about the line AB for the equilibrium of the machine, we have

$$P.b + T.a = T.c.$$

$$\therefore P = T\frac{c-a}{b} = \frac{W}{2}\frac{c-a}{b}.$$

Hence the mechanical advantage $= \dfrac{W}{P} = \dfrac{2b}{c-a}$.

By making the radii c and a of the two portions of the axle very nearly equal, we can make the mechanical advantage very great, without unduly weakening the machine.

165. Weston's Differential Pulley.

In this machine there are two blocks; the upper contains two pulleys of nearly the same size which turn together as one pulley; the lower consists of one pulley to which the weight W is attached.

The figure represents a section of the machine.

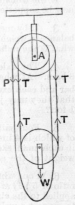

An endless chain passes round the larger of the upper pulleys, then round the lower pulley and the smaller of the upper pulleys; the remainder of the chain hangs slack and is joined on to the first portion of the chain. The effort P is applied as in the figure. The chain is prevented from slipping by small projections on the surfaces of the upper pulleys, or by depressions in the pulleys into which the links of the chain fit.

If T be the tension of the portions of the chain which support the weight W, we have, since these portions are approximately nearly vertical, on neglecting the weight of the chain and the lower pulley,

$$2T = W \quad\dots\dots\dots\dots\dots(1).$$

If R and r be the radii of the larger and smaller pulleys of the upper block we have, by taking moments about the centre A of the upper block,

$$P.R + T.r = T.R.$$

Hence

$$P = T\frac{R-r}{R} = \frac{W}{2}\frac{R-r}{R}.$$

The mechanical advantage of this system therefore

$$= \frac{W}{P} = \frac{2R}{R-r}.$$

Since R and r are nearly equal this mechanical advantage is therefore very great.

The differential pulley-block avoids one great disadvantage of the differential wheel and axle. In the latter machine a very great amount of rope is required in order to raise the weight through an appreciable distance.

EXAMPLES. XXVII.

1. If the radii of the wheel and axle be respectively 2 feet and 3 inches, find what power must be applied to raise a weight of 56 lbs.

2. If the radii of the wheel and axle be respectively 30 inches and 5 inches, find what weight would be supported by a force equal to the weight of 20 lbs., and find also the pressures on the supports on which the axle rests.

If the thickness of the ropes be each 1 inch, find what weight would now be supported.

3. If by means of a wheel and axle a power equal to 3 lbs. weight balance a weight of 30 lbs., and if the radius of the axle be 2 inches, what is the radius of the wheel?

4. The axle of a capstan is 16 inches in diameter and there are 8 bars. At what distance from the axis must 8 men push, 1 at each bar and each exerting a force equal to the weight of $26\frac{2}{3}$ lbs., in order that they may just produce a strain sufficient to raise the weight of 1 ton?

5. Four sailors raise an anchor by means of a capstan, the radius of which is 4 ins. and the length of the spokes 6 feet from the capstan; if each man exert a force equal to the weight of 112 lbs., find the weight of the anchor.

6. Four wheels and axles, in each of which the radii are in the ratio of 5 : 1, are arranged so that the circumference of each axle is applied to the circumference of the next wheel; what effort is required to support a weight of 1875 lbs. ?

7. The radii of a wheel and axle are 2 feet and 2 ins. respectively, and the strings which hang from them are tied to the two ends of a uniform rod, 2 feet 2 ins. in length and 10 lbs. in weight; what weight must be also hung from one of the strings that the rod may hang in a horizontal position?

8. A pulley is suspended by a vertical loop of string from a wheel-and-axle and supports a weight of 1 cwt., one end of the string being wound round the axle and the other in a contrary direction round the wheel. Find the power which acting at one end of an arm, 2 feet in length, so as to turn the axle, will support the weight, assuming the radii of the wheel and axle to be 1 foot and 2 ins.

9. In the Differential Wheel and Axle, if the radius of the wheel be 1 foot and the radii of the two portions of the axle be 5 and 4 ins. respectively, what power will support a weight of 56 lbs.?

10. In the Differential Wheel and Axle, if the radius of the wheel be 18 ins. and the radii of the two portions of the axle be 6 and 4 ins. respectively, what weight will be supported by an effort equal to 20 lbs. weight?

11. In a wheel and axle the radius of the wheel is 1 foot and that of the axle is 1 inch; if 2 weights, each 10 lbs., be fastened to 2 points on the rim of the wheel, so that the line joining them subtends an angle of 120° at the centre of the wheel, find the greatest weight which can be supported by a string hanging from the axle in the usual way.

12. In a wheel and axle, if the radius of the wheel be six times that of the axle, and if by means of an effort equal to 5 lbs. wt. a body be lifted through 50 feet, find the amount of work expended.

13. A capstan, of diameter 20 inches, is worked by means of a lever, which measures 5 feet from the axis of the capstan. Find the work done in drawing up by a rope a body, of weight one ton, over 35 feet of the surface of a smooth plane inclined to the horizon at an angle $\cos^{-1}\frac{4}{5}$. Find also the force applied to the end of the lever, and the distance through which the point of application moves.

14. Verify the Principle of Work in the cases of the Differential Wheel-and-Axle and Weston's Differential Pulley, finding the Velocity-Ratio in each case.

V. The Common Balance.

166. The Common Balance consists of a rigid beam *AB* (Art. 167), carrying a scale-pan suspended from each end, which can turn freely about a fulcrum *O* outside the beam. The fulcrum and the beam are rigidly connected and, if the balance be well constructed, at the point *O* is a hard steel wedge, whose edge is turned downward and which rests on a small plate of agate.

The body to be weighed is placed in one scale-pan and in the other are placed weights, whose magnitudes are known; these weights are adjusted until the beam of the balance rests in a horizontal position. If *OH* be perpendicular to the beam, and the arms HA and HB be of equal length, and if the centre of gravity of the beam lie in the line OH, and the scale-pans be of equal weight, then the weight of the body is the same as the sum of the weights placed in the other scale-pan.

If the weight of the body be not equal to the sum of the weights placed in the other scale-pan, the balance will not rest with its beam horizontal, but will rest with the beam inclined to the horizon.

In the best balances the beam is usually provided with a long pointer attached to the beam at H. The end of this pointer travels along a graduated scale and, when the beam is horizontal, the pointer is vertical and points to the zero graduation on the scale.

167. *To find the position of equilibrium of a balance when the weights placed in the scale-pans are not equal.*

Let the weights placed in the scale-pans be P and W, the former being the greater; let S be the weight of each scale-pan, and let the weight of the beam (and the parts rigidly connected with it) be W', acting at a point K on OH.

[*The figure is drawn out of proportion so that the points may be distinctly marked; K is actually very near the beam.*]

When in equilibrium let the beam be inclined at an angle θ to the horizontal, so that OH is inclined at the same angle θ to the vertical.

Let OH and OK be h and k respectively, and let the length of AH or HB be a.

Let horizontal lines through O and H meet the vertical lines through the ends A and B of the beam in the points L, M, L' and M' respectively.

Also let the vertical lines through H and K meet LM in F and G respectively.

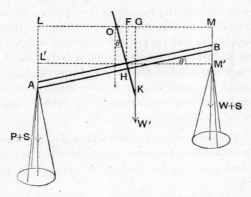

When the system is in equilibrium, the moments of the forces about O must balance.

$$\therefore \ (P + S) . OL = (W + S) OM + W' . OG,$$

$$i.e., \ (P + S) (FL - FO) = (W + S) (FM + OF) + W' . OG,$$

$$\therefore \ (P + S) (a \cos \theta - h \sin \theta) = (W + S) (a \cos \theta + h \sin \theta) + W' . k \sin \theta.$$

[For $\quad OF = OH \cos FOH = h \sin \theta$; $\quad OG = OK \sin \theta$;

and $\qquad\qquad FL = HL' = a \cos \theta.$]

$$\therefore \ a \cos \theta (P - W) = \sin \theta [W'k + (P + W + 2S) h].$$

$$\therefore \ \tan \theta = \frac{(P - W) a}{W'k + (P + W + 2S) h}.$$

168. *Requisites of a good balance.*

(1) The balance must be **true.**

This will be the case if the arms of the balance be equal, if the weights of the scale-pans be equal, and if the centre of gravity of the beam be on the line through the fulcrum perpendicular to the beam; for the beam will now be horizontal when equal weights are placed in the scale-pans.

To test whether the balance is true, first see if the beam is horizontal when the scale-pans are empty; then make the beam horizontal by putting sufficient weights in one scale-pan to balance the weight of a body placed in the other; now interchange the body and the weights; if they still balance one another, the balance must be true; if in the second case the beam assumes any position inclined to the vertical, the balance is not true.

(2) The balance must be **sensitive,** *i.e.,* the beam must, for any difference, however small, between the weights in the scale-pans, be inclined at an appreciable angle to the horizon.

For a *given* difference between P and W, the greater the inclination of the beam to the horizon the more sensitive is the balance; also the less the difference between the weights required to produce a given inclination θ, the greater is the sensitiveness of the balance.

Hence, when $P - W$ is given, the sensitiveness increases as θ increases, and therefore as $\tan \theta$ increases; also, when θ is given, it varies as

$$\frac{1}{P - W}.$$

The sensitiveness is therefore appropriately measured by

$$\frac{\tan \theta}{P - W},$$

i.e. by

$$\frac{a}{W'k + (P + W + 2S)\,h}. \quad \text{(Art. 167.)}$$

Hence, the sensitiveness of a balance will be great if the arm a be fairly long in comparison with the distances h and k and the weight W' of the beam be as small as is consistent with the length and rigidity of the machine.

If h is not zero, it follows that the sensitiveness depends on the values of P and W, *i.e.* depends on the loads in the scale-pans. In a balance for use in a chemical laboratory this is undesirable. Such balances are therefore made with h zero, *i.e.* with the point O in the figure coinciding with H. The sensibility then varies inversely with k, the distance of the centre of gravity of the beam below O or H.

But we must not make both h and k zero; for then the points O and K would both coincide with H. In this case the balance would either when the weights in the scale-pans were equal, be, as in Art. 144, in equilibrium in *any* position or else, if the weights in the scale-pans were not equal, it would take up a position as nearly vertical as the mechanism of the machine would allow.

(3) The balance must be **stable** and must quickly take up its position of equilibrium.

The determination of the time taken by the machine to take up its position of equilibrium is essentially a dynamical question. We may however *assume* that this condition is best satisfied when the moment of the forces about the fulcrum O is greatest. When the weights in the scale-pans are each P, the moment of the forces tending to restore equilibrium

$$= (P + S)(a \cos \theta + h \sin \theta) - (P + S)(a \cos \theta - h \sin \theta)$$
$$+ W' \cdot k \sin \theta$$
$$= [2(P + S) h + W' \cdot k] \sin \theta.$$

This expression is greatest when h and k are greatest.

Since the balance is most sensitive when h and k are small, and most stable when these quantities are large, we see that in any balance great sensitiveness and quick weighing are to a certain extent incompatible. In practice this is not very important; for in balances where great sensitiveness is required (such as balances used in a laboratory) we can afford to sacrifice quickness of weighing; the opposite is the case when the balance is used for ordinary commercial purposes.

To insure as much as possible both the qualities of sensitiveness and quick weighing, the balance should be made with fairly light long arms, and at the same time the distance of the fulcrum from the beam should be considerable.

169. Double weighing. By this method the weight of a body may be accurately determined even if the balance be not accurate.

Place the body to be weighed in one scale-pan and in the other pan put sand, or other suitable material, sufficient to balance the body. Next remove the body, and in its place put known weights sufficient to again balance the sand. The weight of the body is now clearly equal to the sum of the weights.

This method is used even in the case of extremely good machines when very great accuracy is desired. It is known as Borda's Method.

170. Ex. 1. *The arms of a balance are equal in length but the beam is unjustly loaded; if a body be placed in each scale-pan in succession and weighed, shew that its true weight is the arithmetic mean between its apparent weights.*

For let the length of the arms be a, and let the horizontal distance of the centre of gravity of the beam from the fulcrum be x.

Let a body, whose true weight is W, appear to weigh W_1 and W_2 successively.

If W' be the weight of the beam, we have

$$W \cdot a = W' \cdot x + W_1 \cdot a,$$

and $$W_2 \cdot a = W' \cdot x + W \cdot a.$$

Hence, by subtraction,

$$(W - W_2)\,a = (W_1 - W)\,a.$$
$$\therefore\ W = \tfrac{1}{2}\,(W_1 + W_2)$$
$$= \text{arithmetic mean between the}$$
$$\text{apparent weights.}$$

Ex. 2. *The arms of a balance are of unequal length, but the beam remains in a horizontal position when the scale-pans are not loaded; shew that, if a body be placed successively in each scale-pan, its true weight is the geometrical mean between its apparent weights.*
[*Method of Gauss.*]

Shew also that if a tradesman appear to weigh out equal quantities of the same substance, using alternately each of the scale-pans, he will defraud himself.

Since the beam remains horizontal when there are no weights in the scale-pans, it follows that the centre of gravity of the beam and scale-pans must be vertically under the fulcrum.

Let a and b be the lengths of the arms of the beam, and let a body, whose true weight is W, appear to weigh W_1 and W_2 successively.

Hence $\qquad\qquad W\,.\,a = W_1\,.\,b$ ....(1),

and $\qquad\qquad W_2\,.\,a = W\,.\,b$ ....(2).

Hence, by multiplication, we have

$$W^2\,.\,ab = W_1 W_2\,.\,ab.$$
$$\therefore\ W = \sqrt{W_1\,.\,W_2},$$

i.e., the true weight is the geometrical mean between the apparent weights.

Again, if the tradesman appear to weigh out in succession quantities equal to W, he really gives his customers $W_1 + W_2$.

Now $\qquad W_1 + W_2 - 2W = W\dfrac{a}{b} + W\dfrac{b}{a} - 2W$

$$= W\frac{a^2 + b^2 - 2ab}{ab} = W\frac{(a - b)^2}{ab}.$$

Now, whatever be the values of a and b, the right-hand member of this equation is always positive, so that $W_1 + W_2$ is always $> 2W$. Hence the tradesman defrauds himself.

Numerical example. If the lengths of the arms be 11 and 12 ins. respectively, and if the nominal quantity weighed be 66 lbs. in each case, the real quantities are $\frac{11}{12}\,.\,66$ and $\frac{12}{11}\,.\,66$, *i.e.*, $60\frac{1}{2}$ and 72, *i.e.*, $132\frac{1}{2}$ lbs., so that the tradesman loses $\frac{1}{2}$ lb.

Ex. 3. *If a balance be unjustly weighted, and have unequal arms, and if a tradesman weigh out to a customer a quantity $2W$ of some substance by weighing equal portions in the two scale-pans, shew that he will defraud himself if the centre of gravity of the beam be in the longer arm.*

Let a and b be the lengths of the arms; and let the weight W' of the machine act at a point in the arm b at a distance x from the fulcrum. Let a body of weight W, placed in the two pans in succession, be balanced by W_1 and W_2 respectively. Then we have

$$W \cdot a = W_1 \cdot b + W' \cdot x,$$

and
$$W_2 \cdot a = W \cdot b + W' \cdot x.$$

$$\therefore W_1 + W_2 - 2W = \frac{W \cdot a - W' \cdot x}{b} + \frac{W \cdot b + W' \cdot x}{a} - 2W$$

$$= \frac{W(b-a)^2}{ab} + W'\frac{b-a}{ab}x.$$

If b be $> a$, the right-hand member of this equation is positive, and then
$$W_1 + W_2 \text{ is } > 2W.$$

Hence, if the centre of gravity of the beam be in the longer arm, the tradesman will defraud himself.

EXAMPLES. XXVIII.

1. The only fault in a balance being the unequalness in weight of the scale-pans, what is the real weight of a body which balances 10 lbs. when placed in one scale-pan, and 12 lbs. when placed in the other?

2. The arms of a balance are $8\frac{3}{4}$ and 9 ins. respectively, the goods to be weighed being suspended from the longer arm; find the real weight of goods whose apparent weight is 27 lbs.

3. One scale of a common balance is loaded so that the apparent weight of a body, whose true weight is 18 ounces, is 20 ounces; find the weight with which the scale is loaded.

4. A substance, weighed from the two arms successively of a balance, has apparent weights 9 and 4 lbs. Find the ratio of the lengths of the arms and the true weight of the body.

5. A body, when placed in one scale-pan, appears to weigh 24 lbs. and, when placed in the other, 25 lbs. Find its true weight to three places of decimals, assuming the arms of the scale-pans to be of unequal length.

6. A piece of lead in one pan A of a balance is counterpoised by 100 grains in the pan B; when the same piece of lead is put into the pan B it requires 104 grains in A to balance it; what is the ratio of the length of the arms of the balance?

7. A body, placed in a scale-pan, is balanced by 10 lbs. placed in the other pan; when the position of the body and the weights are interchanged, 11 lbs. are required to balance the body. If the length of the shorter arm be 12 ins., find the length of the longer arm and the weight of the body.

8. The arms of a false balance, whose weight is neglected, are in the ratio of 10 : 9. If goods be alternately weighed from each arm, shew that the seller loses $\frac{5}{9}$ths per cent.

9. If the arms of a false balance be 8 and 9 ins. long respectively, find the prices really paid by a person for tea at two shillings per lb., if the tea be weighed out from the end of (1) the longer, (2) the shorter arm.

10. A dealer has correct weights, but one arm of his balance is $\frac{1}{20}$th part shorter than the other. If he sell two quantities of a certain drug, each apparently weighing $9\frac{1}{2}$ lbs., at 40s. per lb., weighing one in one scale and the other in the other, what will he gain or lose ?

11. When a given balance is loaded with equal weights, it is found that the beam is not horizontal, but it is not known whether the arms are of unequal length, or the scale-pans of unequal weight; 51·075 grains in one scale balance 51·362 in the other, and 25·592 grains balance 25·879 grains ; shew that the arms are equal, but that the scale-pans differ in weight by ·287 grains.

12. P and Q balance on a common balance; on interchanging them it is found that we must add to Q one-hundredth part of itself; what is the ratio of the arms and the ratio of P to Q?

13. A true balance has one scale unjustly loaded ; if a body be successively weighed in the two scales and appear to weigh P and Q pounds respectively, find the amount of the unjust load and also the true weight of the body.

14. The arms of a false balance are unequal and the scale loaded ; a body, whose true weight is P lbs., appears to weigh w lbs. when placed in one scale and w' lbs. when placed in the other ; find the ratio of the arms and the weight with which the scale is loaded.

15. In a loaded balance with unequal arms, P appears to weigh Q, and Q appears to weigh R ; find what R appears to weigh.

16. A piece of wood in the form of a long wedge, of uniform width, one end being $\frac{1}{2}$-inch and the other $\frac{1}{4}$-inch thick, is suspended by its centre of gravity and used as the beam of a balance, the goods to be weighed being suspended from the longer arm ; find the true weight of goods whose apparent weight is 20 lbs.

17. The arms of a false balance are a and b, and a weight W balances P at the end of the shorter arm b, and Q at the end of the arm a ; shew that

$$\frac{a}{b} = \frac{P - W}{W - Q}.$$

18. If a man, sitting in one scale of a weighing-machine, press with a stick against any point of the beam between the point from which the scale is suspended and the fulcrum, shew that he will appear to weigh more than before.

VI. The Steelyards.

171. The **Common**, or Roman, Steelyard is a machine for weighing bodies and consists of a rod, AB, movable about a fixed fulcrum at a point C.

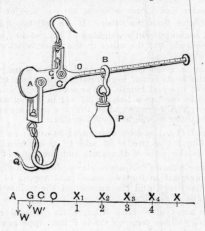

At the point A is attached a hook or scale-pan to carry the body to be weighed, and on the arm CB slides a movable weight P. The point at which P must be placed, in order that the beam may rest in a horizontal position, determines the weight of the body in the scale-pan. The arm CB has numbers engraved on it at different points of its length, so that the graduation at which the weight P rests gives the weight of the body.

172. *To graduate the Steelyard.* Let W' be the weight of the steelyard and the scale-pan, and let G be the point of the beam through which W' acts. The beam is usually constructed so that G lies in the shorter arm AC.

When there is no weight in the scale-pan, let O be the point in CB at which the movable weight P must be placed to balance W'.

Taking moments about C, we have

$$W' \cdot GC = P \cdot CO \dots\dots\dots\dots(i).$$

This condition determines the position of the point O which is the zero of graduation.

When the weight in the scale-pan is W, let X be the point at which P must be placed. Taking moments, we have

$$W \cdot CA + W' \cdot GC = P \cdot CX \dots\dots\dots(ii).$$

By subtracting equation (i) from equation (ii), we have

$$W \cdot CA = P \cdot OX.$$

$$\therefore OX = \frac{W}{P} \cdot CA \dots\dots\dots\dots(iii).$$

First, let $W = P$; then, by (iii), we have

$$OX = CA.$$

Hence, if from O we measure off a distance $OX_1 (= CA)$, and if we mark the point X_1 with the figure 1, then, when the movable weight rests here, the body in the scale-pan is P lbs.

Secondly, let $W = 2P$; then, from (iii), $OX = 2CA$.

Hence from O mark off a distance $2CA$, and at the extremity put the figure 2. Thirdly, let $W = 3P$; then, from (iii), $OX = 3CA$, and we therefore mark off a distance from O equal to $3CA$, and mark the extremity with the figure 3.

Hence, to graduate the steelyard, we must mark off from O successive distances CA, $2CA$, $3CA$,... and at their extremities put the figures 1, 2, 3, 4,.... The intermediate spaces can be subdivided to shew fractions of P lbs.

If the movable weight be 1 lb., the graduations will shew pounds.

Cor. Since the distances between successive graduations are equal, it follows that the distances of the points of graduations from the fulcrum, corresponding to equal increments of weight, form an arithmetical progression whose common difference is the distance between the fulcrum and the point at which the body to be weighed is attached.

173. When the centre of gravity G of the machine is in the longer arm, the point O from which the graduations are to be measured must lie in the shorter arm. The theory will be the same as before, except that in this case we shall have to add the equations (i) and (ii).

174. The **Danish** steelyard consists of a bar AB, terminating in a heavy knob, or ball, B. At A is attached a hook or scale-pan to carry the body to be weighed.

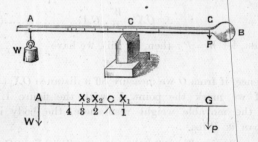

The weight of the body is determined by observing about what point of the bar the machine balances.

[This is often done by having a loop of string, which can slide along the bar, and finding where the loop must be to give equilibrium.]

175. *To graduate the Danish steelyard.* Let P be the weight of the bar and scale-pan, and let G be their common centre of gravity. When a body of weight W is placed in the scale-pan, let C be the position of the fulcrum.

By taking moments about C, we have
$$AC \cdot W = CG \cdot P = (AG - AC) \cdot P.$$
$$\therefore \ AC (P + W) = P \cdot AG.$$
$$\therefore \ AC = \frac{P}{P + W} \cdot AG \ \dots\dots\dots\dots\dots(i).$$

First, let $W = P$; then $AC = \frac{1}{2}AG$.

Hence bisect AG and at the middle point, X_1, engrave the figure 1; when the steelyard balances about this point the weight of the body in the scale-pan is P.

Secondly, let $W = 2P$; then $AC = \frac{1}{3}AG$.

Take a point at a distance from A equal to $\frac{1}{3}AG$ and mark it 2.

Next, let W in succession be equal to $3P$, $4P$, ...; from (i), the corresponding values of AC are $\frac{1}{4}AG$, $\frac{1}{5}AG$, ... Take points of the bar at these distances from A and mark them 3, 4, ...

Finally, let $W = \frac{1}{2}P$; then, from (i), $AC = \frac{2}{3}AG$;
and let $W = \frac{1}{3}P$; then, from (i), $AC = \frac{3}{4}AG$.

Take points whose distances from A are $\frac{2}{3}AG$, $\frac{3}{4}AG$, $\frac{4}{5}AG$, ..., and mark them $\frac{1}{2}$, $\frac{1}{3}$, $\frac{1}{4}$, ...

It will be noticed that the point G can be easily determined; for it is the position of the fulcrum when the steelyard balances without any weight in the scale-pan.

Cor. Since AX_1, AX_2, AX_3, ... are inversely proportional to the numbers 2, 3, 4, ... they form an harmonical progression; hence the distances of the points of graduation from the scale-pan (corresponding to equal increments of the body to be weighed) are in harmonical progression.

Ex. *A Danish steelyard weighs 6 lbs., and the distance of its centre of gravity from the scale-pan is 3 feet; find the distances of the successive points of graduation from the fulcrum.*

Taking the notation of the preceding article, we have $P = 6$, and $AG = 3$ feet.
$$\therefore \ AC = \frac{6}{6 + W} \times 3 = \frac{18}{W + 6} \text{ feet.}$$

$$\therefore \text{ when } W=1,\ AX_1=\tfrac{18}{7}=2\tfrac{4}{7} \text{ feet,}$$
$$\text{when } W=2,\ AX_2=\tfrac{18}{8}=2\tfrac{1}{4} \text{ feet,}$$
$$\text{when } W=3,\ AX_3=\tfrac{18}{9}=2 \text{ feet,}$$

....

$$\text{when } W=\tfrac{1}{2},\ AX_{\frac{1}{2}}=\frac{18}{\tfrac{1}{2}+6}=2\tfrac{10}{13} \text{ feet,}$$

and so on.

These give the required graduations.

EXAMPLES. XXIX.

1. A common steelyard weighs 10 lbs.; the weight is suspended from a point 4 inches from the fulcrum, and the centre of gravity of the steelyard is 3 inches on the other side of the fulcrum; the movable weight is 12 lbs.; where should the graduation corresponding to 1 cwt. be situated?

2. A heavy tapering rod, $14\tfrac{1}{2}$ inches long and of weight 3 lbs., has its centre of gravity $1\tfrac{2}{3}$ inches from the thick end and is used as a steelyard with a movable weight of 2 lbs.; where must the fulcrum be placed, so that it may weigh up to 12 lbs., and what are the intervals between the graduations that denote pounds?

3. In a steelyard, in which the distance of the fulcrum from the point of suspension of the weight is one inch and the movable weight is 6 ozs., to weigh 15 lbs. the weight must be placed 8 inches from the fulcrum; where must it be placed to weigh 24 lbs.?

4. The fulcrum is distant $1\tfrac{1}{3}$ inches from the point at which are suspended the goods to be weighed, and is distant 2 inches from the centre of gravity of the bar; the bar itself weighs 3 lbs. and a 2 lb. weight slides on it. At what distance apart are the graduations marking successive pounds' weight, and what is the least weight that can be weighed?

5. A steelyard, AB, 4 feet long, has its centre of gravity 11 inches, and its fulcrum 8 inches, from A. If the weight of the machine be 4 lbs. and the movable weight be 3 lbs., find how many inches from B is the graduation marking 15 lbs.

6. A uniform bar, AB, 2 feet long and weighing 3 lbs., is used as a steelyard, being supported at a point 4 inches from A. Find the greatest weight that can be weighed with a movable weight of 2 lbs., and find also the point from which the graduations are measured.

7. A uniform rod being divided into 20 equal parts, the fulcrum is placed at the first graduation. The greatest and least weights which the instrument can weigh are 20 and 2 lbs.; find its weight and the magnitude of the movable weight.

8. A uniform rod, 2 feet long and of weight 3 lbs., is used as a steelyard, whose fulcrum is 2 inches from one end, the sliding weight being 1 lb. Find the greatest and the least weights that can be measured.

Where should the sliding weight be to shew 20 lbs.?

9. The beam of a steelyard is 33 inches in length; the fulcrum is distant 4 inches and the centre of gravity of the beam $5\frac{1}{3}$ inches from the point of attachment of the weight; if the weight of the beam be 6 lbs. and the heaviest weight that can be weighed be 24 lbs., find the magnitude of the movable weight.

10. A steelyard is formed of a uniform bar, 3 feet long and weighing $2\frac{1}{4}$ lbs., and the fulcrum is distant 4 inches from one end; if the movable weight be 1 lb., find the greatest and least weights that can be weighed by the machine and the distance between the graduations when it is graduated to shew pounds.

11. A common steelyard, supposed uniform, is 40 inches long, the weight of the beam is equal to the movable weight, and the greatest weight that can be weighed by it is four times the movable weight; find the position of the fulcrum.

12. In a Danish steelyard the distance between the zero graduation and the end of the instrument is divided into 20 equal parts and the greatest weight that can be weighed is 3 lbs. 9 ozs.; find the weight of the instrument.

13. Find the length of the graduated arm of a Danish steelyard, whose weight is 1 lb., and in which the distance between the graduations denoting 4 and 5 lbs. is one inch.

14. In a Danish steelyard the fulcrum rests halfway between the first and second graduation; shew that the weight in the scale-pan is $\frac{7}{5}$ths of the weight of the bar.

15. If the weight of a steelyard be worn away to one-half, its length and centre of gravity remaining unaltered, what corrections must be applied to make the weighing true, if the distance of the zero point of graduation from the fulcrum were originally one-third of the distance between successive graduations, and if the movable weight be one pound?

16. A steelyard by use loses $\frac{1}{10}$th of its weight, its centre of gravity remaining unaltered; shew how to correct its graduations.

17. A shopman, using a common steelyard, alters the movable weight for which it has been graduated; does he cheat himself or his customers?

18. In a weighing machine constructed on the principle of a common steelyard, the pounds are read off by graduations reading from 0 to 14 lbs., and the stones by a weight hung at the end of the arm; if the weight corresponding to one stone be 7 ounces, the movable weight $\frac{1}{2}$ lb., and the length of the arm measured from the fulcrum 1 foot, shew that the distance between successive graduations is $\frac{3}{4}$ inch.

19. A weighing machine is constructed so that for each complete stone placed in the weighing pan an additional mass of m ounces has to be placed at the end of the arm, which is one foot in length measured from the fulcrum, whilst the odd pounds in the weighing pan are measured by a mass of n ounces sliding along the weighing arm. Shew that the distances between the graduations for successive lbs. must be $\frac{6m}{7n}$ inches, and that the distance from the fulcrum of the point of suspension of the weight is $\frac{3m}{56}$ inches.

VII. The Screw.

176. A Screw consists of a cylinder of metal round the outside of which runs a protuberant thread of metal.

Let $ABCD$ be a solid cylinder, and let $EFGH$ be a

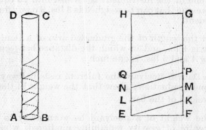

rectangle, whose base EF is equal to the circumference of the solid cylinder. On EH and FG take points

$$L, N, Q... \quad \text{and} \quad K, M, P...$$

such that $\quad EL, LN,...FK, KM, MP ...$
are all equal, and join $EK, LM, NP,....$

Wrap the rectangle round the cylinder, so that the point E coincides with A and EH with the line AD. On being wrapped round the cylinder the point F will coincide with E at A.

The lines EK, LM, NP, ... will now become a continuous spiral line on the surface of the cylinder and, if we imagine the metal along this spiral line to become protuberant, we shall have the thread of a screw.

It is evident, by the method of construction, that the thread is an inclined plane running round the cylinder and that its inclination to the horizon is the same everywhere and equal to the angle KEF. This angle is often called the **angle of the screw**, and the distance between two consecutive threads, measured parallel to the axis, is called the **pitch** of the screw.

It is clear that FK is equal to the distance between consecutive threads on the screw, and that EF is equal to the circumference of the cylinder on which the thread is traced.

$$\therefore \ \tan(\text{angle of screw}) = \frac{FK}{EF}$$

$$= \frac{\text{pitch of screw}}{\text{circumference of a circle whose radius is the distance from the axis of any point of the screw.}}$$

The section of the thread of the screw has, in practice, various shapes. The only kind that we shall consider has the section rectangular.

177. The screw usually works in a fixed support, along the inside of which is cut out a hollow of the same shape as the thread of the screw, and along which the thread slides. The only movement admissible to the screw is to revolve about its axis, and at the same time to move in a direction parallel to its length.

If the screw were placed in an upright position, and a weight placed on its top, the screw would revolve and descend since there is supposed to be no friction between it and its support. Hence, if the screw is to remain in equilibrium, some force must act on it; this force is usually applied at one end of a horizontal arm, the other end of which is rigidly attached to the screw.

178. *In a smooth screw, to find the relation between the effort and the weight.*

Let a be the distance of any point on the thread of the screw from its axis, and b the distance, AB, from the axis of the screw, of the point at which the effort is applied.

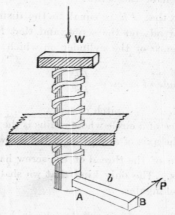

The screw is in equilibrium under the action of the effort P, the weight W, and the reactions at the points in which the fixed block touches the thread of the screw. Let $R, S, T, \ldots$ denote the reactions of the block at different points of the thread of the screw. These will be all perpendicular to the thread of the screw, since it is smooth.

Let a be the inclination of the thread of the screw to the horizon.

The horizontal and vertical components of the reaction R are $R \sin a$ and $R \cos a$ respectively.

Similarly, we may resolve S, T, ...

Hence the reactions of the block are equivalent to a set of forces $R \cos a$, $S \cos a$, $T \cos a$, ... vertically, and a set $R \sin a$, $S \sin a$, $T \sin a$, ... horizontally. These latter forces, though they act at different points of the screw, all act at the same distance

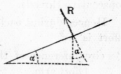

from the axis of the screw; they also tend to turn the screw in the opposite direction to that of P.

Equating the vertical forces, we have

$$W = R \cos a + S \cos a + \ldots = (R + S + T + \ldots) \cos a \ldots (1).$$

Also, taking moments about the axis of the screw, we have, by Art. 93,

$$P \cdot b = R \sin a \cdot a + S \sin a \cdot a + T \sin a \cdot a + \ldots$$
$$= a \sin a \, (R + S + T + \ldots) \ldots\ldots\ldots\ldots\ldots (2).$$

From equations (1) and (2) we have, by division,

$$\frac{P \cdot b}{W} = \frac{a \sin a}{\cos a},$$

$$\therefore \frac{P}{W} = \frac{a}{b} \tan a = \frac{2\pi a \tan a}{2\pi b}.$$

But, by Art. 176,

$2\pi a \tan a =$ distance between consecutive threads $=$ pitch of the screw.

15—2

Also $2\pi b$ = circumference of the circle described by the end B of the effort-arm.

Hence the mechanical advantage $= \dfrac{W}{P} = \dfrac{2\pi b}{2\pi a \tan \alpha}$

$$= \frac{\text{circumference of a circle whose radius is the effort-arm}}{\text{distance between consecutive threads of the screw}}.$$

Verification of the Principle of Work.

For each revolution made by the effort-arm the screw rises through a distance equal to the distance between two consecutive threads.

Hence, during each revolution, the work done by the effort is

P × circumference of the circle described by the end of the effort-arm,

and that done against the weight is

W × distance between two consecutive threads.

These are equal by the relation just proved.

*179. Theoretically, the mechanical advantage in the case of the screw can be made as large as we please, by decreasing sufficiently the distance between the threads of the screw. In practice, however, this is impossible; for, if we diminish the distance between the threads to too small a quantity, the threads themselves would not be sufficiently strong to bear the strain put upon them.

By means of **Hunter's Differential Screw** this difficulty may be overcome.

In this machine we have a screw AD working in a fixed block. The inside of the screw AD is hollow and is grooved to admit a smaller screw DE. The screw DE is fastened at E to a block, so that it cannot rotate, but can only move in the direction of its length.

When the effort-arm AB has made one revolution, the screw AD has advanced a distance equal to the distance between two consecutive threads, and at the same time the smaller screw goes into DA a distance equal

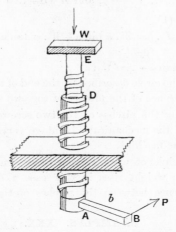

to the distance between two consecutive threads of the smaller screw. Hence the smaller screw, and therefore also the weight, advances a distance equal to the *difference* of these two distances.

When in equilibrium let R, S, T, ... be the reactions between the larger screw and its block, and R', S', T', ... the reactions between the inner and outer screws; let a and a' be the radii, and a and a' the angles of the screws.

As in the last article, since the outer screw is in equilibrium, we have

$$P \cdot b = (R + S + T + ...) \sin a \cdot a - (R' + S' + ...) \sin a' \cdot a'$$
$$\dots\dots\dots(1),$$

and $(R + S + T + ...) \cos a = (R' + S' + ...) \cos a' \dots(2).$

Also, since the inner screw is in equilibrium, we have
$$W = (R' + S' + T' \ldots) \cos \alpha' \ldots\ldots\ldots\ldots\ldots(3).$$

From (2) and (3), we have
$$R' + S' + \ldots = \frac{W}{\cos \alpha'}, \text{ and } R + S + \ldots = \frac{W}{\cos \alpha}.$$

Hence, from (1),
$$P \cdot b = W \cdot a \tan \alpha - W \cdot a' \tan \alpha'.$$

$$\therefore \frac{W}{P} = \frac{2\pi b}{2\pi a \tan \alpha - 2\pi a' \tan \alpha'}$$

$$= \frac{\text{circum. of the circle described by the end of the power-arm}}{\text{difference of the pitches of the two screws}}.$$

By making the pitches of the two screws nearly equal,
we can make the mechanical advantage very great without
weakening the machine.

The principle of work is seen to be true in this case
also; for the weight rises in this case a distance equal
to the difference between the pitches of the screws.

EXAMPLES. XXX.

1. Find what mass can be lifted by a smooth vertical screw of
$1\frac{1}{2}$ ins. pitch, if the power be a force of 25 lbs. wt. acting at the end of
an arm, $3\frac{1}{2}$ feet long.

2. What must be the length of the power-arm of a screw, having
6 threads to the inch, so that the mechanical advantage may be 216?

3. What force applied to the end of an arm, 18 ins. long, will
produce a pressure of 1100 lbs. wt. upon the head of a screw, when
seven turns cause the screw to advance through $\frac{2}{3}$ rds of an inch?

4. A screw, whose pitch is $\frac{1}{4}$ inch, is turned by means of a lever,
4 feet long; find the force which will raise 15 cwt.

5. The arm of a screw-jack is 1 yard long, and the screw has
2 threads to the inch. What force must be applied to the arm to
raise 1 ton?

6. What is the thrust caused by a screw, having 4 threads to the
inch, when a force of 50 lbs. wt. is applied to the end of an arm, 2 feet
long?

7. What thrust will a screw, whose arm is 2 feet and with 10 threads per foot of its length, produce, if the effort be a force of 112 lbs. weight?

8. If the effort be applied at the end of an arm of 1 foot in length, and if the screw make seven complete turns in 1 foot of its length, find the effort that will support a weight of 1 ton.

9. If the lever by which a screw is worked be 6 feet in length, determine the distance between two successive threads of the screw, in order that a thrust of 10 lbs. wt. applied to each end of the lever may produce a thrust of 1000 lbs. wt. at the end of the screw.

10. Find the mechanical advantage in a differential screw, having 5 threads to the inch and 6 threads to the inch, the effort being applied at the circumference of a wheel of diameter 4 feet.

11. Find the mechanical advantage in a differential screw, the larger screw having 8 threads to the inch and the smaller 9 threads, the length of the effort-arm being 1 foot.

12. If the axis of a screw be vertical and the distance between the threads 2 inches, and a door, of weight 100 lbs., be attached to the screw as to a hinge, find the work done in turning the door through a right angle.

13. Prove that the tension of a stay is equal to 9 tons' weight if it be set up by a force of 49 lbs. at a leverage of 2 feet acting on a double screw having a right-handed screw of 5 threads to the inch and a left-handed one of 6 threads to the inch.

[For one complete turn of the screw its ends are brought nearer by a distance of $(\frac{1}{5} + \frac{1}{6})$ inch. Hence the principle of work gives

$$T \times (\tfrac{1}{5} + \tfrac{1}{6}) \times \tfrac{1}{12} = 49 \times 2\pi \cdot 2,$$

where T is the tension of the stay in lbs. wt.]

CHAPTER XIII.

FRICTION.

180. In Art. 20 we defined smooth bodies to be bodies such that, if they be in contact, the only action between them is perpendicular to both surfaces at the point of contact. With smooth bodies, therefore, there is no force tending to prevent one body sliding over the other. If a perfectly smooth body be placed on a perfectly smooth inclined plane, there is no action between the plane and the body to prevent the latter from sliding down the plane, and hence the body will not remain at rest on the plane unless some external force be applied to it.

Practically, however, there are no bodies which are perfectly smooth; there is always *some* force between two bodies in contact to prevent one sliding upon the other. Such a force is called the force of friction.

Friction. Def. *If two bodies be in contact with one another, the property of the two bodies, by virtue of which a force is exerted between them at their point of contact to prevent one body sliding on the other, is called friction; also the force exerted is called the force of friction.*

181. Friction is a self-adjusting force; no more friction is called into play than is sufficient to prevent motion.

Let a heavy slab of iron with a plane base be placed on a horizontal table. If we attach a piece of string to some point of the body, and pull in a horizontal direction passing through the centre of gravity of the slab, a resistance is felt which prevents our moving the body; this resistance is exactly equal to the force which we exert on the body.

If we now stop pulling, the force of friction also ceases to act; for, if the force of friction did not cease to act, the body would move.

The amount of friction which can be exerted between two bodies is not, however, unlimited. If we continually increase the force which we exert on the slab, we find that finally the friction is not sufficient to overcome this force, and the body moves.

182. Friction plays an important part in the mechanical problems of ordinary life. If there were no friction between our boots and the ground, we should not be able to walk; if there were no friction between a ladder and the ground, the ladder would not rest, unless held, in any position inclined to the vertical; without friction nails and screws would not remain in wood, nor would a locomotive engine be able to draw a train.

183. The laws of statical friction are as follows:

Law I. *When two bodies are in contact, the direction of the friction on one of them at its point of contact is opposite to the direction in which this point of contact would commence to move.*

Law II. *The magnitude of the friction is, when there is equilibrium, just sufficient to prevent the body from moving.*

184. Suppose, in Art. 156, Case I., the plane to be rough, and that the body, instead of being supported by a force, rested freely on the plane. In this case the force P is replaced by the friction, which is therefore equal to $W \sin \alpha$.

Ex. 1. In what direction does the force of friction act in the case of (1) the wheel of a carriage, (2) the feet of a man who is walking?

Ex. 2. A body, of weight 30 lbs., rests on a rough horizontal plane and is acted upon by a force, equal to 10 lbs. wt., making an angle of 30° with the horizontal; shew that the force of friction is equal to about 8·66 lbs. wt.

Ex. 3. A body, resting on a rough horizontal plane, is acted on by two horizontal forces, equal respectively to 7 and 8 lbs. wt., and acting at an angle of 60°; shew that the force of friction is equal to 13 lbs. wt. in a direction making an angle $\sin^{-1}\dfrac{4\sqrt{3}}{13}$ with the first force.

Ex. 4. A body, of weight 40 lbs., rests on a rough plane inclined at 30° to the horizon, and is supported by (1) a force of 14 lbs. wt. acting up the plane, (2) a force of 25 lbs. acting up the plane, (3) a horizontal force equal to 20 lbs. wt., (4) a force equal to 30 lbs. wt. making an angle of 30° with the plane.

Find the force of friction in each case.

Ans. (1) 6 lbs. wt. up the plane; (2) 5 lbs. wt. down the plane; (3) 2·68 lbs. wt. up the plane; (4) 5·98 lbs. wt. down the plane.

185. The above laws hold good, in general; but the amount of friction that can be exerted is limited, and equilibrium is sometimes on the point of being destroyed, and motion often ensues.

Limiting Friction. Def. *When one body is just on the point of sliding upon another body, the equilibrium is said to be limiting, and the friction then exerted is called limiting friction.*

186. The direction of the limiting friction is given by Law I. (Art. 183).

The magnitude of the limiting friction is given by the three following laws.

Law III. *The magnitude of the limiting friction always bears a constant ratio to the normal reaction, and this ratio depends only on the substances of which the bodies are composed.*

Law IV. *The limiting friction is independent of the extent and shape of the surfaces in contact, so long as the normal reaction is unaltered.*

Law V. *When motion ensues, by one body sliding over the other, the direction of friction is opposite to the direction of motion; the magnitude of the friction is independent of the velocity, but the ratio of the friction to the normal reaction is slightly less than when the body is at rest and just on the point of motion.*

The above laws are experimental, and cannot be accepted as rigorously accurate, though they represent, however, to a fair degree of accuracy the facts under ordinary conditions.

For example, if one body be pressed so closely on another that the surfaces in contact are on the point of being crushed, Law III. is no longer true; the friction then increases at a greater rate than the normal reaction.

187. Coefficient of Friction. The constant ratio of the limiting friction to the normal pressure is called the coefficient of friction, and is generally denoted by μ; hence, if F be the friction, and R the normal pressure, between two bodies when equilibrium is on the point of being destroyed, we have $\dfrac{F}{R} = \mu$, and hence $F = \mu R$.

The values of μ are widely different for different pairs of substances in contact; no pairs of substances are, however, known for which the coefficient of friction is as great as unity.

188. *To verify the laws of friction by experiment.*

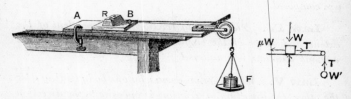

Experiment 1. Take a large smooth piece of wood (A) and clamp it firmly so as to be horizontal. Take a second piece of wood (B) to act as a sliding piece and make it as smooth as possible; attach a light string to it and pass the string over a light pulley fixed at the end of the piece A, and at the other end of the string attach a scale-pan.

The pulley should be so placed that the part of the string, which is not vertical, should be horizontal.

Upon the sliding piece put a known weight R, and into the scale-pan put known weights, F, until the slider is just on the point of motion. The required weight F can be very approximately ascertained by gently tapping the fixed piece A.

Consider now the right-hand diagram.

Let W be the total weight of R and the sliding piece, and W' the total weight of F and the scale-pan. Since the slider is just on the point of motion the friction on it is μW; also the tension T of the string is equal to W', since it just balances the scale-pan and F.

From the equilibrium of the slider we have

$$\mu W = T = W'.$$
$$\therefore \ \mu = \frac{W'}{W}.$$

Next, put a different weight on the slider, and adjust the corresponding weight F until the slider is again on the point of motion and calculate the new values, W_1 and W_1', of W and W'. Then, as before,

$$\mu = \frac{W_1'}{W_1}.$$

Perform the experiment again with different weights on the slider and obtain the values of

$$\frac{W_2'}{W_2}, \quad \frac{W_3'}{W_3}, \ \dots$$

Then, approximately, it will be found that
$$\frac{W'}{W}, \quad \frac{W_1'}{W_1}, \quad \frac{W_2'}{W_2}, \ldots$$
will be the same.

Hence the truth of the first part of Law III. viz. that *the value of μ is independent of the normal reaction.*

Experiment 2. Take another piece of wood (B) whose shape is quite different from the piece used in Experiment 1. [This should be obtained by cutting it from the same piece of well-planed wood from which the first piece B was taken.]

The area of this piece B in contact with the board A should differ considerably from that in Experiment 1, whether greater or less is immaterial.

Perform the Experiment 1 over again and deduce the corresponding value of μ. It will be found to be, within the limits of experiment, the same as in Experiment 1. But the only difference in the two experiments is the extent of the rough surfaces in contact.

Hence the truth of Law IV.

Experiment 3. Take another piece of a different kind of wood (C) and plane it well. Cut out from it pieces, of different area, but with surfaces otherwise as nearly alike as possible.

Perform Experiments 1 and 2 over again and obtain the value of μ. This value of μ will be found to differ from the value of μ found when the slider was made of wood B. Hence the truth of the second part of Law III. viz. that *the ratio depends on the substances of which the bodies are composed.*

Experiment 4. Perform the above three experiments over again but in this case choose F not so that the slider shall just be on the point of motion, but so that *the slider shall move with a constant velocity.* The truth of Law V. will then approximately appear.

However carefully the surfaces of the wood used in the previous experiments be prepared, the student must expect to find some considerable discrepancies in the actual numerical results obtained. There must also be applied a correction for the force necessary to make the pulley turn. However light and well-made it may be, there will always be a certain amount of friction on its axis. Hence the tensions of the string on each side of it will not quite be equal, as we have assumed; in other words some part of F will be used in turning the pulley.

This method is the one used by Morin in A.D. 1833.

189. Angle of Friction. When the equilibrium is limiting, if the friction and the normal reaction be compounded into one single force, the angle which this force makes with the normal is called the angle of friction, and the single force is called the resultant reaction.

Let A be the point of contact of the two bodies, and let AB and AC be the directions of the normal force R and the friction μR.

Let AD be the direction of the resultant reaction S, so that the angle of friction is BAD. Let this angle be λ.

Since R and μR are the components of S, we have

$$S \cos \lambda = R,$$

and $\qquad S \sin \lambda = \mu R.$

Hence, by squaring and adding, we have

$$S = R \sqrt{1 + \mu^2},$$

and, by division,

$$\tan \lambda = \mu,$$

Hence we see that *the coefficient of friction is equal to the tangent of the angle of friction.*

190. Since the greatest value of the friction is μR, it follows that the greatest angle which the direction of resultant reaction can make with the normal is λ, *i.e.*, $\tan^{-1} \mu$.

Hence, if two bodies be in contact and if, with the common normal as axis, and the point of contact as vertex, we describe a cone whose semi-vertical angle is $\tan^{-1} \mu$, it is possible for the resultant reaction to have any direction lying within, or upon, this cone, but it cannot have any direction lying without the cone.

This cone is called the **Cone of friction.**

191. The following table, taken from Prof. Rankine's *Machinery and Millwork*, gives the coefficients and angles of friction for a few substances.

SUBSTANCES		μ	λ
Wood on wood	—Dry	·25 to ·5	$14°$ to $26\frac{1}{2}°$
,, ,, ,,	—Soaped	·04 to ·2	$2°$ to $11\frac{1}{2}°$
Metals on metals	—Dry	·15 to ·2	$8\frac{1}{2}°$ to $11\frac{1}{2}°$
,, ,, ,,	—Wet	·3	$16\frac{1}{2}°$
Leather on metals	—Dry	·56	$29\frac{1}{2}°$
,, ,, ,,	—Wet	·36	$20°$
,, ,, ,,	—Oily	·15	$8\frac{1}{2}°$

192. *If a body be placed upon a rough inclined plane,
and be on the point of sliding down the plane under the
action of its weight and the reactions of the plane* only, *the
angle of inclination of the plane to the horizon is equal to
the angle of friction.*

Let θ be the inclination of the plane to the horizon, W
the weight of the body, and R
the normal reaction.

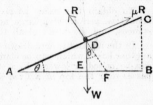

Since the body is on the
point of motion *down* the
plane, the friction acts *up*
the plane and is equal to μR.

Resolving perpendicular
and parallel to the plane, we
have

$$W \cos \theta = R,$$

and $$W \sin \theta = \mu R.$$

Hence, by division,

$$\tan \theta = \mu = \tan \text{ (angle of friction)},$$

$$\therefore \ \theta = \text{the angle of friction}.$$

This may be shewn otherwise thus:

Since the body is in equilibrium under the action of its weight and
the resultant reaction, the latter must be vertical; but, since the
equilibrium is limiting, the resultant reaction makes with the normal
the angle of friction.

Hence the angle between the normal and the vertical is the angle
of friction, *i.e.,* the inclination of the plane to the horizon is the angle
of friction.

On account of the property just proved the angle of
friction is sometimes called the angle of repose.

The student must carefully notice that, when the body
rests on the inclined plane *supported by an external force*, it
must not be assumed that the coefficient of friction is equal
to the tangent of inclination of the plane to the horizon.

193. *To determine the coefficient of friction experimentally, and to verify the laws of friction.* [Second Method.]

By means of the theorem of the previous article the coefficient of friction between two bodies may be experimentally obtained.

For let an inclined plane be made of one of the substances and let its face be made as smooth as is possible; on this face let there be placed a slab, having a plane face, composed of the other substance.

If the angle of inclination of the plane be gradually increased, until the slab *just* slides, the tangent of the angle of inclination is the co-efficient of friction.

To obtain the result as accurately as possible, the experiment should be performed a large number of times with the same substances, and the mean of all the results taken.

In the apparatus here drawn we have a board hinged at one end to another board which can be clamped to the table. The hinged board can be raised or lowered by a string attached to it whose other end passes over the top of a fixed support.

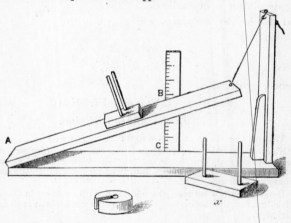

On the hinged board can be placed sliders of different sizes and materials upon which various weights can be placed. Each slider x has two thin brass rods screwed to it on which weights can be piled so that they shall not slip during the experiment. A graduated vertical scale is attached to the lower board, so that the height of the hinged board at B is easily seen. The value of $\dfrac{BC}{AC}$, *i.e.*, tan θ of Art. 185, is then easily obtained.

By this apparatus the laws of friction can be verified; for, within the limits of experiment, it will be found that the value of $\dfrac{BC}{AC}$, *i.e.*, μ,

(1) is always the same so long as the slide x is made of the same material in the same state of preparedness of surface,

(2) is independent of the weights put upon the slide, or of its shape,

(3) is different for different substances.

This method is the one used by Coulomb in the year 1785.

194. Equilibrium on a rough inclined plane.

A body is placed on a rough plane inclined to the horizon at an angle greater than the angle of friction, and is supported by a force, acting parallel to the plane, and along a line of greatest slope; to find the limits between which the force must lie.

Let a be the inclination of the plane to the horizon, W the weight of the body, and R the normal reaction (Fig. I., Art. 156).

(i) Let the body be on the point of motion *down* the plane, so that the friction acts *up* the plane and is equal to μR; let P be the force required to keep the body at rest.

Resolving parallel and perpendicular to the plane, we have

$$P + \mu R = W \sin a \quad \dots\dots\dots\dots(1),$$
and
$$R = W \cos a \quad \dots\dots\dots\dots(2).$$
$$\therefore \ P = W (\sin a - \mu \cos a).$$

If $\mu = \tan \lambda$, we have

$$P = W [\sin a - \tan \lambda \cos a]$$
$$= W \left[\frac{\sin a \cos \lambda - \sin \lambda \cos a}{\cos \lambda} \right] = W \frac{\sin (a - \lambda)}{\cos \lambda} \dots(3).$$

(ii) Let the body be on the point of motion *up* the plane, so that the friction acts *down* the plane and is equal to μR; let P_1 be the force required to keep the body at rest. In this case, we have

$$P_1 - \mu R = W \sin \alpha,$$

and $\hspace{3cm} R = W \cos \alpha.$

Hence $P_1 = W (\sin \alpha + \mu \cos \alpha)$

$$= W [\sin \alpha + \tan \lambda \cos \alpha] = W \frac{\sin (\alpha + \lambda)}{\cos \lambda} \ldots\ldots(4).$$

These values, P and P_1, are the limiting values of the force, if the body is to remain in equilibrium; if the force lie between P and P_1, the body remains in equilibrium, but is not on the point of motion in either direction.

Hence, for equilibrium, the force must lie between the values $W \dfrac{\sin (\alpha \pm \lambda)}{\cos \lambda}$.

It will be noted that the value of P_1 may be obtained from that of P by changing the sign of μ.

195. If the power P act at an angle θ with the inclined plane (as in Art. 156, Case III.), when the body is on the point of motion *down* the plane and the friction acts therefore *up* the plane, the equations of equilibrium are

$$P \cos \theta + \mu R = W \sin \alpha \quad \ldots\ldots\ldots\ldots(1),$$

$$P \sin \theta + R = W \cos \alpha \quad \ldots\ldots\ldots\ldots(2).$$

Hence, multiplying (2) by μ, and subtracting, we have

$$P = W \frac{\sin \alpha - \mu \cos \alpha}{\cos \theta - \mu \sin \theta} = W \frac{\sin (\alpha - \lambda)}{\cos (\theta + \lambda)}.$$

By substituting this value of P in (2), the value of R may be found.

When the body is on the point of motion *up* the plane we have, by changing the sign of μ,

$$P_1 = W \frac{\sin (\alpha + \lambda)}{\cos (\theta - \lambda)}.$$

Cor. The force that will just be on the point of moving the body up the plane is least when

$$W \frac{\sin(\alpha + \lambda)}{\cos(\theta - \lambda)} \text{ is least,}$$

i.e., when $\cos(\theta - \lambda)$ is unity,

i.e., when $\theta = \lambda$.

Hence the force required to move the body up the plane will be least when it is applied in a direction making with the inclined plane an angle equal to the angle of friction.

196. The results of the previous article may be found by geometric construction.

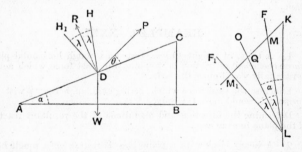

Draw a vertical line KL to represent W on any scale that is convenient (*e.g.* one inch per lb. or one inch per 10 lbs.).

Draw LO parallel to the direction of the normal reaction R. Make OLF, OLF_1 each equal to the angle of friction λ, as in the figure.

Then LF, LF_1 are parallel to the directions DH, DH_1 of the resulting reaction at D according as the body is on the point of motion down or up the plane.

Draw KMM_1 parallel to the supporting force P to meet LF, LF_1 in M and M_1.

Then clearly KLM and KLM_1 are respectively the triangles of forces for the two extreme positions of equilibrium.

Hence, on the same scale that KL represents W, KM and KM_1 represent the P and P_1 of the previous article.

Clearly $OLK = \angle$ between R and the vertical $= \alpha$, so that

$$\angle MLK = \alpha - \lambda \quad \text{and} \quad \angle M_1LK = \alpha + \lambda.$$

Similarly

$$\angle KQO = \angle \text{ between the directions of } R \text{ and } P = 90° - \theta,$$

so that $\angle KQL = 90° + \theta, \quad \angle KM_1L = 90° + \theta - \lambda,$

and $\angle KML = 90° + \theta + \lambda.$

Hence

$$\frac{P}{W} = \frac{KM}{KL} = \frac{\sin KLM}{\sin KML} = \frac{\sin (\alpha - \lambda)}{\sin (90° + \theta + \lambda)} = \frac{\sin (\alpha - \lambda)}{\cos (\theta + \lambda)},$$

and

$$\frac{P_1}{W} = \frac{KM_1}{KL} = \frac{\sin KLM_1}{\sin KM_1L} = \frac{\sin (\alpha + \lambda)}{\sin (90° + \theta - \lambda)} = \frac{\sin (\alpha + \lambda)}{\cos (\theta - \lambda)}.$$

Cor. It is clear that KM_1 is least when it is drawn perpendicular to LF_1, *i.e.* when P_1 is inclined at a right angle to the direction of resultant reaction DH_1, and therefore at an angle λ to the inclined plane.

EXAMPLES. XXXI.

1. A body, of weight 40 lbs., rests on a rough horizontal plane whose coefficient of friction is ·25; find the least force which acting horizontally would move the body.

Find also the least force which, acting at an angle $\cos^{-1}\frac{3}{5}$ with the horizontal, would move the body.

Determine the direction and magnitude of the resultant reaction of the plane in each case.

2. A heavy block with a plane base is resting on a rough horizontal plane. It is acted on by a force at an inclination of 45° to the plane, and the force is gradually increased till the block is just going to slide. If the coefficient of friction be ·5, compare the force with the weight of the block.

3. A mass of 30 lbs. is resting on a rough horizontal plane and can be just moved by a force of 10 lbs. wt. acting horizontally; find the coefficient of friction and the direction and magnitude of the resultant reaction of the plane.

4. Shew that the least force which will move a weight W along a rough horizontal plane is $W \sin \phi$, where ϕ is the angle of friction.

5. The inclination of a rough plane to the horizon is $\cos^{-1}\frac{12}{13}$; shew that, if the coefficient of friction be $\frac{1}{3}$, the least force, acting parallel to the plane, that will support 1 cwt. placed on the plane is $8\frac{8}{13}$ lbs. wt.; shew also that the force that would be on the point of moving the body up the plane is $77\frac{7}{13}$ lbs. wt.

6. The base of an inclined plane is 4 feet in length and the height is 3 feet; a force of 8 lbs., acting parallel to the plane, will just prevent a weight of 20 lbs. from sliding down; find the coefficient of friction.

7. A body, of weight 4 lbs., rests in limiting equilibrium on a rough plane whose slope is 30°; the plane being raised to a slope of 60°, find the force along the plane required to support the body.

8. A weight of 30 lbs. just rests on a rough inclined plane, the height of the plane being $\frac{3}{5}$ths of its length. Shew that it will require a force of 36 lbs. wt. acting parallel to the plane just to be on the point of moving the weight up the plane.

9. A weight of 60 lbs. is on the point of motion down a rough inclined plane when supported by a force of 24 lbs. wt. acting parallel to the plane, and is on the point of motion up the plane when under the influence of a force of 36 lbs. wt. parallel to the plane; find the coefficient of friction.

10. Two inclined planes have a common vertex, and a string, passing over a small smooth pulley at the vertex, supports two equal weights. If one of the planes be rough and the other smooth, find the relation between the two angles of inclination of the two planes when the weight on the smooth plane is on the point of moving down.

11. Two unequal weights on a rough inclined plane are connected by a string which passes round a fixed pulley in the plane; find the greatest inclination of the plane consistent with the equilibrium of the weights.

12. Two equal weights are attached to the ends of a string which is laid over the top of two equally rough planes, having the same altitude and placed back to back, the angles of inclination of the planes to the horizon being 30° and 60° respectively; shew that the weights will be on the point of motion if the coefficient of friction be $2-\sqrt{3}$.

13. A particle is placed on the outside surface of a rough sphere whose coefficient of friction is μ. Shew that it will be on the point of motion when the radius from it to the centre makes an angle $\tan^{-1}\mu$ with the vertical.

14. How high can a particle rest inside a hollow sphere, of radius a, if the coefficient of friction be $\frac{1}{\sqrt{3}}$?

15. At what angle of inclination should the traces be attached to a sledge that it may be drawn up a given hill with the least exertion?

16. A cubical block of stone, of weight 5 cwt., is to be drawn along a rough horizontal plane by a force P inclined at 40° to the horizontal. If the angle of friction be 25°, find, by a graphic construction, the least value of P.

17. A body, of weight 1 cwt., rests on a plane inclined at 25° to the horizon, being just prevented from sliding down by a force of 15 lbs. acting up the plane; find, by a graphic construction, the force that will just drag it up and the value of the coefficient of friction.

197. *To find the work done in dragging a body up a rough inclined plane.*

From Art. 194, Case II., we know that the force P_1 which would just move the body up the plane is

$$W (\sin a + \mu \cos a).$$

Hence the work done in dragging it from A to C

$= P_1 \times AC$ (Fig. Art. 156)

$= W (\sin a + \mu \cos a) . AC$

$= W . AC \sin a + \mu W . AC \cos a$

$= W . BC + \mu W . AB$

= work done in dragging the body through the same vertical height without the intervention of the plane

+ the work done in dragging it along a horizontal distance equal to the base of the inclined plane and of the same roughness as the plane.

198. From the preceding article we see that, if our inclined plane be rough, the work done by the power is more than the work done against the weight. This is true for any machine; the principle may be expressed thus,

In any machine, the work done by the power is equal to the work done against the weight, together with the work done against the frictional resistances of the machine, and the work done against the weights of the component parts of the machine.

The ratio of the work done on the weight to the work done by the effort is, for any machine, called the efficiency of the machine, so that

$$\text{Efficiency} = \frac{\text{Useful work done by the machine}}{\text{Work supplied to the machine}}.$$

Let P_0 be the effort required if there were no friction, and P the actual effort. Then, by Art. 138,

Work done against the weight

$= P_0 \times$ distance through which its point of application moves,

and work supplied to the machine

$= P \times$ distance through which its point of application moves.

Hence, by division,

$$\text{Efficiency} = \frac{P_0}{P}$$

$$= \frac{\text{Effort when there is no friction}}{\text{Actual effort}}.$$

We can never get rid entirely of frictional resistances, or make our machine without weight, so that some work must always be lost through these two causes. Hence the efficiency of the machine can never be so great as unity. The more nearly the efficiency approaches to unity, the better is the machine.

There is no machine by whose use we can create work, and in practice, however smooth and perfect the machine may be, we always lose work. The only use of any machine is to multiply the force we apply, whilst at the same time the distance through which the force works is more than proportionately lessened.

199. Equilibrium of a rough screw. *To find the relation between the effort and the resistance in the case of a screw, when friction is taken into account.*

Using the same notation as in Art. 178, let the screw be on the point of motion *downwards*, so that the friction acts *upwards* along the thread. [As in Art. 176, its section is rectangular.]

In this case the vertical pressures of the block are

$$R (\cos a + \mu \sin a), \quad S (\cos a + \mu \sin a),\ldots$$

and the horizontal components of these pressures are

$$R (\sin a - \mu \cos a), \quad S (\sin a - \mu \cos a),\ldots$$

Hence the equations (1) and (2) of Art. 178 become

$$W = (R + S + T + \ldots)(\cos a + \mu \sin a) \quad \ldots\ldots(1),$$

and

$$P . b = a (R + S + T + \ldots)(\sin a - \mu \cos a) \ldots\ldots(2).$$

Hence, by division,

$$\frac{P . b}{W} = a \frac{\sin a - \mu \cos a}{\cos a + \mu \sin a} = a \frac{\sin a \cos \lambda - \cos a \sin \lambda}{\cos a \cos \lambda + \sin a \sin \lambda}$$

$$= a \frac{\sin (a - \lambda)}{\cos (a - \lambda)}.$$

$$\therefore \frac{P}{W} = \frac{a}{b} \tan (a - \lambda).$$

Similarly, if the screw be on the point of motion upwards, we have, by changing the sign of μ,

$$\frac{P_1}{W} = \frac{a}{b} \frac{\sin a + \mu \cos a}{\cos a - \mu \sin a} = \frac{a}{b} \tan (a + \lambda).$$

If the effort have any value between P and P_1, the screw will be in equilibrium, but the friction will not be limiting friction.

It will be noted that if the angle a of the screw be equal to the angle of friction, λ, then the value of the effort P is zero. In this case the screw will just remain in equilibrium supported only by the friction along the thread of the screw. If $a < \lambda$, P will be negative, *i.e.* the screw will not descend unless it is forced down.

Ex. 1. *If the circumference of a screw be two inches, the distance between its threads half an inch, and the coefficient of friction $\frac{1}{5}$, find the limits between which the effort must lie, so that the screw may be in equilibrium when it is supporting a body of weight 1 cwt., the length of the effort-arm being 12 inches.*

Here $\qquad 2\pi a = 2$, and $2\pi a \tan \alpha = \frac{1}{2}$.

$$\therefore \ a = \frac{1}{\pi}, \text{ and } \tan \alpha = \frac{1}{4}.$$

Also $\qquad\qquad \tan \lambda = \frac{1}{5}$, and $b = 12$.

Hence the force which would *just* support the screw

$$= 112 \times \frac{a}{b} \tan (\alpha - \lambda)$$

$$= 112 \times \frac{1}{12\pi} \times \frac{\frac{1}{4} - \frac{1}{5}}{1 + \frac{1}{4} \cdot \frac{1}{5}} = \frac{112}{12\pi} \times \frac{1}{21} = \frac{14}{99} \text{ lbs. wt.} = \cdot \dot{1}\dot{4} \text{ lbs. wt.}$$

Again, the force which would just be on the point of moving the screw upwards

$$= 112 \times \frac{a}{b} \tan (\alpha + \lambda) = \frac{112}{12\pi} \times \frac{\frac{1}{4} + \frac{1}{5}}{1 - \frac{1}{4} \cdot \frac{1}{5}} = \frac{112}{12\pi} \times \frac{9}{19}$$

$$= 1\frac{85}{209} \text{ lbs. wt.} = 1\cdot4067 \text{ lbs. wt.}$$

Hence the screw will be in equilibrium if the effort lie between $\cdot\dot{1}\dot{4}$ and $1\cdot4067$ lbs. wt.

If the screw were smooth, the force required would

$$= 112 \frac{a}{b} \tan \alpha = \frac{112}{12\pi} \times \frac{1}{4} = \frac{49}{66} = \cdot742 \text{ lbs. wt.}$$

The efficiency therefore, by Art. 198,

$$= \frac{\cdot742}{1\cdot4067} = \cdot527.$$

Ex. 2. The coefficient of friction of wrought iron on wood being ·15, shew that the least angle of inclination of the thread of a screw, so that it may slide into a prepared hole in the wood under the influence of its own weight, is $\tan^{-1}\frac{3}{20}$.

Ex. 3. If the circumference of a screw be $\frac{3}{2}$ inch, the coefficient of friction ·15, the length of the power-arm 12 inches, and if there be 3 threads to the inch, find the forces which will respectively just support, and just move, the screw when it supports a weight W. Find also the value of the effort, when the same screw is smooth, and deduce its efficiency.

Ans. $\qquad \dfrac{W}{16\pi}(\cdot07); \qquad \dfrac{W}{16\pi}(\cdot385); \qquad \dfrac{W}{16\pi}(\cdot2); \qquad \cdot577.$

Ex. 4. *Shew that the efficiency of a screw is greatest when its angle is* $45° - \dfrac{\lambda}{2}$.

The force required to lift the weight W, when there is friction,

$$= W \frac{a}{b} \tan \overline{a + \lambda},$$

and where there is no friction it

$$= W \frac{a}{b} \tan a.$$

As in Art. 198 the efficiency, E,

$$= \text{the ratio of these}$$

$$= \frac{\tan a}{\tan (a + \lambda)} = \frac{\sin a \cos (a + \lambda)}{\cos a \sin \overline{a + \lambda}}.$$

$$\therefore 1 - E = 1 - \frac{\sin a \cos (a + \lambda)}{\cos a \sin (a + \lambda)} = \frac{\sin \lambda}{\cos a \sin (a + \lambda)}$$

$$= \frac{2 \sin \lambda}{\sin (2a + \lambda) + \sin \lambda}.$$

$$\therefore E \text{ is greatest when } 1 - E \text{ is least,}$$

$$\textit{i.e. when } \sin (2a + \lambda) \text{ is greatest,}$$

$$\textit{i.e. when } 2a + \lambda = 90°,$$

and then

$$a = 45° - \frac{\lambda}{2}.$$

200. *Wheel and Axle with the pivot resting on rough bearings.*

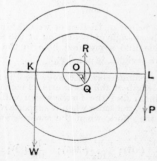

Let the central circle represent the pivots A or B of Fig. Art. 159 (much magnified) when looked at endways.

The resultant action between these pivots and the bearings on which they rest must be vertical, since it balances P and W.

Also it must make an angle λ, the angle of friction, with the normal at the point of contact Q, if we assume that P is just on the point of overcoming W.

Hence Q cannot be at the lowest point of the pivot, but must be as denoted in the figure, where OQ makes an angle λ with the vertical. The resultant reaction at Q is thus vertical.

Since R balances P and W,

$$\therefore \ R = P + W \quad\dots\dots\dots\dots\dots\dots(1).$$

Also, by taking moments about O, we have

$$P \cdot b - R \cdot c \sin \lambda = W \cdot a \dots\dots\dots\dots(2),$$

where c is the radius of the pivot and b, a the radii of the wheel and the axle (as in Art. 159).

Solving (1) and (2), we have

$$P = W \frac{a + c \sin \lambda}{b - c \sin \lambda}.$$

If P be only just sufficient to support W, *i.e.* if the machine be on the point of motion in the direction $\big)$, then, by changing the sign of λ, we have

$$P_1 = W \frac{a - c \sin \lambda}{b + c \sin \lambda}.$$

In this case the point of contact Q is on the left of the vertical through O.

201. The Wedge is a piece of iron, or metal, which has two plane faces meeting in a sharp edge. It is used to split wood or other tough substances, its edge being forced in by repeated blows applied by a hammer to its upper surface.

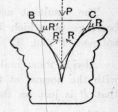

The problem of the action of a wedge is essentially a dynamical one.

We shall only consider the statical problem when the wedge is just kept in equilibrium by a steady force applied to its upper surface.

Let ABC be a section of the wedge and let its faces be equally inclined to the base BC. Let the angle CAB be α.

Let P be the force applied to the upper face, R and R' the normal reactions of the wood at the points where the wedge touches the wood, and μR and $\mu R'$ the frictions, it being assumed that the wedge is on the point of being pushed in.

We shall suppose the force P applied at the middle point of BC and that its direction is perpendicular to BC and hence bisects the angle BAC.

Resolving along and perpendicular to BC, we have

$$\mu R \sin \frac{\alpha}{2} - R \cos \frac{\alpha}{2} = \mu R' \sin \frac{\alpha}{2} - R' \cos \frac{\alpha}{2} \ldots\ldots(1),$$

and
$$P = \mu (R + R') \cos \frac{\alpha}{2} + (R + R') \sin \frac{\alpha}{2} \ \ldots\ldots(2).$$

From equation (1) we have $R = R'$, and then (2) gives

$$P = 2R \left(\mu \cos \frac{\alpha}{2} + \sin \frac{\alpha}{2} \right).$$

Hence
$$\frac{2R}{P} = \frac{1}{\mu \cos \dfrac{a}{2} + \sin \dfrac{a}{2}} = \frac{\cos \lambda}{\sin \dfrac{a}{2} \cos \lambda + \cos \dfrac{a}{2} \sin \lambda}$$

$$= \frac{\cos \lambda}{\sin \left(\dfrac{a}{2} + \lambda \right)},$$

if λ be the coefficient of friction. *angle*

The splitting power of the wedge is measured by R. For a given force P this splitting power is therefore greatest when a is least.

Theoretically this will be when a is zero, *i.e.* when the wedge is of infinitesimal strength. Practically the wedge has the greatest splitting power when it is made with as small an angle as is consistent with its strength.

202. If there be no friction between the wedge and wood (though this is practically an impossible supposition), we should have $\lambda = 0$, and therefore

$$\frac{2R}{P} = \frac{1}{\sin \dfrac{a}{2}} = \operatorname{cosec} \frac{a}{2}.$$

203. If the force of compression exerted by the wood on the wedge be great enough the force P may not be large enough to make the wedge on the point of motion down; in fact the wedge may be on the point of being forced out.

If P_1 be the value of P in this case, its value is found by changing the sign of μ in Art. 201, so that we should have

$$P_1 = 2R \left(\sin \frac{a}{2} - \mu \cos \frac{a}{2} \right)$$

$$= 2R \frac{\sin \left(\dfrac{a}{2} - \lambda \right)}{\cos \lambda}.$$

If $\dfrac{a}{2}$ be $> \lambda$, the value of P_1 is positive.

If $\dfrac{a}{2}$ be $< \lambda$, P_1 is negative and the wedge could therefore only be on the point of slipping out if a pull were applied to its upper surface.

If $\dfrac{a}{2} = \lambda$, the wedge will just stick fast without the application of any force.

Ex. Prove that the multiplication of force produced by a screw-press, in which the distance between successive threads is c and the power is applied at the extremities of a cross-bar of length $2b$, is the same as that produced by a thin isosceles wedge of angle a such that

$$\sin \frac{a}{2} = c \div 4\pi b.$$

204. Friction exerts such an important influence on the practical working of machines that the theoretical investigations are not of much actual use and recourse must for any particular machine be had to experiment. The method is the same for all kinds of machines.

The velocity-ratio can be obtained by experiment; for in all machines it equals the distance through which the effort moves divided by the corresponding distance through which the weight, or resistance, moves. Call it n.

Let the weight raised be W. Then the theoretical effort P_0, corresponding to no friction, is $\dfrac{W}{n}$. Find by experiment the actual value of the effort P which just raises W. The actual mechanical advantage of the machine is $\dfrac{W}{P}$, and the efficiency of it is, by Art. 198, $\dfrac{P_0}{P}$. The

product of the efficiency and the velocity ratio $= \dfrac{P_0}{P} \cdot \dfrac{W}{P_0} = \dfrac{W}{P}$

$=$ the mechanical advantage.

205. As an example take the case of a class-room model of a differential wheel and axle on which some experiments were performed. The machine was not at all in good condition and was not cleaned before use, and no lubricants were used for the bearings of either it or its pulley.

With the notation of Art. 164 the values of a, b, and c were found to be $1\frac{1}{2}$, 3, and $6\frac{3}{4}$ inches, so that the value of the velocity ratio n

$$= \frac{2b}{c - a} = \frac{2 \times 6\frac{3}{4}}{3 - 1\frac{1}{2}} = 9.$$

This value was also verified by experiment; for it was found that for every inch that W went up, P went down nine inches.

P was measured by means of weights put into a scale-pan whose weight is included in that of P; similarly for W.

The weight of the pulley to which W is attached was also included in the weight of W.

The corresponding values of P and W, in grammes' weight are given in the following table; the value of P was that which just overcame the weight W. The third column gives the corresponding values of P_0, *i.e.* the effort which would have been required had there been no frictional resistances.

W	P	$P_0 = \dfrac{W}{n}$	$E = \dfrac{P_0}{P}$	$M = \dfrac{W}{P}$
50	28	5·55	·2	1·79
100	36	11·11	·31	2·78
150	45	16·67	·37	3·3
250	60	27·78	·46	4·17
450	90	50	·56	5
650	119	72·22	·61	5·46
850	147	94·44	·64	5·78
1050	175	116·67	·67	6
1250	203	138·88	·68	6·16
1450	232	161·11	·694	6·25

The fourth column gives the values of E, the corresponding efficiency, and the last column gives the values of M, the mechanical advantages.

On plotting out on squared paper the above results, which the student should do for himself, the points giving P are found to roughly be on a straight line going through the third and last of the above. Hence, according to the theory of graphs, the relation between P and W is of the form $P = aW + b$, where a and b are constants.

Also $P = 45$ when $W = 150$, and $P = 232$ when $W = 1450$.

$$\therefore \quad 45 = 150a + b \text{ and } 232 = 1450a + b.$$

Solving, we have $a = ·144$ and $b = 23·4$ approximately, so that

$$P = ·144W + 23·4.$$

This is called the Law of the Machine.

Also $\qquad P_0 = \tfrac{1}{9}W = ·111W.$

Hence $\qquad E = \dfrac{P_0}{P} = \dfrac{·111W}{·144W + 23·4},$

and
$$M = \frac{W}{P} = \frac{W}{\cdot 144W + 23\cdot 4}.$$

These give E and M for any weight W.

The values of E and M get bigger as W increases. Assuming the above value of E to be true for all values of W, then its greatest value is when W is infinitely great, and

$$= \frac{\cdot 111}{\cdot 144} = \text{about} \cdot 77,$$

so that in this machine at least 23 % of the work put into it is lost.

The corresponding greatest value of the mechanical advantage

$$= \frac{1}{\cdot 144} = \text{about } 7.$$

If the machine had been well cleaned and lubricated before the experiment, much better results would have been obtained.

206. Just as in the example of the last article, so, with any other machine, the actual efficiency is found to fall considerably short of unity.

There is one practical advantage which, in general, belongs to machines having a comparatively small efficiency.

It can be shewn that, in any machine in which the magnitude of the effort applied has no effect on the friction, the load does not run down of its own accord when no effort is applied provided that the efficiency is less than $\frac{1}{2}$.

Examples of such machines are a Screw whose pitch is small and whose " Power " or effort is applied horizontally as in Art. 178, and an Inclined Plane where the effort acts up the plane as in Art. 194.

In machines where the friction does depend on the effort applied no such general rule can be theoretically proved, and each case must be considered separately. But it may be taken as a rough general rule that where the effort has a comparatively small effect on the amount of friction then the load will not run down if the efficiency be less than $\frac{1}{2}$. Such a machine is said not to "reverse" or "overhaul."

Thus in the case of the Differential Pulley (Art. 165), as usually constructed the efficiency is less than $\frac{1}{2}$, and the load W does not run down when no force P is applied, that is, when the machine is left alone and the chain let go.

This property of not overhauling compensates, in great measure, for the comparatively small efficiency.

In a wheel and axle the mechanical advantage is usually great and the efficiency usually considerably more than $\frac{1}{2}$; but the fact that it reverses does not always make it a more useful machine than the Differential Pulley.

The student, who desires further information as to the practical working of machines, should consult Sir Robert Ball's *Experimental Mechanics* or works on Applied Mechanics.

EXAMPLES. XXXII.

1. How much work is done in drawing a load of 6 cwt. up a rough inclined plane, whose height is 3 feet and base 20 feet, the coefficient of friction being $\frac{2}{15}$?

2. A weight of 10 tons is dragged in half an hour through a length of 330 feet up an inclined plane, of inclination 30°, the co-efficient of friction being $\frac{1}{\sqrt{3}}$; find the work expended and the H.P. of the engine which could do the work.

3. A tank, 24 feet long, 12 feet broad, and 16 feet deep, is filled by water from a well the surface of which is always 80 feet below the top of the tank; find the work done in filling the tank, and the H.P. of an engine, whose efficiency is ·5, that will fill the tank in 4 hours.

4. The diameter of the circular piston of a steam engine is 60 inches and it makes 11 strokes per minute, the length of each stroke being 8 feet, the mean pressure per square inch on the piston being 15 lbs., and the efficiency of the engine ·65. Find the number of cubic feet of water that it will raise per hour from a well whose depth is 300 feet, on the supposition that no work is wasted.

5. The diameter of the piston of an engine is 80 inches, the mean pressure of steam 12 lbs. per square inch, the length of the stroke 10 feet and the number of double strokes per minute is 11. The engine is found to raise $42\frac{1}{2}$ cub. ft. of water per minute from a depth of 500 fathoms. Shew that its efficiency is ·6 nearly.

6. The radii of a wheel and axle are 4 feet and 6 inches. If a force of 56 lbs. wt. is required to overcome a resistance of 200 lbs. wt. what is the efficiency of the machine?

7. In some experiments with a block and tackle (second system of pulleys), in which the velocity-ratio was 4, the weights lifted were 10, 80, and 160 lbs. and the corresponding values of the effort were 23, 58, and 85 lbs. Find the efficiency in each case.

8. With a certain machine it is found that, with efforts equal to 12 and 7·5 lbs. wt. respectively, resistances equal to 700 and 300 lbs. wt. are overcome; assuming that $P = a + bW$, find the values of a and b.

9. In some experiments with a screw-jack the values of the load W were 150, 180, 210, 240 and 270 lbs. wt. and the corresponding values of the effort P were found to be 20·9, 22·7, 25·75, 28·4 and 31·4 lbs. wt.; plot the results on squared paper and assuming that $P = a + bW$, find the approximate values of a and b.

10. In some experiments with a model block and tackle (the second system of pulleys), the values of W (including the weight of the lower block) and P expressed in grammes' weight were found to be as follows:

$$W = 75, \quad 175, \quad 275, \quad 475, \quad 675, \quad 875, \quad 1075;$$

$$P = 25, \quad 48, \quad 71, \quad 119, \quad 166, \quad 214, \quad 264.$$

Also there were five strings at the lower block. Find an approximate relation between P and W and the corresponding values for the efficiency and mechanical advantage.

Draw the graphs of P, P_0, E, and M.

11. The following table gives the load in tons upon a crane, and the corresponding effort in lbs. wt.:

Load   1,   3,   5,   7,   8,   10,   11.
Effort   9,   20,   28,   37,   42,   51,   56.

Find the law of the machine, and calculate the efficiency at the loads 5 and 10 tons given that the velocity-ratio is 500.

12. A weight is lifted by a screw-jack, of pitch $\frac{1}{4}$ inch, the force being applied at right angles to a lever of length 15 inches. The values of the weight in tons, and the corresponding force in lbs., are given in the following table:

Weight   1,   2·5,   5,   7,   8,   10.
Force   24,   32,   46,   57,   63,   73.

Find the law of the machine, and calculate its efficiency for the weights 4 and 9 tons.

CHAPTER XIV.

FRICTION (continued).

207. In this chapter we give some further examples of the solution of problems where friction is involved.

Ex. 1. *A uniform ladder is in equilibrium, with one end resting on the ground, and the other end against a vertical wall; if the ground and wall be both rough, the coefficients of friction being μ and μ' respectively, and if the ladder be on the point of slipping at both ends, find the inclination of the ladder to the horizon.*

Let AB be the ladder, and G its centre of gravity; let R and S be the normal reactions at A and B respectively; the end A of the ladder is on the point of slipping *from* the wall, and hence the friction μR is *towards* the wall; the end B is on the point of motion vertically *downwards*, and therefore the friction $\mu'S$ acts *upwards*.

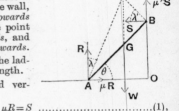

Let θ be the inclination of the ladder to the ground, and $2a$ its length.

Resolving horizontally and vertically, we have

$$\mu R = S \qquad \qquad \qquad \qquad (1),$$

and
$$R + \mu'S = W \qquad \qquad \qquad (2).$$

Also, taking moments about A, we have

$$W \cdot a \cos\theta = \mu'S \cdot 2a \cos\theta + S \cdot 2a \sin\theta,$$

$$\therefore \ W \cos\theta = 2S(\mu' \cos\theta + \sin\theta) \qquad \qquad (3).$$

From (1) and (2), we have

$$\mu(W - \mu'S) = S,$$

and
$$\therefore \ \mu W = S(1 + \mu\mu') \qquad \qquad (4).$$

By (3) and (4), we have, by division,

$$\frac{\cos\theta}{\mu} = \frac{2(\mu'\cos\theta + \sin\theta)}{1 + \mu\mu'},$$

$$\therefore \cos\theta(1 - \mu\mu') = 2\mu\sin\theta.$$

Hence $$\tan\theta = \frac{1 - \mu\mu'}{2\mu}.$$

Otherwise thus;

Let λ and λ' be the angles of friction at A and B; draw AC making an angle λ with the normal at A, and BC making an angle λ' with the normal at B, as in the figure.

By Art. 189, AC and BC are the directions of the resultant reactions at A and B.

The ladder is kept in equilibrium by these resultant reactions and its weight; hence their directions must meet in a point and therefore the vertical line through G must pass through C.

Formula (1) of Art. 79 gives

$$(a+a)\cot CGB = a\cot ACG - a\cot BCG,$$

i.e. $$2\tan\theta = \cot\lambda - \tan\lambda' = \frac{1}{\mu} - \mu'.$$

$$\therefore \tan\theta = \frac{1 - \mu\mu'}{2\mu}.$$

Ex. 2. *A ladder is placed in a given position with one end resting on the ground and the other against a vertical wall. If the ground and wall be both rough, the angles of friction being λ and λ' respectively, find by a graphic construction how high a man can ascend the ladder without its slipping.*

Let AB (Fig. Ex. 1) be the ladder.

Draw AC and BC making the angles of friction with the normals at A and B to the wall and ground respectively.

Draw CG vertically to meet AB in G. If the centre of gravity of the man and ladder together be between A and G the ladder will rest; if not, it will slide.

For if this centre of gravity be between G and B the vertical through it will meet BC, the limiting direction of friction at B, in a point P such that the $\angle PAR$ is greater than the angle of friction at A, and so equilibrium will be impossible.

If this centre of gravity be between G and A equilibrium will be possible; for even if the friction were limiting at A the vertical through this centre of gravity would meet AC in a point P such that the angle PBS would be $< \lambda'$, so that equilibrium would be possible. Similarly we may shew that if the friction be limiting at B, there is still equilibrium.

If then G_1 be the centre of gravity of the ladder, G_2 the highest possible position of the man, and W_1 and W_2 be their respective weights, then G_2 is determined by the relation

$$W_1 . GG_1 = W_2 . GG_2. $$

EXAMPLES. XXXIII.

1. A uniform ladder, 13 feet long, rests with one end against a smooth vertical wall and the other on a rough horizontal plane at a point 5 feet from the wall; find the friction between the ladder and the ground, if the weight of the ladder be 56 lbs.

2. A uniform ladder rests with one end on a horizontal floor and the other against a vertical wall, the coefficients of friction being respectively $\frac{3}{7}$ and $\frac{1}{3}$; find the inclination of the ladder when it is about to slip.

3. If in the last example the coefficient of friction in each case be $\frac{1}{3}$, shew that the ladder will slip when its inclination to the vertical is $\tan^{-1} \frac{3}{4}$.

4. A uniform ladder rests in limiting equilibrium with one end on a rough floor, whose coefficient of friction is μ, and with the other against a smooth vertical wall; shew that its inclination to the vertical is $\tan^{-1}(2\mu)$.

5. A uniform ladder is placed against a wall; if the ground and wall be equally rough, the coefficient of friction being $\tan\theta$, shew that the limiting inclination of the ladder to the vertical is 2θ.

When the ladder is in this position can it be ascended without its slipping?

6. A uniform ladder rests in limiting equilibrium with one end on a rough horizontal plane, and the other against a smooth vertical wall; a man then ascends the ladder; shew that he cannot go more than half-way up.

7. A uniform ladder rests with one end against a smooth vertical wall and the other on the ground, the coefficient of friction being $\frac{3}{4}$; if the inclination of the ladder to the ground be 45°, shew that a man, whose weight is equal to that of the ladder, can just ascend to the top of the ladder without its slipping.

8. A uniform ladder, of length 70 feet, rests against a vertical wall with which it makes an angle of 45°, the coefficients of friction between the ladder and the wall and ground respectively being $\frac{1}{3}$ and $\frac{1}{2}$. If a man, whose weight is one-half that of the ladder, ascend the ladder, how high will he be when the ladder slips?

If a boy now stand on the bottom rung of the ladder what must be his least weight so that the man may go to the top of the ladder?

9. Two equal ladders, of weight w, are placed so as to lean against each other with their ends resting on a rough horizontal floor; given the coefficient of friction, μ, and the angle $2a$, that they make with each other, find what weight on the top would cause them to slip.

Explain the meaning of the result when $\tan a > 2\mu$ or $< \mu$.

10. A uniform ladder rests, at an angle of 45° with the horizon, with its upper extremity against a rough vertical wall and its lower extremity on the ground. If μ and μ' be the coefficients of limiting friction between the ladder and the ground and wall respectively, shew that the least horizontal force which will move the lower extremity towards the wall is $\frac{1}{2} W \cdot \dfrac{1 + 2\mu - \mu\mu'}{1 - \mu'}$.

11. In Ex. 9 if the weight be placed at the middle point of one leg and be heavy enough to cause slipping, shew that the other leg will be the one that will slide first.

208. Ex. 1. *A uniform cylinder is placed with its plane base on a rough inclined plane and the inclination of the plane to the horizon is gradually increased; shew that the cylinder will topple over before it slides if the ratio of the diameter of the base of the cylinder to its height be less than the coefficient of friction.*

Let ϕ be the inclination of the plane to the horizon when the cylinder is on the point of tumbling over. The vertical line through the centre of gravity G of the cylinder must just fall within the base.

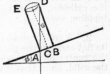

Hence, if AB be the base, the line GA must be vertical.

Let C be the middle point of the base, r its radius, and let h be the height of the cylinder,

$$\therefore \ \tan \phi = \cot CAG = \frac{AC}{CG} = \frac{r}{\frac{1}{2}h} = \frac{2r}{h} \ \ldots\ldots\ldots\ldots(1).$$

Also the inclination θ of the plane to the horizon, when the cylinder is about to slide, is given by

$$\tan \theta = \mu \ \ldots\ldots\ldots\ldots\ldots\ldots\ldots\ldots\ldots(2).$$

Hence the cylinder will topple before it slides if ϕ be less than θ,

$$\textit{i.e., if } \frac{2r}{h} \text{ be} < \mu.$$

Ex. 2. *A rectangle ABCD rests on a vertical plane, with its base AB on a rough table; a gradually increasing force acts along DC; will equilibrium be broken by sliding or toppling?*

Let F be the force, and W the weight of the rectangle.

Let $AB = 2a$ and $BC = h$.

If the rectangle topples it will clearly turn about B, and this will be when the moments of F and W about B just balance,

$$i.e., \text{ when } F \cdot h = W \cdot a \ldots\ldots(1).$$

Also the rectangle will slide when F is equal to the limiting friction,

$$i.e., \text{ when } F = \mu W \ldots\ldots(2).$$

The rectangle will topple or slide according as the value of F given by (1) is less or greater than the value of F given by (2),

$$i.e., \text{ according as } \frac{a}{h} \lessgtr \mu,$$

i.e., according as μ is $\gtrless$ the ratio of the base to twice the height of the rectangle.

EXAMPLES. XXXIV.

1. A cylinder rests with its circular base on a rough inclined plane, the coefficient of friction being $\frac{1}{2}$. Find the inclination of the plane and the relation between the height and diameter of the base of the cylinder, so that it may be on the point of sliding and also of toppling over.

2. A solid cylinder rests on a rough horizontal plane with one of its flat ends on the plane, and is acted on by a horizontal force through the centre of its upper end; if this force be just sufficient to move the solid, shew that it will slide, and not topple over, if the coefficient of friction be less than the ratio of the radius of the base of the cylinder to its height.

3. An equilateral triangle rests in a vertical plane with its base resting on a rough horizontal plane; a gradually increasing horizontal force acts on its vertex in the plane of the triangle; prove that the triangle will slide before it turns about the end of its base, if the coefficient of friction be less than $\frac{1}{3}\sqrt{3}$.

4. A conical sugarloaf, whose height is equal to twice the diameter of its base, stands on a table rough enough to prevent sliding; one end is gently raised till the sugarloaf is on the point of falling over; find the inclination of the plane to the horizon in this position.

5. A cone, of given vertical angle $2a$, rests on a rough plane which is inclined to the horizon. As the inclination of the plane is increased, shew that the cone will slide, before it topples over, if the coefficient of friction be less than $4 \tan a$.

6. A right cone is placed with its base on a rough inclined plane; if $\dfrac{1}{\sqrt{3}}$ be the coefficient of friction, find the angle of the cone when it is on the point of both slipping and turning over.

7. A cone rests on a rough table, and a cord fastened to the vertex of the cone passes over a smooth pulley at the same height as the top of the cone, and supports a weight. Shew that, if the weight be continually increased, the cone will turn over, or slide, according as the coefficient of friction is $>$ or $< \tan a$, where a is the semi-vertical angle of the cone.

8. A cubical block rests on a rough inclined plane with its edges parallel to the edges of the plank. If, as the plank is gradually raised, the block turn on it before slipping, what is the least value that the coefficient of friction can have?

9. The triangular lamina ABC, right-angled at B, stands with BC upon a rough horizontal plane. If the plane be gradually tilted round an axis in its own plane perpendicular to BC, so that the angle B is lower than the angle C, shew that the lamina will begin to slide, or topple over, according as the coefficient of friction is less, or greater, than $\tan A$.

10. A square uniform metallic plate $ABCD$ rests with its side BC on a perfectly rough plane inclined to the horizon at an angle a. A string AP attached to A, the highest point of the plate, and passing over a smooth pulley at P, the vertex of the plane, supports a weight w, and AP is horizontal. If W be the weight of the plate, shew that, as w increases, it will begin to turn when

$$ w > W \frac{1 + \tan a}{2} . $$

11. A block, of weight one ton, is in the form of a rectangular parallelopiped, 8 feet high, standing on a square base whose side is 6 feet. It is placed on a rough weightless board with the sides of its base parallel to the length and breadth of the board, and the centre of the base is distant 6 feet from one extremity of the board. The board is now tilted round this extremity until the block topples without sliding; find the work done.

209. Ex. *A uniform rod rests in limiting equilibrium within a rough hollow sphere; if the rod subtend an angle $2a$ at the centre of the sphere, and if λ be the angle of friction, shew that the angle of inclination of the rod to the horizon is*

$$tan^{-1}\left[\frac{tan\,(a+\lambda)-tan\,(a-\lambda)}{2}\right].$$

Let AB be the rod, G its centre of gravity, and O the centre of the sphere, so that

$$\angle\,GOA = \angle\,GOB = a.$$

Through A and B draw lines AC and BC making an angle λ with the lines joining A and B to the centre. By Art. 189, these are the directions of the resultant reactions, R and S, at A and B respectively.

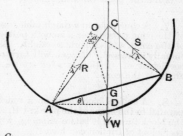

Since these reactions and the weight keep the rod in equilibrium, the vertical line through G must pass through C.

Let AD be the horizontal line drawn through A to meet CG in D so that the angle GAD is θ.

The angle $\qquad CAG = \angle\,OAG - \lambda = 90° - a - \lambda,$

and the angle $\qquad CBG = \angle\,OBG + \lambda = 90° - a + \lambda.$

Hence theorem (2) of Art. 79 gives

$$(a+a)\cot CGB = a\cot CAB - a\cot CBA,$$

$$i.e.\ 2\tan\theta = \cot\,(90°-a-\lambda) - \cot\,(90°-a+\lambda)$$

$$= \tan\,(a+\lambda) - \tan\,(a-\lambda) \quad\dots\dots\dots\dots\dots(1).$$

Otherwise thus; The solution may be also obtained by using the conditions of Art. 83.

Resolving the forces along the rod, we have

$$R\cos\,(90°-a-\lambda) - S\cos\,(90°-a+\lambda) = W\sin\theta,$$

$$i.e.\ R\sin\,(a+\lambda) - S\sin\,(a-\lambda) = W\sin\theta\dots\dots\dots\dots\dots(2).$$

Resolving perpendicular to the rod, we have

$$R\cos\,(a+\lambda) + S\cos\,(a-\lambda) = W\cos\theta\dots\dots\dots\dots\dots(3).$$

By taking moments about A, we have

$$S\,.\,AB\sin\,(90°-a+\lambda) = W\,.\,AG\cos\theta,$$

$$i.e.\ 2S\cos\,(a-\lambda) = W\cos\theta \quad\dots\dots\dots\dots\dots(4).$$

From equations (3) and (4), we have

$$R\cos\,(a+\lambda) = S\cos\,(a-\lambda) = \tfrac{1}{2}W\cos\theta.$$

Substituting these values of R and S in (2), we have

$$\tan(a+\lambda) - \tan(a-\lambda) = 2\tan\theta.$$

Numerical example. If the rod subtend a right angle at the centre of the sphere, shew that its inclination to the horizon is twice the angle of friction.

210. Ex. *Two bodies, of weights W_1 and W_2, are placed on an inclined plane and are connected by a light string which coincides with a line of greatest slope of the plane; if the coefficients of friction between the bodies and the plane be respectively μ_1 and μ_2, find the inclination of the plane to the horizon when both bodies are on the point of motion, it being assumed that the smoother body is below the other.*

The lower body would slip when the inclination is $\tan^{-1}\mu_1$, but the upper would not do so till the inclination had the value $\tan^{-1}\mu_2$. When the two are tied together the inclination for slipping would be between these two values. Let it be θ and let R_1 and R_2 be the normal reactions of the bodies; also let T be the tension of the string.

The frictions $\mu_1 R_1$ and $\mu_2 R_2$ both act up the plane.

For the equilibrium of W_1, we have

$$W_1 \sin\theta = T + \mu_1 R_1,$$

and

$$W_1 \cos\theta = R_1.$$

$$\therefore T = W_1(\sin\theta - \mu_1\cos\theta) \quad\quad\quad\ldots\ldots\ldots\ldots(1).$$

For the equilibrium of W_2, we have

$$W_2 \sin\theta + T = \mu_2 R_2,$$

and

$$W_2 \cos\theta = R_2.$$

$$\therefore T = \mu_2 R_2 - W_2 \sin\theta = W_2(\mu_2\cos\theta - \sin\theta) \quad\ldots\ldots(2).$$

Hence, from (1) and (2),

$$W_1(\sin\theta - \mu_1\cos\theta) = W_2(\mu_2\cos\theta - \sin\theta).$$

$$\therefore (W_1 + W_2)\sin\theta = (W_1\mu_1 + W_2\mu_2)\cos\theta.$$

$$\therefore \tan\theta = \frac{W_1\mu_1 + W_2\mu_2}{W_1 + W_2}.$$

Ex. 1. Two equal bodies are placed on a rough inclined plane, being connected by a light string; if the coefficients of friction be respectively $\frac{1}{2}$ and $\frac{1}{3}$, shew that they will both be on the point of motion when the inclination of the plane is $\tan^{-1}\frac{5}{12}$.

Ex. 2. Shew that the greatest angle at which a plane may be inclined to the horizon so that three equal bodies, whose coefficients of friction are $\frac{1}{2}$, $\frac{5}{8}$, and $\frac{3}{8}$ respectively, when rigidly connected together, may rest on it without slipping, is $\tan^{-1}\frac{1}{2}$.

211. **Ex.** *A particle is placed on a rough plane, whose inclination to the horizon is* α, *and is acted upon by a force P acting parallel to the plane and in a direction making an angle* β *with the line of greatest slope in the plane; if the coefficient of friction be* μ *and the equilibrium be limiting, find the direction in which the body will begin to move.*

Let W be the weight of the particle, and R the normal reaction.

The forces perpendicular to the inclined plane must vanish.

$$\therefore R = W \cos \alpha \ \ldots\ldots\ldots(1).$$

The other component of the weight will be $W \sin \alpha$, acting down the line of greatest slope.

Let the friction, μR, act in the direction AB, making an angle θ with the line of greatest slope, so that the particle would begin to move in the direction BA produced.

Since the forces acting along the surface of the plane are in equilibrium, we have, by Lami's Theorem,

$$\frac{\mu R}{\sin \beta} = \frac{W \sin \alpha}{\sin (\theta + \beta)} = \frac{P}{\sin \theta} \ \ldots\ldots\ldots\ldots(2).$$

From (1) and (2), eliminating R and W, we have

$$\cos \alpha = \frac{R}{W} = \frac{\sin \alpha \sin \beta}{\mu \sin (\theta + \beta)}.$$

Hence $$\sin (\theta + \beta) = \frac{\tan \alpha \sin \beta}{\mu} \ \ldots\ldots\ldots\ldots\ldots(3),$$

giving the angle θ.

Numerical Example. Suppose the inclination of the plane to be $30°$, the coefficient of friction to be $\frac{1}{3}$, and the angle between the force P and the line of greatest slope to be $30°$.

In this case we have

$$\sin (\theta + 30°) = \frac{\tan 30° \cdot \sin 30°}{\frac{1}{3}} = \frac{\sqrt{3}}{2} = \sin 60° \ldots\ldots\ldots(4).$$

Hence θ is $30°$, and the body begins to slide down the plane in a direction making an angle of $30°$ with the line of greatest slope.

The force P could be easily shewn to be $\frac{W}{6}\sqrt{3}$.

If the force be on the point of overcoming the weight, it can be easily shewn [or it follows from (4), since another solution is $\theta = 90°$], that the friction μR acts horizontally, so that the particle would start in a horizontal direction, and that the corresponding value of P is $\frac{W}{3}\sqrt{3}$.

EXAMPLES. XXXV.

1. A ladder, whose centre of gravity divides it into two portions of length a and b, rests with one end on a rough horizontal floor, and the other end against a rough vertical wall. If the coefficients of friction at the floor and wall be respectively μ and μ', shew that the inclination of the ladder to the floor, when the equilibrium is limiting, is

$$\tan^{-1} \frac{a - b\mu\mu'}{\mu (a+b)}.$$

2. A weightless rod is supported horizontally between two rough inclined planes at right angles to each other, the angle of friction λ being less than the inclination of either plane. Shew that the length of that portion of the rod on which a weight may be placed without producing motion is $\sin 2a \cdot \sin 2\lambda$ of the whole length of the rod, where a is the inclination of either plane to the horizon.

3. A heavy uniform rod is placed over one and under the other of two horizontal pegs, so that the rod lies in a vertical plane; shew that the length of the shortest rod which will rest in such a position is

$$a (1 + \tan a \cot \lambda),$$

where a is the distance between the pegs, a is the angle of inclination to the horizon of the line joining them, and λ is the angle of friction.

4. A uniform heavy rod, 1 foot long, one end of which is rough and the other smooth, rests within a circular hoop in a vertical plane, the radius of the hoop being 10 inches. If the rod is in limiting equilibrium when its rough end is at the lowest point of the hoop, shew that the coefficient of friction is $\frac{2}{4}\frac{4}{3}$.

5. A heavy uniform rod rests with its extremities on a rough circular hoop fixed in a vertical plane; the rod subtends an angle of 120° at the centre of the hoop, and in the limiting position of equilibrium is inclined to the horizon at an angle θ. If $\sqrt{3}\mu = \tan a$, μ being the coefficient of friction, shew that

$$\tan \theta : \tan 2a :: 2 : \sqrt{3}.$$

6. A and B are two small equal heavy rings which slide on a rough horizontal rod, the coefficient of friction being $3^{-\frac{3}{2}}$. Another equal heavy ring C slides on a weightless smooth string connecting A and B; shew that, in the position of limiting equilibrium, ABC is an equilateral triangle.

7. One end of a heavy uniform rod AB can slide along a rough horizontal rod AC, to which it is attached by a ring; B and C are joined by a string. If ABC be a right angle when the rod is on the point of sliding, μ the coefficient of friction, and a the angle between AB and the vertical, shew that

$$\mu = \frac{\tan a}{\tan^2 a + 2}.$$

8. A uniform rod slides with its ends on two fixed equally rough rods, one being vertical and the other inclined at an angle α to the horizon. Shew that the inclination θ to the horizon of the movable rod, when it is on the point of sliding, is given by

$$\tan\theta = \frac{1 \mp 2\mu\tan\alpha - \mu^2}{2(\tan\alpha \pm \mu)}.$$

9. A uniform ladder, whose length is a and whose weight is W, makes an angle θ with the horizontal, and rests with one end against a vertical wall and the other upon a horizontal floor, the wall and floor being equally rough, and the coefficient of friction being $\tan\lambda$. Shew that a man, whose weight is P, can never get nearer to the top of the ladder than $\dfrac{W\cot 2\lambda + P\cot\lambda - (W+P)\tan\theta}{2P}\, a\sin 2\lambda$.

10. The poles supporting a lawn-tennis net are kept in a vertical position by guy ropes, one to each pole, which pass round pegs 2 feet distant from the poles. If the coefficient of limiting friction between the ropes and pegs be $\frac{4}{3}$, shew that the inclination of the latter to the vertical must not be less than $\tan^{-1}\frac{2}{11}$, the height of the poles being 4 feet.

11. A chest in the form of a rectangular parallelopiped, whose weight without the lid is 200 lbs., and width from back to front 1 foot, has a lid weighing 50 lbs. and stands with its back 6 inches from a smooth wall and parallel to it. If the lid be open and lean against the wall, find the least coefficient of friction between the chest and the ground that there may be no motion.

12. A heavy circular disc, whose plane is vertical, is kept at rest on a rough inclined plane by a string parallel to the plane and touching the circle. Shew that the disc will slip on the plane if the coefficient of friction be less than $\frac{1}{2}\tan i$, where i is the slope of the plane.

13. A particle resting on a rough table, whose coefficient of friction is μ, is fastened by a string, of length a, to a fixed point A on the table. Another string is fastened to the particle and, after passing over the smooth edge of the table, supports an equal particle hanging freely. Shew that the particle on the table will rest at any point P of the circle, whose centre is A and whose radius is a, which is such that the string AP is kept taut and the distance of the second string from A is not greater than μa.

14. A heavy rod, of length $2a$, lies over a rough peg with one extremity leaning against a rough vertical wall; if c be the distance of the peg from the wall and λ be the angle of friction both at the peg and the wall, shew that, when the point of contact of the rod with the wall is above the peg, then the rod is on the point of sliding downwards when

$$\sin^3 \theta = \frac{c}{a} \cos^2 \lambda,$$

where θ is the inclination of the rod to the wall. If the point of contact of the rod and wall be below the peg, prove that the rod is on the point of slipping downwards when

$$\sin^2 \theta \sin (\theta + 2\lambda) = \frac{c}{a} \cos^2 \lambda,$$

and on the point of slipping upwards when

$$\sin^2 \theta \sin (\theta - 2\lambda) = \frac{c}{a} \cos^2 \lambda.$$

15. A circular disc, of radius a and weight W, is placed within a smooth sphere, of radius b, and a particle, of weight w, is placed on the disc. If the coefficient of friction between the particle and the disc be μ, find the greatest distance from the centre of the disc at which the particle can rest.

16. A smooth sphere, of given weight W, rests between a vertical wall and a prism, one of whose faces rests on a horizontal plane; if the coefficient of friction between the horizontal plane and the prism be μ, shew that the least weight of the prism consistent with equilibrium is $W \left(\dfrac{\tan a}{\mu} - 1 \right)$, where a is the inclination to the horizon of the face in contact with the sphere.

17. Two equal rods, of length $2a$, are fastened together so as to form two sides of a square, and one of them rests on a rough peg. Shew that the limiting distances of the points of contact from the middle point of the rod are $\dfrac{a}{2}(1 \pm \mu)$, where μ is the coefficient of friction.

18. Two uniform rods, AC and BC, are rigidly joined at C so that they form one uniform bent rod, whose two portions are at right angles. This bent rod is supported on the edge of a rough table which touches AC at its middle point. If BC be three times AC, shew that the tangent of the inclination of AC to the horizon is $\frac{1}{3}$.

Find also the least value of the coefficient of friction that the rod may rest with the point A on the edge of the table.

19. A heavy string rests on two given inclined planes, of the same material, passing over a small pulley at their common vertex. If the string be on the point of motion, shew that the line joining its two ends is inclined to the horizon at the angle of friction.

20. On a rough inclined plane $\left(\mu = \frac{1}{2}\right)$ a weight W is just supported by a force $\dfrac{W}{2}$ acting up the plane and parallel to it. Find the magnitude and direction of the least additional force, acting along the plane, which will prevent motion when the force $\dfrac{W}{2}$ acts along the plane, but at 60° with the line of greatest slope.

21. A weight W is laid upon a rough plane $\left(\mu = \dfrac{1}{\sqrt{3}}\right)$, inclined at 45° to the horizon, and is connected by a string passing through a smooth ring, A, at the top of the plane, with a weight P hanging vertically. If $W = 3P$, shew that, if θ be the greatest possible inclination of the string AW to the line of greatest slope in the plane, then

$$\cos \theta = \frac{2\sqrt{2}}{3}.$$

Find also the direction in which W would commence to move.

22. A weight W rests on a rough inclined plane inclined at an angle a to the horizon, and the coefficient of friction is $2 \tan a$. Shew that the least horizontal force along the plane which will move the body is $\sqrt{3} W \sin a$, and that the body will begin to move in a direction inclined at 60° to the line of greatest slope on the plane.

23. If two equal weights, unequally rough, be connected by a light rigid rod and be placed on an inclined plane whose inclination, a, to the horizon is the angle whose tangent is the geometric mean between the coefficients of friction, shew that the greatest possible inclination to the line of greatest slope which the rod can make when at rest is $\cos^{-1}\left(\dfrac{\mu_1 + \mu_2}{2\sqrt{2\mu_1\mu_2}}\right)$, where μ_1 and μ_2 are the coefficients of friction.

24. A heavy particle is placed on a rough plane inclined at an angle a to the horizon, and is connected by a stretched weightless string AP to a fixed point A in the plane. If AB be the line of greatest slope and θ the angle PAB when the particle is on the point of slipping, shew that $\sin \theta = \mu \cot a$.

Interpret the result when $\mu \cot a$ is greater than unity.

25. A hemispherical shell rests on a rough plane, whose angle of friction is λ; shew that the inclination of the plane base of the rim to the horizon cannot be greater than $\sin^{-1}(2 \sin \lambda)$.

26. A solid homogeneous hemisphere rests on a rough horizontal plane and against a smooth vertical wall. Shew that, if the coefficient of friction be greater than $\frac{3}{8}$, the hemisphere can rest in any position and, if it be less, the least angle that the base of the hemisphere can make with the vertical is $\cos^{-1}\frac{8\mu}{3}$.

If the wall be rough (coefficient of friction μ') shew that this angle is $\cos^{-1}\left(\frac{8\mu}{3}\cdot\frac{1+\mu'}{1+\mu\mu'}\right)$.

27. A heavy homogeneous hemisphere rests with its convex surface in contact with a rough inclined plane; shew that the greatest possible inclination of the plane to the horizon is $\sin^{-1}\frac{3}{8}$.

Shew that a homogeneous sphere cannot rest in equilibrium on any inclined plane, whatever its roughness.

28. If a hemisphere rest in equilibrium with its curved surface in contact with a rough plane inclined to the horizon at an angle $\sin^{-1}\frac{3}{16}$, find the inclination of the plane base of the hemisphere to the vertical.

29. A uniform hemisphere, of radius a and weight W, rests with its spherical surface on a horizontal plane, and a rough particle, of weight W', rests on the plane surface; shew that the distance of the particle from the centre of the plane face is not greater than $\frac{3W\mu a}{8W'}$, where μ is the coefficient of friction.

30. A sphere, whose radius is a and whose centre of gravity is at a distance c from the centre, rests in limiting equilibrium on a rough plane inclined at an angle a to the horizon; shew that it may be turned through an angle

$$2\cos^{-1}\left(\frac{a\sin a}{c}\right),$$

and still be in limiting equilibrium.

CHAPTER XV.

MISCELLANEOUS.

212. Bodies connected by smooth hinges. When two bodies are hinged together, it usually happens that, either a rounded end of one body fits loosely into a prepared hollow in the other body, as in the case of a ball-and-socket joint; or that a round pin, or other separate fastening, passes through a hole in each body, as in the case of the hinge of a door.

In either case, if the bodies be smooth, the action on each body at the hinge consists of a single force. Let the figure represent a section of the joint connecting two bodies. If it be smooth the actions at all the points of the joint pass through the centre of the pin and thus have as resultant a single force passing through O. Also the action

of the hinge on the one body is equal and opposite to the action of the hinge on the other body; for forces, equal and opposite to these actions, keep the pin, or fastening, in equilibrium, since its weight is negligible.

If the joint be not smooth, then at the points of contact A, B, C, D, ... there will also be frictional resistances acting in directions perpendicular to OA, OB, OC, ... The forces acting on such a joint will not, in general, reduce to a single force but to a force and a couple (Art. 87).

In solving questions concerning smooth hinges, the direction and magnitude of the action at the hinge are usually both unknown. Hence it is generally most convenient to assume the action of a smooth hinge on one body to consist of two unknown components at right angles to one another; the action of the hinge on the other body will then consist of components equal and opposite to these.

The forces acting on each body, together with the actions of the hinge on it, are in equilibrium, and the general conditions of equilibrium of Art. 83 will now apply.

In order to avoid mistakes as to the components of the reaction acting on each body, it is convenient, as in the second figure of the following example, not to produce the beams to meet but to leave a space between them.

213. Ex. *Three equal uniform rods, each of weight W, are smoothly jointed so as to form an equilateral triangle. If the system be supported at the middle point of one of the rods, shew that the action at the lowest angle is $\dfrac{\sqrt{3}}{6} W$, and that at each of the others is $W\sqrt{\dfrac{13}{12}}$.*

Let ABC be the triangle formed by the rods, and D the middle point of the side AB at which the system is supported.

Let the action of the hinge at A on the rod AB consist of two components, respectively equal to Y and X, acting in vertical and horizontal directions; hence the action of the hinge on AC consists of components equal and opposite to these.

Since the whole system is symmetrical about the vertical line through D, the action at B will consist of components, also equal to Y and X, as in the figure.

Let the action of the hinge C on CB consist of Y_1 vertically upwards, and X_1 horizontally to the right, so that the action of the same hinge on CA consists of two components opposite to these, as in the figure.

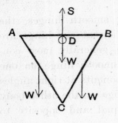
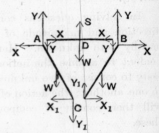

For AB, resolving vertically, we have
$$S = W + 2Y \quad \dots\dots\dots\dots\dots\dots(1),$$
where S is the vertical reaction of the peg at D.

For CB, resolving horizontally and vertically, and taking moments about C, we have
$$X + X_1 = 0 \quad \dots\dots\dots\dots\dots\dots(2),$$
$$W = Y + Y_1 \quad \dots\dots\dots\dots\dots\dots(3),$$
and
$$W \cdot a \cos 60° + X \cdot 2a \sin 60° = Y \cdot 2a \cos 60° \dots\dots\dots(4).$$

For CA, by resolving vertically, we have
$$W = Y - Y_1 \quad \dots\dots\dots\dots\dots\dots(5).$$

From equations (3) and (5) we have
$$Y_1 = 0, \text{ and } Y = W.$$

Hence equation (4) is
$$X = \tfrac{1}{2} W \cot 60° = \frac{W}{2\sqrt{3}} = \frac{\sqrt{3}}{6} W.$$

Therefore, from (2),
$$X_1 = -\frac{\sqrt{3}}{6} W.$$

Also (1) gives
$$S = 3W.$$

Hence the action of the hinge at B consists of a force $\sqrt{X^2 + Y^2}$ $\left(i.e.\ W\sqrt{\dfrac{13}{12}}\right)$, acting at an angle $\tan^{-1}\dfrac{Y}{X}$ ($i.e.\ \tan^{-1} 2\sqrt{3}$), to the horizon; also the action of the hinge at C consists of a horizontal force equal to $\dfrac{\sqrt{3}}{6} W$.

A priori reasoning would have shewn us that the action of the hinge at C must be horizontal; for the whole system is symmetrical about the line CD, and, unless the component Y_1 vanished, the reaction at C would not satisfy the condition of symmetry.

EXAMPLES. XXXVI.

1. Two equal uniform beams, AB and BC, are freely jointed at B and A is fixed to a hinge at a point in a wall about which AB can turn freely in a vertical plane. At what point in BC must a vertical force be applied to keep the two beams in one horizontal line, and what is the magnitude of the force?

2. Two uniform beams, AC and CB, are smoothly hinged together at C, and have their ends attached at two points, A and B, in the same horizontal line. If they be made of the same material and be of total weight 60 lbs., and if each be inclined at an angle of 60° to the horizon, shew that the action of the hinge at the point C is a horizontal force of $5\sqrt{3}$ lbs. weight.

3. A pair of compasses, each of whose legs is a uniform bar of weight W, is supported, hinge downwards, by two smooth pegs placed at the middle points of the legs in the same horizontal line, the legs being kept apart at an angle $2a$ with one another by a weightless rod joining their extremities; shew that the thrust in this rod and that the action at the hinge are each $\frac{1}{2}W \cot a$.

4. Two equal uniform rods, AB and AC, each of weight W, are smoothly jointed at A and placed in a vertical plane with the ends B and C resting on a smooth table. Equilibrium is preserved by a string which attaches C to the middle point of AB. Shew that the tension of the string and the reaction of the rods at A are both equal to

$$\frac{W}{4} \operatorname{cosec} a \sqrt{1 + 8\cos^2 a},$$

and that each is inclined at an angle $\tan^{-1}\left(\frac{1}{3}\tan a\right)$ to the horizon, where a is the inclination of either rod to the horizon.

5. Two equal beams, AC and BC, freely jointed together at C, stand with their ends, A and B, in contact with a rough horizontal plane, and with the plane ABC vertical. If the coefficient of friction be $\frac{1}{2}$, shew that the angle ACB cannot be greater than a right angle, and find the thrust at C in any position of equilibrium.

6. Three uniform heavy rods, AB, BC, and CA, of lengths 5, 4, and 3 feet respectively, are hinged together at their extremities to form a triangle. Shew that the whole will balance, with AB horizontal, about a fulcrum which is distant $1\frac{1}{5}$ of an inch from the middle point towards A.

Prove also that the vertical components of the actions at the hinges A and B, when the rod is balanced, are $\dfrac{187}{600}W$ and $\dfrac{163}{600}W$ respectively, where W is the total weight of the rods.

7. Two equal rods, AB and BC, are jointed at B, and have their middle points connected by an inelastic string of such a length that, when it is straightened, the angle ABC is a right angle; if the system be freely suspended from the point A, shew that the inclination of AB to the vertical will be $\tan^{-1} \frac{1}{3}$, and find the tension of the string and the action at the hinge.

8. Two equal bars, AB and BC, each 1 foot long and each of weight W, are jointed together at B and suspended by strings OA, OB, and OC, each 1 foot long, from a fixed peg O; find the tensions of the three strings and the magnitude of the action at the hinge, the strings and bars being all in one plane.

9. Three uniform beams AB, BC, and CD, of the same thickness, and of lengths l, $2l$, and l respectively, are connected by smooth hinges at B and C, and rest on a perfectly smooth sphere, whose radius is $2l$, so that the middle point of BC and the extremities, A and D, are in contact with the sphere; shew that the pressure at the middle point of BC is $\frac{91}{100}$ of the weight of the beams.

10. Three uniform rods AB, BC, and CD, whose weights are proportional to their lengths a, b, and c, are jointed at B and C and are in a horizontal position resting on two pegs P and Q; find the actions at the joints B and C, and shew that the distance between the pegs must be

$$\frac{a^2}{2a+b} + \frac{c^2}{2c+b} + b.$$

11. AB and AC are similar uniform rods, of length a, smoothly jointed at A. BD is a weightless bar, of length b, smoothly jointed at B, and fastened at D to a smooth ring sliding on AC. The system is hung on a small smooth pin at A. Shew that the rod AC makes with the vertical an angle

$$\tan^{-1} \frac{b}{a + \sqrt{a^2 - b^2}}.$$

12. A square figure $ABCD$ is formed by four equal uniform rods jointed together, and the system is suspended from the joint A, and kept in the form of a square by a string connecting A and C; shew that the tension of the string is half the weight of the four rods, and find the direction and magnitude of the action at either of the joints B or D.

13. Four equal rods are jointed together to form a rhombus, and the opposite joints are joined by strings forming the diagonals, and the whole system is placed on a smooth horizontal table. Shew that their tensions are in the same ratio as their lengths.

214. **Funicular,** *i.e.* **Rope, Polygon.** If a light cord have its ends attached to two fixed points, and if at different points of the cord there be attached weights, the figure formed by the cord is called a funicular polygon.

Let O and O_1 be the two fixed points at which the ends of the cord are tied, and let A_1, A_2, ... A_n be the points of the cord at which are attached bodies, whose weights are w_1, w_2, ... w_n respectively.

Let the lengths of the portions

OA_1, A_1A_2, A_2A_3, ... A_nO_1, be a_1, a_2, a_3, ... a_{n+1}, respectively, and let their inclinations to the horizon be

$$a_1, \quad a_2, \quad \ldots a_{n+1}.$$

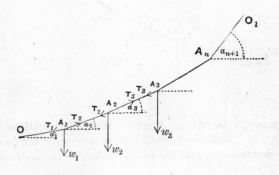

Let h and k be respectively the horizontal and vertical distances between the points O and O_1, so that

$$a_1 \cos a_1 + a_2 \cos a_2 + \ldots + a_{n+1} \cos a_{n+1} = h \ldots (1),$$
and $\quad a_1 \sin a_1 + a_2 \sin a_2 + \ldots + a_{n+1} \sin a_{n+1} = k \ldots (2).$

Let T_1, T_2, ... T_{n+1} be respectively the tensions of the portions of the cord.

Resolving vertically and horizontally for the equilibrium of the different weights in succession, we have

$$T_2 \sin a_2 \; - T_1 \sin a_1 = w_1, \text{ and } T_2 \cos a_2 \; - T_1 \cos a_1 = 0 \; ;$$

$$T_3 \sin a_3 \; - T_2 \sin a_2 = w_2, \text{ and } T_3 \cos a_3 \; - T_2 \cos a_2 = 0 \; ;$$

$$T_4 \sin a_4 \; - T_3 \sin a_3 = w_3, \text{ and } T_4 \cos a_4 \; - T_3 \cos a_3 = 0 \; ;$$

....

$$T_{n+1} \sin a_{n+1} - T_n \sin a_n = w_n, \text{ and } T_{n+1} \cos a_{n+1} - T_n \cos a_n = 0.$$

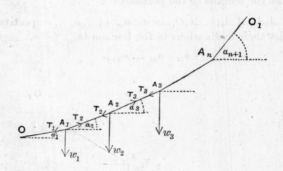

These $2n$ equations, together with the equations (1) and (2), are theoretically sufficient to determine the $(n+1)$ unknown tensions, and the $(n+1)$ unknown inclinations

$$a_1, \quad a_2, \; \dots a_{n+1}.$$

From the right-hand column of equations, we have

$$T_1 \cos a_1 = T_2 \cos a_2 = T_3 \cos a_3 = \dots = T_{n+1} \cos a_{n+1}$$
$$= K \text{ (say)} \quad \dots \dots (3),$$

so that the horizontal component of the tension of the cord is constant throughout and is denoted by K.

From (3), substituting for T_1, T_2, ... T_{n+1} in the left-hand column of equations, we have

$$\tan a_2 - \tan a_1 = \frac{w_1}{K},$$

$$\tan a_3 - \tan a_2 = \frac{w_2}{K},$$

$$\tan a_4 - \tan a_3 = \frac{w_3}{K},$$

$$\dots\dots\dots\dots\dots\dots\dots$$

$$\tan a_{n+1} - \tan a_n = \frac{w_n}{K}.$$

If the weights be all equal, the right-hand members of this latter column of equations are all equal and it follows that $\tan a_1$, $\tan a_2$, ... $\tan a_{n+1}$, are in arithmetical progression.

Hence when a set of equal weights are attached to different points of a cord, as above, the tangents of inclination to the horizon of successive portions of the cord form an arithmetical progression whose constant difference is the weight of any attached particle divided by the constant horizontal tension of the cords.

215. Graphical construction. If, in the Funicular Polygon, the inclinations of the different portions of cord be given, we can easily, by geometric construction, obtain the ratios of w_1, w_2, ... w_n.

For let C be any point and CD the horizontal line through C. Draw CP_1, CP_2, ... CP_{n+1} parallel to the cords OA_1, A_1A_2, ... A_nO_1, so that the angles P_1CD, P_2CD, ... are respectively a_1, a_2, ...

Draw any vertical line cutting these lines in D, P_1, P_2....

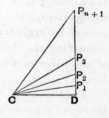

Then, by the previous article,

$$\frac{w_1}{K} = \tan a_2 - \tan a_1 = \frac{DP_2}{CD} - \frac{DP_1}{CD} = \frac{P_1P_2}{CD},$$

$$\frac{w_2}{K} = \tan a_3 - \tan a_2 = \frac{DP_3}{CD} - \frac{DP_2}{CD} = \frac{P_2P_3}{CD},$$

and so on.

Hence the quantities K, w_1, w_2, ... w_n are respectively proportional to the lines CD, P_1P_2, P_2P_3, ... P_nP_{n+1}, and hence their ratios are determined.

This result also follows from the fact that CP_2P_1 is a triangle of forces for the weight at A_1, CP_3P_2 similarly for the weight at A_2, and so on.

Similarly, if the weights hung on at the joints be given and the directions of any two of the cords be also known, we can determine the directions of the others. We draw a vertical line and on it mark off P_1P_2, P_2P_3, ... proportional to the weights W_1, W_2,.... If the directions of the cords OA_1, A_1A_2 are given, we draw P_1O, P_2O parallel to them and thus determine the point O. Join O to P_3, P_4, ... etc., and we have the directions of the rest of the cords.

216. Tensions of Elastic Strings. All through this book we have assumed our strings and cords to be inextensible, *i.e.* that they would bear any tension without altering their length.

In practice, all strings are extensible, although the extensibility is in many cases extremely small, and practically negligible. When the extensibility of the string cannot be neglected, there is a simple experimental law connecting the tension of the string with the amount of extension of the string. It may be expressed in the form

The tension of an elastic string varies as the extension of the string beyond its natural length.

Suppose a string to be naturally of length one foot; its tension, when the length is 13 inches, will be to its tension, when of length 15 inches, as

$$13 - 12 : 15 - 12, i.e., \text{ as } 1 : 3.$$

This law may be verified experimentally thus; take a spiral spring, or an india-rubber band. Attach one end A to a fixed point and at the other end B attach weights, and observe the amount of the extensions produced by the weights. These extensions will be found to be approximately proportional to the weights. The amount of the weights used must depend on the strength of the spring or of the rubber band; the heaviest must not be large enough to injure or permanently deform the spring or band.

217. The student will observe carefully that the tension of the string is not proportional to its stretched length, but to its extension.

The above law was discovered by Hooke (A.D. 1635— 1703), and enunciated by him in the form *Ut tensio, sic vis.* From it we easily obtain a formula giving us the tension in any case.

Let a be the unstretched length of a string, and T its tension when it is stretched to be of length x. The extension is now $x - a$, and the law states that

$$T \propto x - a.$$

This is generally expressed in the form

$$T = \lambda \cdot \frac{x - a}{a},$$

the constant of variation being $\dfrac{\lambda}{a}$.

The quantity λ depends only on the thickness of the string and on the material of which it is made, and is called the *Modulus of Elasticity of the String.*

It is equal to the force which would stretch the string, if placed on a smooth horizontal table, to twice its natural length; for, when $x = 2a$, we have the tension

$$= \lambda \frac{2a - a}{a} = \lambda.$$

No elastic string will however bear an unlimited

stretching; when the string, through being stretched, is on the point of breaking, its tension then is called the *breaking tension*.

Hooke's Law holds also for steel and other bars, but the extensions for which it is true in these cases are extremely small. We cannot stretch a bar to twice its natural length; but λ will be 100 times the force which will extend the bar by $\frac{1}{100}$th of its natural length. For if $x - a = \dfrac{a}{100}$, then

$$T = \frac{\lambda}{100}.$$

The value of T will depend also on the thickness of the bar, and the bar is usually taken as one square inch section. Thus the modulus of elasticity of a steel bar is about 13500 tons per square inch.

By the method of Art. 134 it is easily seen - that the work done in stretching an elastic string is equal to the extension multiplied by the mean of the initial and final tensions.

Ex. *ABC is an elastic string, hanging vertically from a fixed point A; at B and C are attached particles, of weights $2W$ and W respectively. If the modulus of elasticity of the string be $3W$, find the ratio of the stretched lengths of the portions of the string to their unstretched lengths.*

Let c and c_1 be the unstretched lengths of AB and BC, and x and y their stretched lengths.

Let T and T_1 be their tensions, so that

$$T = \lambda \frac{x - c}{c} = 3W \frac{x - c}{c},$$

and

$$T_1 = \lambda \frac{y - c_1}{c_1} = 3W \frac{y - c_1}{c_1}.$$

From the equilibrium of B and C, we have

$$T - T_1 = 2W, \text{ and } T_1 = W.$$

Hence

$$T = 3W.$$

$$\therefore 3W \frac{x - c}{c} = 3W, \text{ and } 3W \frac{y - c_1}{c_1} = W.$$

$$\therefore x = 2c, \text{ and } y = \tfrac{4}{3}c_1,$$

so that the stretched lengths are respectively twice and four-thirds of the natural lengths.

EXAMPLES. XXXVII.

1. ABC is an elastic string, whose modulus of elasticity is $4W$, which is tied to a fixed point at A. At B and C are attached weights each equal to W, the unstretched lengths of AB and BC being each equal to c. Shew that, if the string and bodies take up a vertical position of equilibrium, the stretched lengths of AB and BC are $\frac{3}{2}c$ and $\frac{5}{4}c$ respectively.

2. An elastic string has its ends attached to two points in the same horizontal plane, and initially it is just tight and unstretched; a particle, of weight W, is tied to the middle point of the string; if the modulus of elasticity be $\frac{W}{\sqrt{3}}$, shew that, in the position of equilibrium, the two portions of the string will be inclined at an angle of 60° to one another.

3. In the previous question, if $2a$ be the distance between the two points, $2c$ the unstretched length of the string, and λ the modulus of elasticity, shew that the inclination, θ, of the strings to the vertical is given by

$$\frac{W}{2\lambda}\tan\theta + \sin\theta = \frac{a}{c}.$$

4. A body rests on a rough inclined plane whose inclination α to the horizon is greater than λ, the angle of friction; it is held at rest by an elastic string attached to it and to a point on the plane. If the modulus of elasticity be equal to the weight of the body, prove that in the position of equilibrium the ratio of the length of the string to its original length is

$$1 + \sin(\alpha - \lambda) \cdot \sec\lambda.$$

5. Four equal jointed rods, each of length a, are hung from an angular point, which is connected by an elastic string with the opposite point. If the rods hang in the form of a square, and if the modulus of elasticity of the string be equal to the weight of a rod, shew that the unstretched length of the string is $\frac{a\sqrt{2}}{3}$.

6. An elastic cord, whose natural length is 10 inches, can be kept stretched to a length of 15 inches by a force of 5 lbs. wt.; find the amount of work done in stretching it from a length of 12 inches to a length of 15 inches.

7. A spiral spring requires a force of one pound weight to stretch it one inch. How much work is done in stretching it three inches more?

Graphic Constructions.

218. *To find the resultant of any number of coplanar forces.*

Let the forces be P, Q, R, and S whose lines of action are as in the left-hand figure.

Draw the figure $ABCDE$ having its sides AB, BC, CD, and DE respectively parallel and proportional to P, Q, R and S. Join AE, so that by the Polygon of Forces AE represents the required resultant in magnitude and direction.

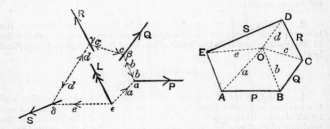

Take any point O and join it to A, B, C, D, and E; let the lengths of these joining lines be a, b, c, d, and e respectively.

Take any point α on the line of action of P, draw $\alpha\beta$ parallel to BO to meet Q in β, $\beta\gamma$ parallel to CO to meet R in γ, and $\gamma\delta$ parallel to DO to meet S in δ.

Through δ and α draw lines parallel respectively to EO and OA to meet in ϵ.

Through ϵ draw ϵL parallel and equal to AE. Then ϵL shall represent the required resultant in magnitude and line of action, on the same scale that AB represents P.

For P, being represented by AB, is equivalent to forces represented by AO and OB and therefore may be replaced by forces equal to a and b in the directions ϵa and βa. So Q may be replaced by b and c in directions $a\beta$ and $\gamma\beta$, R by c and d in directions $\beta\gamma$ and $\delta\gamma$, and S by forces d and e in directions $\gamma\delta$ and $\epsilon\delta$.

The forces P, Q, R, and S have therefore been replaced by forces acting along the sides of the figure $a\beta\gamma\delta\epsilon$, of which the forces along $a\beta$, $\beta\gamma$ and $\gamma\delta$ balance.

Hence we have left forces at ϵ which are parallel and equal to AO and OE, whose resultant is AE.

Since ϵL is drawn parallel and equal to AE, it therefore represents the required resultant in magnitude and line of action.

Such a figure as $ABCDE$ is called a Force Polygon and one such as $a\beta\gamma\delta\epsilon$ is called a Link or Funicular Polygon, because it represents a set of links or cords in equilibrium.

219. If the point E of the Force Polygon coincides with the point A it is said to close, and then the resultant force vanishes.

If the Force Polygon closed, but the Funicular Polygon did not close, *i.e.* if $\delta\epsilon a$ was not a straight line, we should have left forces acting at δ and a parallel to OE and AO, *i.e.* we should in this case have two equal, opposite, and parallel forces forming a couple.

If however the Funicular Polygon also closed, then $\delta\epsilon a$ would be a straight line and these two equal, opposite, and parallel forces would now be in the same straight line and would balance.

Hence, if the forces P, Q, R, S are in equilibrium, both their Force and Funicular Polygons must close.

220. If the forces be parallel the construction is the same as in the previous article. The annexed figure is

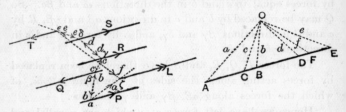

drawn for the case in which the forces are parallel and two of the five forces are in the opposite direction to that of the other three.

Since P, R, and S are in the same direction we have AB, CD, and DE in one direction, whilst BC and EF which represent Q and T are in the opposite direction.

The proof of the construction is the same as in the last article. The line ζL, equal and parallel to AF, represents the required resultant both in magnitude and line of action.

This construction clearly applies to finding the resultant weight of a number of weights.

221. *A closed polygon of light rods freely jointed at their extremities is acted upon by a given system of forces*

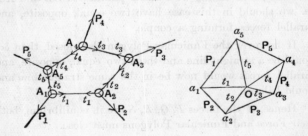

acting at the joints which are in equilibrium; find the actions along the rods.

Let A_1A_2, A_2A_3, ... A_5A_1 be a system of five rods freely jointed at their ends and at the joints let given forces P_1, P_2, P_3, P_4, and P_5 act as in the figure.

Let the consequent actions along the rods be t_1, t_2, t_3, t_4, and t_5, as marked.

Draw the pentagon $a_5a_1a_2a_3a_4$ having its sides parallel and proportional to the forces P_1, P_2, ... P_5. Since the forces are in equilibrium this polygon is a closed figure.

Through a_1 draw a_1O parallel to A_1A_2 and through a_5 draw a_5O parallel to A_5A_1.

Now the triangle a_5Oa_1 has its sides parallel to the forces P_1, t_1, and t_5 which act on the joint A_1. Its sides are therefore proportional to these forces; hence, on the same scale that a_5a_1 represents P_1, the sides Oa_5 and a_1O represent t_5 and t_1.

Join Oa_2, Oa_3, and Oa_4.

The sides a_1a_2 and Oa_1 represent two of the forces, P_2 and t_1, which act on A_2. Hence a_2O, which completes the triangle a_1Oa_2, represents the third force t_2 in magnitude and direction.

Similarly Oa_3 and Oa_4 represent t_3 and t_4 respectively.

The lines Oa_1, Oa_2, Oa_3, Oa_4 and Oa_5 therefore represent, both in magnitude and direction, the forces along the sides of the framework. The figure $a_1a_2a_3a_4a_5$ is called the force polygon.

A similar construction would apply whatever be the number of sides in the framework.

222. It is clear that the figure and construction of the preceding article are really the same as those of Art. 218.

If the right-hand figure represents a framework of rods a_1a_2, a_2a_3, a_2a_4 ... acted on at the joints by forces along a_1O, a_2O, ... then the polygon $A_1A_2A_3A_4A_5$ of the left-hand figure is clearly its force polygon, since A_1A_2, A_2A_3 ... are respectively parallel to a_1O, a_2O ....

Hence either of these two polygons may be taken as the Framework, or Funicular Polygon, and then the other is the Force Polygon. For this reason such figures are called Reciprocal.

As another example we give a triangular framework acted on at its joints by three forces P_1, P_2, P_3 in equilibrium whose force polygon is $a_2a_3a_1$; conversely, $A_2A_3A_1$ is the force polygon for the triangle $a_1a_2a_3$ acted on by forces T_1, T_2, and T_3.

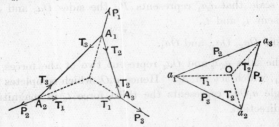

223. **Ex. 1.** *A framework, ABCD, consisting of light rods stiffened by a brace AC, is supported in a vertical plane by supports at A and B, so that AB is horizontal; the lengths of AB, BC, CD and DA are 4, 3, 2, and 3 feet respectively; also AB and CD are parallel, and AD and BC are equally inclined to AB. If weights of 5 and 10 cwt. respectively be placed at C and D, find the reactions of the supports at A and B, and the forces exerted by the different portions of the framework.*

Let the forces in the sides be as marked in the figure and let P and Q be the reactions at A and B.

Draw a vertical line $\alpha\beta$, 5 inches in length, to represent the weight 10 cwt. at D; also draw $\alpha\delta$ parallel to AD and $\beta\delta$ parallel to CD.

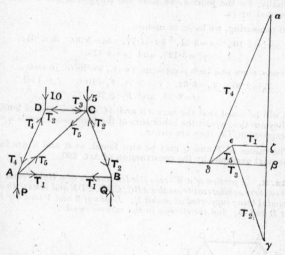

Then $\alpha\beta\delta$ is the Triangle of Forces for the joint D, and the forces at D must be in the directions marked.

Note that the force at C in the bar DC must be along DC or CD, and that at D in the same bar along CD or DC.

[This is an important general principle; for any bar, which undergoes stress, is either resisting a tendency to compress it, or a tendency to stretch it.

In the first case, the action at each end is from its centre towards its ends, in which case it is called a Strut; in the second case it is towards its centre, when it is called a Tie.

In *either* case the actions at the two ends of the rod are equal and opposite.]

Draw $\beta\gamma$ vertical and equal to $2\frac{1}{2}$ ins. to represent the weight at C. Draw $\gamma\epsilon$ parallel to BC and $\delta\epsilon$ parallel to AC. Then $\delta\beta\gamma\epsilon\delta$ is the Polygon of Forces for the joint C, so that the actions at C are as marked.

Draw $\epsilon\zeta$ horizontal to meet $\alpha\gamma$ in ζ.

Then $\epsilon\gamma\zeta$ is the Triangle of Forces for B, so that the reaction Q is represented by $\gamma\zeta$, and T_1 by $\zeta\epsilon$.

Finally, for the joint A, we have the polygon $\delta\epsilon\zeta a\delta$, so that P is represented by ζa.

On measuring, we have, in inches,

$$\epsilon\zeta=1\cdot 10, \quad \gamma\epsilon=3\cdot 31, \quad \delta\beta=1\cdot 77, \quad \delta a=5\cdot 30, \quad \delta\epsilon=\cdot 91,$$
$$\gamma\zeta=3\cdot 125, \text{ and } \zeta a=4\cdot 375.$$

Hence, since one inch represents 2 cwt., we have, in cwts.,

$$T_1=2\cdot 20, \quad T_2=6\cdot 62, \quad T_3=3\cdot 54, \quad T_4=10\cdot 6, \quad T_5=1\cdot 82,$$
$$Q=6\cdot 25, \text{ and } P=8\cdot 75.$$

It will be noted that the bars AB and AC are in a state of tension, *i.e.* they are ties, whilst the other bars of the framework are in a state of compression, *i.e.* they are struts.

The values of P and Q may be also found, as R and S are found in the next example, by the construction of Art. 220.

Ex. 2. *A portion of a Warren Girder consists of a light frame composed of three equilateral triangles ABC, CBD, CDE and rests with ACE horizontal being supported at A and E. Loads of 2 and 1 tons are hung on at B and D; find the stresses in the various members.*

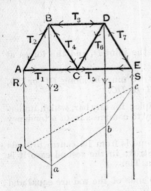
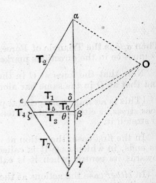

Draw $a\beta$, $\beta\gamma$ vertical, and equal to 2 inches and 1 inch respectively, to represent 2 tons and 1 ton. Take any pole O and join Oa, $O\beta$, $O\gamma$.

Take any point a on the line of action of the 2 ton wt.; draw ad parallel to aO to meet the reaction R in d, and ab parallel to βO to meet the vertical through D in b, and then bc parallel to γO to meet S in c. Join cd. Then $abcd$ is the funicular polygon of which (if we draw $O\delta$ parallel to cd) $\alpha\beta\gamma\delta$ is the force polygon (in this case a straight line). Hence $\delta\alpha$ represents R and $\gamma\delta$ represents S.

Let the forces exerted by the rods, whether thrusts or tensions, be T_1, T_2, ... as marked.

Draw $\delta\epsilon$ parallel to CA and $\alpha\epsilon$ parallel to AB; then $\alpha\epsilon\delta$ is a triangle of forces for the joint A, so that $\alpha\epsilon$ and $\epsilon\delta$ represent T_2 and T_1.

Draw $\epsilon\zeta$ and $\beta\zeta$ parallel to BC and BD respectively. Then $\epsilon\alpha\beta\zeta$ is the polygon of forces for the joint B so that T_4 and T_3 are given by $\epsilon\zeta$ and $\zeta\beta$ respectively.

Draw $\delta\theta$ parallel to DC; then $\delta\epsilon\zeta\theta$ is the polygon of forces for the joint C and hence $\zeta\theta$ and $\theta\delta$ represent T_5 and T_6.

Draw $\gamma\iota$ parallel to DC to meet $\epsilon\zeta$ produced in ι; then $\zeta\beta\gamma\iota$ is the polygon of forces for the joint D so that $\gamma\iota$ and $\iota\zeta$ represent T_6 and T_7 respectively; [it follows that $\gamma\iota$ must be equal and parallel to $\delta\theta$, and hence $\iota\theta$ must be equal and parallel to $\gamma\delta$ and therefore represent S.]

Finally $\iota\theta\zeta$ is the triangle of forces for the joint E.

Hence if we measure off the lengths $\alpha\delta$, $\delta\gamma$, $\epsilon\delta$, $\epsilon\alpha$, $\zeta\beta$, $\epsilon\zeta$, $\zeta\theta$, $\theta\delta$, $\iota\zeta$ in inches, we shall have the values of R, S, T_1, T_2, T_3, T_4, T_5, T_6, T_7 respectively expressed in tons' wt.

They are found to be 1·75, 1·25, 1·01, 2·02, ·87, ·29, ·72, ·29, and 1·44 tons' wt. respectively.

From the figure it is clear that AC, CE and CD are ties and that the others are struts.

EXAMPLES. XXXVIII.

[The following are to be solved by graphic methods.]

1. A uniform triangular lamina ABC, of 30 lbs. weight, can turn in a vertical plane about a hinge at B; it is supported with the side AB horizontal by a peg placed at the middle point of BC. If the sides AB, BC, and CA be respectively 6, 5, and 4 feet in length, find the pressure on the prop and the strain on the hinge.

2. A uniform ladder, 30 feet long, rests with one end against a smooth wall and the other against the rough ground, the distance of its foot from the wall being 10 feet; find the resultant force exerted by the ground on the foot of the ladder if the weight of the ladder be 150 lbs. (1) when there is no extra weight on the ladder, (2) when 1 cwt. is placed $\frac{3}{4}$ of the way up.

3. It is found by experiment that a force equal to the weight of 10 lbs. acting along the plane is required to make a mass of 10 lbs. begin to move up a plane inclined at 45° to the horizon; find the coefficient of friction between the mass and the plane.

4. Three forces equal respectively to the weights of 5·05 lbs., 4·24 lbs., and 3·85 lbs. act at three given points of a flat disc resting on a smooth table. Place the forces, by geometric construction, so as to keep the disc in equilibrium, and measure the number of degrees in each of the angles which they make with one another.

5. A uniform rectangular block, of which $ABCD$ is the symmetrical section through its centre of gravity, rests with CD in contact with a rough horizontal plane $(\mu = \frac{1}{2})$; the weight of the block is 40 lbs. and a force equal to 10 lbs. wt. acts at D in the direction CD; if the lengths of BC and CD be respectively 3 and 5 feet, find the value of the least force which, applied at the middle point of CB parallel to the diagonal DB, would move the block.

6. A body, of weight 100 lbs., rests on a rough plane whose slope is 1 in 3, the coefficient of friction being $\frac{1}{2}$; find the magnitude of the force which, acting at an angle of 40° with the plane, is on the point of dragging the body up the plane. Find also the force which, acting at an angle of 40° with the plane, is on the point of dragging the body down the plane.

7. ABC is a triangle whose sides AB, BC, CA are respectively 12, 10, and 15 inches long and BD is the perpendicular from B on CA. Find by means of a force and funicular polygon the magnitude and the line of action of the resultant of the following forces; 8 from A to C, 8 from C to B, 3 from B to A, and 2 from B to D.

8. AB is a straight line, 3 feet long; at A and B act parallel forces equal to 7 and 5 cwt. respectively which are (1) like, (2) unlike; construct for each case the position of the point D at which their resultant meets AB and measure its distance from A.

9. Loads of 2, 4, 3 cwt. are placed on a beam 10 ft. long at distances of 1 ft.; 3 ft.; 7 ft. from one end. Find by an accurate drawing the line of action of the resultant.

10. A horizontal beam 20 feet long is supported at its ends and carries loads of 3, 2, 5, and 4 cwt. at distances of 3, 7, 12, and 15 feet respectively from one end. Find by means of a funicular polygon the thrusts on the two ends.

11. A triangular frame of jointed rods ABC, right-angled at A, can turn about A in a vertical plane. The side AB is horizontal and the corner C rests against a smooth vertical stop below A. If $AB=3$ ft., $AC=1$ ft., and a weight of 50 lbs. be hung on at B, find graphically the stresses in the various bars.

12. Forces equal to 1, 2, 4, and 4 lbs. weight respectively act along the sides AB, BC, CD, and DA of a square. Prove that their resultant is 3·6 lbs. weight in a direction inclined at $\tan^{-1}\frac{3}{2}$ to CB and intersecting BC produced at G, where CG is equal to $\frac{5}{3} BC$.

13. AC and CB are two equal beams inclined to one another at an angle of 40°, the ends A and B resting on the ground, which is rough enough to prevent any slipping, and the plane ACB being inclined at an angle of 70° to the ground. At C is attached a body of weight 10 cwt., and the system is supported by a rope, attached to C, which is in the vertical plane passing through C and the middle point of AB. If the rope be attached to the ground and be inclined at an angle of 50° to the ground, find the tension of the rope and the action along the beams. [This arrangement is called a Sheer-legs.]

14. A beam, AB, of weight 140 lbs., rests with one end A on a rough horizontal plane, the other end, B, being supported by a cord, passing over a smooth pulley at C, whose horizontal and vertical distances from A are respectively 15 and 20 feet. If the length of the beam be 15 feet, and it be on the point of slipping when the end B is at a height of 9 feet above the horizontal plane, find the magnitudes of the coefficient of friction, the tension of the chord, and the resultant reaction at A.

15. A triangular framework ABC, formed of three bars jointed at its angular points, is in equilibrium under the action of three forces P, Q, and R acting outwards at its angular points, the line of action of each being the line joining its point of application to the middle of the opposite bar. If the sides BC, CA, and AB be 9 ft., 8 ft., and 7 ft. in length respectively, and if the force P be equal to 50 lbs. wt., find the values of Q and R, and the forces acting along the bars of the framework.

16. A and B are two fixed pegs, B being the higher, and a heavy rod rests on B and passes under A; shew that, the angle of friction between the rod and the pegs being the same for both, the rod will rest in any position in which its centre of gravity is beyond B, provided that the inclination of AB to the horizon is less than the angle of friction; also, for any greater inclination, determine graphically the limiting distance of the centre of gravity beyond B consistent with equilibrium.

17. A uniform beam AB, weighing 100 lbs., is supported by strings AC and BD, the latter being vertical, and the angles CAB and ABD are each 105°. The rod is maintained in this position by a horizontal force P applied at B. Shew that the value of P is about 25 lbs. weight.

18. AB and AC are two equal rods of no appreciable weight smoothly jointed together at A, which rest in a vertical plane with their ends upon a smooth horizontal plane BC. D is a point in AB such that $AD = \frac{1}{3}AB$ and E and F are the points of trisection of AC, E being the nearer to A. A fine string connects D and F and is of such a length that the angle A is 60°. Shew that, if a weight W be attached to E, the tension of the string is $\dfrac{W}{2}$.

19. $ABCDEF$ is a regular hexagon. Shew that the forces which must act along AC, AF, and DE to produce equilibrium with a force of 40 lbs. weight acting along EC are respectively 10, 17·32, and 34·64 lbs. weight.

20. Fig. 1 consists of a symmetrical system of light rods freely jointed and supported vertically at the extremities; vertical loads of 10 and 5 cwt. are placed at the points indicated; find the thrusts or tensions of the rods, if the side rods are inclined at 50° to the horizon.

21. Fig. 2 consists of a symmetrical system of light rods freely jointed and supported by vertical reactions at A and B; if a weight of 10 cwt. be placed at D find the thrusts or tensions in the rods, given that $\angle DAB = 55°$ and $\angle CAB = 35°$.

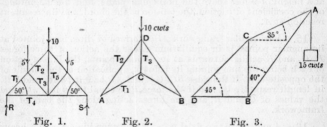

Fig. 1.   Fig. 2.   Fig. 3.

22. A crane is constructed as in Fig. 3, and 15 cwt. is hung on at A; find the forces along the parts AC and AB.

If the post BC be free to move, and BD be rigidly fixed, find the pull in the tie CD.

23. A portion of a Warren girder consists of three equilateral triangles ABC, ADC, BCE, the lines AB, DCE being horizontal and the latter the uppermost. It rests on vertical supports at A and B and carries 5 tons at D and 3 tons at E. Find the reactions at the supports and the stresses in the four inclined members.

24. $ABCD$ consists of a quadrilateral consisting of four light rods loosely jointed, which is stiffened by a rod BD; at A and C act forces equal to 40 lbs. weight. Given that $AB = 2$ ft., $BC = 3$ ft., $CD = 4$ ft., $DA = 4\frac{1}{2}$ ft., and $DB = 5$ ft., find the tensions or thrusts of the rods.

CHAPTER XVI.

SOME ADDITIONAL PROPOSITIONS.

224. Formal proof of the Parallelogram of Forces.

The proof is divided into two portions, (I) as regards the direction, (II) as regards the magnitude of the resultant.

I. DIRECTION.

(a) Equal Forces.

Let the forces be equal and represented by OA and OB.

Complete the parallelogram $OACB$, and join OC. Then OC bisects the angle AOB.

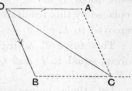

Since the forces are equal, it is clear that the resultant must bisect the angle between them; for there is no reason to shew why the resultant should lie on one side of OC which would not equally hold to shew that the resultant should lie on the other side of OC. Hence, as far as regards direction, we may assume the truth of the theorem for equal forces.

(β) **Commensurable Forces.**

Lemma. *If the theorem be true, as far as regards direction, for a pair of forces P and Q, and also for a pair of forces P and R acting at the same angle, to shew that it is true for the pair of forces P and (Q + R).*

Let the forces act at a point A of a rigid body, and let AB be the direction of P, and ACD that of Q and R.

Let AB and AC represent the forces P and Q in magnitude.

Since, by the principle of The Transmissibility of Force, the force R may be supposed to act at any point in its line of action, let it act at C and be represented by CD.

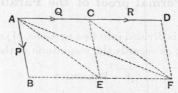

Complete the parallelograms $ABEC$ and $ABFD$.

The resultant of P and Q is, by supposition, equal to some force T acting in the direction AE; let them be replaced by this resultant and let its point of application be removed to E.

This force T, acting at E, may now be replaced by forces, equal to P and Q, acting in the directions CE and EF respectively.

Let their points of application be removed to C and F.

Again, by the supposition, the resultant of P and R, acting at C, is equivalent to some force acting in the direction CF; let them be replaced by their resultant and let its point of application be removed to F.

All the forces have now been applied at F without altering their combined effect; hence F must be a point on the line of action of their resultant; therefore AF is the direction of the required resultant.

Hence the Lemma is proved.

Application of the lemma.

By (a) we know that the theorem is true for forces which are each equal to S.

Hence, by the lemma, putting P, Q, and R each equal to S, we see that the theorem is true for forces S and $2S$. Again, by the lemma, since the theorem is true for forces (S, S) and $(S, 2S)$ we see that it is true for forces $(S, 3S)$. Similarly for forces $(S, 4S)$ and so on.

Continuing in this way we see that it is true for forces S and mS, where m is any positive integer.

Again, from the lemma, putting P equal to mS, and Q and R both equal to S, the theorem is true for forces mS and $2S$.

Again, putting P equal to mS, Q to $2S$, and R to S, the theorem is true for forces mS and $3S$.

Proceeding in this way we see that the theorem is true for forces mS and nS, where m and n are positive integers.

Also any two commensurable forces can be represented by mS and nS.

(γ) Incommensurable Forces.

Let P and Q be incommensurable forces, and let AB and AC represent them.

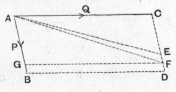

Complete the parallelogram $ABDC$.

If the resultant of P and Q be not in the line AD let it act in the line AE meeting CD in E.

Divide AC into any number of equal parts x, *each less than ED*, and from CD cut off successively portions, each equal to x. The last point of subdivision F must fall between E and D, *since x is less than ED*.

Draw FG parallel to CA to meet AB in G, and join AF.

The lines AC and AG represent commensurable forces, and therefore their resultant is, by (β), in the direction $A\breve{F}$.

Hence the resultant of forces AC and AB must lie within the angle BAF. But this resultant acts in the direction AE, which is without the angle BAF.

But this is absurd.

Hence AE cannot be the direction of the resultant.

In a similar manner it can be shewn that no other line, except AD, can be the direction of the resultant.

Hence AD is the direction of the resultant.

II. MAGNITUDE.

As before let AB and AC represent the forces P and Q. Complete the parallelogram $ABDC$.

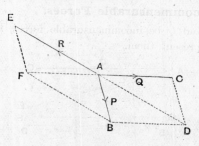

Take a force R, represented both in magnitude and direction by AE, to balance the resultant of P and Q.

Then, by the first part of the proof, *AE is in the same straight line with AD.* AE shall also be equal to AD.

Complete the parallelogram $AEFB$.

Since the three forces P, Q, and R are in equilibrium, each of them is equal and opposite to the resultant of the other two.

Now the resultant of P and R is in the direction AF; hence AC, the direction of Q, is in the same straight line with AF.

Therefore $ADBF$ is a parallelogram, and hence DA equals BF.

But, since $AEFB$ is a parallelogram, BF equals AF.

Therefore AD equals AE, and hence AD is equal, in magnitude as well as direction, to the resultant of P and Q.

The above proof is known as **Duchayla's Proof.**

225. Centre of gravity of a uniform circular arc.

Let AB be a circular arc, subtending an angle $2a$ at its centre O, and let OC bisect the angle AOB.

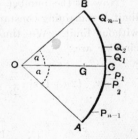

Let the arc AB be divided into $2n$ equal portions, the points of division, starting from C, being $P_1, P_2, \ldots P_{n-1}$ towards A, and $Q_1, Q_2, \ldots Q_{n-1}$ towards B.

At each of these points of division, and at the extremities A and B, and also at the point C, let there be placed equal particles, each of mass m.

Let the arc joining two successive particles subtend an angle β at the centre O, so that $2n\beta = 2a$.

Since the system of particles is symmetrical with respect to the line OC, the centre of gravity, G, must lie on the line OC. Let $\bar{x}$ be the distance OG.

Then, by Art. 111,

$$\bar{x} = \frac{mr + 2m \cdot r\cos\beta + 2m \cdot r\cos 2\beta + \ldots + 2mr\cos n\beta}{m + 2m + 2m + \ldots + 2m}$$

$$= \frac{r}{2n+1}\left[1 + 2\cos\beta + 2\cos 2\beta + \ldots + 2\cos n\beta\right]$$

$$= \frac{r}{2n+1}\left[1 + 2\frac{\cos\dfrac{n+1}{2}\beta\sin\dfrac{n\beta}{2}}{\sin\dfrac{\beta}{2}}\right], \quad [\textit{Trig. Art. 242}]$$

by summing the trigonometrical series,

$$= \frac{r}{2n+1}\left[1 + \frac{\sin\left(n+\dfrac{1}{2}\right)\beta - \sin\dfrac{\beta}{2}}{\sin\dfrac{\beta}{2}}\right]$$

$$= r\frac{\sin\left(n+\dfrac{1}{2}\right)\beta}{(2n+1)\sin\dfrac{\beta}{2}} = r\frac{\sin\left(a+\dfrac{a}{2n}\right)}{(2n+1)\sin\dfrac{a}{2n}} \quad \ldots\ldots\ldots\ldots\ldots(\text{i}).$$

Now let the number of particles be increased without limit, a remaining constant, and consequently β decreasing without limit. We thus obtain the case of a uniform circular arc.

Now $(2n+1)\sin\dfrac{a}{2n} = \dfrac{(2n+1)}{2n}\,a \cdot \dfrac{\sin\dfrac{a}{2n}}{\dfrac{a}{2n}}$

$$= \left[1 + \frac{1}{2n}\right] \cdot a \cdot \frac{\sin\dfrac{a}{2n}}{\dfrac{a}{2n}} = a,$$

when n is made indefinitely great.

Hence, in the case of a uniform circular arc, (i) becomes

$$\bar{x} = r\,\frac{\sin \alpha}{\alpha}\;*.$$

Cor. In the case of a semicircular arc, in which $\alpha = \dfrac{\pi}{2}$, the distance of the centre of gravity from the centre

$$= r\,\frac{\sin \dfrac{\pi}{2}}{\dfrac{\pi}{2}} = \frac{2r}{\pi}.$$

226. Centre of gravity of a sector of a circle.

With the same notation as in the last article, let P and Q be two consecutive points on the circular boundary of the sector, so that PQ is very approximately a straight line, and OPQ is a triangle with a very small vertical angle at O.

Take P' on OP such that $OP' = \frac{2}{3}OP$; when PQ is very small, P' is the centre of gravity of the triangle OPQ.

---

* The Student who is acquainted with the Integral Calculus can obtain this result very much easier thus;

Let P be a point on the arc such that $\angle POC = \theta$, and P' a very close point such that $\angle P'OP = \delta\theta$.

If M be the mass of the whole arc the mass of the element PP' is $\dfrac{\delta\theta}{2\alpha}\,.\,M$, and the abscissa of the point P is $r\cos\theta$. Hence, by Art. 111,

$$\bar{x} = \frac{\displaystyle\int_{-\alpha}^{+\alpha} \frac{\delta\theta}{2\alpha} M\,.\,r\cos\theta}{\displaystyle\int_{-\alpha}^{+\alpha} \frac{\delta\theta}{2\alpha} M} = r\,\frac{\displaystyle\int_{-\alpha}^{+\alpha} \cos\theta\,d\theta}{\displaystyle\int_{-\alpha}^{+\alpha} d\theta}$$

$$= r\,\frac{\Big[\sin\theta\Big]_{-\alpha}^{+\alpha}}{\Big[\theta\Big]_{-\alpha}^{+\alpha}} = r\,\frac{\sin\alpha}{\alpha}.$$

Also, by symmetry, it is clear that the centre of gravity must lie on OC.

By joining O to an indefinitely large number of consecutive points on the arc AB, the sector can be divided into an indefinitely large number of triangles, each of whose centres of gravity lies on the dotted circular arc, whose radius is $\frac{2}{3}r$.

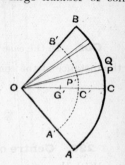

Hence the centre of gravity of the sector is the same as that of the circular arc $A'C'B'$, so that, by the last article,

$$OG' = OC' \frac{\sin \alpha}{\alpha} = \frac{2}{3} r \frac{\sin \alpha}{\alpha}.$$

Cor. If the sector be a semi-circle, $\alpha = \frac{\pi}{2}$, and the distance $OG' = \frac{4r}{3\pi}$.

227. Centre of gravity of the segment of a circle.

The segment of a circle ACB is the difference between the sector $OACB$ and the triangle OAB.

Using the same notation as in the two previous articles, let G_1 and G_2 be respectively the centres of gravity of the triangle AOB and the segment ACB. Also let G be the centre of gravity of the sector, and let AB meet OC in D.

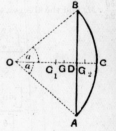

We have, by Art. 109,

$$OG = \frac{\triangle AOB \times OG_1 + \text{segment } ACB \times OG_2}{\triangle AOB + \text{segment } ACB} \quad \ldots(i).$$

But $$OG_1 = \tfrac{2}{3}OD = \tfrac{2}{3}r\cos a,$$

and $$OG = \tfrac{2}{3}r\,\frac{\sin a}{a}.$$

Also $$\triangle AOB = \tfrac{1}{2}r^2 \sin 2a,$$

and segment $ABC =$ sector $AOB - \triangle AOB$

$$= \tfrac{1}{2}r^2 \cdot 2a - \tfrac{1}{2}r^2 \sin 2a.$$

Hence equation (i) becomes

$$\tfrac{2}{3}r\,\frac{\sin a}{a} = \frac{\tfrac{1}{2}r^2 \sin 2a \times \tfrac{2}{3}r\cos a + \tfrac{1}{2}r^2\,(2a - \sin 2a) \times OG_2}{\tfrac{1}{2}r^2 \cdot 2a}$$

$$= \frac{\tfrac{2}{3}r\cos a \sin 2a + OG_2\,(2a - \sin 2a)}{2a};$$

$$\therefore \ \tfrac{4}{3}r\sin a - \tfrac{2}{3}r\cos a \sin 2a = OG_2\,(2a - \sin 2a);$$

$$\therefore \ OG_2 = \tfrac{4}{3}r\,\frac{\sin a - \cos^2 a \sin a}{2a - \sin 2a}$$

$$= \tfrac{4}{3}r\,\frac{\sin^3 a}{2a - \sin 2a}.$$

228. Centre of gravity of a Zone of a Sphere.

To prove that the centre of gravity of the surface of any zone of a sphere is midway between its plane ends.

[A zone is the portion of a sphere intercepted between any two parallel planes.]

Let $ABCD$ be the section of the zone which is made by a plane through the centre of the sphere perpendicular to its plane ends.

In the plane of the paper let ROR' be the diameter parallel to the plane ends. Draw the tangents RU and

$R'U'$ at its ends, and let AB and CD meet them in the points a, b, c, and d.

Consider the figure obtained by revolving the above figure about EOE'. The arc AD will trace out the zone and the line ad will trace out a portion of the circumscribing cylinder.

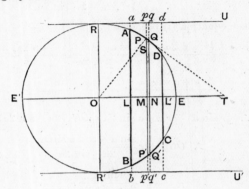

We shall shew that the areas of the portions of the zone and cylinder intercepted between the planes ab and cd are the same.

Take any point P on the arc between A and D and another point Q *indefinitely close* to P. Draw the lines $pPMP'p'$ and $qQNQ'q'$ perpendicular to OE as in the figure.

Let PQ meet $E'E$ in T and draw QS perpendicular to PM.

Since Q is the very next point to P on the arc, the line PQ is, by the definition of a tangent, the tangent at P and hence OPT is a right angle. Also in the limit, when

P and Q are very close to one another, the area traced out by PQ, which really lies between $2\pi MP . PQ$ and $2\pi NQ . PQ$, is equal to either of them.

We then have

$$\frac{\text{element of the zone}}{\text{element of the cylinder}} = \frac{\text{area traced out by } PQ}{\text{area traced out by } pq}$$

$$= \frac{2\pi . MP . PQ}{2\pi . Mp . pq} = \frac{MP}{Mp} . \frac{PQ}{SQ} = \frac{MP}{Mp} . \frac{1}{\cos SQP}$$

$$= \frac{MP}{Mp} . \frac{1}{\cos OTP} = \frac{MP}{Mp} . \frac{1}{\sin MOP} = \frac{MP}{Mp} . \frac{OP}{MP}$$

$$= \frac{OP}{Mp} = 1.$$

The portions of the zone and cylinder cut off by these two indefinitely close planes are therefore the same and hence their centres of gravity are the same.

If we now take an indefinitely large number of thin sections of the zone and cylinder starting with AB and

---

By Integral Calculus. Let $\angle AOE = \alpha$, $\angle DOE = \beta$, and $\angle POE = \theta$. The element of area at $P = a\delta\theta \times 2\pi a \sin \theta$, and the abscissa of P is $a \cos \theta$. Hence, by Art. 111,

$$\bar{x} = \frac{\int_{\beta}^{\alpha} 2\pi a^2 \sin \theta \delta \theta . a \cos \theta}{\int_{\beta}^{\alpha} 2\pi a^2 \sin \theta d\theta} = a \frac{\int_{\beta}^{\alpha} \sin \theta \cos \theta d\theta}{\int_{\beta}^{\alpha} \sin \theta d\theta}$$

$$= a \frac{\left[\frac{1}{2} \sin^2 \theta\right]_{\beta}^{\alpha}}{\left[-\cos \theta\right]_{\beta}^{\alpha}} = \frac{a}{2} \frac{\sin^2 \alpha - \sin^2 \beta}{\cos \beta - \cos \alpha}$$

$$= \frac{a}{2} \frac{\cos^2 \beta - \cos^2 \alpha}{\cos \beta - \cos \alpha} = \frac{a}{2} (\cos \beta + \cos \alpha)$$

$$= \tfrac{1}{2} [OL + OL'].$$

ending with CD the corresponding sections have the same mass and the same centre of gravity.

The centre of gravity of the zone and cylinder are therefore the same, and the centre of gravity of the latter is clearly the middle point of LL'.

Hence the centre of gravity of any zone of a sphere is midway between its plane ends.

229. *Centre of gravity of a* **hollow hemisphere.**

Let AB pass through the centre of the sphere and therefore coincide with RR'. Also let D and C move up to coincide with E, so that the bounding plane DC becomes a point at E.

The zone thus becomes the hemisphere $RDECR'$ and its centre of gravity is therefore at the middle point of OE, *i.e.*, it bisects the radius of the sphere perpendicular to the plane base of the hemisphere.

230. *To find the position of the centre of gravity of a* **solid hemisphere.**

*Let LAM be the section of the hemisphere made by the

---

* **By Integral Calculus.** Let P be any point on the arc AL; draw PN perpendicular to OA and let $ON = x$, $NP = y$; then clearly
$$x^2 + y^2 = a^2,$$
where a is the radius of the hemisphere.

The element of volume included between PN and the plane at distance $x + \delta x$ is $\pi y^2 \delta x$. Also the abscissa of P is x.

Hence, by Art. 111,

$$\bar{x} = \frac{\int_0^a \pi y^2 \delta x \cdot x}{\int_0^a \pi y^2 \delta x} = \frac{\int_0^a x(a^2 - x^2)\,\delta x}{\int_0^a (a^2 - x^2)\,\delta x}$$

$$= \frac{\left[\dfrac{a^2 x^2}{2} - \dfrac{x^4}{4}\right]_0^a}{\left[a^2 x - \dfrac{x^3}{3}\right]_0^a} = \frac{\dfrac{a^4}{2} - \dfrac{a^4}{4}}{a^3 - \dfrac{a^3}{3}} = \frac{3}{8}a.$$

plane of the paper, and let OA be the radius of the hemisphere which is perpendicular to its plane base.

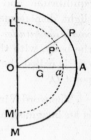

Take any point P on the hemisphere and consider an exceedingly small element of the surface at P. The centre of gravity of the very thin pyramid, whose base is this small element and whose vertex is O, is at a point P' on OP, such that $OP' = \frac{3}{4}OP$. (Art. 107.)

The weight of this very thin pyramid may therefore be considered concentrated at P'.

Let the external surface of the hemisphere be entirely divided up into very small portions and the corresponding pyramids drawn. Their centres of gravity all lie on the hemisphere $L'P'aM'$ whose centre is O and whose radius is $Oa\,(=\frac{3}{4}OA)$.

Hence the centre of gravity of the solid hemisphere is the same as that of the hemispherical shell $L'P'aM'$, *i.e.* it is at G, where

$$OG = \tfrac{1}{2}Oa = \tfrac{3}{8}OA.$$

231. In a similar manner we may obtain the position of the centre of gravity of a spherical sector which is the figure formed by the revolution of a circular sector, such as the figure $OAQEBO$, in the figure of Art. 228, about the bisecting radius OE.

The distance of its centre of gravity from O is easily seen to be $\frac{3}{8}(OL + OE)$.

232. There are some points which are not quite satisfactory in the foregoing proofs. For a strict demonstration the use of the Calculus is required.

233. Virtual Work.

When we have a system of forces acting on a body in equilibrium and we suppose that the body undergoes a slight displacement, *which is consistent with the geometrical conditions under which the system exists,* and if a point Q of the body, with this imagined displacement, goes to Q', then QQ' is called the Virtual Velocity, or Displacement, of the point Q.

The word Virtual is used to imply that the displacement is an imagined, and not an actual, displacement.

234. If a force R act at a point Q of the body and QQ' be the virtual displacement of Q and if $Q'N$ be the perpendicular from Q' on the direction of R, then the product $R \cdot QN$ is called the Virtual Work or Virtual Moment of the force R. As in Art. 127 this work is positive, or negative, according as QN is in the same direction as R, or in the opposite direction.

235. *The virtual work of a force is equal to the sum of the virtual works of its components.*

Let the components of R in two directions at right angles be X and Y, R being inclined at an angle ϕ to the direction of X, so that

$$X = R \cos \phi \text{ and } Y = R \sin \phi.$$

Let the point of application Q of R be removed, by a virtual displacement, to Q' and draw $Q'N$ perpendicular to R and let

$$\angle NQQ' = \alpha.$$

The sum of the virtual works of X and Y

$$= X . QL + Y . QM$$

$$= R \cos \phi . QQ' \cos (\phi + \alpha) + R \sin \phi . QQ' \sin (\phi + \alpha)$$

$$= R . QQ' \left[\cos \phi \cos (\phi + \alpha) + \sin \phi \sin (\phi + \alpha) \right]$$

$$= R . QQ' \cos \alpha$$

$$= R . QN$$

$$= \text{the virtual work of } R.$$

236. The principle of virtual work states that *If a system of forces acting on a body be in equilibrium and the body undergo a slight displacement consistent with the geometrical conditions of the system, the algebraic sum of the virtual works is zero; and conversely if this algebraic sum be zero the forces are in equilibrium. In other words, if each force R have a virtual displacement r in the direction of its line of action, then $\Sigma (R . r) = 0$; also conversely if $\Sigma (R . r)$ be zero, the forces are in equilibrium.*

In the next article we give a proof of this theorem for coplanar forces.

237. *Proof of the principle of virtual work for any system of forces in one plane.*

Take any two straight lines at right angles to one another in the plane of the forces and let the body undergo a slight displacement. This can clearly be done by turning the body through a suitable small angle α radians about O and then moving it through suitable distances a and b parallel to the axis.

[The student may illustrate this by moving a book from any position on a table into any other position, the book throughout the motion being kept in contact with the table.]

Let Q be the point of application of any force R, whose coordinates referred to O are x and y and whose polar coordinates are r and θ, so that $x = r \cos \theta$ and $y = r \sin \theta$, where $OQ = r$ and $XOQ = \theta$.

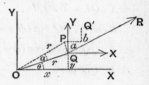

When the small displacement has been made the coordinates of the new position Q' of Q are

$$r \cos (\theta + a) + a \text{ and } r \sin (\theta + a) + b,$$

i.e. $\qquad r \cos \theta \cos a - r \sin \theta \sin a + a$

and $\qquad r \sin \theta \cos a + r \cos \theta \sin a + b,$

i.e. $\qquad r \cos \theta - a \cdot r \sin \theta + a$

and $\qquad r \sin \theta + a \cdot r \cos \theta + b,$

since a is very small.

The changes in the coordinates of Q are therefore

$$a - a \cdot r \sin \theta \text{ and } b + a \cdot r \cos \theta,$$

i.e. $\qquad a - ay \text{ and } b + ax.$

If then X and Y be the components of R, the virtual work of R, which is equal to the sum of the virtual works of X and Y, is

$$X (a - ay) + Y (b + ax),$$

i.e. $\qquad a \cdot X + b \cdot Y + a (Yx - Yy).$

Similarly we have the virtual work of any other force of the system, a, b, and a being the same for each force.

The sum of the virtual works will therefore be zero if

$$a \Sigma (X) + b \Sigma (Y) + a \Sigma (Yx - Xy) \text{ be zero.}$$

If the forces be in equilibrium then $\Sigma (X)$ and $\Sigma (Y)$ are the sums of the components of the forces along the axes OX and OY and hence, by Art. 83, they are separately equal to zero.

Also $Yx - Xy$ = sum of the moments of X and Y about the origin O = moment of R about O.   (Art. 62.)

Hence $\Sigma\,(Yx - Xy)$ = sum of the moments of all the forces about O, and this sum is zero, by Art. 83.

It follows that if the forces be in equilibrium the sum of their virtual works is zero.

238. Conversely, if the sum of the virtual works be zero for any displacement, the forces are in equilibrium.

With the same notation as in the last article, the sum of the virtual works is

$$a\Sigma\,(X) + b\Sigma\,(Y) + a\Sigma\,(Yx - Xy) \quad\ldots\ldots\ldots(1),$$

and this is given to be zero *for all displacements.*

Choose a displacement such that the body is displaced only through a distance a parallel to the axis of x. For this displacement b and a vanish, and (1) then gives

$$a\Sigma\,(X) = 0,$$

so that $\Sigma\,(X) = 0$, *i.e.* the sum of the components parallel to OX is zero.

Similarly, choosing a displacement parallel to the axis of y, we have the sum of the components parallel to OY zero also.

Finally, let the displacement be one of simple rotation round the origin O. In this case a and b vanish and (1) gives

$$\Sigma\,(Yx - Xy) = 0,$$

so that the sum of the moments of the forces about O vanish.

The three conditions of equilibrium given in Art. 83 therefore hold and the system of forces is therefore in equilibrium.

239. As an example of the application of the Principle of Virtual Work we shall solve the following problem.

Six equal rods AB, BC, CD, DE, EF, and FA are each of weight W and are freely jointed at their extremities so as to form a hexagon; the rod AB is fixed in a horizontal position and the middle points of AB and DE are joined by a string; prove that its tension is 3W.

Let G_1, G_2, G_3, G_4, G_5, and G_6 be the middle points of the rods.

Since, by symmetry, BC and CD are equally inclined to the vertical the depths of the points C, G_3 and D below AB are respectively 2, 3, and 4 times as great as that of G_2.

Let the system undergo a displacement in the vertical plane of such a character that D and E are always in the vertical lines through B and A and DE is always horizontal.

If G_2 descend a vertical distance x, then G_3 will descend $3x$, G_4 will descend $4x$, whilst G_5 and G_6 will descend $3x$ and x respectively.

The sum of the virtual works done by the weights

$$= W.x + W.3x + W.4x + W.3x + W.x$$
$$= 12W.x.$$

If T be the tension of the string, the virtual work done by it will be

$$T \times (-4x).$$

For the displacement of G_4 is in a direction opposite to that in which T acts and hence the virtual work done by it is negative.

The principle of virtual work then gives

$$12W.x + T(-4x) = 0,$$

i.e. $$T = 3W.$$

240. Roberval's Balance. This balance, which is a common form of letter-weigher, consists of four rods AB, BE, ED, and DA freely jointed at the corners A, B, E, and D, so as to form a parallelogram, whilst the middle points, C and F, of AB and ED are attached to fixed points C and F which are in a vertical straight line. The rods AB and DE can freely turn about C and F.

To the rods AD and BE are attached scale-pans. In one of these is placed the substance W which is to be weighed and in the other the counterbalancing weight P.

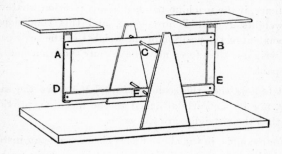

We shall apply the Principle of Virtual Work to prove that it is immaterial on what part of the scale-pans the weights P and W are placed.

Since $CBEF$ and $CADF$ are parallelograms it follows that, whatever be the angle through which the balance is turned, the rods BE and AD are always parallel to CF and therefore are always vertical.

If the rod AB be turned through a small angle the point B rises as much as the point A falls. The rod BE therefore rises as much as AD falls, and the right-hand scale-pan rises as much as the left-hand one falls. In such a displacement the virtual work of the weights of the rod BE and its scale-pan is therefore equal and opposite to the virtual work of the weights of AD and its scale-pan. These virtual works therefore cancel one another in the equation of virtual work.

Also if the displacement of the right-hand scale-pan be p upwards, that of the left-hand one is p downwards.

The equation of virtual work therefore gives

$$P \cdot p + W(-p) = 0,$$

i.e.
$$P = W.$$

Hence, if the machine balance in any position whatever, the weights P and W are equal, and this condition is independent of the position of the weights in the scale-pans. The weights therefore may have any position on the scale-pans.

It follows that the scale-pans need not have the same shape, nor be similarly attached to the machine, provided only that their weights are the same.

For example, in the above figure either scale-pan instead of pointing away from CF may point towards it, and no change would be requisite in the position of the other.

EXAMPLES. XXXIX.

1. Four equal heavy uniform rods are freely jointed so as to form a rhombus which is freely suspended by one angular point and the middle points of the two upper rods are connected by a light rod so that the rhombus cannot collapse. Prove that the tension of this light rod is $4W \tan \alpha$, where W is the weight of each rod and 2α is the angle of the rhombus at the point of suspension.

2. A string, of length a, forms the shorter diagonal of a rhombus formed of four uniform rods, each of length b and weight W, which are hinged together.

If one of the rods be supported in a horizontal position prove that the tension of the string is

$$\frac{2W(2b^2 - a^2)}{b\sqrt{4b^2 - a^2}}.$$

3. A regular hexagon $ABCDEF$ consists of 6 equal rods which are each of weight W and are freely jointed together. The hexagon rests in a vertical plane and AB is in contact with a horizontal table; if C and F be connected by a light string, prove that its tension is $W\sqrt{3}$.

4. A tripod consists of three equal uniform bars, each of length a and weight w, which are freely jointed at one extremity, their middle points being joined by strings of length b. The tripod is placed with its free ends in contact with a smooth horizontal plane and a weight W is attached to the common joint; prove that the tension of each string is

$$\tfrac{2}{3}(2W + 3w)\,\frac{b}{\sqrt{9a^2 - 12b^2}}.$$

5. A square framework, formed of uniform heavy rods of equal weight W, jointed together, is hung up by one corner. A weight W is suspended from each of the three lower corners and the shape of the square is preserved by a light rod along the horizontal diagonal. Prove that its tension is $4W$.

6. Four equal rods, each of length a, are jointed to form a rhombus $ABCD$ and the angles B and D are joined by a string of length l. The system is placed in a vertical plane with A resting on a horizontal plane and AC is vertical. Prove that the tension of the string is $2W\,\dfrac{l}{\sqrt{4a^2 - l^2}}$, where W is the weight of each rod.

7. A heavy elastic string, whose natural length is $2\pi a$, is placed round a smooth cone whose axis is vertical and whose semivertical angle is α. If W be the weight and λ the modulus of elasticity of the string, prove that it will be in equilibrium when in the form of a circle whose radius is $a\left(1 + \dfrac{W}{2\pi\lambda}\cot\alpha\right)$.

8. Two equal uniform rods AB and AC, each of length $2b$, are freely jointed at A and rest on a smooth vertical circle of radius a. Shew, by the Principle of Virtual Work, that, if 2θ be the angle between them, then

$$b\sin^3\theta = a\cos\theta.$$

9. Solve Ex. 13, page 278, by the application of the Principle of Virtual Work.

EASY MISCELLANEOUS EXAMPLES.

1. Find the resultant of two forces, equal to the weights of 13 and 14 lbs. respectively, acting at an obtuse angle whose sine is $\frac{12}{13}$.

2. Resolve a force of 100 lbs. weight into two equal forces acting at an angle of 60°.

3. *ABCD* is a square; forces of 1 lb. wt., 6 lbs. wt. and 9 lbs. wt. act in the directions *AB*, *AC*, and *AD* respectively; find the magnitude of their resultant correct to two places of decimals.

4. The resultant of two forces, acting at an angle of 120°, is perpendicular to the smaller component. The greater component is equal to 100 lbs. weight; find the other component and the resultant.

5. If *E* and *F* be the middle points of the diagonals *AC* and *BD* of the quadrilateral *ABCD*, and if *EF* be bisected in *G*, prove that the four forces represented in magnitude and direction by *AG*, *BG*, *CG*, and *DG*, will be in equilibrium.

6. A stiff pole 12 feet long sticks horizontally out from a vertical wall. It would break if a weight of 28 lbs. were hung at the end. How far out along the pole may a boy who weighs 8 stone venture with safety?

7. A rod weighing 4 ounces and of length one yard is placed on a table so that one-third of its length projects over the edge. Find the greatest weight which can be attached by a string to the end of the rod without causing it to topple over.

8. A uniform beam, of weight 30 lbs., rests with its lower end on the ground, the upper end being attached to a weight by means of a horizontal string passing over a small pulley. If the beam be inclined at 60° to the vertical, prove that the pressure on the lower end is nearly 40 lbs. wt., and that the weight attached to the string is nearly 26 lbs. wt.

9. Find the centre of parallel forces which are equal respectively to 1, 2, 3, 4, 5, and 6 lbs. weight, the points of application of the forces being at distances 1, 2, 3, 4, 5, and 6 inches respectively measured from a given point *A* along a given line *AB*.

10. The angle *B* of a triangle *ABC* is a right angle, *AB* being 8 inches and *BC* 11 inches in length; at *A*, *B*, and *C* are placed particles whose weights are 4, 5, and 6 respectively; find the distance of their centre of gravity from *A*.

11. On the side AB of an equilateral triangle and on the side remote from C is described a rectangle whose height is one half of AB; prove that the centre of gravity of the whole figure thus formed is the middle point of AB.

12. From a regular hexagon one of the equilateral triangles with its vertex at the centre, and a side for base, is cut away. Find the centre of gravity of the remainder.

13. A pile of six pennies rests on a horizontal table, and each penny projects the same distance beyond the one below it. Find the greatest possible horizontal distance between the centres of the highest and lowest pennies.

14. The pressure on the fulcrum when two weights are suspended in equilibrium at the end of a straight lever, 12 inches long, is 20 lbs. wt. and the ratio of the distances of the fulcrum from the ends is 3 : 2. Find the weights.

15. A straight lever of length 5 feet and weight 10 lbs. has its fulcrum at one end and weights of 3 and 6 lbs. are fastened to it at distances of 1 foot and 3 feet from the fulcrum; it is kept horizontal by a force at its other end; find the pressure on the fulcrum.

16. Find the relation between the effort P and the weight W in a system of 5 movable pulleys in which each pulley hangs by a separate string, the weight of each pulley being P.

17. In the system of 5 weightless pulleys in which each string is attached to a weightless bar from which the weights hang, if the strings be successively one inch apart, find to what point of the bar the weight must be attached, so that the bar may be always horizontal.

18. A body, of mass 5 lbs., rests on a smooth plane which is inclined at 30° to the horizon and is acted on by a force equal to the weight of 2 lbs. acting parallel to the plane and upwards, and by a force equal to P lbs. weight acting at an angle of 30° to the plane. Find the value of P if the body be in equilibrium.

19. If one scale of an accurate balance be removed and no mass be placed in the other scale, prove that the inclination of the beam to the horizon is $\tan^{-1}\dfrac{Sa}{W'k+Sh}$, where $2a$ is the length of the beam, h and k are respectively the distances of the point of suspension from the beam and the centre of gravity of the balance, and S and W' are respectively the weight of the scale-pan and the remainder of the balance.

20. If the distance of the centre of gravity of the beam of a common steelyard from its fulcrum be 2 inches, the movable weight 4 ozs., and the weight of the beam 2 lbs., find the distance of the zero of graduations from the centre of gravity. Also, if the distance between the fulcrum and the end at which the scale-pan is attached be 4 inches, find the distance between successive graduations.

21. If the circumference of a screw be 20 inches and the distance between successive threads ·75 inch, find its mechanical advantage.

22. The height of a rough plane is to its base as 3 to 4 and it is found that a body is just supported on it by a horizontal force equal to half the weight of the body; find the coefficient of friction between the body and the plane.

23. A ladder, 30 feet long, rests with one end against a smooth vertical wall and with the other on the ground, which is rough, the coefficient of friction being $\frac{1}{2}$; find how high a man whose weight is 4 times that of the ladder can ascend before it begins to slip, the foot of the ladder being 6 feet from the wall.

24. A cylindrical shaft has to be sunk to a depth of 100 fathoms through chalk whose density is 2·3 times that of water; the diameter of the shaft being 10 feet, what must be the H.P. of the engine that can lift out the material in 12 working days of 8 hours each?

**HARDER MISCELLANEOUS EXAMPLES.

1. If O be the centre of the circle circumscribing the triangle ABC, and if forces act along OA, OB, and OC respectively proportional to BC, CA, and AB, shew that their resultant passes through the centre of the inscribed circle.

2. Three forces act along the sides of a triangle ABC, taken in order, and their resultant passes through the orthocentre and the centre of gravity of the triangle; shew that the forces are in the ratio of

$$\sin 2A \sin (B - C) : \sin 2B \sin (C - A) : \sin 2C \sin (A - B).$$

Shew also that their resultant acts along the line joining the centres of the inscribed and circumscribing circles, if the forces be in the ratio

$$\cos B - \cos C : \cos C - \cos A : \cos A - \cos B.$$

3. Three forces PA, PB, and PC, diverge from the point P and three others AQ, BQ, and CQ converge to a point Q. Shew that the resultant of the six is represented in magnitude and direction by $3PQ$ and that it passes through the centre of gravity of the triangle ABC.

4. T is the orthocentre, and O the circumcentre of a triangle ABC; shew that the three forces AT, BT, and CT have as resultant the force represented by twice OT.

5. Find the centre of gravity of three particles placed at the centres of the escribed circles of a triangle, if they be inversely proportional to the radii of these circles.

6. $ABCD$ is a rectangle; find a point P in AD such that, when the triangle PDC is taken away, the remaining trapezoid $ABCP$ may, when suspended from P, hang with its sides AP and BC horizontal.

7. A triangular lamina ABC, obtuse-angled at C, stands with the side AC in contact with a table. Shew that the least weight, which suspended from B will overturn the triangle, is

$$\tfrac{1}{3} W \frac{a^2 + 3b^2 - c^2}{c^2 - a^2 - b^2},$$

where W is the weight of the triangle.

Interpret the above if $\quad c^2 > a^2 + 3b^2$.

8. A pack of cards is laid on a table, and each card projects in the direction of the length of the pack beyond the one below it; if each project as far as possible, shew that the distances between the extremites of successive cards will form a harmonical progression.

9. If aA, bB, cC ... represent n forces, whose points of application are a, b, c ... and whose extremities are A, B, C, ..., shew that their resultant is given in magnitude and direction by $n \cdot gG$, where g is the centre of inertia of n equal particles a, b, c, ..., and G the centre of inertia of n equal particles A, B, C, ...

What follows if g coincide with G?

10. From a body, of weight W, a portion, of weight w, is cut out and moved through a distance x; shew that the line joining the two positions of the centre of gravity of the whole body is parallel to the line joining the two positions of the centre of gravity of the part moved.

11. Two uniform rods, AB and AC, of the same material are rigidly connected at A, the angle BAC being $60°$, and the length of AB being double that of AC. If G be the centre of inertia of the rods, shew that $BG = AC \sqrt{\dfrac{19}{12}}$, and, if the system be suspended freely from the end B of the rod AB, shew that the action at A consists of a vertical force equal to one-third of the weight, W, of the system, and a couple whose moment is

$$\tfrac{2}{3} W \frac{AC}{\sqrt{19}}.$$

12. If the hinges of a gate be 4 feet apart and the gate be 10 feet wide and weigh 500 lbs., shew that, on the assumption that all the weight is borne by the lower hinge, the stress on the upper hinge must be 625 lbs. wt.

13. A step-ladder in the form of the letter A, with each of its legs inclined at an angle a to the vertical, is placed on a horizontal floor, and is held up by a cord connecting the middle points of its legs, there being no friction anywhere; shew that, when a weight W is placed on one of the steps at a height from the floor equal to $\dfrac{1}{n}$ of the height of the ladder, the increase in the tension of the cord is $\dfrac{1}{n} W \tan a$.

14. A cylinder, of radius r, whose axis is fixed horizontally, touches a vertical wall along a generating line. A flat beam of uniform material, of length $2l$ and weight W, rests with its extremities in contact with the wall and the cylinder, making an angle of $45°$ with the vertical. Shew that, in the absence of friction, $\dfrac{l}{r} = \dfrac{\sqrt{5}-1}{\sqrt{10}}$, that the pressure on the wall is $\frac{1}{2}W$, and that the reaction of the cylinder is $\frac{1}{2}\sqrt{5}W$.

15. A uniform rod, of length $35a$, rests partly within and partly without a smooth cylindrical cup of radius a. Shew that in the position of equilibrium the rod makes an angle of $60°$ with the horizon, and prove also that the cylinder will topple over unless its weight be at least six times that of the rod.

16. A tipping basin, whose interior surface is spherical, is free to turn round an axis at a distance c below the centre of the sphere and at a distance a above the centre of gravity of the basin, and a heavy ball is laid at the bottom of the basin; shew that it will tip over if the weight of the ball exceed the fraction $\dfrac{a}{c}$ of the weight of the basin.

17. A thin hemispherical shell, closed by a plane base, is filled with water and, when suspended from a point on the rim of the base, it hangs with the base inclined at an angle a to the vertical. Shew that the ratio of the weight of the water to that of the shell is $\tan a - \frac{1}{3} : \frac{3}{8} - \tan a$.

18. A hollow cylinder, composed of thin metal open at both ends, of radius a, is placed on a smooth horizontal plane. Inside it are placed two smooth spheres, of radius r, one above the other, $2r$ being $>a$ and $<2a$. If W be the weight of the cylinder and W' the weight of one of the spheres, shew that the cylinder will just stand upright, without tumbling over, if
$$W \cdot a = 2W'(a-r).$$

19. An isosceles triangular lamina, with its plane vertical, rests, vertex downwards, between two smooth pegs in the same horizontal line; shew that there will be equilibrium if the base make an angle $\sin^{-1}(\cos^2 \alpha)$ with the vertical, 2α being the vertical angle of the lamina and the length of the base being three times the distance between the pegs.

20. A prism, whose cross section is an equilateral triangle, rests with two edges horizontal on smooth planes inclined at angles α and β to the horizon. If θ be the angle that the plane through these edges makes with the vertical, shew that

$$\tan \theta = \frac{2\sqrt{3} \sin \alpha \sin \beta + \sin (\alpha + \beta)}{\sqrt{3} \sin (\alpha \sim \beta)}.$$

21. A thin board in the form of an equilateral triangle, of weight 1 lb., has one-quarter of its base resting on the end of a horizontal table, and is kept from falling over by a string attached to its vertex and to a point on the table in the same vertical plane as the triangle. If the length of the string be double the height of the vertex of the triangle above the base, find its tension.

22. A solid cone, of height h and semi-vertical angle α, is placed with its base against a smooth vertical wall and is supported by a string attached to its vertex and to a point in the wall; shew that the greatest possible length of the string is $h \sqrt{1 + \frac{16}{9} \tan^2 \alpha}$.

23. The altitude of a cone is h and the radius of its base is r; a string is fastened to the vertex and to a point on the circumference of the circular base, and is then put over a smooth peg; shew that, if the cone rest with its axis horizontal, the length of the string must be $\sqrt{h^2 + 4r^2}$.

24. Three equal smooth spheres on a smooth horizontal plane are in contact with one another, and are kept together by an endless string in the plane of their centres, just fitting them; if a fourth equal sphere be placed on them, shew that the tension of the string is to the weight of either sphere as $1 : 3\sqrt{6}$.

25. A smooth rod, of length $2a$, has one end resting on a plane of inclination α to the horizon, and is supported by a horizontal rail which is parallel to the plane and at a distance c from it. Shew that the inclination θ of the rod to the inclined plane is given by the equation $c \sin \alpha = a \sin^2 \theta \cos (\theta - \alpha)$.

26. A square board is hung flat against a wall, by means of a string fastened to the two extremities of the upper edge and hung round a perfectly smooth rail; when the length of the string is less than the diagonal of the board, shew that there are three positions of equilibrium.

27. A hemispherical bowl, of radius r, rests on a smooth horizontal table and partly inside it rests a rod, of length $2l$ and of weight equal to that of the bowl. Shew that the position of equilibrium is given by the equation

$$l \sin (\alpha + \beta) = r \sin \alpha = -2r \cos (\alpha + 2\beta),$$

where α is the inclination of the base of the hemisphere to the horizon, and 2β is the angle subtended at the centre by the part of the rod within the bowl.

28. A uniform rod, of weight W, is suspended horizontally from two nails in a wall by means of two vertical strings, each of length l, attached to its ends. A smooth weightless wedge, of vertical angle $30°$, is pressed down with a vertical force $\dfrac{W}{2}$ between the wall and the rod, without touching the strings, its lower edge being kept horizontal and one face touching the wall. Find the distance through which the rod is thrust from the wall.

29. AB is a smooth plane inclined at an angle α to the horizon, and at A, the lower end, is a hinge about which there works, without friction, a heavy uniform smooth plank AC, of length $2a$. Between the plane and the plank is placed a smooth cylinder, of radius r, which is prevented from sliding down the plane by the pressure of the plank from above. If W be the weight of the plank, W' that of the cylinder, and θ the angle between the plane and the plank, shew that

$$\frac{W'r}{Wa} = \cos (\alpha + \theta) \; \frac{1 - \cos \theta}{\sin \alpha} .$$

30. Two equal circular discs—of radius r—with smooth edges, are placed on their flat sides in the corner between two smooth vertical planes inclined at an angle 2α, and touch each other in the line bisecting the angle; prove that the radius of the least disc that can be pressed between them, without causing them to separate, is $r (\sec \alpha - 1)$.

31. A rectangular frame $ABCD$ consists of four freely jointed bars, of negligible weight, the bar AD being fixed in a vertical position. A weight is placed on the upper horizontal bar AB at a given point P and the frame is kept in a rectangular shape by a string AC. Find the tension of the string, and shew that it is unaltered if this weight be placed on the lower bar CD vertically under its former position.

32. A uniform rod MN has its ends in two fixed straight rough grooves OA and OB, in the same vertical plane, which make angles α and β with the horizon; shew that, when the end M is on the point of slipping in the direction AO, the tangent of the angle of inclination of MN to the horizon is $\dfrac{\sin (\alpha - \beta - 2\epsilon)}{2 \sin (\beta + \epsilon) \sin (\alpha - \epsilon)}$, where ϵ is the angle of friction.

33. A rod, resting on a rough inclined plane, whose inclination a to the horizon is greater than the angle of friction λ, is free to turn about one of its ends, which is attached to the plane; shew that, for equilibrium, the greatest possible inclination of the rod to the line of greatest slope is $\sin^{-1}(\tan\lambda\cot a)$.

34. Two equal uniform rods, of length $2a$, are jointed at one extremity by a hinge, and rest symmetrically upon a rough fixed sphere of radius c. Find the limiting position of equilibrium, and shew that, if the coefficient of friction be $c \div a$, the limiting inclination of each rod to the vertical is $\tan^{-1}\sqrt[3]{c \div a}$.

35. A uniform straight rod, of length $2c$, is placed in a horizontal position as high as possible within a hollow rough sphere, of radius a. Shew that the line joining the middle point of the rod to the centre of the sphere makes with the vertical an angle $\tan^{-1}\dfrac{\mu a}{\sqrt{a^2 - c^2}}$.

36. A rough rod is fixed in a horizontal position, and a rod, having one end freely jointed to a fixed point, is in equilibrium resting on the fixed rod; if the perpendicular from the fixed point upon the fixed rod be of length b and be inclined to the horizon at an angle a, shew that the portion of the fixed rod upon any point of which the movable rod may rest is of length

$$\frac{2\mu b\cos a}{\sqrt{\sin^2 a - \mu^2\cos^2 a}},$$

where μ is the coefficient of friction.

37. A glass rod is balanced, partly in and partly out of a cylindrical tumbler, with the lower end resting against the vertical side of the tumbler. If a and β be the greatest and least angles which the rod can make with the vertical, shew that the angle of friction is

$$\tfrac{1}{2}\tan^{-1}\frac{\sin^3 a - \sin^3 \beta}{\sin^2 a\cos a + \sin^2 \beta\cos \beta}.$$

38. A rod rests partly within and partly without a box in the shape of a rectangular parallelopiped, and presses with one end against the rough vertical side of the box, and rests in contact with the opposite smooth edge. The weight of the box being four times that of the rod, shew that if the rod be about to slip and the box be about to tumble at the same instant, the angle that the rod makes with the vertical is $\tfrac{1}{2}\lambda + \tfrac{1}{2}\cos^{-1}(\tfrac{1}{3}\cos\lambda)$, where λ is the angle of friction.

39. A uniform heavy rod lies on a rough horizontal table and is pulled perpendicularly to its length by a string attached to any point. About what point will it commence to turn?

Shew also that the ratio of the forces, required to move the rod, when applied at the centre and through the end of the rod perpendicular to the rod, is $\sqrt{2}+1 : 1$.

40. Two equal heavy particles are attached to a light rod at equal distances c, and two strings are attached to it at equal distances a from the middle point; the rod is then placed on a rough horizontal table, and the strings are pulled in directions perpendicular to the rod and making the same angle θ with the vertical on opposite sides of the rod. Find the least tensions that will turn the rod and shew that, if the coefficient of friction be $\dfrac{a}{c}$, the tension will be least when θ is $45°$.

41. Two equal similar bodies, A and B, each of weight W, are connected by a light string and rest on a rough horizontal plane, the coefficient of friction being μ. A force P, which is less than $2\mu W$, is applied at A in the direction BA, and its direction is gradually turned through an angle θ in the horizontal plane. Shew that, if P be greater than $\sqrt{2}\mu W$, then both the weights will slip when $\cos\theta = \dfrac{P}{2\mu W}$, but, if P be less than $\sqrt{2}\mu W$ and be greater than μW, then A alone will slip when $\sin\theta = \dfrac{\mu W}{P}$.

42. A uniform rough beam AB lies horizontally upon two others at points A and C; shew that the least horizontal force applied at B in a direction perpendicular to BA, which is able to move the beam, is the lesser of the two forces $\frac{1}{2}\mu W$ and $\mu W\dfrac{b-a}{2a-b}$, where AB is $2a$, AC is b, W is the weight of the beam, and μ the coefficient of friction.

43. A uniform rough beam AB, of length $2a$, is placed horizontally on two equal and equally rough balls, the distance between whose centres is b, touching them in C and D; shew that, if b be not greater than $\dfrac{4a}{3}$, a position of the beam can be found in which a force P exerted at B perpendicular to the beam will cause it to be on the point of motion both at C and D at the same time.

44. A uniform heavy beam is placed, in a horizontal position, between two unequally rough fixed planes, inclined to the horizon at given angles, in a vertical plane perpendicular to the planes. Find the condition that it may rest there.

45. A uniform rod is in limiting equilibrium, one end resting on a rough horizontal plane and the other on an equally rough plane inclined at an angle a to the horizon. If λ be the angle of friction, and the rod be in a vertical plane, shew that the inclination, θ, of the rod to the horizon is given by

$$\tan\theta = \frac{\sin(a - 2\lambda)}{2\sin\lambda\sin(a - \lambda)}.$$

Find also the normal reactions of the planes.

46. If a pair of compasses rest across a smooth horizontal cylinder of radius c, shew that the frictional couple at the joint to prevent the legs of the compasses from slipping must be

$$W(c\cot a\operatorname{cosec}a - a\sin a),$$

where W is the weight of each leg, $2a$ the angle between the legs, and a the distance of the centre of gravity of a leg from the joint.

47. The handles of a drawer are equidistant from the sides of the drawer and are distant c from each other; shew that it will be impossible to pull the drawer out by pulling one handle, unless the length of the drawer from back to front exceed μc.

48. If one cord of a sash-window break, find the least coefficient of friction between the sash and the window-frame in order that the other weight may still support the window.

49. A circular hoop, of radius one foot, hangs on a horizontal bar and a man hangs by one hand from the hoop. If the coefficient of friction between the hoop and the bar be $1 \div \sqrt{3}$, find the shortest possible distance from the man's hand to the bar, the weight of the hoop being neglected.

50. A square, of side $2a$, is placed with its plane vertical between two smooth pegs, which are in the same horizontal line and at a distance c; shew that it will be in equilibrium when the inclination of one of its edges to the horizon is either $45°$ or $\frac{1}{2}\sin^{-1}\frac{a^2 - c^2}{c^2}$.

51. Three equal circular discs, A, B, and C, are placed in contact with each other upon a smooth horizontal plane, and, in addition, B and C are in contact with a rough vertical wall. If the coefficient of friction between the circumferences of the discs and also between the discs and wall be $2 - \sqrt{3}$, shew that no motion will ensue when A is pushed perpendicularly towards the wall with any force P.

52. If the centre of gravity of a wheel and axle be at a distance a from the axis, shew that the wheel can rest with the plane through the axis and the centre of gravity inclined at an angle less than θ to the vertical, where $\sin \theta = \dfrac{b}{a} \sin \phi$, b being the radius of the axle, and ϕ the angle of friction.

53. A particle, of weight w, rests on a rough inclined plane, of weight W, whose base rests on a rough table, the coefficients of friction being the same. If a gradually increasing force be applied to the particle w along the surface of the inclined plane, find whether it will move up the plane before the plane slides on the table, the angle of inclination of the plane being a.

54. A rough cylinder, of weight W', lies with its axis horizontal upon a plane, whose inclination to the horizontal is a, whilst a man, of weight W (with his body vertical), stands upon the cylinder and keeps it at rest. If his feet be at A and a vertical section of the cylinder through A touch the plane at B, shew that the angle, θ, subtended by AB at the centre of the section, the friction being sufficient to prevent any sliding, is given by the equation

$$W \sin (\theta + a) = (W + W') \sin a.$$

55. Two rough uniform spheres, of equal radii but unequal weights W_1 and W_2, rest in a spherical bowl, the line joining their centres being horizontal and subtending an angle $2a$ at the centre of the bowl; shew that the coefficient of friction between them is not less than $\dfrac{W_1 - W_2}{W_1 + W_2} \tan \left(45° - \dfrac{a}{2} \right)$.

56. Two rigid weightless rods are firmly jointed, so as to be at right angles, a weight being fixed at their junction, and are placed over two rough pegs in the same horizontal plane, whose coefficients of friction are μ and μ'. Shew that they can be turned either way from their symmetrical position through an angle $\dfrac{1}{2} \tan^{-1} \dfrac{\mu + \mu'}{2}$, without slipping.

57. A sphere, of weight W, is placed on a rough plane, inclined to the horizon at an angle a, which is less than the angle of friction; shew that a weight $W \dfrac{\sin a}{\cos a - \sin a}$, fastened to the sphere at the upper end of the diameter which is parallel to the plane, will just prevent the sphere from rolling down the plane.

What will be the effect of slightly decreasing or slightly increasing this weight?

58. Two equal uniform rods are joined rigidly together at one extremity of each to form a V, with the angle at the vertex 2α, and are placed astride a rough vertical circle of such a radius that the centre of gravity of the V is in the circumference of the circle, the angle of friction being ϵ. Shew that, if the V be just on the point of motion when the line joining its vertex with the centre of the circle is horizontal, then $\sin \epsilon = \sqrt{\sin \alpha}$.

If the rods be connected by a hinge and not rigidly connected and the free ends be joined by a string, shew that the joining string will not meet the circle if $\sin \alpha$ be $< \frac{1}{3}$; if this condition be satisfied, shew that if the V is just on the point of slipping when the line joining its vertex to the centre is horizontal, the tension of the string will be $\dfrac{W}{2} \sqrt{1 + \operatorname{cosec} \alpha}$, where W is the weight of either rod.

59. A vertical rectangular beam, of weight W, is constrained by guides to move only in its own direction, the lower end resting on a smooth floor. If a smooth inclined plane of given slope be pushed under it by a horizontal force acting at the back of the inclined plane, find the force required.

If there be friction between the floor and the inclined plane, but nowhere else, what must be the least value of μ so that the inclined plane may remain, when left in a given position under the beam, without being forced out?

60. A circular disc, of weight W and radius a, is suspended horizontally by three equal vertical strings, of length b, attached symmetrically to its perimeter. Shew that the magnitude of the horizontal couple required to keep it twisted through an angle θ is

$$Wa^2 \frac{\sin \theta}{\sqrt{b^2 - 4a^2 \sin^2 \dfrac{\theta}{2}}}.$$

61. Two small rings, each of weight W, slide one upon each of two rods in a vertical plane, each inclined at an angle α to the vertical; the rings are connected by a fine elastic string of natural length $2a$, and whose modulus of elasticity is λ; the coefficient of friction for each rod and ring is $\tan \beta$; shew that, if the string be horizontal, each ring will rest at any point of a segment of the rod whose length is

$$W\lambda^{-1} a \operatorname{cosec} \alpha \left\{ \cot (\alpha - \beta) - \cot (\alpha + \beta) \right\}.$$

62. A wedge, with angle $60°$, is placed upon a smooth table, and a weight of 20 lbs. on the slant face is supported by a string lying on that face which, after passing through a smooth ring at the top, supports a weight W hanging vertically; find the magnitude of W.

Find also the horizontal force necessary to keep the wedge at rest

(1) when the ring is not attached to the wedge,

(2) when it is so attached.

Solve the same question supposing the slant face of the wedge to be rough, the coefficient of friction being $\frac{1}{\sqrt{3}}$ and the 20 lb. weight on the point of moving down.

63. Shew that the power necessary to move a cylinder, of radius r and weight W, up a smooth plane inclined at an angle α to the horizon by means of a crowbar of length l inclined at an angle β to the horizon is

$$\frac{Wr}{l} \frac{\sin \alpha}{1 + \cos(\alpha + \beta)}.$$

64. A letter-weigher consists of a uniform plate in the form of a right-angled isosceles triangle ABC, of mass 3 ozs., which is suspended by its right angle C from a fixed point to which a plumb-line is also attached. The letters are suspended from the angle A, and their weight read off by observing where the plumb-line intersects a scale engraved along AB, the divisions of which are marked 1 oz., 2 oz., 3 oz., etc. Shew that the distances from A of the divisions of the scale form a harmonic progression.

65. A ladder, of length l feet and weight W lbs., and uniform in every respect throughout, is raised by two men A and B from a horizontal to a vertical position. A stands at one end and B, getting underneath the ladder, walks from the other end towards A holding successive points of the ladder above his head, at the height of d feet from the ground, the force he exerts being vertical. Find the force exerted by B when thus supporting a point n feet from A, and shew that the work done by him in passing from the nth to the $(n-1)^{\text{th}}$ foot is $\dfrac{Wld}{2n(n-1)}$.

When must A press his feet *downwards* against his end of the ladder?

66. Prove that an ordinary drawer cannot be pushed in by a force applied to one handle until it has been pushed in a distance $a \cdot \mu$ by forces applied in some other manner, where a is the distance between the handles and μ is the coefficient of friction.

67. Three equal uniform rods, each of weight W, have their ends hinged together so that they form an equilateral triangle; the triangle rests in a horizontal position with each rod in contact with a smooth cone of semivertical angle α whose axis is vertical; prove that the action at each hinge is $\dfrac{W \cot \alpha}{\sqrt{3}}$.

68. A reel, consisting of a spindle of radius c with two circular ends of radius a, is placed on a rough inclined plane and has a thread wound on it which unwinds when the reel rolls downwards. If μ be the coefficient of friction and α be the inclination of the plane to the horizontal, shew that the reel can be drawn up the plane by means of the thread if μ be not less than $\dfrac{c \sin \alpha}{a - c \cos \alpha}$.

69. Prove the following geometrical construction for the centre of gravity of any uniform plane quadrilateral $ABCD$; find the centres of gravity, X and Y, of the triangles ABD, CBD; let XY meet BD in U; then the required centre of gravity is a point G on XY, such that $YG = XU$.

70. There is a small interval between the bottom of a door and the floor, and a wedge of no appreciable weight has been thrust into this interval, the coefficient of friction between its base and the floor being known. If the angle of the wedge be smaller than a certain amount, shew that no force can open the door, the slant edge of the wedge being supposed smooth.

71. On the top of a fixed rough cylinder, of radius r, rests a thin uniform plank, and a man stands on the plank just above the point of contact. Shew that he can walk slowly a distance $(n+1)\, r\epsilon$ along the plank without its slipping off the cylinder, if the weight of the plank is n times that of the man and ϵ is the angle of friction between the plank and the cylinder.

72. A hoop stands in a vertical plane on a rough incline which the plane of the hoop cuts in a line of greatest slope. It is kept in equilibrium by a string fastened to a point in the circumference, wound round it, and fastened to a peg in the incline further up and in the same plane. If λ is the angle of friction, θ the angle the hoop subtends at the peg, and α that of the incline, shew that there is limiting equilibrium when $\theta = \alpha + \cos^{-1} \left[\dfrac{\sin(\alpha - \lambda)}{\sin \lambda} \right]$. What will happen if θ has a greater value?

73. Shew that the least force which applied to the surface of a heavy uniform sphere will just maintain it in equilibrium against a rough vertical wall is
$$W \cos \epsilon \quad \text{or} \quad W \tan \epsilon [\tan \epsilon - \sqrt{\tan^2 \epsilon - 1}]$$
according as $\epsilon < \text{or} > \cos^{-1} \dfrac{\sqrt{5} - 1}{2}$, where W is the weight and ϵ the angle of friction.

74. A uniform rod, of weight W, can turn freely about a hinge at one end, and rests with the other against a rough vertical wall making an angle α with the wall. Shew that this end may rest anywhere on an arc of a circle of angle $2\tan^{-1}[\mu\tan\alpha]$, and that in either of the extreme positions the pressure on the wall is $\frac{1}{2}W[\cot^2\alpha+\mu^2]^{-\frac{1}{2}}$, where μ is the coefficient of friction.

75. If the greatest possible cube be cut out of a solid hemisphere of uniform density, prove that the remainder can rest with its curved surface on a perfectly rough inclined plane with its base inclined to the horizon at an angle

$$\sin^{-1}\left[\frac{8\,(3\pi-\sqrt{6})}{9\pi-8}\sin\alpha\right],$$

where α is the slope of the inclined plane.

76. A cylindrical cork, of length l and radius r, is slowly extracted from the neck of a bottle. If the normal pressure per unit of area between the bottle and the unextracted part of the cork at any instant be constant and equal to P, shew that the work done in extracting it is $\pi\mu r l^2 P$, where μ is the coefficient of friction.

ANSWERS TO THE EXAMPLES.

I. (Pages 15, 16.)

1. (i) 25; (ii) $3\sqrt{3}$; (iii) 13; (iv) $\sqrt{61}$; (v) $60°$;
(vi) 15 or $\sqrt{505}$; (vii) 3.

2. 20 lbs. wt. ; 4 lbs. wt.

3. $\sqrt{2}$ lbs. wt. in a direction south-west.

4. 205 lbs. wt.

5. P lbs. wt. at right angles to the first component.

6. 2 lbs. wt.   7. 20 lbs. wt.   8. 17 lbs. wt.

9. $60°$.   10. 3 lbs. wt. ; 1 lb. wt.

11. (i) $120°$; (ii) $\cos^{-1}\left(-\dfrac{7}{8}\right)$, $i.e.$ $151°\ 3'$.

12. $\cos^{-1}\left(-\dfrac{1}{2}\dfrac{A^2 + B^2}{A^2 - B^2}\right)$.

13. In the direction of the resultant of the two given forces.

14. (i) $23 \cdot 8$; (ii) $6 \cdot 64$; (iii) $68°\ 12'$; (iv) $2 \cdot 56$.

II. (Pages 19, 20.)

1. $5\sqrt{3}$ and 5 lbs. wt.   2. (i) $\frac{1}{2}P\sqrt{2}$; (ii) $1\frac{2}{13}P$.

3. 50 lbs. wt.

4. Each is $\dfrac{1}{3} 100\sqrt{3}$, $i.e.$ $57 \cdot 735$, lbs. wt.

5. $36 \cdot 603$ and $44 \cdot 83$ lbs. wt. nearly.

6. $P(\sqrt{3} - 1)$ and $\dfrac{P}{2}(\sqrt{6} - \sqrt{2})$, *i.e.* $P \times \cdot732$ and $P \times \cdot5176$.

8. $F\sqrt{3}$ and $2F$.

9. $F\sqrt{2}$ at $135°$ with the other component.

10. $10\sqrt{5}$ at an angle $\tan^{-1}\frac{1}{2}$ (*i.e.* $22\cdot36$ at $26°\ 34'$) with the vertical.

11. $33\cdot62$ lbs. wt. ; $51\cdot8$ lbs. wt.

III.   (Pages 25, 26.)

1. $1 : 1 : \sqrt{3}.$ 2. $\sqrt{3} : 1 : 2.$ 3. $120°.$

4. $90°, 112°\ 37'\ (=180° - \cos^{-1}\frac{5}{13})$, and $157°\ 23'$.

9. $R_1 = 34\cdot4$ lbs. wt., $a_1 = 81°$; $R_2 = 6\cdot5$ lbs. wt., $a_2 = 169°$.

10. $101\frac{1}{2}°$; $57°$.   11. 52 ; $95°$.

12. $67\cdot2$; $101.$ 13. 46 ; $138°$.

14. $29\cdot6$; $14°$.   15. $2\cdot66$ cwts.

IV.   (Pages 26—28.)

1. $40.$ 2. $\cos^{-1}\left(-\dfrac{1}{4}\right)$, *i.e.* $104°\ 29'$.

3. $2\sqrt{3}$ and $\sqrt{3}$ lbs. wt.

4. $15\sqrt{3}$ and 15 lbs. wt.   5. $5 : 4.$

6. 5 and $13.$ 9. 12 lbs. wt.

16.   The straight line passes through C and the middle point of AB.

19.   The required point bisects the line joining the middle points of the diagonals.

20.   Through B draw BL, parallel to AC, to meet CD in L ; bisect DL in X ; the resultant is a force through X, parallel to AD, and equal to twice AD.

V. (Pages 33—35.)

1. 4 lbs. wt. in the direction AQ.

2. $\sqrt{50 + 32\sqrt{2}}$ at an angle $\tan^{-1}\dfrac{7 + 4\sqrt{2}}{17}$, *i.e.* 9·76 lbs. wt. at 36° 40′, with the first force.

3. $2P$ in the direction of the middle force.

4. $7P$ at $\cos^{-1}\frac{11}{14}$, *i.e.* 38° 13′, with the third force.

5. $\sqrt{3}P$ at 30° with the third force.

6. 12·31 making an angle $\tan^{-1}5$, *i.e.* 78° 41′, with AB.

7. 14·24 lbs. wt.

8. 5 lbs. wt. opposite the second force.

9. $\frac{1}{4}P(\sqrt{5}+1)\sqrt{10+2\sqrt{5}}$ bisecting the angle between Q and R.

10. 10 lbs. wt. towards the opposite angular point.

11. $\sqrt{125 + 68\sqrt{3}}$ lbs. wt. at an angle $\tan^{-1}\dfrac{64 + 19\sqrt{3}}{23}$, *i.e.* 15·58 lbs. wt. at 76° 39′, with the first force.

13. $P \times 5{\cdot}027$ towards the opposite angular point of the octagon.

14. 17·79 lbs. wt. at 66° 29′ with the fixed line.

15. 9·40 lbs. wt. at 39° 45′ with the fixed line.

16. 39·50 lbs. wt. at 111° 46′ with the fixed line.

17. 42·5 kilog. wt. at 30° with OA.

VI. (Pages 38—41.)

1. $\dfrac{W}{2}(\sqrt{6}-\sqrt{2})$; $W(\sqrt{3}-1)$.

2. $2\frac{2}{3}$ and $3\frac{1}{3}$ lbs. wt.   **3.** 126 and 32 lbs. wt.

4. 56 and 42 lbs. wt.   **5.** 48 and 36 lbs. wt.

6. 4, 8, and 12 lbs. wt.   **7.** W.

8. 120 lbs. wt.

9. The inclined portions of the string make 60° with the vertical and the thrust is $W\sqrt{3}$.

10. 7·23 lbs. wt.   11. The weights are equal.

12. 1·34 inches.   13. $2\frac{4}{5}$ and $9\frac{3}{5}$ lbs. wt.

14. 14 lbs. wt.   15. 6 ft. 5 ins. ; 2 ft. 4 ins.

16. They are each equal to the weight of the body.

18. $2P\cos\dfrac{a}{2}$, where a is the angle at the bit between the two portions of the rein.

20. $\dfrac{W}{2}\sec\dfrac{C}{2}$.   22. W ; $W\sqrt{2}$.

VII. (Pages 45, 46.)

1. 42·9 lbs. wt. ; 19·91 lbs. wt.

2. $1\frac{1}{3}$ and $1\frac{2}{3}$ tons wt.

3. 37·8 and 85·1 lbs. wt.   4. 15·2 lbs.

5. 3·4, 6·6, 3·67, 7·55 and 5 cwt. respectively.

6. 160 lbs. and 120 lbs. wt. ; 128 and 72 lbs. wt.

7. 20 cwts. and 6 cwts.

8. 244·84 and 561·34 lbs. wt.

9. 2·73 and ·93 tons wt.

10. (1) 3, $1\frac{1}{3}$ and 1 ton wt. ; (2) 2, $\frac{1}{3}$ and 1 ton wt.

11. A thrust of 5·01 tons wt. in AC, and a pull of 1·79 tons wt. in CD.

VIII. (Pages 55—57.)

1. (i) $R=11$, $AC=7$ ins. ; (ii) $R=30$, $AC=1$ ft. 7 ins. ; (iii) $R=10$, $AC=1$ ft. 6 ins.

2. (i) $R=8, AC=25$ ins. ; (ii) $R=8, AC=-75$ ins. ; (iii) $R=17$, $AC=-19\frac{1}{17}$ ins.

3. (i) $Q=9$, $AB=8\frac{1}{2}$ ins. ; (ii) $P=2\frac{3}{4}$, $R=13\frac{3}{4}$; (iii) $Q=6\frac{3}{4}$, $R=12\frac{3}{4}$.

4. (i) $Q=25$, $AB=3\frac{3}{50}$ ins. ; (ii) $P=24\frac{3}{4}$, $R=13\frac{3}{4}$; (iii) $Q=2\frac{4}{7}$, $R=3\frac{3}{7}$.

5. 15 and 5 lbs. wt.   **6.** $43\frac{1}{3}$ and $13\frac{1}{3}$ lbs. wt.

8. 98 and 70 lbs. wt.

9. The block must be 2 ft. from the stronger man.

10. 4 ft. 3 ins.   **11.** 1 lb. wt.   **12.** 1 foot.

13. 20 lbs. ; 4 ins. ; 8 ins.   **14.** $14\frac{3}{8}$ ins. ; $10\frac{5}{8}$ ins.

16. 40 and 35 lbs. wt.   **17.** $\frac{1}{2}W$.

18. The force varies inversely as the distance between his hand and his shoulder.

19. (i) 100 and 150 lbs. wt. ; (ii) 50 and 100 lbs. wt. ; (iii) 25 and 75 lbs. wt.

20. 1 lb. wt. at 5 ft. from the first.

21. 77·55 and 34·45 lbs. wt. approx.

IX. (Pages 71—74.)

1. 10·1.   **2.** $5\sqrt{3}$ ft.-lbs.

3. $75\sqrt{3} = 129\cdot9$ lbs. wt.

4. 3 ft. 8 ins. from the 6 lb. wt.

5. At a point distant 6·6 feet from the 20 lbs.

6. $2\frac{6}{7}$ ft. from the end.   **7.** $2\frac{2}{3}$ lbs.

8. $2\frac{1}{3}$ lbs.

9. (1) 4 tons wt. each ; (2) $4\frac{1}{3}$ tons wt., $3\frac{2}{3}$ tons wt.

10. B is 3 inches from the peg.   **11.** $\frac{6}{7}$ cwt.

12. One-quarter of the length of the beam.

13. 55 lbs. wt.

14. The weight is $3\frac{1}{2}$ lbs. and the point is $8\frac{1}{2}$ ins. from the 5 lb. wt.

15. 3 ozs.   **16.** $85\frac{1}{2}$, $85\frac{1}{2}$, and 29 lbs. wt.

17. 96, 96 and 46 lbs. wt.

18. $1\frac{17}{28}$ ins. from the axle.

19. $2\sqrt{2}$ lbs. wt., parallel to CA, and cutting AD at P, where AP equals $\frac{9}{2}AD$.

20. $2P$ acting along DC.

21. The resultant is parallel to AC and cuts AD at P, where AP is $\frac{2}{5}$ ft.

22. $20\sqrt{5}$ lbs. wt. cutting AB and AD in points distant from A 8 ft. and 16 ft. respectively.

23. $P\sqrt{3}$ perpendicular to BC and cutting it at Q where BQ is $\frac{3}{2}BC$.

29. The required height is $\frac{1}{2}l\sqrt{2}$, where l is the length of the rope.

31. A straight line dividing the exterior angle between the two forces into two angles the inverse ratio of whose sines is equal to the ratio of the forces.

33. 225 lbs. wt.

X. (Page 79.)

2. 9 ft.-lbs.   **3.** 6.

4. A force equal, parallel, and opposite, to the force at C, and acting at a point C' in AC, such that CC' is $\frac{2}{5}AB$.

XI. (Pages 92—96.)

2. $45°$.   **3.** $10\sqrt{2}$ and 10 lbs. wt.

4. The length of the string is AC.

5. $\frac{2}{3}W\sqrt{3}$; $\frac{1}{3}W\sqrt{3}$.

8. $\dfrac{a}{l}$ must be < 1 and $> \frac{1}{2}$.

12. $\frac{3}{5}\sqrt{5}$ and $\frac{6}{5}\sqrt{5}$ lbs. wt.

14. $W \operatorname{cosec} a$ and $W \cot a$.   **15.** $\frac{1}{3}W\sqrt{3}$.

16. $30°$; $\frac{2}{3}W\sqrt{3}$; $\frac{1}{3}W\sqrt{3}$.   **17.** $\sqrt{7} : 2\sqrt{3}$.

18. $\frac{40}{3}\sqrt{3}$ lbs. wt.   **19.** $6\frac{2}{3}$ lbs. wt.

21. $h\sqrt{h^2 + a^2 \sin^2 a}/(h + a \cos a)$, where $2a$ is the height of the picture.

22. The reactions are
$$\frac{b}{a+b}\,\frac{r}{\sqrt{r^2-ab}}\,W \text{ and } \frac{a}{a+b}\,\frac{r}{\sqrt{r^2-ab}}\,W.$$

25. 3·16 ft. ; 133 and 118·8 lbs. wt.

26. 15·5 lbs. wt.   **27.** 6·75 and 16·6 lbs. wt.

28. 2·83 and 3·61 cwts.   **29.** 26·8 and 32·1 lbs. wt.

XII. (Pages 107—111.)

1. $\frac{1}{4} W \sqrt{3}.$ 2. $\frac{1}{6} W \sqrt{3}.$

4. $\frac{1}{2} W \cot a$; $\frac{5}{6} W \cot a.$

6. $\dfrac{W \sin \beta}{\sin (a + \beta)}$; $\dfrac{W \sin a}{\sin (a + \beta)}$; $\tan^{-1}\left(\dfrac{\cot \beta - \cot a}{2}\right).$

8. $\frac{3}{5}$ lb. wt.   11. $AC = a$; the tension $= 2 W \sqrt{3}.$

14. The reactions at the edge and the base are respectively 3·24 and 4·8 ozs. wt. nearly.

15. $W \cdot r/2 \sqrt{R^2 - r^2}.$ 18. $W \dfrac{a}{b}.$ 23. $\frac{1}{8} W \sqrt{6}.$

24. $133\frac{1}{3}$ and $166\frac{2}{3}$ lbs. wt.

26. $17\frac{11}{36}$ and $2\frac{5}{36}$ lbs. wt.   27.   20 lbs. wt.

XIII. (Page 113.)

1. The force is $4 \sqrt{2}$ lbs. wt. inclined at 45° to the third force, and the moment of the couple is $10a$, where a is the side of the square.

2. The force is $5P \sqrt{2}$, parallel to DB, and the moment of the couple is $3Pa$, where a is the side of the square.

3. The force is 6 lbs. wt., parallel to CB, and the moment of the couple is $\dfrac{21 \sqrt{3}a}{2}$, where a is the side of the hexagon.

XIV. (Pages 117, 118.)

1. The side makes an angle $\tan^{-1} 2$ with the horizon.

2. $15a.$ 3. $(n + 2) \sqrt{b^2 + c^2}.$

4. A weight equal to the weight of the table.

6. 10 lbs.

7. On the line joining the centre to the leg which is opposite the missing leg, and at a distance from the centre equal to one-third of the diagonal of the square.

8.   120 lbs.   9. $\sin^{-1}\dfrac{p}{p+w}$.

11. The pressure on A is $W\dfrac{\cos A}{2\sin B\sin C}$.

XV. (Pages 128, 129.)

1. $1\frac{1}{3}$, $1\frac{3}{5}$, and $1\frac{3}{5}$ feet.   2. 2, $2\frac{2}{3}$, and $1\frac{3}{5}$ feet.

3. $2\sqrt{5}$, 3, and 3 inches.

6.   The pressure at the point A of the triangle is

$$\frac{w}{3} + W\frac{a}{c\sin B},$$

where a is the perpendicular distance of the weight W from the side BC.

10.   60°.   12. $\cos^{-1}\frac{7}{25}$, *i.e.* 73° 44'.

XVI. (Pages 131, 132.)

1. $4\frac{2}{3}$ inches from the end.

2.   15 inches from the end.

3. $2\frac{5}{9}$ feet.   4. $\frac{20}{21}$ inch from the middle.

5. $7\frac{1}{3}$ inch from the first particle.

6.   It divides the distance between the two extreme weights in the ratio of 7 : 2.

7. $5:1$.   8.   1·335... feet.   9. $\dfrac{2n}{3}$ inches.

10.   12 lbs. ; the middle point of the rod.

XVII. (Pages 137, 138.)

1.   One-fifth of the side of the square.

2. $\dfrac{3a}{4}$ from AB ; $\dfrac{a}{4}$ from AD.

3.   At a point whose distances from AB and AD are 16 and 15 inches respectively.

4. $7\frac{1}{3}$ and $8\frac{1}{3}$ inches.   **5.** $\dfrac{a}{6}\sqrt{19}$; $\dfrac{a}{30}\sqrt{283}$.

7. At the centre of gravity of the lamina.

8. $8\frac{1}{3}$ and $11\frac{1}{3}$ inches.   **10.** $2:1:1$.

12. At a point whose distances from BC and CA are respectively $\frac{3}{13}$ths and $\frac{4}{13}$ths of the distances of A and B from the same two lines.

14. It divides the line joining the centre to the fifth weight in the ratio of $5:9$.

18. One-quarter of the side of the square.

20. $4\frac{1}{3}$ inches from A.

21. It passes through the centre of the circle inscribed in the triangle.

XVIII. (Pages 141—143.)

1. $2\frac{1}{24}$ inches from the joint.

2. $5\frac{7}{8}$ inches from the lower end of the figure.

3. It divides the beam in the ratio of $5:11$.

4. At the centre of the base of the triangle.

5. $7\frac{3}{5}$ inches.

7. One inch from the centre of the larger sphere.

8. Its distance from the centre of the parallelogram is one-ninth of a side.

9. The distance from the centre is one-twelfth of the diagonal.

10. The distance from the centre is $\frac{1}{21}$th of the diagonal of the square.

11. It divides the line joining the middle points of the opposite parallel sides in the ratio of $5:7$.

12. $\frac{1}{3}\sqrt{3}$ inches from O.   **14.** $\dfrac{5a}{18}$.

15. A' bisects AD, where D is the middle point of BC.

16. It divides GA in the ratio $\sqrt{m}-1:m\sqrt{m}-3\sqrt{m}+1$.

17.   The height of the triangle is $\dfrac{3-\sqrt{3}}{2}$, *i.e.* ·634, of the side of the square.

18. $\frac{15}{194}$ inches from the centre.

19.   The centre of the hole must be 16 inches from the centre of the disc.

20.   It is at a distance $\dfrac{b^3}{a^2+ab+b^2}$ from the centre of the larger sphere.

21. $\frac{45}{56}h$, where h is the height of the cone.

22.   13·532 inches.

23.   The height, x, of the part scooped out is one-third of the height of the cone.

24.   3080 miles nearly.

XIX.   (Pages 145—148.)

1.   By 7, 8, and 9 lbs. wt. respectively.

2. $1\frac{7}{10}$ inch.   6. $5:4$.

10.   At the centre of gravity of the triangle.

14. $2\sin^{-1}\frac{1}{3}$.   15. $\sqrt{6}:1$.

16.   The height of the cone must be to the height of the cylinder as $2-\sqrt{2}:1$, *i.e.* as ·5858 : 1.

19.   It divides the axis of the original cone in the ratio $3:5$.

XX.   (Pages 159—162.)

1. $6\frac{2}{3}$ inches.   2. $\dfrac{6}{\sqrt[3]{\pi}}$ inches.   4. $\dfrac{W}{6}$.

7.   120 ; $\frac{1}{120}$th.

8.   18 if they overlap in the direction of their lengths, and 8 if in the direction of their breadths.

11. $\sqrt{3}$ times the radius of the hemisphere.

12. $1:\sqrt{2}$.   14. $4r$.

18. The string makes an angle $\cos^{-1}\left(\dfrac{W\sin a}{P}\right)$ with the plane where a is its inclination to the horizon; the equilibrium is stable.

19. The line from the fixed point to the centre is inclined at an angle $\sin^{-1}\left[\dfrac{W-w}{p+W+w}\dfrac{r}{c}\right]$ to the vertical; the equilibrium is stable.

XXI. (Pages 168—170.)

1. (1) $168\frac{3}{4}$ ft.-tons; $117\frac{6}{7}$ ft.-tons. **2.** 1000 feet.

3. 6×10^7 ft.-lbs. **4.** 21120. **5.** $9\frac{27}{32}$ hours.

6. $8\frac{13}{14}$. **7.** $71\frac{1}{44}$ mins. **9.** 4·4352.

10. 660,000 ft.-lbs.; 30 H.P.

11. $111\frac{17}{28}$ tons wt. **13.** 176 ft.-lbs.; ·21$\dot{3}$ H.P.

14. 24·2... ft.-lbs.; $\frac{5}{192}n(n+1)$ ft.-lbs.

16. 3 ft.-lbs. **18.** 166 ft.-lbs.

XXII. (Pages 178—180.)

1. 5 feet.

2. 4 feet from the first weight; toward the first weight.

3. 11 : 9. **4.** 2 lbs. **6.** 4 lbs.

7. $9\frac{4}{5}$ lbs.

8. 6 ins. from the 27 ounces; $1\frac{5}{7}$ inch.

9. 1 foot. **10.** 360 stone wt. **11.** 21 lbs. wt.

12. 15 lbs. wt. **13.** $2\sqrt{2}$ at 45° to the lever.

14. 50 lbs. wt.

15. The long arm makes an angle $\tan^{-1}\dfrac{7}{\sqrt{3}}$ with the horizon.

16. $8\frac{1}{2}$ lbs. wt. **19.** 20 lbs.

20. The weight of $2\frac{1}{2}$ cwt. **21.** $\dfrac{n}{6}(\sqrt{3}-1)a$.

XXIII.   (Pages 186, 187.)

1.   (i) 320 ; (ii) 7 ; (iii) 3.
2.   (i) 7 ; (ii) $45\frac{1}{2}$; (iii) 7 ; (iv) 6.
3.   290 lbs.   4. $10\frac{3}{4}$ lbs.   5.   5 lbs.
7.   5 lbs.   9.   49 lbs. ; 1 lb. each.
10. $4w$; $21w$.   12. $9\frac{5}{17}$ lbs. wt.   13.   18 lbs. wt.

XXIV.   (Pages 189, 190.)

1.   6 lbs.   2.   4 strings ; 2 lbs.
3.   47 lbs. ; 6 pulleys.   4.   7 strings ; 14 lbs.
5. $\dfrac{W}{n+1}$, where n is the number of strings ; $\dfrac{W}{n-1}$.
6.   9 stone wt.
7.   The cable would support $2\frac{1}{4}$ tons.   8. n.
9.   75 lbs. ; $166\frac{2}{3}$ lbs.   10. $1\frac{3}{22}$ cwt.

XXV.   (Pages 195, 196.)

1.   (i) 30 lbs. ; (ii) 4 lbs. ; (iii) 4.
2.   (i) 161 lbs. wt. ; (ii) 16 lbs. wt. ; (iii) $\frac{1}{2}$ lb. ; (iv) 5.
3.   10 lbs. wt. ; the point required divides the distance between the first two strings in the ratio of 23 : 5.
4. $1\frac{11}{15}$ inch from the end.   5. $18\frac{6}{53}$.
6. $\frac{4}{7}$ inch from the end.
8. $W = 7P + 4w$; 8 ozs. ; 1 lb. wt.
9.   4 ; 1050 lbs.   10.   4.
12. $W = P(2^n - 1) + W'(2^{n-1} - 1)$.

XXVI.   (Pages 201—203.)

1.   12 lbs. wt. ; 20 lbs. wt.   2.   30° ; $W\dfrac{\sqrt{3}}{2}$.
3.   103·92 lbs. wt.   5.   3 : 4 ; $2P$.
6. $\sqrt{3} : 1$.   7. $\cos^{-1}\frac{11}{16}$; $\sin^{-1}\frac{1}{4}$ to the plane.

8. $\dfrac{1}{\sqrt{3}}$ lbs. wt.; $\dfrac{7}{\sqrt{3}}$ lbs. wt.   9.   6 lbs. wt.

11. $16\frac{1}{2}$ lbs.   12. $\dfrac{\sin a}{\sin \beta - \sin a}$ tons.

14.   The point divides the string in the ratio $1 : \sin a$.

16.   17·374 lbs. wt.; 46·884 lbs. wt.

17.   10·318 lbs. wt.; 12·208 lbs. wt.

18.   16·12 lbs. wt.; 34·056 lbs. wt.

XXVII.   (Pages 208, 209.)

1.   7 lbs. wt.

2.   120 lbs. wt.; 70 lbs. wt. on each; $110\frac{10}{11}$ lbs. wt.

3.   20 inches.   4.   7 feet.   5. $3\frac{4}{5}$ tons.

6.   3 lbs. wt.   7.   55 lbs.   8. $23\frac{1}{3}$ lbs. wt.

9. $2\frac{1}{3}$ lbs. wt.   10.   360 lbs.   11.   120 lbs.

12.   1500 ft.-lbs.

13.   47040 ft.-lbs.; 2 cwt.; 210 feet.

14. $\dfrac{2b}{c-a}$; $\dfrac{2R}{R-r}$.

XXVIII.   (Pages 216, 217.)

1.   11 lbs.   2. $26\frac{1}{4}$ lbs.   3.   2 ozs.

4. $2 : 3$; 6 lbs.   5.   24·494 lbs.   6. $5 : \sqrt{26}$.

7. $\frac{6}{5}\sqrt{110}$ inches; $\sqrt{110}$ lbs.

9. $2s.\ 3d.$; $1s.\ 9\frac{1}{3}d.$

10.   He will lose one shilling.

12. $10 : \sqrt{101}$; $\sqrt{101} : 10$.

13. $\dfrac{P-Q}{2}$; $\dfrac{P+Q}{2}$.

14. $w - P : P - w'$; $\dfrac{ww' - P^2}{P - w'}$.

15. $R - \dfrac{(Q-R)^2}{P-Q}$.   16.   16 lbs.

XXIX. (Pages 222—224).

1. $34\frac{5}{6}$ inches from the fulcrum.

2. 2 inches from the end; 1 inch.

3. 32 inches from the fulcrum.

4. $\frac{2}{3}$ inch; $4\frac{1}{2}$ lbs.   5. 4 inches.

6. 16 lbs.; 8 inches beyond the point of attachment of the weight.

7. $\frac{2}{9}$ lb.; $\frac{18}{19}$ lb.

8. 26 lbs.; 15 lbs.; 10 inches from the fulcrum.

9. 3 lbs.   10. $15\frac{7}{8}$ lbs.; $6\frac{7}{8}$ lbs.; 4 inches

11. It is 10 inches from the point at which the weight is attached.

12. 3 ozs.   13. 30 inches.

15. The machine being graduated to shew lbs. the weights indicated must each be increased by $\frac{1}{6}$th of a lb.

16. The numbers marked on the machine must each be increased by $\dfrac{x}{y}\dfrac{W}{10}$, where x and y are respectively the distances of the centre of gravity of the machine and its end from the fulcrum, and W is the weight of the machine.

17. He cheats his customers, or himself, according as he decreases, or increases, the movable weight.

XXX. (Pages 230, 231.)

(*In the following examples π is taken to be $2\frac{2}{7}$.*)

1. 4400 lbs.   2. $5\frac{8}{11}$ inches.   3. $\frac{25}{27}$ lbs. wt.

4. $1\frac{69}{176}$ lbs. wt.   5. $4\frac{94}{99}$ lbs. wt.

6. $13\frac{23}{49}$ tons wt.   7. $6\frac{2}{7}$ tons wt.

8. $50\frac{10}{11}$ lbs. wt.   9. $4\frac{92}{175}$ inches.

10. $4525\frac{5}{7}$.   11. $5430\frac{6}{7}$.   12. $4\frac{1}{6}$ ft.-lbs.

XXXI. (Pages 244—246.)

1. 10 lbs. wt.; $12\frac{1}{2}$ lbs. wt.; $10\sqrt{17}$ and $\frac{15}{2}\sqrt{17}$ lbs. wt. respectively, inclined at an angle $\tan^{-1}4$ with the horizontal.

2. $\dfrac{P}{W} = \dfrac{\sqrt{2}}{3} = \cdot4714.$

3. $10\sqrt{10}$ lbs. wt. at an angle $\tan^{-1}3$ with the horizon.

6. $\frac{1}{4}.$ 　　7. $\frac{4}{3}\sqrt{3}$ lbs. wt. 　　9. $\dfrac{\sqrt{3}}{15}.$

10. $\sin\beta = \sin\alpha + \mu\cos\alpha.$

11. $\tan^{-1}\left(\mu\dfrac{W_1 + W_2}{W_1 - W_2}\right)$, where W_1 and W_2 are the two weights.

14. $a \times \cdot134.$

15. At an angle equal to the angle of friction.

16. 2·19 cwts. 　　　　17. 79·7 lbs. wt.; ·32.

XXXII. (Pages 257—259.)

1. 3808 ft.-lbs. 　　2. 7,392,000 ft.-lbs.; $7\frac{7}{15}$ H.P.

3. 23,040,000 ft.-lbs.; $5\frac{9}{11}$ H.P.

4. 7766. 　　　　　　　　6. ·446.

7. ·11, ·34, and ·47 nearly.

8. $a = 4\cdot125$; $b = \cdot01125.$

(The answers to the following four questions will be only approximations.)

9. $a = 5\cdot3$; $b = \cdot097.$

10. $P = 7\cdot3 + \cdot236\,W$;

$$E = \dfrac{W}{36\cdot5 + 1\cdot18\,W}; \quad M = \dfrac{W}{7\cdot3 + \cdot236\,W}.$$

11. $P = 4\cdot3 + 4\cdot7\,W$; ·8 and ·88.

12. $P = 18\cdot5 + 5\cdot5\,W$; ·59 and ·79.

XXXIII. (Pages 262, 263.)

1. $11\frac{2}{3}$ lbs. wt.   2. $45°$.

5. It can be ascended as far as the centre.

8. 50 feet; one-quarter of the weight of the ladder.

9. $w\dfrac{2\mu - \tan\alpha}{\tan\alpha - \mu}$; if $\tan\alpha > 2\mu$, the weight is negative, *i.e.* the ladder would have to be *held up* in order that there should be equilibrium; if $\tan\alpha < \mu$, the weight is again negative, and we should then only get limiting equilibrium if the ladder were held up, and in this case the feet would be on the point of moving *towards* one another.

XXXIV. (Pages 264, 265.)

1. $\tan^{-1}\frac{1}{2}$; height = twice diameter.   4. $45°$.

6. $2\tan^{-1}\dfrac{\sqrt{3}}{12} = 2\tan^{-1}(\cdot1443) = 16°\ 26'$.

8. Unity.

XXXV. (Pages 269—273.)

11. $\dfrac{\sqrt{3}}{30} = \cdot0577$.   15. $\mu\left(\dfrac{W}{w}+1\right)\sqrt{b^2-a^2}$.

18. $\frac{7}{9}$.

20. The required force is $\frac{2}{5}W$ at an angle $\cos^{-1}\frac{11}{14}$ with the line of greatest slope.

21. In a direction making an angle $\cos^{-1}\dfrac{5\sqrt{3}}{9}(=15°\ 48')$ with the line of greatest slope.

24. If $\mu\cot\alpha$ be greater than unity, there is no *limiting* position of equilibrium, *i.e.*, the particle will rest in any position.

28. $60°$.

XXXVI. (Pages 277, 278.)

1. At P, where BP equals $\frac{1}{3}BC$; $\frac{3W}{2}$.

5. $\frac{W}{2} \tan \frac{ACB}{2}$.

7. $\frac{3W}{\sqrt{5}}$; $\frac{W}{5} \sqrt{10}$ at $\tan^{-1} \frac{1}{3}$ to the horizontal.

8. $\frac{W}{2}$; $\frac{3W}{2}$; $\frac{\sqrt{3}W}{4}$.

10. Half the weight of the middle rod.

12. One-eighth of the total weight of the rods, acting in a horizontal direction.

XXXVII. (Page 285.)

6. $\frac{7}{8}$ ft.-lb.

7. $\frac{5}{8}$ ft.-lb.

XXXVIII. (Pages 293—296.)

1. 39 lbs. wt. ; 25·8 lbs. wt. at 1° 40′ to the horizon.

2. 152·3 and 267·96 lbs. wt.   3. ·41.

4. 124°, 103°, 133°.   5. 26·9 lbs. wt.

6. 74 lbs. wt. ; 12·7 lbs. wt.

7. A force 2·6 lbs. along a line which cuts BC and AC produced in points K and L such that $CK = 19·25$ ins. and $CL = 17·6$ ins.

8. (1) $1\frac{1}{4}$ ft. ; (2) $7\frac{1}{2}$ ft. in the direction opposite to AB.

9. 3·9 ft. from the end.

10. 7·15 lbs. wt. and 6·85 lbs. wt.

11. 150, 158·115, and 50 lbs. wt.

13. Each equals the wt. of 10 cwt.

14. ·46 ; 91·2 and 57·2 lbs. wt.

15. 58·1, 65·8, 37·4, 33·2, and 29 lbs. wt. respectively.

20. $T_1 = 13{\cdot}05$; $T_2 = 9{\cdot}79$; $T_3 = 3{\cdot}26$; $T_4 = 8{\cdot}39$; $T_5 = 5$ cwts. T_4 and T_5 are ties; the others are struts.

21. $T_1 = 8{\cdot}39$; $T_2 = 11{\cdot}98$; $T_3 = 9{\cdot}62$. T_2 is a strut; T_1 and T_3 are ties.

22. $37{\cdot}2$, $47{\cdot}5$ and $43{\cdot}1$ cwts.

23. 6 tons and 2 tons; $5{\cdot}77$, $1{\cdot}155$, $1{\cdot}155$ and $3{\cdot}464$; of these last four the first, third and fourth are struts and the second is a tie.

24. The tensions of AB, BC, CD, DA are $32{\cdot}4$, $36{\cdot}4$, $16{\cdot}8$ and $25{\cdot}5$ lbs. wt.; the thrust of BD is $36{\cdot}7$ lbs. wt.

EASY MISCELLANEOUS EXAMPLES.
(Pages 318—320.)

1. 15 lbs. wt. at an angle $\tan^{-1}\frac{4}{3}$ with the second force.

2. Each component is $57{\cdot}735\ldots$ lbs. wt.

3. $14{\cdot}24$ lbs. wt.   **4.**   50 and $86{\cdot}6025\ldots$ lbs. wt.

6. 3 feet.   **7.** 2 ozs.   **9.** $4\frac{1}{3}$ inches from A.

10. $7\frac{1}{3}$ inches.

12. It divides the line joining the centre to the middle point of the opposite side in the ratio 2 : 13.

13. $\frac{5}{6}$ths of the diameter of a penny.

14. 8 and 12 lbs. wt.   **15.** $9\frac{4}{5}$ lbs. wt.

16. $W = P$.

17. The required point divides the distance between the two extreme strings in the ratio 13 : 49.

18. $\frac{1}{3}\sqrt{3}$ lbs. wt.   **20.**   18 inches; 4 inches.

21. $26\frac{2}{3}$.   **22.** $\frac{2}{11}$.

23. He can ascend the whole length.

24. $10\frac{935}{1344}$.

HARDER MISCELLANEOUS EXAMPLES.
(Pages 320—332.)

5. The centre of the inscribed circle.

6. P divides AD in the ratio $1 : \sqrt{3}$.

9. The forces are in equilibrium.

21. $\frac{2}{6}$ lb. wt.

28. $\frac{l}{2}$.

31. $W \dfrac{x \sqrt{a^2 + b^2}}{ab}$, where a and b are the lengths of the sides of the frame and AP is x.

39. At a point distant $\sqrt{c^2 + a^2} - a$ from the centre of the rod, where $2c$ is the length of the rod, and a is the distance from the centre of the given point.

40. $\dfrac{\mu c W}{a \sin \theta + \mu c \cos \theta}$, where W is the weight of each particle.

44. The difference between the angles of inclination of the planes to the horizon must be not greater than the sum of the angles of friction.

45. $W \cos \lambda \sin (a - \lambda) \operatorname{cosec} a$, and $W \cos \lambda \sin \lambda \operatorname{cosec} a$, where W is the weight of the rod.

48. The ratio of the depth to the width of the sash.

49. $\sqrt{3}$ feet.

53. The particle will move first, if $\mu W > (1 + \mu^2)\, w \cos a \sin a$, where a is the inclination of the face of the plane.

57. The equilibrium will be broken.

59. $W \tan i$; $\dfrac{W}{W + W'} \tan i$, where W' is the weight of the inclined plane.

62. $W = 10\sqrt{3}$; the force is (i) $5\sqrt{3}$ lbs. weight, and (ii) zero.

$W = \dfrac{20\sqrt{3}}{3}$; the force is (i) $\dfrac{10}{\sqrt{3}}$ lbs. wt., and (ii) zero.

65. He must press downwards when B has raised more than half the ladder.

Pitt Press Mathematical Series

THE ELEMENTS

OF

STATICS AND DYNAMICS.

_____

PART II. ELEMENTS OF DYNAMICS.

CAMBRIDGE UNIVERSITY PRESS
C. F. CLAY, Manager
LONDON: Fetter Lane, E.C. 4

NEW YORK: G. P. PUTNAM'S SONS
BOMBAY, CALCUTTA, MADRAS: MACMILLAN AND CO., Ltd.
TORONTO: J. M. DENT AND SONS, Ltd.
TOKYO: THE MARUZEN-KABUSHIKI-KAISHA

THE ELEMENTS

OF

STATICS AND DYNAMICS

BY

S. L. LONEY, M.A.

PROFESSOR OF MATHEMATICS AT THE ROYAL HOLLOWAY COLLEGE
(UNIVERSITY OF LONDON),
SOMETIME FELLOW OF SIDNEY SUSSEX COLLEGE, CAMBRIDGE.

PART II. DYNAMICS.

FIFTEENTH EDITION

CAMBRIDGE:
AT THE UNIVERSITY PRESS
1918

First Edition, 1891.
Second Edition, December 1892.
Reprinted, October 1893, *May* 1895,
November 1896, *February* 1899,
Jan. 1901, *July* 1902, *May* 1904.
New Edition (revised and enlarged), May 1906
Reprinted, October 1907, *November* 1908, *October* 1911,
November 1915, *March* 1918.

PREFACE.

THE present book forms Part II. of *The Elements of Statics and Dynamics*, of which Part I. (*Statics*) has already been published.

It aims at being useful for Schools and the less advanced students of Colleges; the examples are, in consequence, large in number, and generally of a numerical and easy character. Except in two articles and a few examples at the end of the Chapter on Projectiles, it is only presumed that the student has a knowledge of Elementary Geometry and Algebra, and of the Elements of Trigonometry.

It is suggested that, on a first reading of the subjects, all articles marked with an asterisk should be omitted.

Part I. and Part II. are, as far as is possible, independent of one another; hence, any teacher, who wishes his pupils to commence with Dynamics, may take Part II. before Part I., by omitting an occasional article which refers to Statics.

Any corrections of mistakes, or hints for improvement, will be gratefully received.

S. L. LONEY.

BARNES, S.W.
March, 1891.

PREFACE TO THE TENTH EDITION.

IT having become desirable to re-set the type for a new Edition, I have taken the opportunity of thoroughly overhauling the whole book. Its general scope is unaltered, but I have introduced more graphical and experimental work; I have, however, confined myself to experiments that can be arranged by a teacher with the simplest of apparatus in an ordinary class-room.

For two new figures on Pages 137 and 175 I am indebted to the kindness of Dr R. T. Glazebrook, who allowed me to make use of blocks prepared for his Mechanics.

I hope that the additions that have been made will add to the usefulness of the book.

S. L. LONEY.

ROYAL HOLLOWAY COLLEGE,
    ENGLEFIELD GREEN, SURREY.
        May 15*th*, 1906.

CONTENTS.

DYNAMICS.

DYNAMICS.

CHAPTER I.

VELOCITY.

1. If at any instant the position of a moving point be P, and at any subsequent instant it be Q, then PQ is the change in its position in the intervening time.

A point is said to be in motion when it changes its position. The path of a moving point is the curve drawn through all the successive positions of the point.

2. Speed. Def. *The speed of a moving point is the rate at which it describes its path.*

A point is said to be moving with uniform speed when it moves through equal lengths of its path in equal times, however small these times may be.

Suppose a train describes 30 miles in each of several consecutive hours. We are not justified in saying that its speed is uniform unless we know that it describes half a mile in *each* minute, 44 feet in *each* second, one-millionth of 30 miles in *each* one-millionth of an hour, and so on.

When uniform, the speed of a point is measured by the distance passed over by it in a unit of time; when variable, by the distance which would be passed over by the point in a unit of time, if it continued to move during that unit of time with the speed which it has at the instant under consideration.

By saying that a train is moving with a speed of 40 miles an hour, we do not mean that it has gone 40 miles in the last hour, or that it will go 40 miles in the next hour, but that, if its speed remained constant for one hour, then it would describe 40 miles in that hour.

When the speed of a point is not uniform, it may be measured at any instant as follows; take the distance s that it describes in the next tenth of a second; then the quantity $\frac{s}{\frac{1}{10}}$, *i.e.* $\frac{\text{space described}}{\text{time taken}}$, is an approximation to the speed required. For a nearer approximation, let s_1 be the distance described by it in the one-hundredth of a second which follows the moment considered; then $\frac{s_1}{\frac{1}{100}}$, *i.e.* $\frac{\text{space described}}{\text{time taken}}$, is a nearer approximation. A still nearer approximation is $\frac{s_2}{\frac{1}{1000}}$, where s_2 is the distance described in the one-thousandth of a second which follows the moment under consideration; and so on, the time being taken smaller and smaller. By this means we obtain a definite notion of the varying velocity at any instant.

In mathematical language this conception amounts to the following; *Let s be the length of the portion of the path described by a moving point in the small time t following the instant under consideration; then the ultimate value of $\frac{s}{t}$, as the time t is taken smaller and smaller, is the measure of the speed of the moving point at the instant under consideration.*

In a similar way the **rate of change** of any quantity (be it money, population of a country, or speed or anything else whose change can be measured) is the ratio of the change in that quantity to the small time in which the change occurs.

3. The units of length and time usually employed in England are a foot and a second.

A foot is the third part of a yard. A yard is defined to be the distance between the centres of two small gold plugs inserted in a solid brass bar which is kept at Westminster.

A day, *i.e.* the time taken by the Earth to rotate once on its axis, is divided into 24 hours, each hour into 60 minutes and each minute into 60 seconds. Hence the definition of a second.

In scientific measurements the unit of length generally used is the centimetre, which is the one hundredth part of a metre. A metre was meant to be defined as one ten-millionth part of a quadrant of the Earth's surface, *i.e.* of the distance from the North Pole to the Equator. In practice it is the length of a certain platinum bar kept in Paris.

One metre = 39·37 inches approximately, and therefore a foot = 30·48 centimetres nearly.

A decimetre is $\frac{1}{10}$th, and a millimetre $\frac{1}{1000}$th of a metre.

4. The unit of speed is the speed of a point which moves uniformly over a unit of length in a unit of time. Hence the unit of speed depends on these two units, and if either, or both of them, be altered, the unit of speed will also, in general, be altered.

5. If a point be moving with speed u, then in each unit of time the point moves over u units of length.

Hence in t units of time the point passes over $u \cdot t$ units of length.

Hence the distance s passed over by a point which moves with speed u for time t is given by $s = u \cdot t$.

It is easy to change a velocity expressed in one set of

units to other units.   For instance a velocity of 60 miles
per hour is equivalent to

$$1 \text{ mile per minute,}$$

or $$\frac{1}{60} \text{ mile per second,}$$

or $$\frac{5280}{60} \text{ feet per second,}$$

i.e. $$88 \text{ feet per second.}$$

Ex. 1.   Shew that the speed of the centre of the earth is about
18·5 miles per second, assuming that it describes a circle of radius
93000000 miles in 365 days.

Ex. 2.   Shew that the speed of light is about 194000 miles per
second assuming that it takes 8 minutes to describe the distance from
the sun to the earth.

6.   Displacement.   The displacement of a moving
point is its change of position.   To know the displacement
of a moving point, we must know both the length and the
direction of the line joining the two positions of the moving
point.   Hence the displacement of a point involves both
magnitude and direction.

Ex. 1.   A man walks 3 miles due east and then 4 miles due
north; shew that his displacement is 5 miles at an angle $\tan^{-1} \frac{4}{3}$
north of east.

Ex. 2.   A ship sails 1 mile due south and then $\sqrt{2}$ miles south-
west; shew that its displacement is $\sqrt{5}$ miles in a direction $\tan^{-1} \frac{1}{2}$
west of south.

Ex. 3.   A vessel proceeded as follows, all the angles being
reckoned from the north towards the east; 5 miles at 225°, 6 north,
2 at 90°, 3 at 135°, 4 at 300°.   The time taken was 2 hours, and the
tide was flowing from east to west at the rate of 3 miles per hour.
Shew graphically that the true distance between the initial and final
positions of the vessel is about 9·18 miles and that it had moved
towards the west a distance of 8·88 miles approximately.

7.   Velocity.   Def.   *The velocity of a moving point
is the rate of its displacement.*

A velocity therefore possesses both magnitude and
direction.

A point is said to be moving with uniform velocity, when it is moving in a constant direction, and passes over equal lengths in equal times, however small these times may be.

When uniform, the velocity of a moving point is measured by its displacement per unit of time; when variable, it is measured, at any instant, by the displacement that the moving point would have in a unit of time, if it moved during that unit of time with the velocity which it has at the instant under consideration.

As in Art. 2, the velocity of a moving point, when not uniform, may be obtained by finding its displacements in the next $\frac{1}{10}$, $\frac{1}{100}$, $\frac{1}{1000}$... of a second after the moment considered, and we thus obtain approximations gradually getting nearer and nearer to the measure required.

Mathematically, *if d be the displacement of the point in the small time t following the instant under consideration, then the ultimate value of $\frac{d}{t}$, as t is taken smaller and smaller, is the velocity at the instant under consideration.*

8. It will be noted that when the moving point is moving in a straight line, the velocity is the same as the speed.

If the motion be not in a straight line the velocity is not the same as the speed. For example, suppose a point to be describing a circle uniformly, so that it passes over equal lengths of the arc in equal times however small; then its direction of motion (*viz.* the tangent to the circle) is different at different points of the circumference; hence in this case the *velocity* of the point (strictly so called) is variable, whilst its *speed* is constant.

9. The magnitude of the unit of velocity is the velocity of a point which undergoes a displacement equal to a unit of length in a unit of time.

When we say that a moving point has velocity v, we mean that it possesses v units of velocity, *i.e.*, that it would undergo a displacement, equal to v units of length, in the unit of time.

If the velocity of a moving point in one direction be denoted by v, an equal velocity in an opposite direction is necessarily denoted by $-v$.

The expression ft./sec. is by some writers used to denote a velocity of one foot per second. Thus "a velocity of 3 ft./sec." means "a velocity of 3 feet per second." So "a velocity of 10 cm./sec." means "a velocity of 10 centimetres per second."

10. Since the velocity of a point is known when its direction and magnitude are both known, we can conveniently represent the velocity of a moving point by a straight line AB; thus, when we say that the velocities of two moving points are represented in magnitude and direction by the straight lines AB and CD, we mean that they move in directions parallel to the lines drawn from A to B, and C to D respectively, and with velocities which are proportional to the lengths AB and CD.

11. A body may have simultaneously velocities in two, or more, different directions. One of the simplest examples of this is when a person walks on the deck of a moving ship from one point of the deck to another. He has one motion with the ship, and another along the deck of the ship, and his motion in space is clearly different from what it would have been had either the ship remained at rest, or had the man stayed at his original position on the deck.

Again, consider the case of a ship steaming with its bow pointing in a constant direction, say due north, whilst a current carries it in a different direction, say south-east, and suppose a sailor is climbing a vertical mast of the ship. The actual change of position and the velocity of the sailor clearly depend on three quantities, *viz.*, the rate and direction of the ship's sailing, the rate and direction of the current, and the rate at which he climbs the mast. His actual velocity is said to be "compounded" of these three velocities.

In the following article we shew how to find the velocity which is equivalent to, or compounded of, two velocities given in magnitude and direction.

12. Theorem. Parallelogram of Velocities.

If a moving point possess simultaneously velocities which are represented in magnitude and direction by the two sides of a parallelogram drawn from a point, they are equivalent to a velocity which is represented in magnitude and direction by the diagonal of the parallelogram passing through the point.

Let the two simultaneous velocities be represented by the lines AB and AC, and let their magnitudes be u and v.

Complete the parallelogram $BACD$.

Then we may imagine the motion of the point to be along the line AB with the velocity u, whilst the line AB moves parallel to the foot of the page so that its end A describes the line AC with velocity v. In the unit of time the moving point will have moved through a distance AB along the line AB, and the line AB will have in the same

time moved into the position CD, so that at the end of the
unit of time the moving point will be at D.

Now, since the two coexistent velocities are constant
in magnitude and direction, the
velocity of the point from A to D
must also be constant in magnitude and direction; hence AD is
the path described by the moving
point in the unit of time.

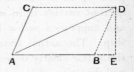

Hence AD represents in magnitude and direction the
velocity which is equivalent to the velocities represented
by AB and AC.

To facilitate his understanding of the previous article the student
may look on AC as the direction of motion of a steamer, whilst AB is
a chalked line, drawn along the deck of the ship, along which a man
is walking at a uniform rate.

13. Def. *The velocity which is equivalent to two or
more velocities is called their* **resultant**, *and these velocities
are called the* **components** *of this resultant.*

The resultant of two velocities u and v in directions
which are inclined to one another at a given angle a may
be easily obtained.

In the figure of Art. 12, let AB and AC represent
the velocities u and v, so that the angle BAC is a.

Then we have, by Trigonometry,

$$AD^2 = AB^2 + BD^2 - 2AB \cdot BD \cos ABD.$$

Hence, if we represent the resultant velocity AD by w,
we have

$$w^2 = u^2 + v^2 + 2uv \cos a, \text{ since } \angle ABD = \pi - a.$$

Also, if we denote the angle BAD by θ, we have

$$\frac{AB}{BD} = \frac{\sin ADB}{\sin BAD} = \frac{\sin DAC}{\sin BAD};$$

$$\therefore \frac{u}{v} = \frac{\sin(a-\theta)}{\sin\theta} = \frac{\sin a \cos\theta - \cos a \sin\theta}{\sin\theta}$$

$$= \sin a \cot\theta - \cos a.$$

$$\therefore \cot\theta = \frac{u + v\cos a}{v\sin a},$$

so that
$$\tan\theta = \frac{v\sin a}{u + v\cos a}.$$

Hence the resultant of two velocities u and v inclined to one another at an angle a, is a velocity $\sqrt{u^2 + v^2 + 2uv\cos a}$ inclined at an angle $\tan^{-1}\dfrac{v\sin a}{u + v\cos a}$ to the direction of the velocity u.

The direction of the resultant velocity may also be obtained as follows; draw DE perpendicular to AB to meet it, produced if necessary, in E; we then have

$$\tan DAB = \frac{ED}{AE} = \frac{BD \sin EBD}{AB + BD \cos EBD}$$

$$= \frac{v\sin a}{u + v\cos a}.$$

14. A velocity can be resolved into two component velocities in an infinite number of ways. For an infinite number of parallelograms can be described having a given line AD as diagonal; and, if $ABDC$ be *any* one of these, the velocity AD is equivalent to the two component velocities AB and AC.

The most important case is when a velocity is to be resolved into two velocities in two directions *at right angles*, one of these directions being given. When we speak of the *component of a velocity in a given direction* it is understood that the other direction in which the given velocity is to be resolved is perpendicular to this given direction.

Thus, suppose we wish to resolve a velocity u, represented by AD, into two components
at right angles to one another, one
of these components being along a
line AB making an angle θ with
AD.

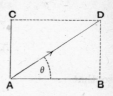

Draw DB perpendicular to AB,
and complete the rectangle $ABDC$.

Then the velocity AD is equivalent to the two component velocities AB and AC.

Also $AB = AD \cos \theta = u \cos \theta$,

and $AC = BD = AD \sin \theta = u \sin \theta$.

We thus have the following important

Theorem. *A velocity u is equivalent to a velocity $u \cos \theta$ along a line making an angle θ with its own direction together with a velocity $u \sin \theta$ perpendicular to the direction of the first component.*

The case in which the angle θ is greater than a right angle may be considered as in Statics, Art. 30.

Ex. 1. A man is walking in a north-easterly direction with a velocity of 4 miles per hour; find the components of his velocity in directions due north and due east respectively.

Ans. Each is $2\sqrt{2}$ miles per hour.

Ex. 2. A point is moving in a straight line with a velocity of 10 feet per second; find the component of its velocity in a direction inclined at an angle of $30°$ to its direction of motion.

Ans. $5\sqrt{3}$ feet per second.

Ex. 3. A body is sliding down an inclined plane whose inclination to the horizontal is $60°$; find the components of its velocity in the horizontal and vertical directions.

Ans. $\dfrac{u}{2}$ and $u\dfrac{\sqrt{3}}{2}$, where u is the velocity of the body.

15. *Components of a velocity in two given directions.*

If we wish to find the components of a velocity u in two given directions making angles α and β with it, we proceed as follows.

Let AD represent u in magnitude and direction. Draw AB and AC making angles α and β with it, and through D draw parallels to complete the parallelogram $ABDC$ as in Art. 12. Since the sides of a triangle are proportional to the sines of the opposite angles, we have

$$\frac{AB}{\sin ADB} = \frac{BD}{\sin BAD} = \frac{AD}{\sin ABD},$$

$$i.e., \quad \frac{AB}{\sin \beta} = \frac{BD}{\sin \alpha} = \frac{AD}{\sin (\alpha + \beta)}.$$

$$\therefore \quad AB = AD \frac{\sin \beta}{\sin (\alpha + \beta)}, \quad \text{and} \quad BD = AD \frac{\sin \alpha}{\sin (\alpha + \beta)}.$$

Hence the component velocities in these two directions are

$$u \frac{\sin \beta}{\sin (\alpha + \beta)} \quad \text{and} \quad u \frac{\sin \alpha}{\sin (\alpha + \beta)}.$$

16. Triangle of Velocities.

If a moving point possess simultaneously velocities represented by the two sides AB and BC of a triangle taken in order, they are equivalent to a velocity represented by AC.

For, completing the parallelogram $ABCD$, the lines AB and BC represent the same velocities as AB and AD and hence have as their resultant the velocity represented by AC.

Cor. 1. If there be simultaneously impressed on a point three velocities represented by the sides of a triangle taken in order, the point will be at rest.

Cor. 2. If a moving point possess velocities represented by $\lambda \cdot OA$ and $\mu \cdot OB$, they are equivalent to a velocity $(\lambda + \mu) \cdot OG$, where G is a point on AB such that

$$\lambda \cdot AG = \mu \cdot GB.$$

For, by the triangle of velocities, the velocity $\lambda \cdot OA$ is equivalent to velocities $\lambda \cdot OG$ and $\lambda \cdot GA$; also the velocity $\mu \cdot OB$ is equivalent to $\mu \cdot OG$ and $\mu \cdot GB$; but the velocities $\lambda \cdot GA$ and $\mu \cdot GB$ destroy one another; hence the resultant velocity is $(\lambda + \mu) \cdot OG$.

17. Parallelopiped of Velocities.

By a proof similar to that for the parallelogram of velocities, it may be shewn that the resultant of three velocities represented by the three edges of a parallelopiped meeting in a point, is a velocity represented by the diagonal of the parallelopiped passing through that angular point. Conversely, a velocity may be resolved into three others.

18. Polygon cf Velocities. If a moving point possess simultaneously velocities represented by the sides AB, BC, CD, ... KL of a polygon (whether the sides of the polygon are, or are not, in one plane), the resultant velocity is represented by AL.

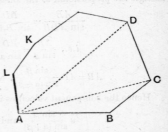

For, by Art. 16, the velocities AB and BC are equivalent to that represented by AC; and again the velocities AC and CD to AD, and so on; so that the final velocity is represented by AL.

Cor. If the point L coincide with A (so that the polygon is a closed figure) the resultant velocity vanishes, and the point is at rest.

19. When a point possesses simultaneously velocities in several different directions in the same plane, their resultant may be found by resolving the velocities along two fixed directions at right angles, and then compounding the resultant velocities in these directions.

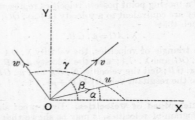

Suppose a point possesses velocities u, v, w,... in directions inclined at angles a, β, γ,... to a fixed line OX, and let OY be perpendicular to OX. The components of u along

OX and OY are respectively $u \cos a$ and $u \sin a$; the components of v are $v \cos \beta$ and $v \sin \beta$; and so for the others.

Hence the velocities are equivalent to

$$u \cos a + v \cos \beta + w \cos \gamma \ldots\ldots\text{parallel to } OX,$$

and $\quad u \sin a + v \sin \beta + w \sin \gamma \ldots\ldots\text{parallel to } OY.$

If their resultant be a velocity V at an angle θ to OX, we must have

$$V \cos \theta = u \cos a + v \cos \beta + w \cos \gamma + \ldots\ldots,$$

and $\quad V \sin \theta = u \sin a + v \sin \beta + w \sin \gamma + \ldots\ldots$

Hence, by squaring and adding,

$$V^2 = (u \cos a + v \cos \beta + \ldots)^2 + (u \sin a + v \sin \beta + \ldots)^2;$$

and, by division, $\tan \theta = \dfrac{u \sin a + v \sin \beta + \ldots}{u \cos a + v \cos \beta + \ldots}.$

These two equations give V and θ.

EXAMPLES. I.

1. *A vessel steams with its bow pointed due north with a velocity of 15 miles an hour, and is carried by a current which flows in a south-easterly direction at the rate of $3\sqrt{2}$ miles per hour. At the end of an hour find its distance and bearing from the point from which it started.*

The ship has two velocities, one being 15 miles per hour northwards, and the other $3\sqrt{2}$ miles per hour south-east.

Now the latter velocity is equivalent to

$\quad 3\sqrt{2} \cos 45°$, that is, 3 miles per hour eastward,

and $\quad 3\sqrt{2} \sin 45°$, that is, 3 miles per hour southward.

Hence the total velocity of the ship is 12 miles per hour northwards and 3 miles per hour eastward.

Hence its resultant velocity is $\sqrt{12^2 + 3^2}$, *i.e.* $\sqrt{153}$ miles per hour in a direction inclined at an angle $\tan^{-1}\frac{1}{4}$ to the north, *i.e.*, 12·37 miles per hour at 14° 2′ east of north.

2. *A point possesses simultaneously velocities whose measures are 4, 3, 2 and 1; the angle between the first and second is 30°, between the second and third 90°, and between the third and fourth 120°; find their resultant.*

Take *OX* along the direction of the first velocity and *OY* perpendicular to it.

The angles which the velocities make with *OX* are respectively 0°, 30°, 120°, and 240°.

Hence, if *V* be the resultant velocity inclined at an angle θ to *OX*, we have

$$V \cos \theta = 4 + 3 \cos 30° + 2 \cos 120° + 1 . \cos 240° ;$$

and $\qquad V \sin \theta = \qquad 3 \sin 30° + 2 \sin 120° + 1 . \sin 240°.$

We therefore have

$$V \cos \theta = 4 + 3 . \frac{\sqrt{3}}{2} + 2 \left(-\frac{1}{2} \right) + 1 \left(-\frac{1}{2} \right) = \frac{5 + 3\sqrt{3}}{2},$$

and $\qquad V \sin \theta = 3 . \frac{1}{2} + 2 . \frac{\sqrt{3}}{2} - 1 . \frac{\sqrt{3}}{2} = \frac{3 + \sqrt{3}}{2}.$

Hence, by squaring and adding,

$$V^2 = 16 + 9\sqrt{3} = 31{\cdot}5885, \quad \text{so that} \quad V = 5{\cdot}62,$$

and, by division,

$$\tan \theta = \frac{3 + \sqrt{3}}{5 + 3\sqrt{3}} = 2\sqrt{3} - 3 = {\cdot}4641 = \tan 24° \, 54'.$$

Hence the resultant is a velocity equal to 5·62 inclined at an angle 24° 54′ to the direction of the first velocity.

Graphically; This result may also be obtained by drawing; mark off *OA* on *OX* equal to 4 inches and draw *AB*, making *AB* equal to 3 inches and *XAB* equal to 30°.

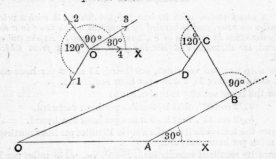

Draw *BC* perpendicular to *AB* and equal to 2 inches, and then *CD* at an angle of 120° with *BC* produced and equal to 1 inch.

Join *OD*.

On measurement, *OD* = 5·62 inches, and the ∠ *AOD* = 25° nearly.

3. The velocity of a ship is $8\frac{2}{11}$ miles per hour, and a ball is bowled across the ship perpendicular to the direction of the ship with a velocity of 3 yards per second; describe the path of the ball in space and shew that it passes over 45 feet in 3 seconds.

4. A boat is rowed with a velocity of 6 miles per hour straight across a river which flows at the rate of 2 miles per hour. If its breadth be 300 feet, find how far down the river the boat will reach the opposite bank below the point at which it was originally directed.

5. A man wishes to cross a river to an exactly opposite point on the other bank; if he can pull his boat with twice the velocity of the current, find at what inclination to the current he must keep the boat pointed.

6. A boat is rowed on a river so that its speed in still water would be 6 miles per hour. If the river flow at the rate of 4 miles per hour, draw a figure to shew the direction in which the head of the boat must point so that the motion of the boat may be at right angles to the current.

7. A stream runs with a velocity of $1\frac{1}{2}$ miles per hour; find in what direction a swimmer, whose velocity is $2\frac{1}{2}$ miles per hour, should start in order to cross the stream perpendicularly.

What direction should be taken in order to cross in the shortest *time?*

8. A ship is steaming in a direction due north across a current running due west. At the end of one hour it is found that the ship has made $8\sqrt{3}$ miles in a direction 30° west of north. Find the velocity of the current, and the rate at which the ship is steaming.

9. Two steamers X and Y are respectively at two points A and B, which are 5 miles apart. X steams away with a uniform velocity of 10 miles per hour in a direction making an angle of 60° with AB. Find in what direction Y must start at the same moment, if it steam with a uniform velocity of $10\sqrt{3}$ miles per hour, in order that it may just come into collision with X; find also at what angle it will strike X and the time that elapses before they meet.

10. A tram-car is moving along a road at the rate of 8 miles per hour; in what direction must a body be projected from it with a velocity of 16 feet per second, so that its resultant motion may be at right angles to the tram car?

11. A ship is sailing north at the rate of 4 feet per second; the current is taking it east at the rate of 3 feet per second, and a sailor is climbing a vertical pole at the rate of 2 feet per second; find the velocity and direction of the sailor in space.

12. Find the components of a velocity u resolved along two lines inclined at angles of 30° and 45° respectively to its direction.

13. A point which possesses velocities represented by 7, 8, and 13 is at rest; find the angle between the directions of the two smaller velocities.

14. A point possesses velocities represented by 3, 19, and 9 inclined at angles of 120° to one another; find by drawing and by calculation their resultant.

15. A point possesses simultaneously velocities represented by u, $2u$, $3\sqrt{3}u$, and $4u$; the angles between the first and second, the second and third, and the third and fourth, are respectively 60°, 90°, and 150°; shew, by drawing and by calculation, that the resultant is u in a direction inclined at an angle of 120° to that of the first velocity.

16. A point has equal velocities in two given directions; if one of these velocities be halved, the angle which the resultant makes with the other is halved also. Shew that the angle between the velocities is 120°.

17. A point possesses velocities represented in magnitude and direction by the lines joining any point on a circle to the ends of a diameter; shew that their resultant is represented by the diameter through the point.

18. A point possesses simultaneously four velocities; the first is 24 ft. per sec.; the second is 36 ft. per sec. at 40° to the first; the third is 45 ft. per sec. at 50° to the second; and the fourth is 60 ft. per sec. at 35° with the third; shew, by a drawing, that the resultant velocity is about 118·5 ft. per sec. at about 82° with the direction of the first component velocity.

20. Average Speed and Velocity. The average speed of a point in a given period of time is the same as the speed of a moving point which moves with uniform speed, and describes the same path as the given point in the given time. Thus the average speed of a moving point in a given period of time is the whole distance described by the point in the given time divided by the whole time. The average speed of an athlete who runs 100 yards in $10\frac{2}{5}$ seconds is $100 \div 10\frac{2}{5}$ or $9\frac{8}{13}$ yards per second.

Again suppose a train describes one mile in the first 5 minutes after leaving a station, then runs 15 mins. at the rate of 20 miles per hour, and finally takes 6 mins. over the last mile before coming to rest.

The total space described $= 1 + \frac{20}{4} + 1 = 7$ miles.

The time taken $= 5 + 15 + 6 = 26$ minutes.

Its average speed $= \frac{7}{26}$ miles per minute $= \frac{7}{26} \times 60$ miles per hour $= 16 \cdot 15$ miles per hour nearly.

The average velocity of a given point in any direction (strictly so called) is the whole displacement in the given direction in the given time divided by the given time.

21. Relative Motion. Rest and motion are relative terms; we do not know what absolute motion is; all motion that we become acquainted with is relative.

For example, when we say that a train is travelling northward at the rate of 40 miles an hour, we mean that that is its velocity relative to the earth, *i.e.* it is the velocity that a person standing at rest on the earth would observe in the train. Beside this motion along the surface it partakes with the rest of the earth in the diurnal motion about the axis of the earth; it also moves with the earth round the sun; and in addition has, in common with the whole solar system, any velocity that that system may have.

22. Consider the case of two trains moving on parallel rails in the same direction with equal velocities and let A and B be two points, one on each train; a person at one of them, A say, would, if he kept his attention fixed on B and if he were unconscious of his own motion, consider B to

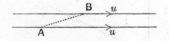

be at rest. The line AB would remain constant in magnitude and direction, and the velocity of B relative to A would be zero.

Next, let the first train be moving at the rate of 20 miles per hour, and let the second train B be moving in the same direction at the rate of 25 miles per hour. In this

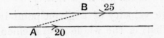

case the line joining A to B would (if we neglect the distance between the rails) be increasing at the rate of 5 miles per hour, and this would be the velocity of B relative to A.

Thirdly, let the second train be moving with a velocity of 25 miles per hour in the opposite direction to that of the first; the line joining A to B would now be increasing at the

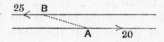

rate of 45 miles per hour in a direction opposite to that of A's motion, and the relative velocity of B with respect to A would be -45 miles per hour.

In each of these cases it will be noticed that the relative velocity of the second train with respect to the

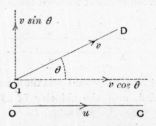

first is obtained by compounding with its own velocity a velocity equal and opposite to that of the first.

Lastly, let the first train be moving along the line OC with velocity u, whilst the second train is moving with velocity v along a line O_1D inclined at an angle θ to OC.

Resolve the velocity v into two components, *viz.*, $v \cos \theta$ parallel to OC and $v \sin \theta$ in the perpendicular direction.

As before, the velocity of B relative to A, parallel to OC, is $v \cos \theta - u$; also, since the point A has no velocity perpendicular to OC, the velocity of B relative to A in that direction is $v \sin \theta$.

Hence the velocity of B relative to A consists of two components, *viz.*, $v \cos \theta - u$ parallel to OC, and $v \sin \theta$ perpendicular to OC. These two components are equivalent to the original velocity v of the train B combined with a velocity equal and opposite to that of A.

Hence we have the following important result;

Relative Velocity. *When the distance between two points is altering, either in direction or in magnitude or in both, then either point is said to have a velocity relative to the other; also the relative velocity of one point B with respect to a second point A is obtained by compounding with the velocity of B a velocity which is equal and opposite to that of A.*

23. It may be advisable for the student to consider relative motion in a slightly different manner. Suppose the velocities of the two points A and B to be represented by the lines AP and BQ, so that in one second the positions of the points change from A and B to P and Q. Complete the parallelogram $APRB$ and join RQ.

By Art. 16 the velocity BQ is equivalent to two velocities represented by BR and RQ; also BR is equal and parallel to AP.

Hence the velocity of B is equivalent to two velocities, one, BR, equal and parallel to that of A, and the other by RQ.

The velocity of B relative to A is therefore represented by RQ.

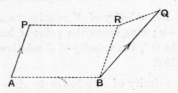

But RQ is the resultant of velocities RB and BQ, *i.e.* of the velocity of B and a velocity equal and opposite to that of A. Hence *the relative velocity of B with respect to A is obtained by compounding with the actual velocity of B a velocity equal and opposite to that of A.*

24. From the previous article it follows that, if two points A and B be moving in the same direction with velocities u and v respectively, the relative velocity of B with respect to A in that direction is $v - u$, and that of A with respect to B is $u - v$.

If they be moving in different directions the relative velocity is found by compounding velocities by means of the parallelogram of velocities.

Ex. *A train is travelling along a horizontal rail at the rate of 30 miles per hour, and rain is driven by the wind, which is in the same direction as the motion of the train, so that it falls with a velocity of 22 feet per second and at an angle of 30° with the vertical. Find the apparent direction of the rain to a person travelling with the train.*

The velocity of the train is 44 feet per second.

Let AB represent the actual velocity of the rain so that, if AE be a vertical line, the angle EAB is 30°.

Draw AC horizontal and opposite to the direction of the train and let it represent in magnitude the velocity, 44 feet per second, of the train.

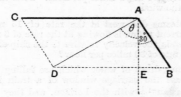

Complete the parallelogram $ABDC$.

Join AD, and let the angle EAD be θ.

AD is the apparent direction of the rain.

From the triangle BAD, we have

$$\frac{BD}{AB} = \frac{\sin DAB}{\sin BDA} = \frac{\sin (\theta + 30°)}{\cos \theta}.$$

$$\therefore \frac{44}{22} = \frac{\sin \theta \cos 30° + \cos \theta \sin 30°}{\cos \theta} = \tan \theta \cos 30° + \sin 30°.$$

$$\therefore 2 = \tan \theta . \frac{\sqrt{3}}{2} + \frac{1}{2}.$$

$$\therefore \tan \theta = \sqrt{3} = \tan 60°.$$

Hence θ is 60°. It follows, since BAD is a right angle, that the apparent direction of the rain is at right angles to its real direction.

EXAMPLES. II.

1. A railway train, moving at the rate of 30 miles per hour, is struck by a stone, moving horizontally and at right angles to the train with a velocity of 33 feet per second. Find the magnitude and direction of the velocity with which the stone appears to meet the train.

2. One ship is sailing due east at the rate of 12 miles per hour, and another ship is sailing due north at the rate of 16 miles per hour; find the relative velocity of the second ship with respect to the first.

3. One ship is sailing south with a velocity of $15\sqrt{2}$ miles per hour, and another south-east at the rate of 15 miles per hour. Find the apparent velocity and direction of motion of the second vessel to an observer on the first vessel.

4. A ship is sailing north-east with a velocity of 10 miles per hour, and to a passenger on board the wind appears to blow from the north with a velocity of $10\sqrt{2}$ miles per hour. Find the true velocity and direction of the wind.

5. A ship steams due west at the rate of 15 miles per hour relative to the current which is flowing at the rate of 6 miles per hour due south. What is the velocity relative to the ship of a train going due north at the rate of 30 miles per hour?

6. In a tunnel, drops of water which are falling from the roof are noticed to pass the carriage window of a train in a direction making an angle $\tan^{-1}\frac{1}{2}$ with the horizon, and they are known to have a velocity of 24 feet per second. Neglecting the resistance of the air, find the velocity of the train.

7. To a man walking at the rate of 2 miles an hour the rain appears to fall vertically; when he increases his speed to 4 miles per hour it appears to meet him at an angle of 45°; find the real direction and speed of the rain.

8. A steamer is going due west at 14 miles per hour, and the wind appears from the drift of the clouds to be blowing at 7 miles per hour from the north-west. Find its actual velocity and make a geometrical construction for its direction.

9. A railway train is moving at the rate of 28 miles per hour, when a pistol shot strikes it in a direction making an angle $\sin^{-1}\frac{3}{5}$ with the train. The shot enters one compartment at the corner furthest from the engine and passes out at the diagonally opposite corner; the compartment being 8 feet long and 6 feet wide, shew that the shot is moving at the rate of 80 miles per hour, and traverses the carriage in $\frac{5}{44}$ths of a second.

10. Two trains, each 200 feet long, are moving towards each other on parallel lines with velocities of 20 and 30 miles per hour respectively. Find the time that elapses from the instant when they first meet until they have cleared each other.

11. The wind blowing exactly along a line of railway, two trains, moving with the same speed in opposite directions, have the steam track of the one double that of the other; shew that the speed of each train is three times that of the wind.

12. *One ship, sailing east with a speed of 15 miles per hour, passes a certain point at noon; and a second ship, sailing north at the same speed, passes the same point at 1.30 p.m.; at what time are they closest together, and what is the distance then?*

Let O be the fixed point, A the position of the second ship at 12.0 noon, so that $OA = 22\frac{1}{2}$ miles.

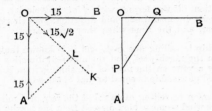

The relative velocity of the first ship with respect to the second is obtained by compounding with its velocity of 15 a velocity equal and opposite to that of the second ship, *i.e.* a velocity of 15 southwards. Hence this relative velocity is $15\sqrt{2}$ in the direction OK, *i.e.* southeast.

Draw AL perpendicular to OK. Then AL is clearly the shortest distance required. It

$$= OA \sin AOL = 22\frac{1}{2} \times \frac{1}{\sqrt{2}} = \frac{45}{4}\sqrt{2} = 15\cdot 9 \text{ miles nearly.}$$

Also the time after 12.0 noon

= the time in which OL is described with the relative velocity $15\sqrt{2}$

$$= \frac{OL}{15\sqrt{2}} = \frac{22\frac{1}{2} \times \frac{1}{\sqrt{2}}}{15\sqrt{2}} = \frac{3}{4} \text{ hour.}$$

Otherwise thus; Let P and Q be the actual positions of the ships at the end of time t, and let $PQ = x$.

Then $\qquad\qquad OP = OA - 15t = 15\left[\frac{3}{2} - t\right],$

and $\qquad\qquad OQ = 15t.$

Hence $\quad x^2 = 15^2\left[(\frac{3}{2} - t)^2 + t^2\right] = 15^2 \times 2\left[t^2 - \frac{3}{2}t + \frac{9}{8}\right]$

$$= 2 \times 15^2 \times \left[(t - \frac{3}{4})^2 + \frac{9}{16}\right].$$

Now a square can never be negative, so that its least value is zero.

Hence the least value of x is when $t = \frac{3}{4}$, and then

$$x = \sqrt{2} \times 15 \times \sqrt{\frac{9}{16}} = \frac{45}{4}\sqrt{2} = 15\cdot 9 \text{ nearly.}$$

13. A ship steaming north at the rate of 12 miles per hour observes a ship, due east of itself and distant 10 miles, which is steaming due west at the rate of 16 miles per hour; after what time are they at the least distance from one another and what is this least distance?

14. Two points are started simultaneously from points A and B which are 5 feet apart, one from A towards B with a velocity which would cause it to reach B in 3 seconds, and the other at right angles to the direction of the former with $\frac{3}{4}$ of its velocity. Find their relative velocity in magnitude and direction, the shortest distance between them, and the time when they are nearest.

15. A ship is sailing due east, and it is known that the wind is blowing from the north-west, and the apparent direction of the wind (as shewn by a vane on the mast of the ship) is from N.N.E.; shew that the speed of the ship is equal to that of the wind.

16. A person travelling eastward at the rate of 4 miles per hour, finds that the wind seems to blow directly from the north; on doubling his speed it appears to come from the north-east; find the direction of the wind and its velocity.

17. A person travelling toward the north-east, finds that the wind appears to blow from the north, but when he doubles his speed it seems to come from a direction inclined at an angle $\cot^{-1} 2$ on the east of north. Find the true direction of the wind.

18. Two points move with velocities v and $2v$ respectively in opposite directions in the circumference of a circle. In what positions is their relative velocity greatest and least and what values has it then?

25. Angular Velocity. Def. *If a point P be in motion in a plane, and if O be a fixed point in the plane and OA a fixed straight line drawn through O, then the rate at which the angle AOP increases is called the angular velocity of the moving point P about O.*

When uniform, the angular velocity is measured by the number of radians in the angle which is turned through by OP in a unit of time.

When variable, it is measured at any instant by what would be the angle turned through by the line OP in a unit of time, if during that unit it continued to turn at the same rate as at the instant under consideration.

Exs. If the line OP turn through 4 right angles (*i.e.* 2π radians) in one second, the angular velocity is 2π.

If it turn through three-quarters of a right angle in one second, the angular velocity is $\dfrac{3}{4} \cdot \dfrac{\pi}{2}$ or $\dfrac{3\pi}{8}$.

If OP make 7 revolutions in one second, the angular velocity is $7 \times 2\pi$ or 14π.

26. The angular velocity can always be expressed in terms of the linear velocity when the path is known.

The only case that we shall consider is when the angular velocity is uniform, and the moving point P is describing a circle about the fixed point O as centre.

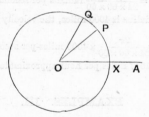

If a moving point describe a circle, its angular velocity about the centre of the circle is equal to its speed divided by the radius of the circle.

Let P be the position of the moving point at any time, and in the unit of time let the point describe the arc PQ. In this time the line OP turns through the angle POQ. Hence the angular velocity is equal to the number of radians in the angle POQ.

But the number of radians in $POQ = \dfrac{\text{arc } PQ}{OP}$.

Also, since the arc PQ is described in one second, it is equal to the speed v.

Hence, if ω be the angular velocity and r the radius of the circle, we have

$$\omega = \frac{v}{r},$$

$$i.e. \ v = r\omega.$$

Exs. (1) If the moving point describe a circle of 3 feet radius with unit angular velocity, the speed is given by $v = 3 \cdot 1 = 3$ feet per second.

(2) If the moving point describe a circle of 5 feet radius with speed 8 feet per second, its angular velocity ω is given by $\omega = \frac{8}{5}$ radian per second.

(3) The earth makes a complete revolution about its own axis in 24 hours. The angular velocity of any point on its surface therefore

$$= \frac{2\pi}{24 \times 60 \times 60} \text{ radians per second.}$$

Since the earth's radius is 4000 miles, the velocity of any point on the equator

$$= \frac{2\pi}{24 \times 60 \times 60} \times 4000 \text{ miles per second}$$

$$= 1047 \text{ miles per hour approximately.}$$

EXAMPLES. III.

1. A wheel turns about its centre, making 200 revolutions per minute; what is the angular velocity of any point on the wheel about the centre?

2. A wheel turns about its centre, making 4 revolutions per second; what is the angular velocity of any point on the wheel about the centre and what is its linear velocity, if the radius of the wheel be 2 feet?

3. If the minute hand of a clock be 6 feet long, find the velocity of the end in feet per second.

What is its angular velocity?

4. Compare the velocities of the extremities of the hour, minute, and second hands of a watch, their lengths being ·48, ·8, and ·24 inches respectively.

5. A treadmill, with axis horizontal and of diameter 40 feet, makes one revolution in 40 seconds. At what rate per hour does a man upon it walk over its surface, supposing he always keeps at the same height above the ground?

6. From a train moving with velocity V a carriage on a road parallel to the line, at a distance d from it, is observed to move so as to appear always in a line with a more distant fixed object whose least distance from the railway is D. Find the velocity of the carriage.

7. A point moves in a circle with uniform speed; shew that its angular velocity about any point on the circumference of the circle is constant.

8. A string has one end attached to the corner of a square board, fixed on a smooth horizontal table, and is wound round the square carrying a particle at its other end; the particle is projected with velocity u at right angles to the side of the square whose side is a; if the length of the string be $4a$, find the time that the string takes to unwrap itself from the square, assuming that the speed of the particle remains the same throughout the motion.

9. *A wheel rolls uniformly on the ground, without sliding, its centre describing a straight line; to find the velocities of different points of its rim.*

Let O be the centre and r the radius of the wheel, and let v be the velocity with which the centre advances. Let A be the point of the wheel in contact with the ground at any instant.

Now the wheel turns uniformly round its centre whilst the centre moves forward in a straight line; also, since each point of the wheel in succession touches the ground, it follows that any point of the wheel describes the perimeter of the wheel relative to the centre, whilst the centre moves through a distance equal to the perimeter; hence the velocity of any point of the wheel relative to the centre is equal in magnitude to the velocity v of the centre.

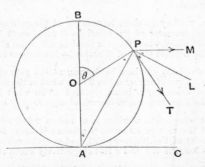

Hence any point P of the wheel possesses two velocities each equal to v, one along the tangent, PT, at P to the circle, and the other in the direction, PM, in which the centre O is moving.

Hence the velocity of $A = v - v = 0$, and so A is at rest for the instant.

So the velocity of $B = v + v = 2v$.

Consider the motion of any other point P. It has two velocities, each equal to v, along PM and PT respectively.

Now, since PM and PT are respectively perpendicular to OB and OP, the $\angle MPT = \angle POB = \theta$ (say).

The resultant of these two velocities v is a velocity $2v \cos \dfrac{\theta}{2}$ along

PL, where $\qquad \angle LPT = \tfrac{1}{2} \angle MPT = \dfrac{\theta}{2} = \angle OPA.$

Hence $\angle APL = \angle OPT = $ a right angle.

Hence the direction of motion of the point P is perpendicular to AP, and its angular velocity about A

$$= \frac{2v \cos \dfrac{\theta}{2}}{AP} = \frac{2v \cos \dfrac{\theta}{2}}{2r \cos \dfrac{\theta}{2}} = \frac{v}{r}$$

= the angular velocity of the wheel about O.

Hence each point of the wheel is turning about the point of contact of the wheel with the ground, with a constant angular velocity whose measure is the velocity of the centre of the wheel divided by the radius of the wheel.

10. An engine is travelling at the rate of 60 miles per hour and its wheel is 4 feet in diameter; find the velocity and direction of motion of each of the two points of the wheel which are at a height of 3 feet above the ground.

11. If a railway carriage be moving at the rate of 30 miles per hour and the diameter of its wheel be 3 feet, what is the angular velocity of the wheel when there is no sliding? Find also the relative velocity of the highest point of the wheel with respect to the centre.

12. If a railway carriage be moving at the rate of 30 miles per hour and the radius of the wheel be 2 feet, what is the angular velocity of the wheel when there is no sliding? Also what is the relative velocity of the highest point of the wheel with respect to the centre?

13. The wheel of a carriage is of radius 2 feet and the carriage is moving at the rate of 10 miles per hour; if there be no slipping, find the velocity of the highest point, and also the velocities of points which are at heights of 1 and 3 feet respectively above the ground.

CHAPTER II.

ACCELERATION.

27. Change of Velocity. Suppose a point at any instant to be moving with a velocity represented by OA, and that at some subsequent time its velocity is represented by OB.

Join AB, and complete the parallelogram $OABC$.

Then the velocities represented by OA and OC are equivalent to the velocity OB. Hence the velocity OC is the velocity which must be compounded with OA to produce the velocity OB. The velocity OC is therefore the change of velocity in the given time.

Thus the change of velocity is not, in general, the difference in magnitude between the magnitudes of the two velocities, but is that velocity which compounded with the original velocity gives the final velocity.

The change of velocity is not constant unless the change is constant both in magnitude and direction.

EXAMPLES. IV.

1. *A point is moving with a velocity of 10 feet per second, and at a subsequent instant it is moving at the same rate in a direction inclined at 30° to the former direction; find the change of velocity.*

On drawing the figure, as in the last article, we have $OA = OB = 10$, and the angle $AOB = 30°$.

Since $OA = OB$, we have $\angle OAB = 75°$, and therefore $\angle AOC = 105°$.

Also $AB = 2OA \sin 15° = 20 \cdot \dfrac{\sqrt{3}-1}{2\sqrt{2}} = 5\,(\sqrt{6}-\sqrt{2}) = 5·176$.

Hence the change in the velocity, *i.e.*, OC, is 5·176 feet per second in a direction inclined at 105° to the original direction of motion.

2. A ship is observed to be moving eastward with a velocity of 3 miles per hour, and at a subsequent instant it is found to be moving northward at the rate of 4 miles per hour; find the change of velocity.

3. A point is moving with a velocity of 5 feet per second, and at a subsequent instant it is moving at the same rate in a direction inclined at 60° to its former direction; find the change of velocity.

4. A point is moving eastward with a velocity of 20 feet per second, and one hour afterwards it is moving north-east with the same speed; find the change of velocity.

5. A point is describing with uniform speed a circle, of radius 7 yards, in 11 seconds, starting from the end of a fixed diameter; find the change in its velocity after it has described one-sixth of the circumference.

28. Acceleration. Def. *The acceleration of a moving point is the rate of change of its velocity.*

Note that the acceleration of a moving point has both magnitude and direction.

The acceleration is uniform when equal changes of velocity take place in equal intervals of time, however small these intervals may be.

When uniform, the acceleration is measured by the change in the velocity in a unit of time; when variable, it is measured at any instant by what would be the change of the velocity in a unit of time, if during that time the acceleration continued the same as at the instant under consideration.

29. The magnitude of the unit of acceleration is the acceleration of a point which moves so that its velocity is changed by the unit of velocity in each unit of time.

Hence a point is moving with n units of acceleration when its velocity is changed by n units of velocity in each unit of time.

Thus a point is moving with 10 centimetre-second units of acceleration when its change of velocity is 10 cms. per second in each second. This acceleration is sometimes called an acceleration of 10 cms./sec².

30. Theorem. Parallelogram of Accelerations.

If a moving point have simultaneously two accelerations represented in magnitude and direction by two sides of a parallelogram drawn from a point, they are equivalent to an acceleration represented by the diagonal of the parallelogram passing through that angular point.

Let the accelerations be represented by the sides AB and AC of the parallelogram $ABDC$, *i.e.* let AB and AC represent the velocities added to the velocity of the point in a unit of time. On the same scale let EF represent the velocity which the particle has at any instant.

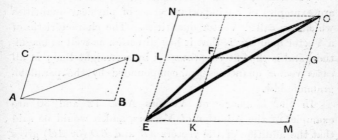

Draw the parallelogram $EKFL$ having its sides parallel to AB and AC; produce EK to M, and EL to N, so that KM and LN are equal to AB and AC respectively.

Complete the parallelograms as in the above figure.

Then the velocity EF is equivalent to velocities EK and EL. But in the unit of time the velocities KM and LN are the changes of velocity.

Therefore at the end of a unit of time the component velocities are equivalent to EM and EN, which are equivalent to EO, and this latter velocity is equivalent to velocities EF and FO.   (Art. 16.)

Hence in the unit of time FO is the change of velocity of the moving point, *i.e.* FO is the resultant acceleration of the point.

But FO is equal and parallel to AD.

Hence AD represents the acceleration which is equivalent to the accelerations AB and AC, *i.e.* AD is the resultant of the accelerations AB and AC.

31.   It follows from the preceding article that accelerations are resolved and compounded in the same way as velocities, and propositions similar to those of Arts. 13—19 will be true when we substitute "acceleration" for "velocity."

Velocities and accelerations, and also forces (Art. 72) are examples of an important class of physical quantities which are called Vector quantities.   The characteristic of a Vector quantity is that it has direction as well as magnitude, and is thus fitly represented by a straight line ; in all cases vector quantities are compounded by the parallelogrammic law.

In the language of Vectors Arts. 12 and 30 are examples of the Addition of Vectors, and it would be said that the addition of the vectors AB and BD (or AC) gives the vector AD.

In contradistinction to Vectors, quantities which only possess magnitude, and not direction, are called Scalars. Kinetic Energy, which will be defined later on, is an example of a physical quantity which is a Scalar ; other examples are a ton of coal, a sum of money, etc.   Scalar quantities are compounded by Simple Addition.

32. Theorem. *A point moves in a straight line, starting with velocity u, and moving with constant acceleration f in its direction of motion; if v be its velocity at the end of time t, and s be its distance at that instant from its starting point, then*

$$(1) \quad v = u + ft,$$

$$(2) \quad s = ut + \tfrac{1}{2}ft^2,$$

$$(3) \quad v^2 = u^2 + 2fs.$$

(1) Since f denotes the acceleration, *i.e.*, the change in the velocity per unit of time, ft denotes the change in the velocity in t units of time.

But, since the particle possessed u units of velocity initially, at the end of time t it must possess $u + ft$ units of velocity, *i.e.*

$$v = u + ft.$$

(2) Let V be the velocity at the middle of the interval so that, by (1), $V = u + f \cdot \dfrac{t}{2}$.

Now the velocity changes uniformly throughout the interval t. Hence the velocity at any instant, preceding the middle of the interval by any time T, is as much less than V, as the velocity at the same time T after the middle of the interval is greater than V.

Hence, since the time t could be divided into pairs of such equal moments, the space described is the same as if the point moved for time t with velocity V.

$$\therefore s = V \cdot t = \left(u + f\frac{t}{2}\right) t = ut + \tfrac{1}{2}ft^2.$$

(3) The third relation can be easily deduced from the first two by eliminating t between them.

For, from (1), $v^2 = (u + ft)^2$
$$= u^2 + 2uft + f^2t^2$$
$$= u^2 + 2f(ut + \tfrac{1}{2}ft^2).$$

Hence, by   (2), $v^2 = u^2 + 2fs.$

33. *Alternative proof of equation* (2).

Let the time t be divided into n equal intervals, each equal to τ, so that $t = n\tau$.

The velocities of the point at the beginnings of these successive intervals are

$$u, \ u + f\tau, \ u + 2f\tau, \ldots\ldots u + (n-1) f\tau.$$

Hence the space s_1 which *would be* moved through by the point, if it moved during each of these intervals τ with the velocity which it has at the *beginning* of each, is

$$s_1 = u \cdot \tau + [u + f\tau] \cdot \tau + \ldots\ldots + [u + f(n-1)\tau] \cdot \tau$$
$$= n \cdot u\tau + f\tau^2 \cdot \{1 + 2 + 3 \ldots\ldots + (n-1)\}$$
$$= n \cdot u\tau + f\tau^2 \cdot \frac{n(n-1)}{1 \cdot 2}, \text{ on summing the A.P.,}$$
$$= ut + \tfrac{1}{2}ft^2 \cdot \left(1 - \frac{1}{n}\right), \text{ since } \tau = \frac{t}{n}.$$

Also the velocities at the ends of these successive intervals are

$$u + f\tau, \ u + 2f\tau, \ldots\ldots u + nf\tau.$$

Hence the space s_2 which *would be* moved through by the point, if it moved during each of these intervals τ with the velocity which it has at the *end* of each, is

$$s_2 = (u + f\tau) \cdot \tau + (u + 2f\tau) \cdot \tau + \ldots\ldots + (u + nf\tau) \cdot \tau$$
$$= nu\tau + f\tau^2 (1 + 2 + 3 \ldots\ldots + n)$$
$$= ut + \tfrac{1}{2}ft^2 \left(1 + \frac{1}{n}\right), \text{ as before.}$$

Now the true space s is intermediate between s_1 and s_2; also the larger we make n and therefore the smaller the intervals τ become, the more nearly do the two hypotheses approach to coincidence.

If we make n infinitely large the values of s_1 and s_2 both become $ut + \tfrac{1}{2}ft^2$.

Hence $s = ut + \tfrac{1}{2}ft^2.$

34. When the moving point starts from rest we have $u = 0$, and the formulae of Art. 32 take the simpler forms

$$v = ft,$$
$$s = \tfrac{1}{2}ft^2,$$
and $v^2 = 2fs.$

35. Graphic Method. Velocity-Time Curve.

To determine, by means of a graph, the distance described in a given time when the velocity of the moving point is varying.

Take two straight lines OX and OY at right angles, and let times be represented by lengths drawn along OX, so that a unit of length in this direction represents a unit of time.

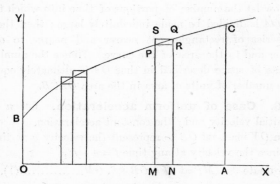

At *each* point M erect a perpendicular MP to represent the velocity of the moving point at the time represented by OM. The tops of all these ordinates will be found to lie on a line such as $BPQC$, which is curved or straight.

We shall shew that the distance described in time OA by the moving point is represented by the area bounded by OB, OA, AC and the curved line BC.

Take an ordinate NQ close to MP. Then during the time MN the point moves with a velocity which is greater than MP and less than NQ. Hence, since the distance described with constant velocity = velocity × time, the distance described by it in time MN is $> MP \cdot MN$ and is $< NQ \cdot MN$, *i.e.* the number of units of space described in time MN is intermediate between the number of units of area in the rectangles PN and QM. Similarly, if we divide OA into any number of equal small parts and erect parallelograms on each.

Hence the number of units in the distance described in time OA is intermediate between the space represented by the sum of the inner rectangles and the sum of the outer rectangles.

Now let the number of portions of time into which the time OA is divided be made indefinitely large; then these two series of rectangles get nearer and nearer to one another and to the area of the curve. Hence the number of units of space described in time OA is ultimately equal to the number of units of area in the area $OACB$.

36. Case of uniform acceleration. Let u be the initial velocity and f the constant acceleration.

On OY mark off OB to represent the velocity u at time 0. Since the velocity at any time $t' = u + ft'$,

the ordinate $\qquad MP$ at $M = OB + f \cdot OM$ ....(1).

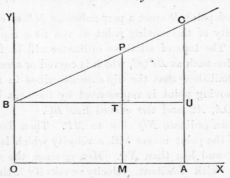

Draw BTU parallel to OX to meet MP in T and AC in U.

Then $\qquad TP = MP - OB = f \cdot OM$, by (1),

so that $\qquad f = \dfrac{TP}{OM} = \dfrac{TP}{BT} = \tan PBT.$

Hence TBP is a constant angle, and therefore P lies on a straight line passing through B.

In this case, therefore, the velocity-time curve is the straight line BC, and $UC = BU \cdot \tan CBU = f \cdot t.$

Hence the number of units of space described in time t

$\qquad$ = the number of units of area in $OACB$

$\qquad$ = area $OBUA$ + area BUC

$\qquad$ = $OA \cdot OB + \frac{1}{2} BU \cdot UC$

$\qquad$ = $OA \left[OB + \frac{1}{2} UC \right] = t \left[u + \frac{1}{2} ft \right]$

$\qquad$ = $ut + \frac{1}{2} ft^2.$

37. In the figure of Art. 35 since RQ is the increase of velocity in time MN the acceleration of the moving point at this instant = the value, when MN is made indefinitely small, of $\dfrac{RQ}{MN}$ $\qquad\qquad$ [Art. 28]

$\qquad$ = the value of $\tan QPR$.

But when MN is made indefinitely small the point Q moves up to P, PQ becomes the tangent at P, and $\tan QPR$ becomes the tangent of the angle that the tangent at P makes with OX.

Hence in the Velocity-Time graph the numerical value of the acceleration is the slope of the curve to the Time-Line.

38. *Space described in any particular second.*

[The student will notice carefully that the formula (2) of Art. 32 gives, not the space traversed in the tth second, but that traversed in t seconds.]

The space described in the tth second

= space described in t seconds − space described in $(t-1)$ seconds

$$= \left[ut + \tfrac{1}{2}ft^2\right] - \left[u(t-1) + \tfrac{1}{2}f(t-1)^2\right]$$
$$= u + \tfrac{1}{2}f\left[t^2 - (t-1)^2\right]$$
$$= u + f\frac{2t-1}{2}.$$

Hence the spaces described in the first, second, third, ... nth seconds of the motion are

$$u + \tfrac{1}{2}f, \ u + \tfrac{3}{2}f, \ \dots \ u + \frac{2n-1}{2}f.$$

These distances form an arithmetical progression whose common difference is f.

Hence, if a body move with a uniform acceleration, the distances described in successive seconds form an arithmetical progression, whose common difference is equal to the number of units in the acceleration.

The space described in any particular second may be otherwise found as follows. As in Art. 32, the space described in the tth second is the same as that which would be described if the point moved during that second with the velocity which it has at the middle of that second.

Now the velocity at the middle of the tth second

$$= \text{velocity at the end of time } (t - \tfrac{1}{2})$$
$$= u + f\left(t - \tfrac{1}{2}\right).$$

Hence the space described in the tth second

$$= u + f\frac{2t-1}{2}.$$

39. Ex. 1. *A train, which is moving at the rate of 60 miles per hour, is brought to rest in 3 minutes with a uniform retardation; find this retardation, and also the distance that the train travels before coming to rest.*

$$60 \text{ miles per hour} = \frac{60 \times 1760 \times 3}{60 \times 60} = 88 \text{ feet per second.}$$

Let f be the acceleration with which the train moves.

Since in 180 seconds a velocity of 88 feet per second is destroyed, we have (by formula (1), Art. 32)

$$0 = 88 + f(180).$$

$$\therefore f = -\frac{22}{45} \text{ ft.-sec. units.}$$

[N.B. f has a negative value because it is a retardation.]

Let x be the distance described. By formula (3), we have

$$0 = 88^2 + 2\left(-\frac{22}{45}\right) \cdot x.$$

$$\therefore x = 88^2 \times \frac{45}{44} = 7920 \text{ feet.}$$

Ex. 2. *A point is moving with uniform acceleration; in the eleventh and fifteenth seconds from the commencement it moves through 720 and 960 cms. respectively; find its initial velocity, and the acceleration with which it moves.*

Let u be the initial velocity, and f the acceleration.

Then $720 =$ distance described in the eleventh second

$$= [u \cdot 11 + \tfrac{1}{2} f \cdot 11^2] - [u \cdot 10 + \tfrac{1}{2} f \cdot 10^2].$$

$$\therefore 720 = u + \frac{21}{2} f \quad\quad\quad\quad\dots\dots(1).$$

So $$960 = [u \cdot 15 + \tfrac{1}{2} f \cdot 15^2] - [u \cdot 14 + \tfrac{1}{2} f \cdot 14^2].$$

$$\therefore 960 = u + \frac{29}{2} f \quad\quad\quad\quad\dots\dots(2).$$

Solving (1) and (2), we have $u = 90$, and $f = 60$.

Hence the point started with a velocity of 90 cms. per second, and moved with an acceleration of 60 cm.-sec. units.

EXAMPLES. V.

1. The quantities u, f, v, s, and t having the meanings assigned to them in Art. 32,

    (1)   Given $u = 2$, $f = 3$, $t = 5$,   find v and s;

    (2)   Given $u = 7$, $f = -1$, $t = 7$,   find v and s;

    (3)   Given $u = 8$, $v = 3$, $s = 9$,   find f and t;

    (4)   Given $v = -6$, $s = -9$, $f = -\frac{3}{2}$,   find u and t.

The units of length and time are a foot and a second.

2. A body, starting from rest, moves with an acceleration equal to 2 ft.-sec. units; find the velocity at the end of 20 seconds, and the distance described in that time.

3. In what time would a body acquire a velocity of 30 miles per hour, if it started with a velocity of 4 feet per second and moved with the ft.-sec. unit of acceleration?

4. With what uniform acceleration does a body, starting from rest, describe 1000 feet in 10 seconds?

5. A body, starting from rest, moves with an acceleration of 3 centimetre-second units; in what time will it acquire a velocity of 30 centimetres per second, and what distance does it traverse in that time?

6. A point starts with a velocity of 100 cms. per second and moves with -2 centimetre-second units of acceleration. When will its velocity be zero, and how far will it have gone?

7. A body, starting from rest and moving with uniform acceleration, describes 171 feet in the tenth second; find its acceleration.

8. A particle is moving with uniform acceleration; in the eighth and thirteenth second after starting it moves through $8\frac{1}{2}$ and $7\frac{1}{2}$ feet respectively; find its initial velocity and its acceleration.

9. In two successive seconds a particle moves through $20\frac{1}{2}$ and $23\frac{1}{2}$ feet respectively; assuming that it was moving with uniform acceleration, find its velocity at the commencement of the first of these two seconds and its acceleration. Find also how far it had moved from rest before the commencement of the first second.

10. A point, moving with uniform acceleration, describes in the last second of its motion $\frac{9}{25}$ths of the whole distance. If it started from rest, how long was it in motion and through what distance did it move, if it described 6 inches in the first second?

11. A point, moving with uniform acceleration, describes 25 feet in the half second which elapses after the first second of its motion, and 198 feet in the eleventh second of its motion; find the acceleration of the point and its initial velocity.

12. A body moves for 3 seconds with a constant acceleration during which time it describes 81 feet; the acceleration then ceases and during the next 3 seconds it describes 72 feet; find its initial velocity and its acceleration.

13. The speed of a train is reduced from 40 miles an hour to 10 miles per hour whilst it travels a distance of 150 yards; if the retardation be uniform, find how much further it will travel before coming to rest.

14. A point starts from rest and moves with a uniform acceleration of 18 ft.-sec. units; find the time taken by it to traverse the first, second, and third feet respectively.

15. A particle starts from a point O with a uniform velocity of 4 feet per second, and after 2 seconds another particle leaves O in the same direction with a velocity of 5 feet per second and with an acceleration equal to 3 ft.-sec. units. Find when and where it will overtake the first particle.

16. A point moves over 7 feet in the first second during which it is observed, and over 11 and 17 feet in the third and sixth seconds respectively; is this consistent with the supposition that it is subject to a uniform acceleration?

17. A point is moving in a north-east direction with a velocity 6, and has accelerations 8 towards the north and 6 towards the east. Find its position after the lapse of one second. [The units are a foot and second.]

18. A particle starts with a velocity of 200 cms. per second and moves in a straight line with a retardation of 10 cms. per sec. per sec.; find how long elapses before it has described 1500 cms. and explain the double answer.

19. Two points move in the same straight line starting at the same moment from the same point in it; the first moves with constant velocity u and the second with constant acceleration f; during the time that elapses before the second catches the first shew that the greatest distance between the particles is $\dfrac{u^2}{2f}$ at the end of time $\dfrac{u}{f}$ from the start.

20. In a run of 12 minutes from rest to rest a train has the following speeds, in miles per hour, at the end of each minute; 25, 40, 50, 50, 45, 40, 40, 45, 45, 35, 20, 0. Draw a curve representing the relation between the speed at any instant and the time from the start, and estimate the average velocity during the run.

21. A point starts from rest, and its velocities at the end of each second up to the seventh are as follows; 5, 18, 38, 62, 78, 81 and 83 feet per second. Sketch the velocity curve on a time base, and estimate the distance through which the point moves in the seven seconds. Estimate also the instant at which the acceleration is greatest and the value of the acceleration at that instant.

22. The velocities of a body are found to be 4, 8·8, 19, 22, 15·7, and 10 feet per second at intervals of 5 seconds from rest. Plot the curve of velocities to a time base, and estimate the distance passed over in the 30 seconds. Find also the acceleration at 16 seconds from the start.

CHAPTER III.

MOTION UNDER GRAVITY.

40. Acceleration of falling bodies. When a heavy body of any kind falls toward the earth, it is a matter of everyday experience that it goes quicker and quicker as it falls, or, in other words, that it moves with an *acceleration*. That it moves with a *constant* acceleration may be roughly shewn by the following experiment first performed by Morin.

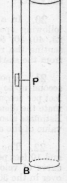

A circular cylinder covered with paper is connected with clock-work and made to rotate about its axis which is vertical. In front of the cylinder is an iron weight, carrying a pencil P, which is compelled by guides to fall in a vertical line and is so arranged that the tip of the pencil just touches the paper on the surface of the cylinder.

When the cylinder is revolving uniformly, the weight is allowed to drop and the pencil traces out a curve on the paper. When the weight has reached the ground the paper is unwrapped and stretched out on a flat surface. The curve marked out by the pencil is found to be such that the vertical distances described by the pencil from the beginning of the motion are always proportional to the squares of the horizontal distances described by it, so that, if Q, R be any two points on the curve, then

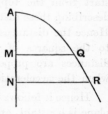

$$\frac{AM}{AN} = \frac{QM^2}{RN^2}.$$

Now since the cylinder revolved uniformly, these horizontal distances are proportional to times that have elapsed from the commencement of the motion. Hence the vertical distance described is proportional to the square of the time from the commencement of the motion.

But, from Art. 34, we know that, if a point move from rest with a constant acceleration, the space described is proportional to the square of the time.

Hence we infer that a falling body moves with a constant acceleration.

41. Galileo's Experiment. That the acceleration of a falling body is constant was first shewn by Galileo by some experiments conducted at Pisa about the year 1590. To avoid the difficulty of measuring the velocity of a freely falling body, which soon becomes very large, he considered the motion down an inclined plane instead, and assumed that the law of motion for a small sphere rolling down a groove in an inclined plane would be similar to that of a freely falling body.

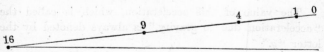

Commencing from the top of his groove, he measured off distances down it proportional to 1, 4, 9, 16, ..., *i.e.* proportional to 1^2, 2^2, 3^2, 4^2,.... He then let his small sphere start from the top, and verified that the times of its describing these distances were proportional to 1, 2, 3, 4,.... Hence the distances described from rest were proportional to the squares of the times. But, as in Art. 34, the distances are proportional to the squares of the times when the acceleration f is constant.

Hence it follows that the acceleration down the inclined plane is constant, and from that Galileo assumed that the acceleration of a freely falling body is constant also.

The great difficulty Galileo had was in measuring time accurately, as the clocks of his time were very inaccurate. He used a vessel of water of large transverse section which had in its bottom a small hole which he could close with his finger. When the ball started he removed his finger, and the water ran out into a vessel placed to receive it. When the ball had reached one of his marks he closed the hole; the water that had meantime run out was then weighed, and formed a fairly accurate measure of the time that had elapsed.

42. From the results of the foregoing, and other more accurate, experiments we learn that, if a body be let fall towards the earth *in vacuo*, it will move with an acceleration which is always the same at the same place on the earth, but which varies slightly for different places.

The value of this acceleration, which is called the "acceleration due to gravity," is always denoted by the letter "g."

When foot-second units are used, the value of g varies from about 32·091 at the equator to about 32·252 at the poles. In the latitude of London its value is about 32·19.

When centimetre-second units are used, the extreme
limits are about 978 and 983 respectively, and in the
latitude of London the value is about 981·17.

The best method of determining the value of "g" is by
means of pendulum experiments; we shall return to the
subject again in Chapter XI.

[*In all numerical examples, unless it is otherwise stated,
the motion may be supposed to be* in vacuo, *and the value
of g taken to be* 32 *when foot-second units, and* 981 *when
centimetre-second units, are used.*]

43.   Vertical motion under gravity.   Suppose a
body is projected vertically from a point on the earth's surface so that it starts with velocity u.   The acceleration of
the body is opposite to the initial direction of motion, and is
therefore denoted by $-g$.   Hence the velocity of the body
continually gets less and less until it vanishes; the body is
then for an instant at rest, but immediately begins to acquire
a velocity in a downward direction, and retraces its steps.

Time to a given height.   The height h at which a body
has arrived in time t is given by substituting $-g$ for f in
equation (2) of Art. 32, and is therefore given by

$$h = ut - \tfrac{1}{2}gt^2.$$

This is a quadratic equation with both roots positive; the
lesser root gives the time at which the body is at the given
height on the way up, and the greater the time at which it
is at the same height on the way down.

Thus the time that elapses before a body, which starts with a
velocity of 64 feet per second, is at a height of 28 feet is given by

$$28 = 64t - 16t^2, \text{ whence } t = \tfrac{1}{2} \text{ or } \tfrac{7}{2}.$$

Hence the particle is at the given height in half a second from the
commencement of its motion, and again in 3 seconds afterwards.

44.　*Velocity at a given height.*

The velocity v at a given height h is, by equation (3) of Art. 32, given by

$$v^2 = u^2 - 2gh.$$

Hence the velocity at a given height is independent of the time from the start, and is therefore the same at the same point whether the body be going upwards or downwards.

45.　*Greatest height attained.*

At the highest point the velocity is just zero; hence, if x be the greatest height attained, we have

$$0 = u^2 - 2gx.$$

Hence the greatest height attained $= \dfrac{u^2}{2g}$.

Also the time T to the greatest height is given by

$$0 = u - gT.$$

$$\therefore T = \frac{u}{g}.$$

46.　*Velocity due to a given vertical fall from rest.*

If a body be dropped from rest, its velocity after falling through a height h is obtained by substituting 0, g, and h for u, f and s in equation (3) of Art. 32;

$$\therefore v = \sqrt{2gh}.$$

EXAMPLES.　VI.

1.　A body is projected from the earth vertically with a velocity of 40 feet per second; find (1) how high it will go before coming to rest, (2) what times will elapse before it is at a height of 9 feet.

2.　A particle is projected vertically upwards with a velocity of 40 feet per second. Find (i) when its velocity will be 25 feet per second, and (ii) when it will be 25 feet above the point of projection.

3. A stone is thrown vertically upwards with a velocity of 60 feet per second. After what times will its velocity be 20 feet per second, and at what height will it then be?

4. Find (1) the distance fallen from rest by a body in 10 seconds, (2) the time of falling 10 feet, (3) the initial vertical velocity when the body describes 1000 feet downwards in 10 seconds.

5. A stone is thrown vertically into a mine-shaft with a velocity of 96 feet per second, and reaches the bottom in 3 seconds; find the depth of the shaft.

6. A body is projected from the bottom of a mine, whose depth is $88g$ feet, with a velocity of $24g$ feet per second; find the time in which the body, after rising to its greatest height, will return to the surface of the earth again.

7. The greatest height attained by a particle projected vertically upwards is 225 feet; find how soon after projection the particle will be at a height of 176 feet.

8. A body moving in a vertical direction passes a point at a height of 54·5 centimetres with a velocity of 436 centimetres per second; with what initial velocity was it thrown up, and for how much longer will it rise?

9. A particle passes a given point moving downwards with a velocity of fifty metres per second; how long before this was it moving upwards at the same rate?

10. A body is projected vertically upwards with a velocity of 6540 centimetres per second; how high does it rise, and for how long is it moving upwards?

11. Given that a body falling freely passes through 176·99 feet in the sixth second, find the value of g.

12. A falling particle in the last second of its fall passes through 224 feet. Find the height from which it fell, and the time of its falling.

13. A body falls freely from the top of a tower, and during the last second of its flight falls $1\frac{6}{25}$ths of the whole distance. Find the height of the tower.

14. A body falls freely from the top of a tower, and during the last second it falls $\frac{9}{25}$ths of the whole distance. Find the height of the tower.

15. A stone A is thrown vertically upwards with a velocity of 96 feet per second; find how high it will rise. After 4 seconds from the projection of A, another stone B is let fall from the same point. Shew that A will overtake B after 4 seconds more.

16. A body is projected upwards with a certain velocity, and it is found that when in its ascent it is 960 feet from the ground it takes 4 seconds to return to the same point again; find the velocity of projection and the whole height ascended.

17. A body projected vertically downwards described 720 feet in t seconds, and 2240 feet in $2t$ seconds; find t, and the velocity of projection.

18. A stone is dropped into a well, and the sound of the splash is heard in $7\frac{7}{10}$ seconds; if the velocity of sound be 1120 feet per second, find the depth of the well.

19. A stone is dropped into a well and reaches the bottom with a velocity of 96 feet per second, and the sound of the splash on the water reaches the top of the well in $3\frac{9}{10}$ seconds from the time the stone starts; find the velocity of sound.

20. Assuming the acceleration of a falling body at the surface of the moon to be one-sixth of its value on the earth's surface, find the height to which a particle will rise if it be projected vertically upward from the surface of the moon with a velocity of 40 feet per second.

47. Motion down a smooth inclined plane.

Let AB be the vertical section of a smooth inclined

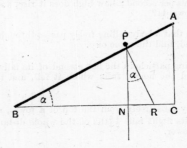

plane inclined at a given angle α to the horizon, and let P be a body on the plane.

If there were no plane to stop its motion, the body would fall vertically with an acceleration g.

Now, by the parallelogram of accelerations, a vertical acceleration g is equivalent to

(1) an acceleration $g \cos \alpha$ perpendicular to the plane in the direction PR,

and (2) an acceleration $g \sin \alpha$ down the plane.

The plane prevents any motion perpendicular to itself.

Hence the body moves down the plane with an acceleration $g \sin \alpha$, and the investigation of its motion is similar to that of a freely falling body, except that instead of g we have to substitute $g \sin \alpha$.

It follows at once that the velocity acquired in sliding from rest down a length l of the plane

$$= \sqrt{2g \sin \alpha \,.\, l} = \sqrt{2g \,.\, l \sin \alpha} = \sqrt{2g \,.\, AC},$$

and is therefore the same as that acquired by a particle in falling freely through a vertical height equal to that of the plane.   In other words the velocity acquired is independent of the inclination of the plane and depends only on the vertical height through which the particle has fallen.

48. If the body be projected up the plane with initial velocity u, an investigation similar to that of Arts. 43—45 will give the motion.   The greatest distance attained, measured up the plane, is $\dfrac{u^2}{2g \sin \alpha}$; the time taken in traversing this distance is $\dfrac{u}{g \sin \alpha}$, and so on.

EXAMPLES. VII.

1. A body is projected with a velocity of 80 feet per second up a smooth inclined plane, whose inclination is 30°; find the distance described, and the time that elapses, before it comes to rest.

2. A heavy particle slides from rest down a smooth inclined plane which is 15 feet long and 12 feet high. What is its velocity when it reaches the ground, and how long does it take?

3. A particle sliding down a smooth plane, 16 feet long, acquires a velocity of $16\sqrt{2}$ feet per second; find the inclination of the plane.

4. What is the ratio of the height to the length of a smooth inclined plane, so that a body may be four times as long in sliding down the plane as in falling freely down the height of the plane starting from rest?

5. A particle is projected (1) upwards, (2) downwards, on a plane which is inclined to the horizon at an angle $\sin^{-1}\frac{3}{5}$; if the initial velocity be 16 feet per second in each case, find the distances described and the velocities acquired in 4 seconds.

6. A particle slides without friction down an inclined plane, and in the 5th second after starting passes over a distance of 2207·25 centimetres; find the inclination of the plane to the horizon.

7. AB is a vertical diameter of a circle, whose plane is vertical, and PQ a diameter inclined at an angle θ to AB. Find θ so that the time of sliding down PQ may be twice that of sliding down AB.

49. Theorem. *The time that a body takes to slide down any smooth chord of a vertical circle, which is drawn from the highest point of the circle, is constant.*

Let AB be a diameter of a vertical circle, of which A is the highest point and AD any chord.

Let $\angle DAB = \theta$; put $AD = x$ and $AB = a$, so that

$$x = a \cos \theta.$$

As in the last article, the acceleration down AD is $g \cos \theta$. Let T be the time from A to D. Then AD is the distance described in time T by a particle starting from rest and moving with acceleration $g \cos \theta$.

$$\therefore x = \tfrac{1}{2} g \cos \theta \cdot T^2.$$

$$\therefore T = \sqrt{\frac{2x}{g \cos \theta}} = \sqrt{\frac{2a}{g}}.$$

This result is independent of θ, and is the same as the time of falling vertically through the distance AB.

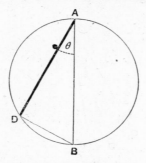

Hence the time of falling down all chords of this circle beginning at A is the same.

The same theorem will be found to be true for all chords of the same circle *ending* in the *lowest* point.

50. Lines of quickest descent. The line of quickest descent from a given point to a curve in the same vertical plane is the straight line down which a body would slide from the given point to the given curve in the shortest *time*.

It is not, in general, the same line as the geometrically shortest line that can be drawn from the given point to the curve. For example, the straight line down which the time from a given point to a given plane is least, is *not* the perpendicular from the given point upon the given plane, except in the case where the given plane is horizontal.

51. Theorem. *The chord of quickest descent from a given point P to a curve in the same vertical plane is PQ, where Q is a point on the curve such that a circle, having P at its highest point, touches the curve at Q.*

For let a circle be drawn, having its highest point at P, to touch the given curve externally in Q. Take *any*

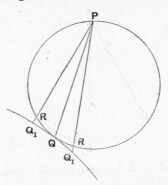

other point Q_1 on the curve, and let PQ_1 meet the circle again in R.

Then, since PQ_1 is $> PR$,

the time down PQ_1 is $>$ time down PR.

But time down $PR =$ time down PQ (Art. 49),

so that the time down PQ_1 is $>$ time down PQ,

and Q_1 is any point on the given curve.

Hence the time down PQ is less than that down any other straight line from P to the given curve.

Similarly it may be shewn that, if we want the chord of quickest descent from a given curve to a given point P, we must describe a circle having the given point P as its lowest point to touch the curve in Q; then QP is the required straight line.

Ex. 1. *To find the straight line of quickest descent from a given point P to a given straight line which is in the same vertical plane as P.*

Let BC be the given straight line. Then we have to describe a circle having its highest point at P to touch the given straight line. Draw PB horizontal to meet BC in B. From BC cut off a portion BQ equal to BP. Then PQ is the required chord; for it is clear that a circle can be drawn to touch BP and BQ at P and Q respectively.

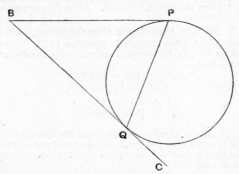

Ex. 2. *To find the line of quickest descent from a given point to a given circle in the same vertical plane.*

Join P to the lowest point B of the given circle to meet the circle again in Q. Then PQ is the required line. For join O, the centre of the circle, to Q and produce to meet the vertical line through P in C.

The $\angle QPC = \angle OBQ$, since OB and CP are parallel,

$$= \angle OQB = \angle CQP.$$

Hence a circle whose centre is C, and radius CP, will have its highest point at P and will touch the given circle at Q.

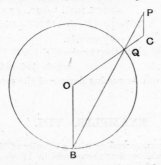

If P be within the given circle, join P to the highest point and produce to meet the circumference in Q; then PQ will be the required line.

52.   Ex. 1. *A cage in a mine-shaft descends with* 2 *ft.-sec. units of acceleration.   After it has been in motion for* 10 *seconds a particle is dropped on it from the top of the shaft.   What time elapses before the particle hits the cage?*

Let T be the time that elapses after the second particle starts. The distance it has fallen through is therefore $\frac{1}{2}gT^2$.   The cage has been in motion for $(T+10)$ seconds, and therefore the distance it has fallen through is

$$\frac{1}{2}\cdot 2\,(T+10)^2 \text{ or } (T+10)^2.$$

Hence we have $(T+10)^2 = \frac{1}{2}gT^2 = 16T^2.$

$$\therefore\quad T+10 = 4T.$$
$$\therefore\quad T = 3\tfrac{1}{3} \text{ seconds.}$$

Ex. 2. *A stone is thrown vertically with the velocity which would just carry it to a height of* 100 *feet.   Two seconds later another stone is projected vertically from the same place with the same velocity; when and where will they meet?*

Let u be the initial velocity of projection.   Since the greatest height is 100 feet, we have

$$0 = u^2 - 2g\,.\,100.$$
$$\therefore\quad u = \sqrt{2g\,.\,100} = 80.$$

Let T be the time after the first stone starts before the two stones meet.

Then the distance traversed by the first stone in time T = distance traversed by the second stone in time $(T-2)$.

$$\therefore\quad 80T - \tfrac{1}{2}gT^2 = 80\,(T-2) - \tfrac{1}{2}g\,(T-2)^2$$
$$= 80T - 160 - \tfrac{1}{2}g\,(T^2 - 4T + 4).$$
$$\therefore\quad 160 = \tfrac{1}{2}g\,(4T-4) = 16\,(4T-4).$$
$$\therefore\quad T = 3\tfrac{1}{2} \text{ seconds.}$$

Also the height at which they meet $= 80T - \tfrac{1}{2}gT^2$

$$= 280 - 196 = 84 \text{ feet.}$$

The first stone will be coming down and the second stone going upwards.

EXAMPLES.   VIII.

1.   From a balloon, ascending with a velocity of 32 ft. per second, a stone is let fall and reaches the ground in 17 seconds; how high was the balloon when the stone was dropped?

2.   If a body be let fall from a height of 64 feet at the same instant that another is sent vertically from the foot of the height

with a velocity of 64 feet per second, what time elapses before they meet?

If the first body starts 1 sec. later than the other, what time will elapse?

3. A tower is 288 feet high; one body is dropped from the top of the tower and at the same instant another is projected vertically upwards from the bottom, and they meet half-way up; find the initial velocity of the projected body and its velocity when it meets the descending body.

4. A body is dropped from the top of a given tower, and at the same instant a body is projected from the foot of the tower, in the same vertical line, with a velocity which would be just sufficient to take it to the same height as the tower; find where they will meet.

5. A particle is dropped from a height h, and after falling $\frac{2}{3}$rds of that distance passes a particle which was projected upwards at the instant when the first was dropped. Find to what height the latter will attain.

6. A body begins to slide down a smooth inclined plane from rest at the top, and at the same instant another body is projected upwards from the foot of the plane with such a velocity that they meet half-way up the plane; find the velocity of projection and determine the velocity of each when they meet.

7. A body is projected upwards with velocity u, and t seconds afterwards another body is similarly projected with the same velocity; find when and where they will meet.

8. A balloon ascends with a uniform acceleration of 4 ft.-sec. units; at the end of half a minute a body is released from it; find the time that elapses before the body reaches the ground.

9. After a ball has been falling under gravity for 5 seconds it passes through a pane of glass and loses half its velocity; if it now reach the ground in 1 second, find the height of the glass above the ground.

10. The space described by a falling body in the last second of its motion is to that described in the last second but one as 3 : 2; find the height from which the body was dropped, and the velocity with which it strikes the ground.

11. A plane is of length 288 feet and of height 64 feet; shew how to divide it into three parts so that a particle at the top of the plane may describe the portions in equal times, and find these times.

12. Shew that the time that a particle takes to slide down a chord of a vertical circle, starting from one end of a horizontal diameter, varies as the square root of the tangent of the inclination of the chord to the vertical.

13. A number of smooth rods meet in a point A and rings placed on them slide down the rods, starting simultaneously from A. Shew that after a time t the rings are all on a sphere of radius $\dfrac{gt^2}{4}$.

14. A number of bodies slide from rest down smooth inclined planes which all commence at the same point and terminate on the same horizontal plane; shew that the velocities acquired are the same.

15. Two heavy bodies descend the height and length respectively of a smooth inclined plane; shew that the times vary as the spaces described and that the velocities acquired are equal.

16. A heavy particle slides down a smooth inclined plane of given height; shew that the time of descent varies as the secant of the inclination of the plane to the vertical.

17. A body slides down smooth chords of a vertical circle ending in its lowest point; shew that the velocity on reaching the lowest point varies as the length of the chord.

18. If two circles touch each other at their highest or lowest points, and a straight line be drawn through the point to meet both circles, shew that the time of sliding from rest down the portion of this line intercepted between the two circles is constant.

19. A plane, of height h and inclination α to the horizon, has a smooth groove cut in it inclined at an angle β to the line of greatest slope; find the time that a particle would take to describe the groove, starting from rest at the top.

---

20. If a length s be divided into n equal parts at the end of each of which the acceleration of a moving point is increased by $\dfrac{f}{n}$, find the velocity of a particle after describing the distance s if it started from rest with acceleration f.

21. A particle starts from rest with acceleration f; at the end of time t it becomes $2f$; it becomes $3f$ at end of time $2t$, and so on. Find the velocity at the end of time nt, and shew that the distance described is

$$\frac{n(n+1)(2n+1)}{12} f \cdot t^2.$$

22. A body starts from rest and moves with uniform acceleration; shew that the distance described in the (n^2+n+1)th second is equal to the distance described in the first n seconds together with the distance described in the first $(n+1)$ seconds.

23. If a particle occupies n seconds less and acquires a velocity of m feet per second more at one place that at another in falling through the same distance, shew that $\dfrac{m}{n}$ equals the geometrical mean between the numerical values of gravity at the two places.

24. A train goes from rest at one station to rest at another, one mile off, being uniformly accelerated for the first $\frac{2}{3}$rds of the journey and uniformly retarded for the remainder, and takes 3 minutes to describe the whole distance. Find the acceleration, the retardation, and the maximum velocity.

25. An engine-driver suddenly puts on his brake and shuts off steam when he is running at full speed; in the first second afterwards the train travels 87 feet, and in the next 85 feet. Find the original speed of the train, the time that elapses before it comes to rest, and the distance it will travel in this interval, assuming the brake to cause a constant retardation. Find also the time the train will take, if it be 96 yards long, to pass a spectator standing at a point 484 yards ahead of the train at the instant when the brake was applied.

26. A railway-train goes from one station to another moving during the first part of the journey with uniform acceleration f; when steam is shut off and the brakes are applied, it moves with uniform retardation f'. If a be the distance between the stations, shew that the time the train takes is

$$\sqrt{2a\,\frac{f+f'}{ff'}}\,.$$

27. During the first quarter of the journey from a station A to a station B the velocity of a train is uniformly accelerated, and during the last quarter it is uniformly retarded, and the middle half of the journey is performed at a uniform speed. Shew that the average speed of the train is $\frac{2}{3}$rds of the full speed.

28. A lift ascending from a pit 600 feet deep rises during the first part of its ascent with uniform acceleration. On nearing the top the upward force is cut off, and the impetus of the lift is just sufficient to carry it to the top. If the whole process occupies 30 secs., find the acceleration during the first part of the ascent, and the maximum velocity attained.

29. A train starts from rest and reaches its greatest speed of 50 miles per hour in 5 minutes. This speed is maintained till it is half a mile from the next stopping place. Find the values of the acceleration and retardation in foot-second units, and the whole time taken for the journey if it be 100 miles. Draw also the velocity-time curve for the whole journey.

CHAPTER IV.

THE LAWS OF MOTION.

53. IN the present chapter we propose to consider the production of motion, and it will be necessary to commence with a few elementary definitions.

Matter is "that which can be perceived by the senses" or "that which can be acted upon by, or can exert, force."

No definition can however be given that would convey an idea of what matter is to anyone who did not already possess that idea. It, like time and space, is a primary conception.

A **Particle** is a portion of matter which is infinitely small in all its dimensions, or, at any rate, so small that for the purpose of our investigations the distances between the different portions of it may be neglected. Sometimes bodies of a finite size can be treated as particles, as in the case of a cricket ball thrown into the air, or of a stone falling to the ground. Again in considering the motion of the Earth round the Sun, the Earth itself may be treated as a particle.

A **Body** is a portion of matter which is bounded by surfaces, and which is limited in every direction, so that it consists of a very large number of material particles.

The **Mass** of a body is the quantity of matter in the body.

Force is that which changes, or tends to change, the state of rest or uniform motion of a body.

These definitions may appear to the student to be vague, but we may illustrate their meaning somewhat as follows.

If we have a small portion of any substance, say iron, resting on a smooth table, we may by a push be able to move it fairly easily ; if we take a larger quantity of the same iron, the same effort on our part will be able to move it less easily. Again, if we take two portions of platinum and wood of exactly the same size and shape, the effect produced on these two substances by equal efforts on our part will be quite different. Once more, if we have a croquet-ball and a cannon-ball, both of the same size, lying at rest on the ground, and we kick each of them with the same force, the effect on the first is greater than that on the second. So also we can distinguish between a cask full of water, and an empty one of the same size, by watching the effect of equal kicks applied to them.

Thus common experience shews us that the same effort applied to different bodies, under seemingly the same conditions, does not always produce the same result. This is because the *masses* of the bodies are different.

54. If to the same mass we apply two forces in succession, and they generate the same velocity in the same time, the forces are said to be equal.

If the same force be applied to two different masses, and if it produce in them the same velocity in the same time, the masses are said to be equal.

The student will notice that we here assume that it is possible to create forces of equal intensity on different occasions, *e.g.* we assume that the force necessary to keep a spiral spring stretched through the same distance is the same when other conditions are unaltered.

Hence by applying the same force in succession we can obtain a number of masses each equal to a standard unit of mass. The foregoing would be a theoretical method of defining equal masses, applicable under all conditions. In practice, we shall find that equal masses have equal weights, so that the process of weighing is the simplest practical method of comparing masses.

55. The British unit of mass is called the Imperial Pound, and consists of a lump of platinum deposited at Westminster, of which there are in addition several accurate copies kept in other places of safety.

The French, or scientific, unit of mass is called a gramme, and is the one-thousandth part of a certain quantity of platinum kept in Paris. The gramme was meant to be defined as the mass of a cubic centimetre of pure water at a temperature of 4° C.

It is a much smaller unit than a Pound.

> One Gramme = about 15·432 grains.
>
> One Pound = about 453·6 grammes.

The system of units in which a centimetre, gramme, and second, are respectively the units of length, mass, and time, is generally called the c.g.s. system of units.

56. Density. The density of a uniform body is the mass of a unit volume of the body; so that, if m be the mass of volume V of a body whose density is ρ, then

$$m = V\rho.$$

57. The **Weight** of a body is the force with which the earth attracts the body.

It can be shewn that every particle of matter in nature attracts every other particle with a force, which varies directly as the product of the masses of the quantities, and inversely as the square of the distance between them; hence it can be deduced that a sphere attracts a particle on, or outside, its surface with a force which varies inversely as the square of the distance of the particle from the centre of the sphere. The earth is not accurately a sphere, and therefore points on its surface are not equidistant from the centre; hence the attraction of the earth for a given mass is not quite the same at all points of its surface, and therefore the weight of a given mass is slightly different at different points of the earth.

58. The **Momentum** of a body is proportional to the product of the mass and the velocity of the body.

If we take as the unit of momentum the momentum of a unit mass moving with unit velocity, then the momentum of a body is mv, where m is the mass and v the velocity of the body. The direction of the momentum is the same as that of the velocity.

Thus the momentum of a body of 100 grammes moving with velocity 275 cms. per sec. is 27500 centimetre-gramme-second units of momentum.

59. We can now enunciate what are commonly called Newton's Laws of Motion. "The first two were discovered by Galileo (about the year 1590) and the third in some of its many forms was known to Hooke, Huyghens, Wallis, Wren and others before the publication of the *Principia*." They were put into formal shape by Newton in his *Principia* published in the year 1686.

They are;

Law I. *Every body continues in its state of rest, or of uniform motion in a straight line, except in so far as it be compelled by external impressed force to change that state.*

Law II. *The rate of change of momentum is proportional to the impressed force, and takes place in the direction of the straight line in which the force acts.*

Law III. *To every action there is an equal and opposite reaction.*

No strictly formal proof, experimental or otherwise, can be given of these three laws. On them however is based the whole system of Dynamics, and on Dynamics the whole theory of Astronomy. Now the results obtained, and the predictions made, from the theory of Astronomy agree so well with the actual observed facts of Astronomy that it is inconceivable that the original laws on which the subject is based should be erroneous. For example, the Nautical Almanac is published four years beforehand; the motions of the Moon and the Planets are therein predicted, and the time and place of Eclipses of the Sun and Moon foretold; and the predictions in it are always correct. Hence the real reason for our belief in the truth of the above three laws of motion is that the conclusions drawn from them agree with our experience.

60. Law I. We never see this law actually exemplified on the Earth because it is practically impossible ever to get rid of all forces during the motion of the body. It may be seen approximately in operation in the case of a piece of dry, hard ice projected along the surface of dry, well swept ice. The only forces acting on the fragment of ice, in the direction of its motion, are the friction between the two portions of ice and the resistance of the air. The smoother the surface of the ice the further the small portion will go, and the less the resistance of the air the further it will go. The above law asserts that **if** the ice were perfectly smooth and **if** there were no resistance of the air and no other forces acting on the body, then it would go on for ever in a straight line with uniform velocity.

The law states a principle sometimes called the **Principle of Inertia,** *viz.*—that a body has no *innate* tendency to change its state of rest or of uniform motion in a straight line. A lump of iron resting on the ground does not move by itself, nor unless it is acted upon by a force external to itself.

If a portion of metal attached to a piece of string be swung round on a smooth horizontal table, then, if the string break, the metal, having no longer any force acting on it, proceeds to move in a straight line, *viz.* the tangent to the circle at the point at which its circular motion ceased.

If a man step out of a rapidly moving train he is generally thrown to the ground; his feet on touching the ground are brought to rest; but, as no force acts on the upper part of his body, it continues its motion as before, and the man falls to the ground.

If a man be riding on a horse which is galloping at a fairly rapid pace and the horse suddenly stops, the rider is in danger of being thrown over the horse's head.

If a man be seated upon the back seat of a dog-cart, and the latter suddenly start, the man is very likely to be left behind.

61. Law II. From this law we derive our method of measuring force.

Let m be the mass of a body, and f the acceleration produced in it by the action of a force whose measure is P.

Then, by the second law of motion,

$P \propto$ rate of change of momentum,

$\propto$ rate of change of mv,

$\propto m \times$ rate of change of v (if m is unaltered),

$\propto m . f$.

$\therefore P = \lambda . mf$, where λ is some constant.

Now let the unit of force be so chosen that it may produce in unit mass the unit of acceleration.

Hence, when $m = 1$ and $f = 1$, we have $P = 1$, and therefore $\lambda = 1$.

The unit of force being thus chosen, we have

$$P = m \cdot f.$$

Therefore, when proper units are chosen, the measure of the force is *equal* to the measure of the rate of change of the momentum.

62. From the preceding article it follows that the magnitude of the unit of force used in Dynamics depends on the units of mass, and acceleration, that we use. The unit of acceleration, again, depends, by Arts. 9 and 29, on the units of length and time. Hence the unit of force depends on our units of mass, length, and time. When these latter units are given the unit of force is a determinate quantity.

When a pound, a foot, and a second are respectively the units of mass, length, and time, the corresponding unit of force is called a **Poundal.**

Hence the equation $P = mf$ is a true relation, m being the number of pounds in the body, P the number of poundals in the force acting on it, and f the number of units of acceleration produced in the mass m by the action of the force P on it.

This relation is sometimes expressed in the form

$$\text{Acceleration} = \frac{\text{Moving Force}}{\text{Mass moved}}.$$

N.B. All through this book the unit of force used will be a poundal, unless it is otherwise stated. Thus, when we say that the tension of a string is T, we mean T poundals.

63. When a gramme, a centimetre, and a second are respectively the units of mass, length, and time, the corresponding unit of force is called a **Dyne**. [This name is derived from the Greek word δύναμις, pronounced Dunamis, which means Force.]

Hence when the equation $P = mf$ is used in this system the force must be expressed in dynes, the mass in grammes, and the acceleration in centimetre-second units.

64. Connection between the unit of force and the weight of the unit of mass.

As explained in Art. 42, we know that, when a body drops freely *in vacuo* it moves with an acceleration which we denote by "g"; also the force which causes this acceleration is that which we call its weight.

Now the unit of force acting on the unit of mass produces in it the unit of acceleration.

Therefore g units of force acting on the unit of mass produce in it g units of acceleration (by the second law).

But the weight of the unit of mass is that which produces in it g units of acceleration.

Hence the weight of the unit of mass = g units of force.

65. *Foot-Pound-Second System of units.* In this system g is equal to 32·2 approximately.

Therefore the weight of one pound is equal to g units of force, *i.e.* to g poundals, where $g = 32·2$ approximately.

Hence a poundal is approximately equal to $\dfrac{1}{32·2}$ times the weight of a pound, *i.e.* to the weight of about half an ounce.

Since g has different values at different points of the earth's surface, and since a poundal is a force which is the same everywhere, it follows that **the weight of a pound is not constant, but has different values at different points of the earth.**

66. *Centimetre-Gramme-Second System of units.* In this system g is equal to 981 approximately.

Therefore the weight of one gramme is equal to g units of force, *i.e.* to g . dynes, where

$$g = 981 \text{ approximately.}$$

Hence a dyne is equal to the weight of about $\frac{1}{981}$ of a gramme.

The dyne is a much smaller unit than a poundal. The approximate relation between them may be easily found as follows:

$$\frac{\text{One Poundal}}{\text{One Dyne}} = \frac{\dfrac{1}{32\cdot2} \text{ wt. of a pound}}{\dfrac{1}{981} \text{ wt. of a gramme}}$$

$$= \frac{981}{32\cdot2} \times \frac{\text{one pound}}{\text{one gramme}} = \frac{981}{32\cdot2} \times 453\cdot6 \text{ (by Art. 55).}$$

Hence One Poundal = about 13800 dynes.

EXAMPLES. IX.

1. *A mass of 20 pounds is acted on by a constant force which in 5 seconds produces a velocity of 15 feet per second. Find the force, if the mass was initially at rest.*

From the equation $v = u + ft$, we have $f = \frac{15}{5} = 3$.

Also, if P be the force expressed in poundals, we have

$$P = 20 \times 3 = 60 \text{ poundals.}$$

Hence P is equal to the weight of about $\frac{60}{32}$, *i.e.* $1\frac{7}{8}$, pounds.

2. *A mass of 10 pounds is placed on a smooth horizontal plane, and is acted on by a force equal to the weight of 3 pounds; find the distance described by it in 10 seconds.*

Here moving force = weight of 3 lbs. = $3g$ poundals;

and mass moved = 10 pounds.

Hence, if ft.-sec. units are used, the acceleration = $\frac{3g}{10}$,

so that the distance required = $\frac{1}{2} \cdot \frac{3g}{10} \cdot 10^2 = 480$ feet.

3. *Find the magnitude of the force which, acting on a kilogramme for 5 seconds, produces in it a velocity of one metre per second.*

Here the velocity acquired = 100 cms. per sec.

Hence the acceleration = 20 c.g.s. units.

Hence the force = 1000×20 dynes = weight of about $\frac{1000 \times 20}{981}$ or $20\cdot4$ grammes.

4. Find the acceleration produced when
    (1) A force of 5 poundals acts on a mass of 10 pounds.
    (2) A force equal to the weight of 5 pounds acts on a mass of 10 pounds.
    (3) A force of 50 pounds weight acts on a mass of 10 tons.

5. Find the force expressed (1) in poundals, (2) in terms of the weight of a pound, that will produce in a mass of 20 pounds an acceleration of 10 foot-second units.

6. Find the force which, acting horizontally for 5 seconds on a mass of 160 pounds placed on a smooth table, will generate in it a velocity of 15 feet per second.

7. Find the magnitude of the force which, acting on a mass of 10 cwt. for 10 seconds, will generate in it a velocity of 3 miles per hour.

8. A force, equal to the weight of 2 lbs., acts on a mass of 40 lbs. for half a minute; find the velocity acquired, and the space moved through, in this time.

9. A body, acted upon by a uniform force, in ten seconds describes a distance of 7 metres; compare the force with the weight of the body, and find the velocity acquired.

10. In what time will a force, which is equal to the weight of a pound, move a mass of 18 lbs. through 50 feet along a smooth horizontal plane, and what will be the velocity acquired by the mass?

11. A body, of mass 200 tons, is acted on by a force equal to 112000 poundals; how long will it take to acquire a velocity of 30 miles per hour?

12. In what time will a force, equal to the weight of 10 lbs., acting on a mass of 1 ton move it through 14 feet?

13. A mass of 224 lbs. is placed on a smooth horizontal plane, and a uniform force acting on it parallel to the table for 5 seconds causes it to describe 50 feet in that time; shew that the force is equal to about 28 lbs. weight.

14. A heavy truck, of mass 16 tons, is standing at rest on a smooth line of rails. A horse now pulls at it steadily in the direction of the line of rails with a force equal to the weight of 1 cwt. How far will it move in 1 minute?

15. A force equal to the weight of 10 grammes acts on a mass of 27 grammes for 1 second; find the velocity of the mass and the distance it has travelled over. At the end of the first second the force ceases to act; how far will the body travel in the next minute?

16. A force equal to the weight of a kilogramme acts on a body continuously for 10 seconds, and causes it to describe 10 metres in that time; find the mass of the body.

17. A horizontal force equal to the weight of 9 lbs. acts on a mass along a smooth horizontal plane; after moving through a space of 25 feet the mass has acquired a velocity of 10 feet per second; find its magnitude.

18. A body is placed on a smooth table and a force equal to the weight of 6 lbs. acts continuously on it; at the end of 3 seconds the body is moving at the rate of 48 feet per second; find its mass.

19. A body, of mass 3 lbs., is falling under gravity at the rate of 100 feet per second. What is the uniform force that will stop it (1) in 2 seconds, (2) in 2 feet?

20. Of two forces, one acts on a mass of 5 lbs. and in one-eleventh of a second produces in it a velocity of 5 feet per second, and the other acting on a mass of 625 lbs. in 1 minute produces in it a velocity of 18 miles per hour; compare the two forces.

21. A mass of 10 lbs. falls 10 feet from rest, and is then brought to rest by penetrating 1 foot into some sand; find the average thrust of the sand on it.

22. A cannon-ball of mass 1000 grammes is discharged with a velocity of 45000 centimetres per second from a cannon the length of whose barrel is 200 centimetres; shew that the mean force exerted on the ball during the explosion is $5·0625 \times 10^9$ dynes.

23. It was found that when 1 foot was cut off from the muzzle of a gun firing a projectile of 100 lbs., the velocity of the projectile was altered from 1490 to 1330 feet per second. Shew that the force exerted on the projectile by the powder-gas at the muzzle, when expanded in the bore, was about 315 tons weight.

24. A bullet moving at the rate of 200 feet per second is fired into a trunk of wood into which it penetrates 9 inches; if a bullet moving with the same velocity were fired into a similar piece of wood 5 inches thick, with what velocity would it emerge, supposing the resistance to be uniform?

25. A motor car travelling at the rate of 40 kilometres per hour is stopped by its brakes in 4 seconds; shew that it will go about 22 metres from the point at which the brakes are first applied, and that the force exerted by them is about ·283 times the weight of the car, and would hold the car at rest on an incline of about 1 in $3\frac{1}{2}$.

67. A poundal and a dyne are called **Absolute Units** because their values are not dependent on the value of g, which varies at different places on the earth's surface. The *weight* of a pound and of a gramme do depend on this value. Hence they are called **Gravitation Units**.

68. *The weight of a body is proportional to its mass and is independent of the kind of matter of which it is composed.* The following is an experimental fact: If we have an air-tight receiver, and if we allow to drop at the same instant, from the same height, portions of matter of any kind whatever, such as a piece of metal, a feather, a piece of paper etc., all these substances will be found to have always fallen through the same distance, and to hit the base of the receiver at the same time, whatever be the substances, or the height from which they are allowed to fall. Since these bodies always fall through the same height in the same time, therefore their velocities [rates of change of space,] and their accelerations [rates of change of velocity,] must be always the same.

The student can approximately perform the above experiment without creating a vacuum. Take a penny and a light substance, say a small piece of paper; place the paper on the penny, held horizontally, and allow both to drop. They will be found to keep together in their fall, although, if they be dropped separately, the penny will reach the ground much quicker than the paper. The penny clears the air out of the way of the paper and so the same result is produced as would be the case if there were no air.

Let W_1 and W_2 poundals be the weights of any two of these bodies, m_1 and m_2 their masses. Then since their accelerations are the same and equal to g, we have

$$W_1 = m_1 g,$$

and

$$W_2 = m_2 g;$$

$$\therefore W_1 : W_2 :: m_1 : m_2,$$

or the weight of a body is proportional to its mass.

Hence bodies whose weights are equal have equal masses; so also the ratio of the masses of two bodies is known when the ratio of their weights is known.

The equation $W = mg$ is a numerical one, and means that the number of units of force in the weight of a body is equal to the product of the number of units of mass in the mass of the body, and the number of units of acceleration produced in the body by its weight.

From the result of Art. 61, combined with this article, we have $\dfrac{P}{W} = \dfrac{f}{g}$, *i.e.* the ratio of any force to the weight of a body is the same as the acceleration produced by the force acting on the body to the acceleration produced by gravity.

This form of the relation between P and f is preferred by some.

69. *Distinction between mass and weight.* The student must carefully notice the difference between the mass and the weight of a body. He has probably been so accustomed to estimate the masses of bodies by means of their weights that he has not clearly distinguished between the two. If it were possible to have a cannon-ball at the centre of the earth it would have no weight there; for the attraction of the earth on a particle at its centre is zero. If, however, it were in motion, the same force would be required to stop it as would be necessary under similar conditions at the surface of the earth. Hence we see that it might be possible for a body to have no weight; its mass however remains unaltered.

The confusion is probably to a great extent caused by the fact that the word "pound" is used in two senses which are scientifically different; it is used to denote both what we more properly call "the mass of one pound" and "the weight of one pound." It cannot be too strongly impressed on the student that, strictly speaking, a pound is a mass and a mass only; when we wish to speak of the force with which the earth attracts this mass we ought to speak of the "weight of a pound." This latter phrase is often shortened into "a pound," but care must be taken to see in which sense this word is used.

It may also be noted here that the expression "a ball of lead weighing 20 lbs." is, strictly speaking, an abbreviation for "a ball of lead whose weight is equal to the weight of 20 lbs." The mass of the lead is 20 lbs.; its weight is $20g$ poundals.

70. *Weighing by Scales and a Spring Balance.* We have pointed out (Art. 42) that the acceleration due to gravity, *i.e.* the value of *g*, varies slightly as we proceed from point to point of the earth's surface. When we weigh out a substance (say tea) by means of a pair of scales, we adjust the tea until the weight of the tea is the same as the weight of sundry pieces of metal whose masses are known, and then, by Art. 68, we know that the mass of the tea is the same as the mass of the metal. Hence a pair of scales really measures masses and not weights, and so the apparent weight of the tea is the same everywhere.

When we use a spring balance, we compare the *weight* of the tea with the *force* necessary to keep the spring stretched through a certain distance. If then we move our tea and spring balance to another place, say from London to Paris, the weight of the tea will be different, whilst the force necessary to keep the spring stretched through the same distance as before will be the same. Hence the weight of the tea will pull the spring through a distance different from the former distance, and hence its apparent weight as shewn by the instrument will be different.

If we have two places, *A* and *B*, at the first of which the numerical value of *g* is greater than at the second, then a given mass of tea will [as tested by the spring balance,] appear to weigh more at *A* than it does at *B*.

Ex. 1. At the equator the value of *g* is 32·09 and in London the value is 32·2; a merchant buys tea at the equator, at a shilling per pound, and sells in London; at what price per pound (apparent) must he sell so that he may neither gain nor lose, if he use the same spring balance for both transactions?

A quantity of tea which weighs 1 lb. at the equator will appear to weigh $\dfrac{32\cdot2}{32\cdot09}$ lbs. in London. Hence he should sell $\dfrac{32\cdot2}{32\cdot09}$ lbs. for one shilling, or at the rate of $\dfrac{3209}{3220}$ shillings per pound.

Ex. 2. At a place *A*, *g* = 32·24, and at a place *B*, *g* = 32·12. A merchant buys goods at £10 per cwt. at *A* and sells at *B*, using the same spring balance. If he is to gain 20 per cent., shew that his selling price must be £12. 0*s*. 10¾*d*. per cwt.

71. Physical Independence of Forces.

The latter part of the Second Law states that the change of motion produced by a force is in the direction in which the force acts.

Suppose we have a particle in motion in the direction *AB* and a force acting on it in the direction *AC*; then the law states that the velocity in the direction AB is unchanged, and that the only change of velocity is in the direction AC; so that to find the real velocity of the particle at the end of a unit of time, we must compound its velocity in the direction AB with the velocity generated in that unit of time by the force in the direction AC. The same reasoning would hold if we had a second force acting on the particle in some other direction, and so for any system of forces. Hence if a set of forces act on a particle at rest, or in motion, their combined effect is found by considering the effect of each force on the particle *just as if the other forces did not exist, and as if the particle were at rest,* and then compounding these effects. This principle is often referred to as that of the *Physical Independence of Forces.*

As an illustration of this principle consider the motion of a ball allowed to fall from the hand of a passenger in a train which is travelling rapidly. It will be found to hit the floor of the carriage at exactly the same spot as it would have done if the carriage had been at rest. This shews that the ball must have continued to move forward with the same velocity that the train had, or, in other words, the weight of the body only altered the motion in the vertical direction, and had no influence on the horizontal velocity of the particle.

Again, if any two small bodies be placed on the edge of a table, and be hit so that they leave the table at the same moment, but with velocities differing as much as possible, then whatever be their masses or their initial velocities, they will be heard to hit the floor at the same instant. It hence follows that the vertical accelerations and velocities produced in the bodies are independent of their masses and also of their initial velocities.

So also, a circus rider, who wishes to jump through a hoop, springs in a vertical direction from the horse's back; his horizontal velocity is the same as that of the horse and remains unaltered; he therefore alights on the horse's back at the spot from which he started.

72. Parallelogram of Forces. We have shewn in Art. 30 that if a particle of mass m have accelerations f_1 and f_2 represented in magnitude and direction by lines AB and AC, then its resultant acceleration f_3 is represented in magnitude and direction by AD, the diagonal of the parallelogram of which AB and AC are adjacent sides.

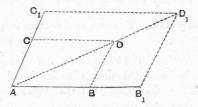

Since the particle has an acceleration f_1 in the direction AB there must be a force $P_1 (= mf_1)$ in that direction, and similarly a force $P_2 (= mf_2)$ in the direction AC. Let AB_1 and AC_1 represent these forces in magnitude and direction. Complete the parallelogram $AB_1D_1C_1$. Then since the forces in the directions AB_1 and AC_1 are proportional to the accelerations in these directions,

$$\therefore AB_1 : AB :: B_1D_1 : BD.$$

Hence, by simple geometry, we have A, D and D_1 in a straight line, and

$$\therefore AD_1 : AD :: AB_1 : AB.$$

It follows that AD_1 represents the force which produces the acceleration represented by AD, and hence is the force which is equivalent to the forces represented by AB_1 and AC_1.

Hence we infer the truth of the Parallelogram of Forces which may be enunciated as follows:

If a particle be acted on by two forces represented in magnitude and direction by the two sides of a parallelogram drawn from a point, they are equivalent to a force represented in magnitude and direction by the diagonal of the parallelogram passing through the point.

Cor. If in Arts. 13—19 which are founded on the
Parallelogram of Velocities we substitute the word "force"
for "velocity" they will still be true.

73. Law III. *To every action there is an equal and
opposite reaction.*

Every exertion of force consists of a mutual action
between two bodies. This mutual action is called the stress
between the two bodies, so that the Action and Reaction
of Newton together form the Stress.

Illustrations. 1. If a book rest on a table, the book presses the
table with a force equal and opposite to that which the table exerts on
the book.

2. If a man raise a weight by means of a string tied to it,
the string exerts on the man's hand exactly the same force that it
exerts on the weight, but in the opposite direction.

3. The attraction of the earth on a body is its weight, and
the body attracts the earth with a force equal and opposite to
its own weight.

4. When a man drags a heavy body along the ground by means
of a rope, the rope drags the man back with a force equal to that
with which it drags the body forward. [The weight of the rope is
neglected.]

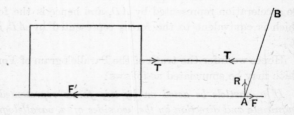

[In the figure AB represents the central line of the man's body.
F and R are the horizontal and vertical forces which the earth exerts
on his feet, and which are equal and opposite to the forces his feet
exert on the earth. T is the tension of the rope which acts in

opposite directions at its ends. F is the horizontal force between the earth and the body.

The man moves because $F > T$.

The body moves because $T > F'$.

Thus at the *commencement* of the motion we have $F > T > F'$.

When the man and body are moving uniformly these three forces are equal.]

5. In the case of a stretched piece of indiarubber, with the ends held in a man's hands, the indiarubber pulls one hand with a force equal and opposite to that with which it pulls the other hand.

The compressed buffers between two railway carriages push one carriage with a force exactly equal and opposite to that with which they push the other carriage.

CHAPTER V.

LAWS OF MOTION (CONTINUED). APPLICATION TO SIMPLE PROBLEMS.

74. Motion of two particles connected by a string.

Two particles, of masses m_1 and m_2, are connected by a light inextensible string which passes over a small smooth fixed pulley. If m_1 be $> m_2$, find the resulting motion of the system, and the tension of the string.

Let the tension of the string be T poundals; the pulley being smooth, this will be the same throughout the string.

Since the string is inextensible, the velocity of m_2 upwards must, throughout the motion, be the same as that of m_1 downwards.

Hence their accelerations [rates of change of velocity] must be the same in magnitude. Let the magnitude of the common acceleration be f.

Now the force on m_1 downwards is $m_1g - T$ poundals.

Hence $m_1g - T = m_1f$ ....(1).

So the force on m_2 upwards is $T - m_2g$ poundals;

$\therefore \ T - m_2g = m_2f$ ....(2).

Adding (1) and (2), we have $f = \dfrac{m_1 - m_2}{m_1 + m_2} g$, which is the common acceleration.

Also, from (2),

$$T = m_2 (f + g) = \frac{2 m_1 m_2}{m_1 + m_2} g \text{ poundals} \quad \ldots\ldots(3).$$

Since the acceleration is known and constant, the equations of Art. 32 give the space moved through and the velocity acquired in any given time.

Experiment. By using the foregoing result the value of g may be roughly obtained if allowance be made for the friction etc. of the pulley.

Fix a light pulley at a convenient height from the ground, so that the distance through which the masses move may be measured. Round the pulley put a light string having at its ends two equal masses [weights of the shape P, in Art. 82, are convenient]. By trial find the mass R which, when placed on the right-hand P, will make it very slowly and uniformly descend to the ground. This mass R is in general small, and we shall neglect it.

Now place on the same P an additional mass Q so that it descends to the ground with an acceleration f which is given by the previous formula. For $m_1 = P + Q$ and $m_2 = P$.

$$\therefore f = \frac{m_1 - m_2}{m_1 + m_2} g = \frac{Q}{2P + Q} g.$$

Measure the distance h through which the weight falls, and the time T that it takes; then

$$h = \tfrac{1}{2} f T^2 = \tfrac{1}{2} \frac{Q}{2P + Q} g T^2.$$

Here everything is known except g which can thus be found.

In an actual experiment the pulley used was a light aluminium one.

The original masses P at the ends of the string were each 265 grammes.

A small mass of the shape Q [Art. 82] equal to 4 grammes when placed on one of the weights P was found to just make it very slowly descend to the ground, so that this weight just overcomes the frictional resistance.

An extra mass of 9 grammes was put on, and the combined weight was then found to descend a distance of 8 feet to the floor in 5·5 seconds. [This time can be found to a considerable degree of accuracy by a stop-watch or by placing an ordinary watch beating four times per second to the ear; the mean of several determinations should be taken.]

Neglecting the 4 grammes put on in order to overcome the friction, we have $m_1 = 265$ and $m_2 = 265 + 9$.

$$\therefore f = \tfrac{9}{539} g,$$

and hence

$$8 = \frac{1}{2} \frac{9g}{539} (5 \cdot 5)^2,$$

$$\therefore g = \frac{8 \times 2 \times 539 \times 4}{9 \times 121} = \text{about } 31 \cdot 7.$$

This is as accurate a result as we can expect to obtain from this experiment.

That the tension of the string is as found may be **experimentally** verified as follows:

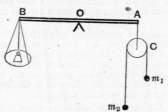

Attach the pulley to the end A of a uniform rod, which can turn about its centre. Then if during the motion the pulley C be at rest, the tension of the string AC must, by result (3),

$$= 2T + \text{wt. of pulley } C = \frac{4m_1 m_2}{m_1 + m_2} g + \text{wt. of pulley,}$$

and hence to keep the beam horizontal weights must be put into the scale-pan at B which will just balance this tension.

As a numerical illustration take $m_1 = 70$ and $m_2 = 30$ grammes; let the mass of the pulley C be 40 grammes and that of the scale-pan B be 10 grammes.

During the motion,

$$2T = \frac{4 \cdot 70 \cdot 30}{70 + 30} g = 84 \text{ grammes weight;}$$

therefore total weight to be placed in the scale-pan

$$= \text{wt. of pulley } C + 84 \text{ grammes} - 10 \text{ grammes} = 114 \text{ grammes.}$$

Put 114 grammes into the scale-pan B; and hold the pulley C, so that it cannot rotate, in such a position that BOA is horizontal; now let motion ensue; the beam will be found to remain horizontal so long as the motion continues; this shows that the tension of the string AC really was 124 grammes as the theory gives.

If the string be slipped off the rim of the pulley, so that no motion can ensue, then, in order to balance m_1 and m_2, the weights that must be put into the scale-pan

= wts. of C, m_1, and m_2 – wt. of the scale-pan

= $40 + 70 + 30 - 10 = 130$ grammes.

Hence when there is motion we see, from experiment, that the tension of the string is less than when the pulley is not free to move.

75. *Two particles, of masses m_1 and m_2, are connected by a light inextensible string; m_2 is placed on a smooth horizontal table and the string passes over a light smooth pulley at the edge of the table, m_1 hanging freely; find the resulting motion.*

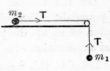

Let the tension of the string be T poundals.

The velocity and acceleration of m_2 along the table must be equal to the velocity and acceleration of m_1 in a vertical direction.

Let f be the common acceleration of the masses.

The force on m_1 downward is $m_1 g - T$;

$$\therefore m_1 g - T = m_1 f \dots\dots\dots\dots\dots\dots(1).$$

The only horizontal force acting on m_2 is the tension T; [for the weight of m_2 is balanced by the reaction of the table].

$$\therefore T = m_2 f \dots\dots\dots\dots\dots\dots(2).$$

Adding (1) and (2), we have

$$m_1 g = (m_1 + m_2) f.$$

$$\therefore f = \frac{m_1}{m_1 + m_2} g,$$

giving the required acceleration.

Hence, from (2), $T = \dfrac{m_1 m_2}{m_1 + m_2} g$ poundals = weight of a body whose mass is

$$\frac{m_1 m_2}{m_1 + m_2}.$$

76.   *Two masses, m_1 and m_2, are connected by a string;
m_2 is placed on a smooth plane inclined at an angle a to the
horizon, and the string, after passing
over a small smooth pulley at the top
of the plane, supports m_1, which hangs
vertically; if m_1 descend, find the resulting motion.*

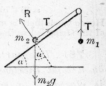

Let the tension of the string be
T poundals.   The velocity and accele-
ration of m_2 up the plane are clearly equal to the velocity
and acceleration of m_1 vertically.

Let f be this common acceleration.   For the motion of
m_1, we have

$$m_1 g - T = m_1 f \quad\quad\quad\quad\quad\ldots\ldots\ldots\ldots\ldots\ldots(1).$$

The weight of m_2 is $m_2 g$ vertically downwards.

The resolved part of $m_2 g$ perpendicular to the inclined
plane is balanced by the reaction R of the plane, since m_2
has no acceleration perpendicular to the plane.

The resolved part of the weight down the inclined plane
is $m_2 g \sin a$, and hence the total force up the plane is

$$T - m_2 g \sin a.$$

Hence $$T - m_2 g \sin a = m_2 f \quad\quad\quad\ldots\ldots\ldots\ldots\ldots(2).$$

Adding (1) and (2), we easily have

$$f = \frac{m_1 - m_2 \sin a}{m_1 + m_2} g.$$

Also, on substitution in (1),

$$T = m_1 (g - f) = m_1 g \left[1 - \frac{m_1 - m_2 \sin a}{m_1 + m_2} \right]$$

$$= \frac{m_1 m_2 (1 + \sin a)}{m_1 + m_2} g,$$

giving the tension of the string.

EXAMPLES. X.

1. A mass of 9 lbs., descending vertically, drags up a mass of 6 lbs. by means of a string passing over a smooth pulley; find the acceleration of the system and the tension of the string.

2. Two particles, of masses 7 and 9 lbs., are connected by a light string passing over a smooth pulley. Find (1) their common accelera- tion, (2) the tension of the string, (3) the velocity at the end of 5 seconds, (4) the distance described in 5 seconds.

3. Two particles, of masses 11 and 13 lbs., are connected by a light string passing over a smooth pulley. Find (1) the velocity at the end of 4 seconds, and (2) the space described in 4 seconds. If at the end of 4 seconds the string be cut, find the distance described by each particle in the next 6 seconds.

4. Masses of 450 and 550 grammes are connected by a thread passing over a light pulley; how far do they go in the first 3 seconds of the motion, and what is the tension of the string?

5. Two masses of 5 and 7 lbs. are fastened to the ends of a cord passing over a frictionless pulley supported by a hook. When they are free to move, shew that the pull on the hook is equal to $11\frac{2}{3}$ lbs. weight.

6. Two equal masses, of 3 lbs. each, are connected by a light string hanging over a smooth peg; if a third mass of 3 lbs. be laid on one of them, by how much is the pressure on the peg increased?

7. Two masses, each equal to P, are connected by a light string passing over a smooth pulley, and a third mass P is laid on one of them; find by how much the pressure on the peg is increased.

8. Two masses, each equal to m, are connected by a string passing over a smooth pulley; what mass must be taken from one and added to the other, so that the system may describe 200 feet in 5 seconds?

9. A mass of 3 lbs., descending vertically, draws up a mass of 2 lbs. by means of a light string passing over a pulley; at the end of 5 seconds the string breaks; find how much higher the 2 lb. mass will go.

10. A body, of mass 9 lbs., is placed on a smooth table at a distance of 8 feet from its edge, and is connected, by a string passing over the edge, with a body of mass 1 lb.; find

    (1)   the common acceleration,

    (2)   the time that elapses before the body reaches the edge of the table,

and   (3)   its velocity on leaving the table.

11. A mass of 350 grammes is placed on a smooth table at a distance of 245·25 cms. from its edge and connected by a light string passing over the edge with a mass of 50 grammes hanging freely; what time will elapse before the first mass will leave the table?

12. A particle, of mass 5 lbs., is placed on a smooth plane inclined at 30° to the horizon, and connected by a string passing over the top of the plane with a particle of mass 3 lbs., which hangs vertically; find (1) the common acceleration, (2) the tension of the string, (3) the velocity at the end of 3 seconds, (4) the space described in 3 seconds.

13. A particle, of mass 4 lbs., is placed at the bottom of a plane, inclined at 45° to the horizon and of length 7 feet, and is connected with a mass of 3 lbs. by a string passing over the top of the plane; find the common acceleration of the masses, and the time that elapses before the first arrives at the top of the plane.

14. A body, of mass 12 lbs., is placed on an inclined plane, whose height is half its length, and connected by a light string passing over a pulley at the top of the plane with a mass of 8 lbs. which hangs freely; find the distance described by the masses in 5 seconds.

15. A mass of 6 ounces slides down a smooth inclined plane, whose height is half its length, and draws another mass from rest over a distance of 3 feet in 5 seconds along a horizontal table which is level with the top of the plane over which the string passes; find the mass on the table.

16. A mass of 4 ozs. is attached by a string passing over a smooth pulley to a larger mass; find the magnitude of the latter so that, if after the motion has continued 3 seconds the string be cut, the former will ascend $\frac{16}{9}$ ft. before descending.

17. Two scale-pans, of mass 3 lbs. each, are connected by a string passing over a smooth pulley; shew how to divide a mass of 12 lbs. between the two scale-pans so that the heavier may descend a distance of 50 feet in the first 5 seconds.

18. Two strings pass over a smooth pulley; on one side they are attached to masses of 3 and 4 lbs. respectively, and on the other to one of 5 lbs.; find the tensions of the strings and the acceleration of the system.

19. A string hung over a pulley has at one end a weight of 10 lbs. and at the other end weights of 8 and 4 lbs. respectively; after being in motion for 5 seconds the 4 lb. weight is taken off; find how much further the weights go before they first come to rest.

20. Two unequal masses are connected by a string passing over a small smooth pulley; during the ensuing motion shew that the thrust of the axis of the pulley upon its supports is always less than the sum of the weights of the masses.

21. A string passing across a smooth table at right angles to two opposite edges has attached to it at the ends two masses P and Q which hang vertically. Prove that, if a mass M be attached to the portion of the string which is on the table, the acceleration of the system when left to itself will be

$$\frac{P-Q}{P+Q+M}g.$$

77. Motion on a rough plane. *A particle slides down a rough inclined plane inclined to the horizon at an angle a; if μ be the coefficient of friction, to determine the motion.*

Let m be the mass of the particle, so that its weight is mg poundals; let R be the normal reaction of the plane, and μR the friction.

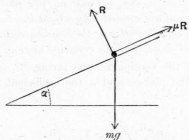

The total force perpendicular to the plane is
$$(R - mg \cos a) \text{ poundals.}$$

The total force down the plane is $(mg \sin a - \mu R)$ poundals.

Now perpendicular to the plane there cannot be any motion, and hence there is no change of motion.

Hence the acceleration, and therefore the total force, in that direction is zero.
$$\therefore \ R - mg \cos a = 0 \dots\dots\dots\dots(1).$$

Also the acceleration down the plane
$$= \frac{\text{moving force}}{\text{mass moved}} = \frac{mg \sin a - \mu R}{m} = g (\sin a - \mu \cos a), \text{ by (1)}.$$

Hence the velocity of the particle after it has moved from rest over a length l of the plane is, by Art. 32, equal to
$$\sqrt{2gl (\sin a - \mu \cos a)}.$$

Similarly, if the particle were projected up the plane, we have to change the sign of μ, and its acceleration in a direction opposite to that of its motion is

$$g\,(\sin \alpha + \mu \cos \alpha).$$

78. *Two equally rough inclined planes, of equal height, whose inclinations to the horizon are α_1 and α_2, are placed back to back; two masses, m_1 and m_2, are placed on their inclined faces and are connected by a light inextensible string passing over a smooth pulley at the common vertex of the two planes; if m_1 descend, find the resulting motion.*

Let T be the tension of the string, R_1 and R_2 the reactions of the planes, and μ the coefficient of friction.

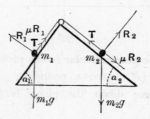

Since m_1 moves *down*, the friction on it acts *up* the plane.

Since m_2 moves *up*, the friction on it acts *down* the plane.

Hence the total force on m_1 down the plane

$$= m_1 g \sin \alpha_1 - T - \mu R_1$$
$$= m_1 g\,(\sin \alpha_1 - \mu \cos \alpha_1) - T.$$

Hence, if f be the common acceleration of the two particles, we have

$$m_1 g\,(\sin \alpha_1 - \mu \cos \alpha_1) - T = m_1 f \ldots\ldots\ldots(1).$$

Similarly, the total force on m_2 up the plane

$$= T - \mu R_2 - m_2 g \sin a_2$$
$$= T - m_2 g \left[\sin a_2 + \mu \cos a_2 \right].$$

Hence

$$T - m_2 g (\sin a_2 + \mu \cos a_2) = m_2 f \ldots\ldots\ldots(2).$$

Adding (1) and (2), we have

$$f(m_1 + m_2) = g \left[\begin{array}{c} m_1 (\sin a_1 - \mu \cos a_1) \\ - m_2 (\sin a_2 + \mu \cos a_2) \end{array} \right],$$

giving the required acceleration.

79. *A train, of mass 50 tons, is ascending an incline of 1 in 100 ; the engine exerts a constant tractive force equal to the weight of 1 ton, and the resistance due to friction etc. may be taken at 8 lbs. weight per ton ; find the acceleration with which the train ascends the incline.*

The train is retarded by the resolved part of its weight down the incline, and by the resistance of friction.

The latter is equal to 8×50 or 400 lbs. wt.

The incline is at an angle a to the horizon, where $\sin a = \frac{1}{100}$.

The resolved part of the weight down the incline therefore

$$= W \sin a = 50 \times 2240 \times \tfrac{1}{100} \text{ lbs. wt.}$$
$$= 1120 \text{ lbs. wt.}$$

Hence the total force to retard the train $= 1520$ lbs. wt.

But the engine pulls with a force equal to 2240 lbs. weight.

Therefore the total force to increase the speed equals $(2240 - 1520)$ or 720 lbs. weight, *i.e.* $720g$ poundals.

Also the mass moved is 50×2240 lbs.

$$\text{Hence the acceleration} = \frac{720\,g}{50 \times 2240}$$

$$= \frac{9g}{1400} \text{ ft.-sec. units.}$$

Since the acceleration is known, we can, by Art. 32, find the velocity acquired, and the space described, in a given time, etc.

EXAMPLES. XI.

1. A mass of 5 lbs. on a rough horizontal table is connected by a string with a mass of 8 lbs. which hangs over the edge of the table; if the coefficient of friction be $\frac{1}{2}$, find the resultant acceleration.

Find also the coefficient of friction if the acceleration be half that of a freely falling body.

2. A mass Q on a horizontal table, whose coefficient of friction is $\sqrt{3}$, is connected by a string with a mass $3Q$ which hangs over the edge of the table; four seconds after the commencement of the motion the string breaks; find the velocity at this instant.

Find also the distance of the new position of equilibrium of Q from its initial position.

3. A mass of 200 grammes is moved along a rough horizontal table by means of a string which is attached to a mass of 40 grammes hanging over the edge of the table; if the masses take twice the time to acquire the same velocity from rest that they do when the table is smooth, find the coefficient of friction.

4. A body, of mass 10 lbs., is placed on a rough plane, whose coefficient of friction is $\frac{1}{\sqrt{3}}$ and whose inclination to the horizon is 30°; if the length of the plane be 4 feet and the body be acted on by a force, parallel to the plane, equal to 15 lbs. weight, find the time that elapses before it reaches the top of the plane and its velocity there.

5. If in the previous question the body be connected with a mass of 15 lbs., hanging freely, by means of a string passing over the top of the plane, find the time and velocity.

6. A rough plane is 100 feet long and is inclined to the horizon at an angle $\sin^{-1} \frac{3}{5}$, the coefficient of friction being $\frac{1}{2}$, and a body slides down it from rest at the highest point; find its velocity on reaching the bottom.

If the body were projected up the plane from the bottom so as just to reach the top, find its initial velocity.

7. A particle slides down a rough inclined plane, whose inclination to the horizon is $\frac{\pi}{4}$ and whose coefficient of friction is $\frac{3}{4}$; shew that the time of descending any space is twice what it would be if the plane were perfectly smooth.

8. Two rough planes, inclined at 30° and 60° to the horizon and of the same height, are placed back to back; masses of 5 and 10 lbs. are placed on the faces and connected by a string passing over the top of the planes; if the coefficient of friction be $\frac{1}{\sqrt{3}}$, find the resulting acceleration.

9. If in the previous question the masses be interchanged, what is the resulting acceleration?

10. A train is moving on horizontal rails at the rate of 15 miles per hour; if the steam be suddenly turned off, find how far it will go before stopping, the resistance being 8 lbs. per ton.

11. If a train of 200 tons, moving at the rate of 30 miles per hour, can be stopped in 60 yards, compare the frictional resistances with the weight of a ton.

12. A train is running on horizontal rails at the rate of 30 miles per hour, the resistance due to friction, etc. being 10 lbs. wt. per ton; if the steam be shut off, find (1) the time that elapses before the train comes to rest, (2) the distance described in this time.

13. In the previous question if the train be ascending an incline of 1 in 112, find the corresponding time and distance.

14. A train of mass 200 tons is running at the rate of 40 miles per hour down an incline of 1 in 120; find the resistance necessary to stop it in half a mile.

15. A train runs from rest for 1 mile down a plane whose descent is 1 foot vertically for each 100 feet of its length; if the resistances be equal to 8 lbs. per ton, how far will the train be carried along the horizontal level at the foot of the incline?

16. A train of mass 140 tons, travelling at the rate of 15 miles per hour, comes to the top of an incline of 1 in 128, the length of the incline being half a mile, and steam is then shut off; taking the resistance due to friction, etc. as 10 lbs. wt. per ton, find the distance it describes on a horizontal line at the foot of the incline before coming to rest.

17. In the preceding question, if on arriving at the foot of the incline a brake-van, of weight 10 tons, have all its wheels prevented from revolving, find the distance described, assuming the coefficient of friction between the wheels and the line to be ·5.

18. An engine, of mass 30 tons, pulls after it a train, of mass 130 tons; supposing the friction to be $\frac{1}{50}$th of the weight of the whole train, calculate the force exerted by the engine if at the end of the first mile from the start the speed be raised to 45 miles per hour.

What incline would be just sufficient to prevent the engine from moving the train?

Also down what incline would the train run with constant velocity, neither steam nor brakes being on?

80. *A body, of mass m lbs., is placed on a horizontal plane which is in motion with a vertical upward acceleration f; find the reaction between the body and the plane.*

Let R be the reaction between the body and the plane.

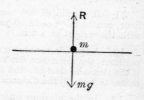

Since the acceleration is vertically upwards, the total force acting on the body must be vertically upwards.

The only force, besides R, acting on the body is its weight mg acting vertically downwards.

Hence the total force is $R - mg$ vertically upwards, and this produces an acceleration f; hence

$$R - mg = mf, \text{ giving } R.$$

In a similar manner it may be shewn that, if the body be moving with a downward acceleration f, the reaction R_1 is given by

$$mg - R_1 = mf.$$

We note that the reaction is greater or less than the weight of the body, according as the acceleration of the body is upwards or downwards.

Ex. 1. *The body is of mass 20 lbs. and is moving with* (1) *an upward acceleration of 12 ft.-sec. units,* (2) *a downward acceleration of the same magnitude; find the reactions.*

In the first case we have

$$R - 20 \cdot g = 20 \cdot 12.$$

$$\therefore R = 20\,(32 + 12) \text{ poundals} = \text{wt. of } 27\tfrac{1}{2} \text{ lbs.}$$

In the second case we have

$$20 \cdot g - R_1 = 20 \cdot 12.$$

$$\therefore R = 20\,(32 - 12) \text{ poundals} = \text{wt. of } 12\tfrac{1}{2} \text{ lbs.}$$

Ex. 2. *Two scale-pans, each of mass M, are connected by a light string passing over a small pulley, and in them are placed masses M_1 and M_2; shew that the reactions of the pans during the motion are*

$$\frac{2M_1\,(M + M_2)}{M_1 + M_2 + 2M} \cdot g \text{ and } \frac{2M_2\,(M + M_1)}{M_1 + M_2 + 2M} \cdot g$$

respectively.

Let f be the common acceleration of the system, and suppose $M_1 > M_2$.

Then, as in Art. 74, we have

$$f = \frac{M_1 - M_2}{2M + M_1 + M_2}\, g.$$

Let P be the reaction between M_1 and the scale-pan on which it rests; then the force on the mass M_1, *considered as a separate body*, is $M_1 g - P$. Also its acceleration is f.

Hence

$$M_1 g - P = M_1 f,$$
$$\therefore P = M_1\,(g - f)$$
$$= \frac{2M_1\,(M + M_2)}{2M + M_1 + M_2}\, g.$$

81. *Three inches of rain fall in a certain district in 12 hours. Assuming that the drops fall freely from a height of a quarter of a mile, find the pressure on the ground per square mile of the district due to the rain during the storm, the mass of a cubic foot of water being 1000 ounces.*

The amount of rain that falls on a square foot during the storm is $\tfrac{1}{4}$ of a cubic foot, and its mass is 250 ounces.

Hence the mass that falls per second

$$= \frac{250}{16} \times \frac{1}{12 \cdot 60 \cdot 60} = \frac{5}{144 \times 96} \text{ lbs. per sq. foot.}$$

The velocity of each raindrop on touching the ground is

$$\sqrt{2 \times g \times 440 \times 3}, \text{ or } 16\,\sqrt{330} \text{ ft. per second.}$$

Therefore the momentum that is destroyed per second is

$$\frac{5}{144 \times 96} \times 16\sqrt{330}, \text{ or } \frac{5\sqrt{330}}{864} \text{ units of momentum.}$$

But the number of units of momentum destroyed per second is equal to the number of poundals in the acting force (Art. 61).

Hence the pressure on the ground per square foot

$$= \frac{5\sqrt{330}}{864} \text{ poundals.}$$

Hence the pressure per square mile

$$= \text{weight of } 9 \times 4840 \times 640 \times \frac{5\sqrt{330}}{32 \times 864} \text{ lbs.}$$

$$= \text{weight of 41 tons approximately.}$$

In general, if a jet of water hit a wall, the pressure on the wall per square foot is mv^2 poundals, where v is the velocity in feet per second and m is the mass of a cubic foot of water in lbs. For a mass mv hits the square foot in each second, and the velocity of each particle of the water is v, so that the total momentum destroyed per second $= mv \times v = mv^2$.

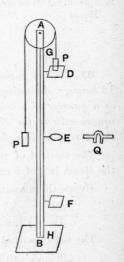

82. Atwood's Machine.

This machine is used to verify the laws of motion and to obtain a rough value for g. In its simplest form it consists of a vertical pillar AB firmly clamped to the ground, and carrying at its top a light pulley which will move very freely. This pillar is graduated and carries two platforms, D and F, and a ring E, all of which can be affixed by screws at any height desired. The platform D can also be instantaneously dropped. Over the pulley passes a fine cord supporting at its ends two long thin equal weights, one of which, P, can freely pass through the ring E. Another small weight Q, called a rider, is provided, which can be laid upon the weight P, but which cannot pass through the ring E.

The weight Q is laid upon P and the platform D is dropped and motion ensues; the weight Q is left behind as the weight P passes through the ring; the weight P then traverses the distance EF with constant velocity, and the time T which it takes to describe this distance is carefully measured.

By Art. 74 the acceleration of the system as the weight falls from D to E is

$$\frac{(Q+P)-P}{(Q+P)+P}\, g, \quad i.e. \quad \frac{Q}{Q+2P}\, g.$$

Denote this by f, and let $DE = h$.

Then the velocity v on arriving at E is given by

$$v^2 = 2fh.$$

After passing E, the distance EF is described with constant velocity v.

Hence, if $EF = h_1$, we have

$$T = \frac{h_1}{v} = \frac{h_1}{\sqrt{2fh}}.$$

$$\therefore h_1^2 = \frac{2Q}{Q+2P}\, ghT^2.$$

Since all the quantities involved can be measured, this relation gives us the value of g.

By giving different values to P, Q, h and h_1, we can in this manner verify all the fundamental laws of motion.

In practice, the value of g cannot by this method be found to any great degree of accuracy, and the interest of Atwood's machine is chiefly of an antiquarian character; the chief causes of discrepancy are the mass of the pulley, which cannot be neglected, the friction of the pivot on which the wheel turns, and the resistance of the air. It is also difficult to accurately measure the times involved in the experiment.

It will be noted that the object of both Galileo's Inclined Plane [Art. 41] and of Atwood's Machine is to lessen the effect of gravity so as to make its results measurable, or, as it has been well expressed, to "dilute" gravity.

The friction of the pivot may be minimised if its ends do not rest on fixed supports, but on the circumferences of four light wheels, called friction wheels, two on each side, which turn very freely.

There are other pieces of apparatus for securing the accuracy of the experiment as far as possible, *e.g.* for instantaneously withdrawing the platform D at the required moment.

83. *By using Atwood's machine to shew that the acceleration of a given mass is proportional to the force acting on it.*

We shall *assume* that the statement is true and see whether the results we deduce therefrom are verified by experiment.

To explain the method of procedure we shall take a numerical example.

Let P be $49\frac{1}{2}$ ozs. and Q 1 oz. so that the mass moved is 100 ozs. and the moving force is the weight of 1 oz.

The acceleration of the system therefore $= \frac{1}{100}g$ (Art. 74).

Let the distance DE be one foot so that the velocity when Q is taken off $= \sqrt{2 \cdot \dfrac{g}{100} \cdot 1} = \dfrac{8}{10}$ ft. per sec., if, for simplicity, we take g equal to 32.

Let the platform F be carefully placed at such a point that the mass will move from E to F in some definite time, say 2 secs.

Then $EF = \dfrac{8}{10} \cdot 2 = \dfrac{8}{5}$ feet.

Now alter the conditions. Make P equal to 48 and Q equal to 4 ozs. The mass moved is still 100 ozs. and the moving force is now the weight of 4 ozs.

The acceleration is now $\frac{4g}{100}$, and the velocity at E

$$= \sqrt{2 \cdot \frac{4g}{100} \cdot 1} = \frac{8}{5} \text{ feet per second.}$$

In 2 seconds the mass would now describe $\frac{16}{5}$ feet, so that, if our hypothesis be correct, the platform F must be twice as far from E as before. *This is found on trial to be correct.*

Similarly if we make $P = 45\frac{1}{2}$ ozs. and $Q = 9$ ozs., so that the mass moved is still 100 ozs., the theory would give us that EF should be $\frac{24}{5}$ feet, and this would be found to be correct.

The experiment should now be tried over again *ab initio* and P and Q be given different values from the above; alterations should then be made in their different values so that $2P + Q$ is constant.

By the same method to shew that the force varies as the mass when the acceleration is constant.

As before let $P = 49\frac{1}{2}$ ozs. and $Q = 1$ oz. so that, as in the last experiment, we have $EF = \frac{8}{5}$ feet.

Secondly, let $P = 99$ ozs. and $Q = 2$ ozs., so that the moving force is doubled and the mass moved is doubled. Hence, if our enunciation be correct, the acceleration should be the same, since

$$\frac{\text{second moving force}}{\text{second mass moved}} = \frac{\text{first moving force}}{\text{first mass moved}}.$$

The distance EF moved through in 2 seconds should therefore be the same as before, and this, on trial, *is found to be the case.*

Similarly if we make $P = 148\frac{1}{2}$ ozs. and $Q = 3$ ozs. the same result would be found to follow.

In actual practice some extra weight R must be put on in order to overcome the friction at the pulley, etc. This should be determined before Q is put on; it will be that weight which will just make the P on which it is placed move very slowly and uniformly down to the ground. This weight R must be kept on when Q is added, and must not be counted as part of Q in the above work.

EXAMPLES. XII.

1. If I jump off a table with a twenty-pound weight in my hand, what is the thrust of the weight on my hand?

2. A mass of 20 lbs. rests on a horizontal plane which is made to ascend (1) with a constant velocity of 1 foot per second, (2) with a constant acceleration of 1 foot per second per second; find in each case the reaction of the plane.

3. A man, whose mass is 8 stone, stands on a lift which moves with a uniform acceleration of 12 ft.-sec. units; find the reaction of the floor when the lift is (1) ascending, (2) descending.

4. A bucket containing 1 cwt. of coal is drawn up the shaft of a coal-pit, and the reaction between the coal and the bottom of the bucket is equal to the weight of 126 lbs. Find the acceleration of the bucket.

5. A balloon ascends with a uniformly accelerated velocity, so that a mass of 1 cwt. produces on the floor of the balloon the same thrust which 116 lbs. would produce on the earth's surface; find the height which the balloon will have attained in one minute from the time of starting.

6. Two scale-pans, each of mass 30 grammes, are suspended by a weightless string passing over a smooth pulley; a mass of 300 grammes is placed in the one, and 240 grammes in the other. Find the tension of the string and the reactions of the scale-pans.

7. A string, passing over a smooth pulley, supports two scale-pans at its ends, the mass of each scale-pan being 1 ounce. If masses of 2 and 4 ounces respectively be placed in the scale-pans, find the acceleration of the system, the tension of the string, and the reactions between the masses and the scale-pans.

8. On a certain day half an inch of rain fell in 3 hours; assuming that the drops are indefinitely small and that the terminal velocity was 10 feet per second, find the impulsive pressure in tons per square mile consequent on their being reduced to rest, assuming that the mass of a cubic foot of water is 1000 ounces and that the rain was uniform and continuous.

9. Find the pressure in lbs. wt. per acre due to the impact of a fall of rain of 3 inches in 24 hours, supposing the rain to have a velocity due to falling freely through 400 feet.

10. A jet of water is projected against a wall so that 300 gallons strike the wall per second with a horizontal velocity of 80 feet per second. Assuming that a gallon contains $277\frac{1}{4}$ cubic inches and that the mass of a cubic foot of water is 1000 ounces, find the reaction of the wall in pounds' weight.

11. The two masses in an Atwood's machine are each 240 grammes, and an additional mass of 10 grammes being placed on one of them it is observed to descend through 10 metres in 10 seconds; hence shew that $g = 980$.

12. Explain how to use Atwood's machine to shew that a body acted on by a constant force moves with constant acceleration.

13. Sixteen balls of equal mass are strung like beads on a string; some are placed on a smooth inclined plane of inclination $\sin^{-1}\frac{1}{3}$, and the rest hang over the top of the plane; how have the balls been arranged if the acceleration at first be $\frac{g}{2}$?

14. Two bodies, of masses P and Q, are connected by a stretched string; P hangs vertically and Q is placed on a smooth plane inclined at 30° to the horizon, the string passing over the top of the plane; if P descend from rest through a given distance in 4 times the time in which it would fall freely from rest through the same distance, find the ratio of P to Q.

15. P hangs vertically and is 9 lbs.; Q is a mass of 6 lbs. on a smooth plane whose inclination to the horizon is 30°; shew that P will drag Q up the whole length of the plane in half the time that Q hanging vertically would take to draw P up the plane.

16. If the height of an inclined plane be 12 feet and the base 16 feet, find how far a particle will move on a horizontal plane after sliding from rest down the length of the inclined plane, supposing it to pass from one plane to the other without loss of velocity, and that the coefficient of friction for each plane is $\frac{1}{8}$.

17. Shew that a train going at the rate of 30 miles per hour will be brought to rest in about 84 yards by continuous brakes, if they press on the wheels with a force equal to three-quarters of the weight of the train, the coefficient of friction being ·16.

18. A train of mass 50 tons is moving on a level at the rate of 30 miles per hour when the steam is shut off, and the brake being applied to the brake-van the train is stopped in a quarter of a mile. Find the mass of the brake-van, taking the coefficient of friction between the wheels and rails to be one-sixth, and supposing the unlocked wheels to roll without sliding.

19. A mass m is drawn up a smooth inclined plane, of height h and length l, by means of a string passing over the vertex of the plane, from the other end of which hangs a mass m'. Shew that, in order that m may just reach the top of the plane, m' must be detached after m has moved through a distance

$$\frac{m+m'}{m'}\frac{hl}{h+l}.$$

20. Two masses are connected by a string passing over a small pulley; shew that, if the sum of the masses be constant, the tension of the string is greater, the less the acceleration.

21. A mass m_1 hanging at the end of a string, draws a mass m_2 along the surface of a smooth table; if the mass on the table be doubled the tension of the string is increased by one-half; find the ratio of m_1 to m_2.

22. Two bodies, of masses 9 and 16 lbs. respectively, are placed on a smooth horizontal table at a distance of 10 feet; if they were now to attract each other with a constant force equal to 1 lb. wt. at all distances, find after what time they would meet.

23. In the case of a single movable pulley the free end of the string passes round a fixed pulley and supports a weight P greater than $\frac{1}{2}W$, where W is the weight suspended from the movable pulley. Find the tension of the string during the ensuing motion, the three parts into which it is divided by the pulleys being parallel.

24. A mass m will just support a mass M in a system of two pulleys in which each string is attached to M, the strings being parallel. A mass m is now attached to M; find the subsequent motion, neglecting the weights of the pulleys.

25. A system of three movable pulleys, in which all the strings are vertical and attached to the beam, is employed to raise a body, of mass 1 cwt., by means of one of mass 15 lbs. attached to a string passing over a smooth fixed pulley. Shew that the body will rise with acceleration $\dfrac{g}{134}$, the masses of the pulleys being neglected.

26. A string, with masses m and m' at its ends, passes over three fixed and under two movable pulleys, each of mass M, hanging down between the fixed pulleys, the parts of the string between the pulleys being vertical. Find the condition that the movable pulleys should neither rise nor fall, and in this case determine the acceleration of m and m'.

27. A rope hangs down over a smooth pulley, and a man of 12 stone lets himself down the portion of rope on one side of the pulley with unit acceleration. Find with what uniform acceleration a man of $11\frac{1}{2}$ stone must pull himself up by the other portion of the rope so that the rope may remain at rest.

28. A man, of mass 12 stone, and a sack, of mass 10 stone, are suspended over a smooth pulley by a rope of negligible weight. If the man pull himself up the rope so as to diminish what would be his acceleration by one-half, find the upward acceleration of the sack in this case, and shew that the acceleration upwards of the man relative to the rope is $\dfrac{g}{10}$.

29. A train, whose mass is 112 tons, is travelling at the uniform rate of 25 miles per hour on a level track, and the resistance due to air, friction, etc. is 16 lbs. per ton. Part of the train, of mass 12 tons, becomes detached. Assuming that the force exerted by the engine is the same throughout, find how much the train will have gained on the detached part after 50 seconds and the velocity of the train when the detached part comes to rest.

30. Two particles, of masses m and $2m$, lie together on a smooth horizontal table. A string which joins them hangs over the edge and supports a pulley carrying a mass $3m$; prove that the acceleration of the latter mass is $\frac{9g}{17}$.

31. *A smooth wedge, of mass M, is placed on a horizontal plane, and a particle, of mass m, slides down its slant face, which is inclined at an angle α to the horizon; prove that the acceleration of the wedge*

is $$\frac{mg \sin \alpha \cos \alpha}{M + m \sin^2 \alpha}.$$

[Let f_1 be the acceleration of the particle in a direction perpendicular to, and towards, the slant face; f_2 the horizontal acceleration of the wedge; and R the normal reaction between the particle and the slant face, so that R acts in one direction on the particle and in the opposite direction on the wedge. Then

$$mf_1 = mg \cos \alpha - R \dots\dots\dots\dots\dots\dots(1),$$

and $$Mf_2 = R \sin \alpha \dots\dots\dots\dots\dots\dots\dots(2).$$

Also, since the particle remains in contact with the slant face, the acceleration f_1 must be the same as the acceleration of the wedge resolved in a direction perpendicular to the slant face.

$$\therefore f_1 = f_2 \sin \alpha \dots\dots\dots\dots\dots\dots(3).$$

Solving (1), (2), and (3), we have f_2.]

CHAPTER VI.

IMPULSE, WORK, AND ENERGY.

84. Impulse. Def. *The impulse of a force in a given time is equal to the product of the force (if constant, and the mean value of the force if variable) and the time during which it acts.*

The impulse of a force P acting for a time t is therefore $P \cdot t$.

The impulse of a force is also equal to the momentum generated by the force in the given time. For suppose a particle, of mass m, moving initially with velocity u is acted on by a constant force P for time t. If f be the resulting acceleration, we have $P = mf$.

But, if v be the velocity of the particle at the end of time t, we have $v = u + ft$.

Hence the impulse $= Pt = mft = mv - mu$

= the momentum generated in the given time.

The same result is also true if the force be variable.

Hence it follows that the second law of motion might have been enunciated in the following form;

The change of momentum of a particle in a given time is equal to the impulse of the force which produces it and is in the same direction.

85. Impulsive Forces. Suppose we have a force P acting for a time τ on a body whose mass is m, and let the velocities of the mass at the beginning and end of this time be u and v. Then by the last article

$$P\tau = m(v-u).$$

Let now the force become bigger and bigger, and the time τ smaller and smaller. Then ultimately P will be almost infinitely big and τ almost infinitely small, and yet their product *may* be finite. For example P may be equal to 10^7 poundals, τ equal to $\dfrac{1}{10^7}$ seconds, and m equal to one pound, in which case the change of velocity produced is the unit of velocity.

To find the whole effect of a finite force acting for a finite time we have to find two things, (1) the change in the velocity of the particle produced by the force during the time it acts, and (2) the change in the position of the particle during this time. Now in the case of an infinitely large force acting for an infinitely short time, the body moves only a very short distance whilst the force is acting, so that this change of position of the particle may be neglected. Hence the total effect of such a force is known when we know the change of momentum which it produces.

Such a force is called an impulsive force. Hence

Def. *An impulsive force is a very great force acting for a very short time, so that the change in the position of the particle during the time the force acts on it may be neglected. Its whole effect is measured by its impulse, or the change of momentum produced.*

In actual practice we never have any experience of an infinitely great force acting for an infinitely short time.

Approximate examples are, however, the blow of a hammer, and the collision of two billiard balls.

The above will be true even if the force be not uniform. In the ordinary case of the collision of two billiard balls the force generally varies very considerably.

Ex. 1. A body, whose mass is 9 lbs., is acted on by a force which changes its velocity from 20 miles per hour to 30 miles per hour. Find the impulse of the force.

Ans. 132 units of impulse.

Ex. 2. A mass of 2 lbs. at rest is struck and starts off with a velocity of 10 feet per second; assuming the time during which the blow lasts to be one-hundredth of a second, find the average value of the force acting on the mass.

Ans. 2000 poundals.

Ex. 3. A glass marble, whose mass is 1 ounce, falls from a height of 25 feet, and rebounds to a height of 16 feet; find the impulse, and the average force between the marble and the floor if the time during which they are in contact be one-tenth of a second.

Ans. $4\frac{1}{2}$ units of impulse; 47 poundals.

86. Impact of two bodies. When two masses A and B impinge, then, by the third law of motion, the action of A on B is, at each instant during which they are in contact, equal and opposite to that of B on A.

Hence the impulse of the action of A on B is equal and opposite to the impulse of the action of B on A.

It follows that the change in the momentum of B is equal and opposite to the change in the momentum of A, and therefore the sum of these changes, measured in the same direction, is zero.

Hence the sum of the momenta of the two masses, measured in the same direction, is unaltered by their impact.

Ex. 1. *A body, of mass 3 lbs., moving with velocity 13 feet per second overtakes a body, of mass 2 lbs., moving with velocity 3 feet per second in the same straight line, and they coalesce and form one body; find the velocity of this single body.*

Let V be the required velocity. Then, since the sum of the momenta of the two bodies is unaltered by the impact, we have

$$(3+2)\,V = 3 \times 13 + 2 \times 3 = 45 \text{ units of momentum,}$$
$$\therefore\ V = 9 \text{ ft. per sec.}$$

Ex. 2. *If in the last example the second body be moving in the direction opposite to that of the first, find the resulting velocity.*

In this case the momentum of the first body is represented by 3×13 and that of the second by -2×3. Hence, if V_1 be the required velocity, we have

$$(3+2)\,V_1 = 3 \times 13 - 2 \times 3 = 33 \text{ units of momentum.}$$
$$\therefore\ V_1 = \tfrac{33}{5} = 6\tfrac{3}{5} \text{ ft. per sec.}$$

87. Motion of a shot and gun.

When a gun is fired, the powder is almost instantaneously converted into a gas at a very high pressure, which by its expansion forces the shot out. The action of the gas is similar to that of a compressed spring trying to recover its natural position. The force exerted on the shot forwards is, at any instant before the shot leaves the gun, equal and opposite to that exerted on the gun backwards, and therefore the impulse of this force on the shot is equal and opposite to the impulse of the force on the gun. Hence the momentum generated in the shot is equal and opposite to that generated in the gun, if the latter be free to move.

Ex. *A shot, whose mass is 400 lbs., is projected from a gun, of mass 50 tons, with a velocity of 900 feet per second; find the resulting velocity of the gun.*

Since the momentum of the gun is equal and opposite to that of the shot we have, if v be the velocity communicated to the gun,

$$50 \times 2240 \times v = 400 \times 900.$$
$$\therefore\ v = 3\tfrac{3}{14} \text{ ft. per sec.}$$

EXAMPLES. XIII.

1.   A body, of mass 7 lbs., moving with a velocity of 10 feet per second, overtakes a body, of mass 20 lbs., moving with a velocity of 2 feet per second in the same direction as the first; if after the impact they move forward with a common velocity, find its magnitude.

2.   A body, of mass 8 lbs., moving with a velocity of 6 feet per second overtakes a body, of mass 24 lbs., moving with a velocity of 2 feet per second in the same direction as the first; if after the impact they coalesce into one body, shew that the velocity of the compound body is 3 feet per second.

If they were moving in opposite directions, shew that after impact the compound body is at rest.

3.   A body, of mass 10 lbs., moving with velocity 4 feet per second meets a body, of mass 12 lbs., moving in the opposite direction with a velocity of 7 feet per second; if they coalesce into one body, shew that it will have a velocity of 2 feet per second in the direction in which the larger body was originally moving.

4.   A shot, of mass 1 ounce, is projected with a velocity of 1000 feet per second from a gun of mass 10 lbs.; find the velocity with which the latter begins to recoil.

5.   A shot of 800 lbs. is projected from a 40-ton gun with a velocity of 2000 feet per second; find the velocity with which the gun would commence to recoil, if free to move in the line of projection.

6.   A shot, of mass 700 lbs., is fired with a velocity of 1700 feet per second from a gun of mass 38 tons; if the recoil be resisted by a constant force equal to the weight of 17 tons, through how many feet will the gun recoil?

7.   A shot, whose mass is 800 lbs., is discharged from an 81-ton gun with a velocity of 1400 feet per second; find the constant force which acting on the gun would stop it after a recoil of 5 feet.

8.   A gun, of mass 1 ton, fires a shot of mass 28 lbs. and recoils up a smooth inclined plane, rising to a height of 5 feet; find the initial velocity of the projectile.

88.   Work.   We have pointed out in Statics, Chapter XI, that a force is said to do work when it moves its point of application in the direction of the force. The work is measured by the product of the force and the distance through which the point of application is moved in the direction of the force. The unit of work used by engineers is a Foot-Pound, which is the work done in raising the weight of one pound through one foot.

The British absolute unit of work is the work done by a poundal in moving its point of application through one foot.

This unit of work is called a **Foot-Poundal.**

With this unit of work the work done by a force of P poundals in moving its point of application through s feet is $P \cdot s$ foot-poundals.

Since the weight of a pound is equal to g-poundals, it follows that a Foot-Pound is equal to g Foot-Poundals.

The c.g.s. unit of work is that done by a dyne in moving its point of application through a centimetre, and is called an **Erg.**

$$\frac{\text{A Foot-Poundal}}{\text{An Erg}} = \frac{\text{Poundal} \times \text{Foot}}{\text{Dyne} \times \text{Centimetre}} = 13800 \times \frac{12}{\cdot 3937} \text{ nearly}$$

[Arts. 66 and 3]

$$= 421390 \text{ approx.}$$

When an agent is performing 1 Joule, *i.e.* 10^7 Ergs, per second it is said to be working with a power of 1 Watt. One Horse-Power is equivalent to about 746 Watts.

89. Ex. 1. *What is the H.P. of an engine which can just keep a train, of mass 150 tons, moving at a uniform rate of 60 miles per hour, the resistances to the motion due to friction, the resistance of the air, etc. being taken at 10 lbs. weight per ton?*

The force to stop the train is equal to the weight of 150×10, *i.e.* 1500, lbs. weight.

Now 60 miles per hour is equal to 88 feet per second.

Hence a force, equal to 1500 lbs. wt., has its point of application moved through 88 feet in a second, and hence the work done is 1500×88 foot-pounds per second.

If x be the H.P. of the engine, the work it does per minute is $x \times 33000$ foot-lbs., and hence the work per second is $x \times 550$ foot-lbs.

$$\therefore \ x \times 550 = 1500 \times 88.$$
$$\therefore \ x = 240.$$

Ex. 2. *Find the least H.P. of an engine which is able in 4 minutes to generate in a train, of mass 100 tons, a velocity of 30 miles per hour on a level line, the resistances due to friction, etc. being equal to 8 lbs. weight per ton, and the pull of the engine being assumed constant.*

Since in 240 seconds a velocity of 44 feet per second is generated the acceleration of the train must be $\dfrac{44}{240}$ or $\dfrac{11}{60}$ foot-second units.

Let the force exerted by the engine be P poundals.

The resistance due to friction is equal to 800 pounds' weight; hence the total force on the train is $P - 800g$ poundals.

Hence
$$P - 800g = 100 \times 2240 \times \frac{11}{60}.$$

$$\therefore \ P = 800 \left(g + \frac{154}{3} \right) \text{ poundals} = 800 \left(1 + \frac{154}{3 \times 32} \right) \text{ lbs. weight}$$

$$= 800 \times \frac{125}{48} \text{ lbs. weight.}$$

When the train is moving at the rate of 30 miles per hour, the work done per second must be $800 \times \dfrac{125}{48} \times 44$ foot-lbs.

Hence, if x be the H.P. of the engine, we have

$$x \times 550 = 800 \times \frac{125}{48} \times 44.$$

$$\therefore \ x = 166\tfrac{2}{3}.$$

Ex. 3. *A train, of mass 100 tons, is ascending uniformly an incline of 1 in 280, and the resistance due to friction, etc. is equal to 16 lbs. per ton; if the engine be of 200 H.P. and be working at full power, find the rate at which the train is going.*

The resistance due to friction, etc. is equal to the weight of 1600 lbs., and the resolved part of the weight of the train down the incline is equal to the weight of $\frac{1}{280}$ of 100 tons, or to the weight of 800 lbs., so that the total force to impede the motion is equal to the weight of 2400 lbs.

Let v be the velocity of the train in feet per second. Then the work done by the engine is that done in dragging a force equal to the weight of 2400 lbs. through v feet per second, and is equivalent to $2400v$ foot-pounds per second.

But the total work which the engine can do is $\dfrac{200 \times 33000}{60}$ or 110,000 foot-pounds per second.

Hence
$$2400v = 110000,$$
or
$$v = \frac{1100}{24},$$

and hence the velocity of the train is $31\tfrac{1}{4}$ miles per hour.

EXAMPLES. XIV.

1. A train, of mass 50 tons, is kept moving at the uniform rate of 30 miles per hour on the level, the resistance of air, friction, etc., being 40 lbs. weight per ton. Find the H.P. of the engine.

2. What is the horse-power of an engine which keeps a train going at the rate of 40 miles per hour against a resistance equal to 2000 lbs. weight?

3. A train, of mass 100 tons, travels at 40 miles per hour up an incline of 1 in 200. Find the H.P. of the engine that will draw the train, neglecting all resistances except that of gravity.

4. A train of mass 200 tons, including the engine, is drawn up an incline of 3 in 500 at the rate of 40 miles per hour by an engine of 600 H.P.; find the resistance per ton due to friction, etc.

5. Find the H.P. of an engine which can travel at the rate of 25 miles per hour up an incline of 1 in 100, the mass of the engine and load being 10 tons, and the resistances due to friction, etc. being 10 lbs. weight per ton.

6. Determine the rate in H.P. at which an engine must be able to work in order to generate a velocity of 20 miles per hour on the level in a train of mass 60 tons in 3 minutes after starting, the resistances to the motion being taken at 10 lbs. per ton, and the acceleration being supposed to be constant.

7. A weight of 10 tons is dragged in half-an-hour through a length of 330 feet up a rough plane inclined at an angle of 30° to the horizon; the coefficient of friction being $\dfrac{1}{\sqrt{3}}$, find the work expended, and the H.P. of an engine by which it will be done.

8. Find the work done by gravity on a stone having a mass of $\frac{1}{2}$ lb. during the tenth second of its fall from rest.

9. A steamer, with engines of 25000 H.P., can be just kept going at the rate of 20 miles per hour. What is the resistance of the water to its motion?

90. Energy. Def. *The Energy of a body is its capacity for doing work and is of two kinds, Kinetic and Potential.*

The **Kinetic Energy** *of a body is the energy which it possesses by virtue of its motion, and is measured by the amount of work that the body can perform against the impressed forces before its velocity is destroyed.*

A falling body, a swinging pendulum, a revolving fly-wheel, and a cannon-ball in motion all possess kinetic energy.

Consider the case of a particle, of mass m, moving with velocity u, and let us find the work done by it before it comes to rest.

Suppose it brought to rest by a constant force P resisting its motion, which produces in it an acceleration $-f$ given by $P = mf$.

Let x be the space described by the particle before it comes to rest, so that $0 = u^2 + 2(-f) \cdot x$;

$$\therefore fx = \tfrac{1}{2}u^2.$$

Hence the kinetic energy of the particle

= work done by it before it comes to rest

$$= Px = mfx = \tfrac{1}{2}mu^2.$$

Hence the kinetic energy of a particle is equal to the product of its mass and one half the square of its velocity.

91. Theorem. *To shew that the change of kinetic energy per unit of space is equal to the acting force.*

If a force P, acting on a particle of mass m, change its velocity from u to v in time t whilst the particle moves through a space s, we have $v^2 - u^2 = 2fs$, where f is the acceleration produced.

$$\therefore \frac{\tfrac{1}{2}mv^2 - \tfrac{1}{2}mu^2}{s} = mf = P \quad \ldots\ldots\ldots(1).$$

This equation proves the proposition when the force is constant.

When the force is variable, the same proof will hold if we take t so small that the force P does not sensibly alter during that interval.

Cor. It follows from equation (1) that the change in the kinetic energy of a particle is equal to the work done on it.

On multiplying the first and third relations of Art. 32 by m, we have

$$m(v-u) = mft = Pt,$$

and
$$\tfrac{1}{2}m(v^2 - u^2) = mfs = Ps.$$

These are often known as the Momentum and Energy Equations respectively. Expressed in words, they state that

$$\text{Change of Momentum} = \text{Force} \times \text{Time},$$

and
$$\text{Change of Kinetic Energy} = \text{Force} \times \text{Space}.$$

92. *The* **Potential Energy** *of a body is the work it can do by means of its position in passing from its present configuration to some standard configuration (usually called its zero position).*

A bent spring has potential energy [as in the case of a watch-spring which, by its uncoiling, keeps a watch going], *viz.* the work it can do in recovering its natural shape.

A body raised to a height above the ground [*e.g.* a clock-weight, when the clock is wound up, a stone at the edge of a precipice, or water stored up in a reservoir] has potential energy, *viz.* the work its weight can do as it falls to the earth's surface, which is usually taken as the zero of potential energy. Compressed air has potential energy, *viz.* the work it can do in expanding to the volume it would occupy in the atmosphere.

93. *A particle of mass m falls from rest at a height h above the ground; to shew that the sum of its potential and kinetic energies is constant throughout the motion.*

Let H be the point from which the particle starts, and O the point where it reaches the ground.

Let v be its velocity when it has fallen through a distance $HP\ (=x)$, so that $v^2 = 2gx$.

Its kinetic energy at $P = \frac{1}{2}mv^2 = mgx$.

Also its potential energy at P

= the work its weight can do as it falls from P to O

$= mg \cdot OP = mg\,(h-x)$.

Hence the sum of its kinetic and potential energies at P

$$= mgh.$$

But its potential energy when at H is mgh, and its kinetic energy there is zero.

Hence the sum of the potential and kinetic energies is the same at P as at H; and, since P is *any* point, it follows that the sum of these two quantities is the same throughout the motion.

As the particle falls to the ground it will be noted that the potential energy which it has when at its highest point (and which was stored up in it as it was lifted into that position) becomes transformed into kinetic energy, and this goes on continually until the particle reaches the ground, when its store of potential energy becomes exhausted.

In the case of a pendulum the potential energy which the bob possesses, when instantaneously at rest in its highest position, becomes converted into kinetic energy as the bob swings down to its lowest position, and is reconverted into potential energy as the bob travels to its next position of instantaneous rest at the end of its swing.

94. The example of the previous article is an extremely simple illustration of the principle of the **Conservation of Energy**, which may be stated as follows:

If a body or system of bodies be in motion under a con-

*servative system of forces, the sum of its kinetic and potential
energies is constant.*

*Forces, of the kind which occur in the material universe,
are said to be conservative when they depend on the position
or configuration* **only** *of the system of bodies, and not on the
velocity or direction of motion of the bodies.*

Thus from a conservative system are excluded forces
of the nature of friction, or forces such as the resistance of
the air which varies as some power of the velocity of the
body. Friction is excluded because, if the direction of
motion of the body be reversed, the direction of the friction
is reversed also.

When the forces are conservative, it is found that the
amount of work required to bring a system from one configuration to another is always the same, and does not
depend on the path pursued by the system during the
alteration of its configuration.

Referring to the case of a particle sliding down a rough
plane of length l (Art. 77), we see that the kinetic energy
of the particle on reaching the ground is

$$\tfrac{1}{2}m\left[2gl\left(\sin a - \mu \cos a\right)\right], \; i.e., \; mgl \sin a - mgl\mu \cos a.$$

Also the potential energy there is zero, so that the sum
of the kinetic and potential energies at the foot of the
plane is

$$mgl \sin a - \mu mgl \cos a.$$

But the potential energy of the particle when at the top
of the plane is $mg \cdot l \sin a$, so that the total loss of visible
mechanical energy of the particle in sliding from the
top to the bottom of the inclined plane is $\mu mgl \cos a$.
This energy has been transformed and appears chiefly in
the form of heat, partly in the moving body, and partly in

the plane; it is ultimately dissipated into the surrounding air.

Other cases of loss of kinetic energy occur in the examples of Art. 86.

In each case the kinetic energy before impact

$$= \frac{1}{2} \cdot 3 \times 13^2 + \frac{1}{2} \cdot 2 \times 3^2 = \frac{507 + 18}{2} = 262\frac{1}{2} \text{ foot-poundals.}$$

In Ex. 1, the kinetic energy after impact

$$= \frac{1}{2} \cdot 5 \cdot 9^2 = \frac{405}{2} = 202\frac{1}{2} \text{ foot-poundals.}$$

In Ex. 2, the kinetic energy after impact

$$= \frac{1}{2} \cdot 5 \times \left(\frac{33}{5}\right)^2 = \frac{1089}{10} = 108 \cdot 9 \text{ foot-poundals.}$$

Hence in the two cases 60 and 153·6 foot-poundals of kinetic energy respectively are lost.

95. Ex. 1. *A bullet, of mass 4 ozs., is fired into a target with a velocity of 1200 feet per second. The mass of the target is 20 lbs. and it is free to move; find the loss of kinetic energy in foot-pounds.*

Let V be the resulting common velocity of the shot and target. Since no momentum is lost (Art. 86) we have

$$\left(20 + \frac{4}{16}\right) V = \frac{4}{16} \times 1200.$$

$$\therefore \quad V = \frac{400}{27}.$$

The original kinetic energy $= \frac{1}{2} \cdot \frac{4}{16} \cdot 1200^2 = 180000$ foot-poundals.

The final kinetic energy $= \frac{1}{2} \left(20 + \frac{4}{16}\right) V^2$

$$= \frac{20000}{9} \text{ foot-poundals.}$$

The energy lost $= 180000 - \frac{20000}{9} = \frac{1600000}{9}$ foot-poundals

$$= \frac{50000}{9} \text{ ft.-lbs.}$$

It will be noted that, in this case, although no momentum is lost by the impact, yet $\frac{80}{81}$ ths of the energy is transformed.

It will be found that, in all cases of impact, kinetic energy is lost or rather transformed.

Ex. 2. *Compare the kinetic energies of the shot and gun in the example of Art.* 87.

The kinetic energy of the shot $= \frac{1}{2} \cdot 400 \times (900)^2$ foot-poundals

$$= \frac{200 \times 900^2}{32} \text{ ft.-lbs.} = \frac{200 \times 900^2}{32 \times 2240} \text{ ft.-tons}$$

$$= 2260 \text{ ft.-tons nearly.}$$

The kinetic energy of the gun

$$= \frac{1}{2} \cdot 50 \times 2240 \times \left(\frac{45}{14}\right)^2 \text{ ft.-poundals}$$

$$= \frac{25}{32} \times \left(\frac{45}{14}\right)^2 \text{ ft.-tons} = 8 \cdot 07 \text{ ft.-tons nearly.}$$

The kinetic energy of the shot is thus 280 times that of the gun, although their momenta are equal.

It is to this great superiority in kinetic energy of the shot that its destructive power is due.

96. When we take into account the energy which has been transformed into heat, sound, light and other forms which modern Physics recognizes as forms of energy, we find that there is no real loss of energy in an isolated system which is left to itself. This doctrine of the indestructibility of energy is the central Principle of Modern Science. It may be expressed thus;

Energy cannot be created nor can it be destroyed, but it may be transformed into any of the forms which it can take.

As a numerical illustration, it may be stated that 778 foot-pounds of work is equivalent to the heat necessary to raise the temperature of 1 lb. of water by 1° Fahrenheit, *i.e.* 778 foot-pounds is the **mechanical equivalent of heat**.

EXAMPLES. XV.

1. A body, of mass 10 lbs., is thrown up vertically with a velocity of 32 feet per second; what is its kinetic energy (1) at the moment of propulsion, (2) after half a second, (3) after one second?

2. Find the kinetic energy measured in foot-pounds of a cannon-ball of mass 25 pounds discharged with a velocity of 200 feet per second.

3. Find the kinetic energy in ergs of a cannon-ball of 10000 grammes discharged with a velocity of 5000 centimetres per second.

4. A cannon-ball, of mass 5000 grammes, is discharged with a velocity of 500 metres per second. Find its kinetic energy in ergs, and, if the cannon be free to move, and have a mass of 100 kilogrammes, find the energy of the recoil.

5. A bullet, of mass 2 ounces, is fired into a target with a velocity of 1280 feet per second. The mass of the target is 10 lbs. and it is free to move; find the loss of kinetic energy by the impact in foot-pounds.

6. Compare (1) the momenta, and (2) the kinetic energies of a bullet of mass 4 ozs. and moving with a velocity of 1200 feet per second, and a cannon-ball of mass 15 lbs. moving with a velocity of 40 feet per second.

Find the uniform forces that would bring each to rest in one second and the distance through which each would move.

97. As a further illustration of the use of the Principles of Momentum and Energy, consider the following examples.

Ex. 1. *A hammer, of mass M lbs., falls from a height of h feet upon the top of a pile, of mass m lbs., and drives it into the ground a distance a feet; find the resistance of the ground, it being assumed to be constant and the pile being supposed inelastic.*

Find also the time during which the pile is in motion, and the kinetic energy lost at the impact.

Let u be the velocity of the hammer on hitting the pile, so that

$$u^2 = 2gh \dots\dots\dots\dots\dots\dots\dots\dots(1).$$

Let v be the velocity of the hammer and pile immediately after the impact. Then the principle of Conservation of Momentum gives

$$(M+m)\,v = Mu \dots\dots\dots\dots\dots\dots\dots(2).$$

If P be the resistance of the ground in poundals, the force to resist the driving of the pile into the ground $= P - (M+m)\,g$.

The Principle of the Conservation of Energy gives

$$\tfrac{1}{2}\,(M+m)\,v^2 = [P - (M+m)\,g]\,.\,a.$$

$$\therefore P = (M+m)\,g + (M+m)\,\frac{v^2}{2a}$$

$$= (M+m)\,g + \frac{M^2}{M+m}\,\frac{u^2}{2a},\ \text{by (2)},$$

$$= (M+m)\,g + \frac{M^2}{M+m}\,g\,\frac{h}{a}.$$

A weight of slightly more than $\dfrac{M^2}{M+m}\,.\,\dfrac{h}{a}$ lbs. placed on the pile would thus slowly overcome the resistance and just drive the pile down.

The principle of Momentum gives the time t during which the pile is in motion. For

$$[P - (M+m)\,g] \times t = \text{change in the momentum}$$
$$= (M+m)\,v = Mu,$$

so that

$$t \times \frac{M^2}{M+m}\,\frac{u^2}{2a} = Mu,$$

and

$$\therefore \; t = \frac{M+m}{M} \cdot \frac{2a}{u} = \frac{M+m}{M}\,a\sqrt{\frac{2}{gh}}.$$

The kinetic energy lost at the impact

$$= \tfrac{1}{2}\,Mu^2 - \tfrac{1}{2}\,(M+m)\,v^2$$
$$= \tfrac{1}{2}\,Mu^2 - \tfrac{1}{2}\,\frac{M^2}{M+m}\,u^2$$
$$= \tfrac{1}{2}\,\frac{Mm}{M+m}\,u^2$$
$$= \frac{m}{M+m} \times \text{energy of the hammer on striking the pile.}$$

The greater that M is compared with m, *i.e.* the greater is the mass of the hammer compared with that of the pile, the less is the fraction of the energy which is destroyed.

Ex. 2. Motion of a bicycle. *A cyclist, whose weight added to that of his machine is 200 lbs., is riding on a level road at the rate of 10 miles an hour; his bicycle is geared up to 70 and the length of the cranks is 7 inches; if the resistance to his motion be 5 lbs. wt. find the downward thrust he must exert on his pedals and the rate at which he works compared with a Horse-Power.*

By saying that a bicycle is "geared up" to 70 inches, we mean that for every revolution of the rider's feet his bicycle advances through a distance equal to the circumference of a wheel of diameter 70 inches, *i.e.* he advances $\pi \cdot 70$ inches.

Let P be the downward thrust, supposed constant, in lbs. wt.

Then in one complete revolution the work done $= 2 \times P \times \frac{14}{12}$ ft.-lbs.

The work done against the resistance to the machine in this time

$$= \pi \cdot \frac{70}{12} \times 5 \text{ ft.-lbs.}$$

Assuming that no work is lost on account of friction, in other words that the bicycle is a theoretically perfect one, we have by equating these works,

$$2 \times P \times \frac{14}{12} = \pi \times \frac{70}{12} \times 5,$$

i.e. $P = \frac{25}{2}\,\pi = 39\tfrac{1}{4}$ lbs. wt. nearly.

The work done by the man per hour $= 5 \times (5280 \times 10)$ foot-pounds.

∴ work done per minute $= 5 \times 88 \times 10$.

∴ rate of working $= \dfrac{5 \times 88 \times 10}{33000}$ H.P. $= \dfrac{2}{15}$ H.P.

If the cyclist were ascending an incline of 1 in 50 at the same rate, find the downward thrust.

For each complete revolution of the pedals he goes forward $\pi . 70$ inches, *i.e.* $\pi . \frac{70}{12}$ ft., and therefore lifts himself and the machine through a vertical distance of $\frac{1}{50} \times \pi . \frac{70}{12}$ ft., and in so doing must perform an extra $\frac{200}{50} \times \pi \times \frac{70}{12}$ ft.-lbs. of work. In this case we then have

$$2 \times P \times \tfrac{14}{12} = \pi . \tfrac{70}{12} \times 5 + \tfrac{200}{50} \times \pi \times \tfrac{70}{12},$$

$$\therefore P = \tfrac{45}{2}\pi = 70\tfrac{3}{4} \text{ lbs. wt. nearly.}$$

EXAMPLES. XVI.

1. A shot of mass m is fired from a gun of mass M with velocity u relative to the gun; shew that the actual velocities of the shot and gun are $\dfrac{Mu}{M+m}$ and $\dfrac{mu}{M+m}$ respectively, and that their kinetic energies are inversely proportional to their masses.

2. A gun is mounted on a gun-carriage movable on a smooth horizontal plane, and the gun is elevated at an angle α to the horizon; a shot is fired and leaves the gun in a direction inclined at an angle θ to the horizon; if the mass of the gun and its carriage be n times that of the shot, shew that $\tan \theta = \left(1 + \dfrac{1}{n}\right) \tan \alpha.$

3. A mass of half a ton, moving with a velocity of 800 feet per second, strikes a fixed target and is brought to rest in a hundredth part of a second. Find the impulse of the blow on the target, and supposing the resistance to be uniform throughout the time taken to bring the body to rest, find the distance through which it penetrates.

4. A mass of 4 cwt. falls from a height of 10 feet upon an inelastic pile of mass 12 cwt.; supposing the mean resistance of the ground to penetration by the pile to be $1\frac{1}{2}$ tons' weight, determine the distance through which the pile is driven at each blow, and the time it takes to travel this distance.

Find also what fraction of the energy is dissipated at each blow.

5. A bullet, of mass 20 grammes, is shot horizontally from a rifle, the barrel of which is one metre long, with a velocity of 200 metres per second into a mass of 50 kilogrammes of wood floating on water. If

the bullet buries itself in the wood without making any splinters or causing it to rotate, find the velocity of the wood immediately after it is struck.

Find also the average force in grammes' weight which is exerted on the bullet by the powder.

6. A hammer, of mass 4 cwt., falls through 4 feet and comes to rest after striking a mass of iron, the duration of the blow being $\frac{1}{50}$th of a second; find the force, supposing it to be uniform, which is exerted by the hammer on the iron.

7. Masses m and $2m$ are connected by a string passing over a smooth pulley; at the end of 3 seconds a mass m is picked up by the ascending body; find the resulting motion.

8. Two equal masses, A and B, are connected by an inelastic thread, 3 feet long, and are laid close together on a smooth horizontal table $3\frac{1}{2}$ feet from its nearest edge; B is also connected by a stretched inelastic thread with an equal mass C hanging over the edge. Find the velocity of the masses when A begins to move and also when B arrives at the edge of the table.

9. Two masses of 5 and 7 lbs. respectively are connected by a string passing over a fixed smooth pulley; at the end of 3 seconds the larger mass impinges on a fixed inelastic horizontal plane; shew that the system will be instantaneously at rest at the end of $2\frac{1}{4}$ seconds more.

10. A string over a pulley supports a mass of 5 lbs. on one side and of 2 and 3 lbs. on the other, the lower mass 2 lbs. being distant 1 foot from the other. The two-pound weight is suddenly raised to the same level as the other and kept from falling. Shew that the string will become taut in half a second, and that the whole system will then move with a uniform velocity of 3·2 ft. per sec.

11. Two equal weights, P and Q, connected by a string passing over a smooth pulley, are moving with a common velocity, P descending and Q ascending. If P be suddenly stopped, and instantly let drop again, find the time that elapses before the string is again tight.

12. A mass M after falling freely through a feet begins to raise a mass m greater than itself and connected with it by means of an inextensible string passing over a fixed pulley. Shew that m will have returned to its original position at the end of time

$$\frac{2M}{m-M}\sqrt{\frac{2a}{g}}.$$

Find also what fraction of the visible energy of M is destroyed at the instant when m is jerked into motion.

13. A light inelastic string passes over a light frictionless pulley and has masses of 12 ozs. and 9 ozs. attached to its ends. On the 9 oz. mass a bar of 7 ozs. is placed which is removed by a fixed ring after it has descended 7 feet from rest. How much further will the 9 oz. mass descend?

If whenever the 9 oz. mass passes up through the ring it carries the bar with it and whenever it passes down through the ring it leaves the bar behind, find the whole time that elapses before the system comes to rest.

14. Two railway carriages are moving side by side with different velocities; what is the ultimate effect of the interchanging of passengers between the carriages?

15. A man of 12 stone ascends a mountain 11000 feet high in 7 hours and the difficulties in his way are equivalent to carrying a weight of 3 stone; one of Watt's horses could pull him up the same height without impediments in 56 minutes; shew that the horse does as much work as 6 such men in the same time.

16. A blacksmith, wielding a 14-lb. sledge, strikes an iron bar 25 times per minute, and brings the sledge to rest upon the bar after each blow. If the velocity of the sledge on striking the iron be 32 feet per second, compare the rate at which he is working with a horse-power.

17. A steam hammer, of mass 20 tons, falls vertically through 5 feet, being pressed downwards by steam pressure equal to the weight of 30 tons; what velocity will it acquire, and how many foot-pounds of work will it do before coming to rest?

18. A train of 150 tons, moving with a velocity of 50 miles per hour, has its steam shut off and the brakes applied, and is stopped in 363 yards. Supposing the resistance to its motion to be uniform, find its value, and find also the mechanical work done by it measured in foot-pounds.

19. A train, of mass 200 tons, is ascending an incline of 1 in 100 at the rate of 30 miles per hour, the resistance of the rails being equal to the weight of 8 lbs. per ton. The steam being shut off, and the brakes applied, the train is stopped in a quarter of a mile. Find the weight of the brake-van, the coefficient of sliding friction of iron on iron being $\frac{1}{6}$.

20. If a bicyclist always works with $\frac{1}{10}$ H.P. and goes 12 miles per hour on the level, shew that the resistance of the road is $3 \cdot 125$ lbs. wt.

If the mass of the machine and its rider be 12 stone, shew that up an incline of 1 in 50 the speed will be reduced to about $5 \cdot 8$ miles per hour.

21. A man can bicycle at the rate of $16\frac{1}{2}$ miles per hour on a smooth road. He exerts a down pressure, equal to 20 lbs. weight, with each foot during the down stroke, and the length of this stroke is 12 inches. If the machine be geared up to 63, find the work he does per minute.

22. A rifle bullet loses $\frac{1}{20}$th of its velocity in passing through a plank; find how many such uniform planks it would pass through before coming to rest, assuming the resistance of the planks to be uniform.

23. A man sculling does E foot-pounds of work, usefully applied, at each stroke. If the total resistance of the water when the boat is moving n miles per hour be R lbs. weight, find the number of strokes he must take per minute to maintain this speed.

24. A bicycle is geared up to 70 inches; the rider works at $\frac{1}{10}$ H.P. and makes 60 revolutions per minute with his feet. Neglecting friction, find the resistance to his motion and the downward thrust on his pedals (supposed constant), if the length of the cranks be $6\frac{3}{4}$ inches.

25. The mass of a rider and his bicycle is 180 lbs.; the machine is running freely down an incline of 1 in 60 at a uniform rate of 8 miles per hour; shew that to go at the same rate up an incline of 1 in 100 he must work at the rate of ·1024 H.P.

26. A horizontal jet delivers 200 pounds of water per minute with a velocity of 10 feet per second against a fixed vertical plate set at right angles to the direction of the jet. What quantity of momentum is destroyed per second and what is the force, in lbs. weight, on the plate?

Find also the rate at which the jet is delivering energy and express it in terms of a horse-power.

27. A hammer, of mass 3 lbs., is used to drive a nail, of mass 2 ozs., into a board, and the hammer when it strikes the nail has a velocity of 8 feet per second. If each blow drives the nail half an inch into the board, find the resistance against which the nail moves, both nail and hammer being treated as inelastic.

Motion of the centre of inertia of a system of particles.

*98. Theorem. *If the velocities at any instant of any number of masses m_1, m_2 ... parallel to any line fixed in space be u_1, u_2, u_3 ..., then the velocity parallel to that line of the centre of inertia of these masses at that instant is*

$$\frac{m_1 u_1 + m_2 u_2 + \dots}{m_1 + m_2 + \dots}.$$

At the instant under consideration let x_1, x_2, x_3... be the distances of the given masses measured along this fixed line from a fixed point in it, and let $\bar{x}$ be the distance of their centre of inertia.

Then (Statics, Art. 111), we have

$$\bar{x} = \frac{m_1 x_1 + m_2 x_2 + \ldots}{m_1 + m_2 + \ldots}.$$

Let x_1', x_2'... be the corresponding distances of these masses at the end of a small time t, and $\bar{x}'$ the corresponding distance of their centre of inertia. Then we have

$$x_1' = x_1 + u_1 t,$$
$$x_2' = x_2 + u_2 t,$$
$$x_3' = x_3 + u_3 t,$$
$$\ldots\ldots\ldots\ldots$$

Also

$$\bar{x}' = \frac{m_1 x_1' + m_2 x_2' + \ldots}{m_1 + m_2 + \ldots},$$

$$\therefore \bar{x}' - \bar{x} = \frac{m_1(x_1' - x_1) + m_2(x_2' - x_2) + \ldots}{m_1 + m_2 + \ldots}$$

$$= \frac{m_1 u_1 t + m_2 u_2 t + \ldots}{m_1 + m_2 + \ldots}.$$

But, if $\bar{u}$ be the velocity of the centre of inertia parallel to the fixed line, we have $\bar{x}' = \bar{x} + \bar{u}t$,

$$\therefore \bar{u} = \frac{\bar{x}' - \bar{x}}{t} = \frac{m_1 u_1 + m_2 u_2 + \ldots}{m_1 + m_2 + \ldots}.$$

Hence the velocity of the centre of inertia of a system of particles in any given direction is equal to the sum of the momenta of the particles in that direction, divided by the sum of the masses of the particles.

Cor. If a system of particles be in motion in a plane, and their velocities and directions of motion are known, we can, by resolving these velocities parallel to two fixed lines and applying the preceding proposition, find the motion of their centre of inertia.

*99.   Theorem.   *If the accelerations at any instant of any number of masses m_1, m_2 ..., parallel to any line fixed in space, be $f_1, f_2, f_3 ...$, then the acceleration of the centre of inertia of these masses parallel to this line is*

$$\frac{m_1 f_1 + m_2 f_2 + \dots}{m_1 + m_2 + \dots}.$$

The proof of this proposition is similar to that of the last article.   We have only to change x_1, u_1, x_1', u_1' into u_1, f_1, u_1', f_1', and make similar changes for the other particles.

Ex. 1.   *Two masses m_1, m_2 are connected by a light string as in Art. 74; find the acceleration of the centre of inertia of the system.*

The acceleration of the mass m_1 is $\dfrac{m_1 - m_2}{m_1 + m_2} g$ vertically downwards, and that of m_2 is the same in the opposite direction.

Here then $f_1 = -f_2 = \dfrac{m_1 - m_2}{m_1 + m_2} g$, so that the acceleration of the centre

of inertia $= \dfrac{m_1 f_1 + m_2 f_2}{m_1 + m_2} = \left(\dfrac{m_1 - m_2}{m_1 + m_2}\right)^2 g$.

Ex. 2.   Two bodies, of masses m and $3m$, are connected by a light string passing over a smooth pulley; shew that during the ensuing motion the acceleration of their centre of inertia is $\dfrac{g}{4}$.

Ex. 3.   Find the velocity of the centre of inertia of two masses of 6 and 4 lbs. which move in parallel lines with velocities of 3 and 8 feet respectively, (1) when they move in the same direction, (2) when they move in opposite directions.

Ans.   (1) 5 feet per second; (2) $1\frac{2}{5}$ feet per second in the direction in which the second body is moving.

Ex. 4.   Two masses, mn and m, start simultaneously from the intersection of two straight lines with velocities v and nv respectively; shew that the path of their centre of inertia is a straight line bisecting the angle between the two given straight lines.

Ex. 5.   Two masses move at a uniform rate along two straight lines which meet and are inclined at a given angle; shew that their centre of inertia describes a straight line with uniform velocity.

CHAPTER VII.

PROJECTILES.

100. In the previous chapters we have considered only motion in straight lines. In the present chapter we shall consider the motion of a particle projected into the air with any direction and velocity. We shall suppose the motion to be within such a moderate distance of the earth's surface, that the acceleration due to gravity may be considered to remain sensibly constant. We shall also neglect the resistance of the air, and consider the motion to be *in vacuo*; for, firstly, the law of resistance of the air to the motion of a particle is not accurately known, and, secondly, even if this law were known, the discussion would require a much larger range of knowledge of pure mathematics than the reader of the present book is supposed to possess.

Def. When a particle is projected into the air, the angle that the direction in which it is projected makes with the horizontal plane through the point of projection is called the **angle of projection**; the path which the particle describes is called its **trajectory**; the distance between the point of projection and the point where the path meets any plane drawn through the point of projection is its **range** on the plane; and the time that elapses before it again meets the horizontal plane through the point of projection is called the **time of flight**.

101. If the earth did not attract a particle to itself, the particle would, if projected into the air, describe a straight line; on account of the attraction of the earth, however, the particle describes a curved line. This curve will be proved in Art. 113 to be always a parabola.

Let P be the point of projection, u the velocity and a the angle of projection; also let PAP' be the path of the particle, A being the highest point, and P' the point where the path again meets the horizontal plane through P.

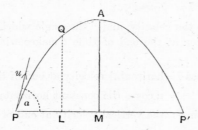

By the principle of the Physical Independence of Forces (Art. 71), the weight of the body only has effect on the motion of the body in the vertical direction; it therefore has no effect on the velocity of the body in the horizontal direction, and this horizontal velocity therefore remains unaltered.

The horizontal and vertical components of the initial velocity of the particle are $u \cos a$ and $u \sin a$ respectively.

The horizontal velocity is, therefore, throughout the motion equal to $u \cos a$.

In the vertical direction the initial velocity is $u \sin a$ and the acceleration is $-g$, [for the acceleration due to gravity is g vertically *downwards*, and we are measuring our positive direction *upwards*]. Hence the vertical motion is the same as that of a particle projected vertically upwards with velocity $u \sin a$, and moving with acceleration $-g$.

The resultant motion of the particle is the same as that of a particle projected with a vertical velocity $u \sin a$ inside a vertical tube of small bore, whilst the tube moves in a horizontal direction with velocity $u \cos a$.

102. *To find the velocity and direction of motion after a given time has elapsed.*

Let v be the velocity, and θ the angle which the direction of motion at the end of time t makes with the horizontal.

Then $v \cos \theta =$ horizontal velocity at end of time t

$= u \cos a$, the constant horizontal velocity.

Also $v \sin \theta =$ the vertical velocity at end of time t

$= u \sin a - gt$.

Hence, by squaring and adding,

$$v^2 = u^2 - 2ugt \sin a + g^2t^2,$$

and, by division, $\quad \tan \theta = \dfrac{u \sin a - gt}{u \cos a}$.

103. *To find the velocity and direction of motion at a given height.*

Let v be the magnitude, and θ the inclination to the horizon, of the velocity of the particle at a given height h. The horizontal and vertical velocities at this point are therefore $v \cos \theta$ and $v \sin \theta$.

Hence

$v \cos \theta = u \cos a$, the constant horizontal velocity...(1).

Also, by Art. 32,

$$v \sin \theta = \sqrt{u^2 \sin^2 \alpha - 2gh} \quad \ldots \ldots \ldots \ldots (2).$$

Squaring and adding (1) and (2), we have

$$v^2 = u^2 - 2gh.$$

Also, by division, $\quad \tan \theta = \dfrac{\sqrt{u^2 \sin^2 \alpha - 2gh}}{u \cos \alpha}.$

104. *To find the greatest height attained by a projectile, and the time that elapses before it is at its greatest height.*

Let A (Fig. Art. 101), be the highest point of the path. The projectile must at A be moving horizontally, and hence the vertical velocity at A must be zero.

Hence, by Art. 32,

$$0 = u^2 \sin^2 \alpha - 2g \cdot MA.$$

$$\therefore MA = \dfrac{u^2 \sin^2 \alpha}{2g},$$

giving the greatest height attained.

Let T be the time from P to A; then T is the time in which a vertical velocity $u \sin \alpha$ is destroyed by gravity.

Hence, by Art. 32, $\quad 0 = u \sin \alpha - gT.$

$$\therefore T = \dfrac{u \sin \alpha}{g},$$

giving the required time.

105. *To find the range on the horizontal plane and the time of flight.*

When the projectile arrives at P' (Fig. Art. 101), the distance it has described in a vertical direction is zero.

Hence, if t be the time of flight, we have by Art. 32 (1),

$$0 = u \sin \alpha t - \tfrac{1}{2} g t^2.$$

$$\therefore t = \dfrac{2u \sin \alpha}{g} = \text{twice the time to the highest point.}$$

During this time t the horizontal velocity remains constant and equal to $u \cos a$.

$$\therefore PP' = \text{horizontal distance described in time } t$$

$$= u \cos a \cdot t = \frac{2u^2 \sin a \cos a}{g}.$$

Hence the range is equal to twice the product of the initial vertical and horizontal velocities divided by g.

106. *For a* **given** *velocity of projection, u, to find the maximum horizontal range, and the corresponding direction of projection.*

If a be the angle of projection, the horizontal range, by the previous article,

$$= \frac{2u^2 \sin a \cos a}{g} = \frac{u^2 \sin 2a}{g}.$$

Also $\sin 2a$ is greatest when $2a = 90°$, that is, when $a = 45°$.

Hence the range on a horizontal plane is greatest when the initial direction of projection is at an angle of $45°$ with the horizontal through the point of projection.

The magnitude of this maximum horizontal range is

$$\frac{u^2}{g} \sin 90°, \; i.e., \; \frac{u^2}{g}.$$

107. *To shew that, with a given velocity of projection, there are for a given horizontal range in general two directions of projection, which are equally inclined to the direction of maximum projection.*

By Art. 105, the range, when the angle of projection is a, is $\dfrac{u^2}{g} \sin 2a$.

Also, when the angle of projection is $\frac{\pi}{2} - a$, the range

$$= \frac{u^2}{g} \sin 2\left(\frac{\pi}{2} - a\right) = \frac{u^2}{g} \sin (\pi - 2a) = \frac{u^2}{g} \sin 2a.$$

Hence we have the same horizontal range for the angles of projection a and $\frac{\pi}{2} - a$.

These directions are equally inclined to the horizon and the vertical respectively, and are therefore equally inclined to the direction of maximum range, which bisects the angle between the horizontal and the vertical.

108. Ex. 1. *A bullet is projected, with a velocity of 640 feet per second, at an angle of 30° with the horizontal; find* (1) *the greatest height attained,* (2) *the range on a horizontal plane and the time of flight, and* (3) *the velocity and direction of motion of the bullet when it is at a height of 576 feet.*

The initial horizontal velocity

$$= 640 \cos 30° = 640 \times \frac{\sqrt{3}}{2} = 320\sqrt{3} \text{ feet per second.}$$

The initial vertical velocity $= 640 \sin 30° = 320$ feet per second.

(1) If h be the greatest height attained, then h is the distance through which a particle, starting with velocity 320 and moving with acceleration $- g$, goes before it comes to rest.

$$\therefore \quad 0 = 320^2 - 2gh;$$

$$\therefore \quad h = \frac{320^2}{2 \times 32} = 1600 \text{ feet.}$$

(2) If t be the time of flight, the vertical distance described in time t is zero.

$$\therefore \quad 0 = 320t - \tfrac{1}{2}gt^2;$$

$$\therefore \quad t = \frac{640}{g} = 20 \text{ seconds.}$$

The horizontal range = the distance described in 20 seconds by a particle moving with a constant velocity of $320\sqrt{3}$ ft. per sec.

$$= 20 \times 320\sqrt{3} = 11085 \text{ feet approximately.}$$

(3) If v be the velocity, and θ the inclination to the horizon, at a height of 576 feet, we have

$$v^2 \sin^2 \theta = 320^2 - 2g \cdot 576 = 32^2 \times 64,$$

and

$$v^2 \cos^2 \theta = (320\sqrt{3})^2 = 32^2 \times 300.$$

Hence, by addition, we have $v = 32 \times \sqrt{364} = 610 \cdot 5$ ft. per sec.

Also, by division,

$$\tan \theta = \sqrt{\frac{16}{75}} = \frac{4\sqrt{3}}{15} = \cdot 46188,$$

so that, from the table of natural tangents, we have $\theta = 24° \ 47'$ approximately.

Ex. 2. *A cricket ball is thrown with a velocity of 96 feet per second; find the greatest range on the horizontal plane, and the two directions in which the ball may be thrown so as to give a range of 144 feet.*

If the angle of projection be α, the range, by Art. 105,

$$= \frac{2 \cdot 96^2 \cdot \sin \alpha \cos \alpha}{g} = \frac{96^2 \cdot \sin 2\alpha}{g}.$$

The maximum range is obtained when $\alpha = 45°$, and therefore

$$= \frac{96^2}{32} = 288 \text{ feet} = 96 \text{ yards.}$$

When the range is 144 feet, the angle α is given by

$$\frac{96^2}{g} \sin 2\alpha = 144.$$

$$\therefore \ \sin 2\alpha = \frac{144 \times 32}{96^2} = \frac{144}{3 \times 96} = \frac{1}{2}.$$

$$\therefore \ 2\alpha = 30°, \text{ or } 150°.$$

$$\therefore \ \alpha = 15°, \text{ or } 75°.$$

Ex. 3. *A cannon ball is projected horizontally from the top of a tower, 49 feet high, with a velocity of 200 feet per second. Find*

(1) *the time of flight,*

(2) *the distance from the foot of the tower of the point at which it hits the ground, and*

(3) *its velocity when it hits the ground.*

(1) The initial vertical velocity of the ball is zero, and hence t, the time of flight, is the time in which a body, falling freely under gravity, would describe 49 feet.

Hence

$$49 = \tfrac{1}{2}g \cdot t^2 = 16t^2.$$

$$\therefore \ t = \tfrac{7}{4} \text{ second.}$$

(2) During this time the horizontal velocity is constant, and therefore the required distance from the foot of the tower

$$= 200 \times \tfrac{7}{4} = 350 \text{ feet.}$$

(3)   The vertical velocity at the end of $\frac{7}{4}$ second $=\frac{7}{4}\times 32=56$ feet per second, and the horizontal velocity is 200 feet per second;

∴   the required velocity $=\sqrt{200^2+56^2}=8\sqrt{674}=207\cdot 7$ feet nearly.

Ex. 4.   *From the top of a cliff, 80 feet high, a stone is thrown so that it starts with a velocity of 128 feet per second, at an angle of 30° with the horizon; find where it hits the ground at the bottom of the cliff.*

The initial vertical velocity is 128 sin 30°, or 64, feet per second, and the initial horizontal velocity is 128 cos 30°, or $64\sqrt{3}$, feet per second.

Let T be the time that elapses before the stone hits the ground.

Then T is the time in which a stone, projected with vertical velocity 64 and moving with acceleration $-g$, describes a distance -80 feet.

$$\therefore \; -80=64T-\tfrac{1}{2}gT^2.$$

Hence $T=5$ seconds.

During this time the horizontal velocity remains unaltered, and hence the distance of the point, where the stone hits the ground, from the foot of the cliff $=320\sqrt{3}=$ about 554 feet.

EXAMPLES.   XVII.

1.   A particle is projected at an angle a to the horizon with a velocity of u feet per second; find the greatest height attained, the time of flight, and the range on a horizontal plane, when

(1) $u=64,$ $a=30°$;

(2) $u=80,$ $a=60°$;

(3) $u=96,$ $a=75°$;

(4) $u=200,$ $a=\sin^{-1}\frac{3}{5}$.

2.   Find the greatest range on a horizontal plane when the velocity of projection is (1) 48, (2) 60, (3) 100 feet per second.

3.   A shot leaves a gun at the rate of 160 metres per second; calculate the greatest distance to which it could be projected, and the height to which it would rise.

4.   If a man can throw a stone 80 metres, how long is it in the air, and to what height does it rise?

5.   A body is projected with a velocity of 80 ft. per sec. in a direction making an angle $\tan^{-1}3$ with the horizon; shew that it rises to a vertical height of 90 feet, that its direction of motion is inclined to the horizon at an angle of 60° when its vertical height above the ground is 60 feet, and that its time of flight is about $4\frac{3}{4}$ secs.

6. A projectile is fired horizontally from a height of 9 feet from the ground, and reaches the ground at a horizontal distance of 1000 feet. Find its initial velocity.

7. A stone is thrown horizontally, with velocity $\sqrt{2gh}$, from the top of a tower of height h. Find where it will strike the level ground through the foot of the tower. What will be its striking velocity?

8. A stone is dropped from a height of 9 feet above the floor of a railway carriage which is travelling at the rate of 30 miles per hour. Find the velocity and direction of the particle in space at the instant when it meets the floor of the carriage.

9. A ship is moving with a velocity of 16 feet per second, and a body is allowed to fall from the top of its mast, which is 144 feet high; find the velocity and direction of motion of the body, (1) at the end of two seconds, (2) when it hits the deck.

10. A shot is fired from a gun on the top of a cliff, 400 feet high, with a velocity of 768 feet per second, at an elevation of 30°. Find the horizontal distance from the vertical line through the gun of the point where the shot strikes the water.

11. From the top of a vertical tower, whose height is $\frac{13}{2}g$ feet, a particle is projected, the vertical and horizontal components of its initial velocity being $6g$ and $8g$ respectively; find the time of flight, and the distance from the foot of the tower of the point at which it strikes the ground.

12. A gun is aimed so that the shot strikes horizontally the top of the spire of Strasburg Cathedral, which is 141 metres high; shew that, if the angle of projection be $\cot^{-1} 5$, then the velocity of projection is nearly 268 metres per second.

13. Find the velocity and direction of projection of a shot which passes in a horizontal direction just over the top of a wall which is 50 yards off and 75 feet high.

14. A particle is projected at an angle of elevation $\sin^{-1} \frac{4}{5}$, and its range on the horizontal plane is 4 miles; find the velocity of projection, and the velocity at the highest point of its path.

15. Two balls are projected from the same point in directions inclined at 60° and 30° to the horizontal; if they attain the same height, what is the ratio of their velocities of projection?

What is this ratio if they have the same horizontal range?

16. The velocity of a particle when at its greatest height is $\sqrt{\frac{2}{5}}$ of its velocity when at half its greatest height; shew that the angle of projection is 60°.

17. Find the angle of projection when the range on a horizontal plane is (1) 4, (2) $4\sqrt{3}$ times the greatest height attained.

18. Find the angle of projection when the range is equal to the distance through which the particle would have to fall in order to acquire a velocity equal to its velocity of projection.

109. Range on an inclined plane. *From a point
on a plane, which is inclined at an angle β to the horizon,
a particle is projected with a velocity u, at an angle α with
the horizontal, in a plane passing through the normal to
the inclined plane and the line of greatest slope; to find
the range on the inclined plane.*

Let PQ be the range on the inclined plane, PT the

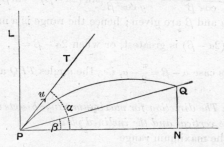

direction of projection, and QN the perpendicular on the
horizontal plane through P.

The initial component of the velocity perpendicular to
PQ is $u \sin (\alpha - \beta)$, and the acceleration in this direction
is $- g \cos \beta$.

Let T be the time which the particle takes to go from
P to Q. Then in time T the space described in a direction
perpendicular to PQ is zero.

Hence $0 = u \sin (\alpha - \beta) . T - \frac{1}{2} g \cos \beta . T^2$, and therefore

$$T = \frac{2u}{g} \frac{\sin (\alpha - \beta)}{\cos \beta}.$$

During this time the horizontal velocity $u \cos \alpha$ remains
unaltered; hence $PN = u \cos \alpha . T$, so that the range

$$PQ = \frac{PN}{\cos \beta} = \frac{u \cos \alpha}{\cos \beta} . T = \frac{2u^2}{g} \frac{\cos \alpha \sin (\alpha - \beta)}{\cos^2 \beta}.$$

110. Maximum range. *To find the direction of projection which gives the maximum range on the inclined plane, and to shew that for any given range there are two directions of projection, which are equally inclined to the direction for maximum range.*

From the preceding article the range

$$= \frac{2u^2}{g} \frac{\cos\alpha \sin(\alpha - \beta)}{\cos^2\beta} = \frac{u^2}{g\cos^2\beta} \{\sin(2\alpha - \beta) - \sin\beta\} \ldots (i).$$

Now u and β are given; hence the range is a maximum when $\sin(2\alpha - \beta)$ is greatest, or when $2\alpha - \beta = \dfrac{\pi}{2}$.

In this case $\alpha - \beta = \dfrac{\pi}{2} - \alpha$, i.e., the angles TPQ and LPT are equal.

Hence *The direction for maximum range bisects the angle between the vertical and the inclined plane.*

Also the maximum range

$$= \frac{u^2}{g\cos^2\beta}(1 - \sin\beta) = \frac{u^2}{g(1 + \sin\beta)}.$$

Again, the range with an angle of elevation α_1 is, by (i), the same as that with elevation α, if

$$\sin(2\alpha_1 - \beta) = \sin(2\alpha - \beta),$$

i.e., if $\qquad 2\alpha_1 - \beta = \pi - (2\alpha - \beta),$

i.e., if $\qquad \alpha_1 = \dfrac{\pi}{2} + \beta - \alpha,$

i.e., if $\qquad \alpha_1 - \left(\dfrac{\pi}{4} + \dfrac{\beta}{2}\right) = \left(\dfrac{\pi}{4} + \dfrac{\beta}{2}\right) - \alpha.$

But $\dfrac{\pi}{4} + \dfrac{\beta}{2}$ is the elevation which gives the greatest range.

Hence for any **given** range on an inclined plane there are two angles of projection, the two corresponding directions of projection being equally inclined to that for the maximum range on the plane.

111. Ex. 1. *From the foot of an inclined plane, whose rise is 7 in 25, a shot is projected with a velocity of 600 feet per second at an angle of 30° with the horizontal, (1) up the plane, (2) down the plane. Find the range in each case.*

Let β be the inclination of the plane, so that

$$\sin \beta = \frac{7}{25} \quad \text{and} \quad \cos \beta = \frac{24}{25}.$$

(1) By Art. 109, the range in the first case

$$= 2 \frac{600^2}{32} \frac{\cos 30° \sin (30° - \beta)}{\cos^2 \beta} = \frac{600^2}{16} \times \frac{\frac{\sqrt{3}}{2} \left(\frac{1}{2} \cdot \frac{24}{25} - \frac{\sqrt{3}}{2} \cdot \frac{7}{25} \right)}{\frac{24^2}{25^2}}$$

$$= \frac{360000}{16} \times \frac{25\sqrt{3} \, (24 - 7\sqrt{3})}{4 \times 576} = \frac{750000}{1024} \, (8\sqrt{3} - 7)$$

$$= 5022 \text{ feet approximately.}$$

(2) The initial velocity perpendicular to the inclined plane is $u \sin (30° + \beta)$ and the acceleration is $- g \cos \beta$. Hence the time of flight, T, is $2 \dfrac{u}{g} \dfrac{\sin (30° + \beta)}{\cos \beta}$. Hence, as in Art. 109, if R_1 be the range, we have

$$R_1 \cos \beta = u \cos 30°. \, T.$$

$$\therefore R_1 = 2 \frac{u^2}{g} \frac{\cos 30° \sin (30° + \beta)}{\cos^2 \beta} = \frac{750000}{1024} \, (8\sqrt{3} + 7), \text{ as in (i),}$$

$$= 15275 \text{ feet approx.}$$

N.B. The range *down* an inclined plane may also be obtained from the formula of Art. 109, by changing β into $- \beta$, so that it is

$$\frac{2u^2}{g} \frac{\cos \alpha \sin (\alpha + \beta)}{\cos^2 \beta}.$$

Ex. 2. *In the previous example, find the greatest range.*

The angle of projection α must

$$= \frac{1}{2} \left(\frac{\pi}{2} + \beta \right) = \frac{\pi}{4} + \frac{\beta}{2}.$$

The range now $= \dfrac{u^2}{g \cos^2 \beta} (1 - \sin \beta)$

$$= \frac{u^2}{g} \frac{1}{1 + \sin \beta} = \frac{600^2}{32} \frac{1}{1 + \dfrac{7}{25}}$$

$$= \frac{360000 \times 25}{32 \times 32} = 8789 \text{ ft. approx.}$$

Similarly the greatest range down the inclined plane would be found to be $\dfrac{600^2}{32} \dfrac{1}{1 - \dfrac{7}{25}}$, *i.e.*, 15625 feet.

Ex. 3. *A particle is projected at an angle* α *with the horizontal from the foot of a plane, whose inclination to the horizon is* β; *shew that it will strike the plane at right angles, if* cot β = 2 tan (α − β).

Let u be the velocity of projection, so that $u \cos (\alpha - \beta)$ and $u \sin (\alpha - \beta)$ are the initial velocities respectively parallel and perpendicular to the inclined plane.

The accelerations in these two directions are $- g \sin \beta$ and $- g \cos \beta$.

Then, as in Art. 109, the time, T, that elapses before the particle reaches the plane again is $\dfrac{2u \sin (\alpha - \beta)}{g \cos \beta}$.

If the direction of motion at the instant when the particle hits the plane be perpendicular to the plane, then the velocity at that instant parallel to the plane must be zero.

Hence
$$u \cos (\alpha - \beta) - g \sin \beta . T = 0.$$
$$\therefore \quad \frac{u \cos (\alpha - \beta)}{g \sin \beta} = T = \frac{2u \sin (\alpha - \beta)}{g \cos \beta},$$
$$\therefore \quad \cot \beta = 2 \tan (\alpha - \beta).$$

112. Motion upon an inclined plane. *A particle moves upon a smooth plane which is inclined at an angle* β *to the horizon, being projected from a point in the plane with velocity* u *in a direction inclined at an angle* α *to the intersection of the inclined plane with a horizontal plane; to find the motion.*

Resolve the acceleration due to gravity into two components; one, $g \sin \beta$, in the direction of the line of greatest slope, and the other, $g \cos \beta$, perpendicular to the inclined plane. The latter acceleration is destroyed by the reaction of the plane.

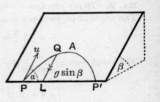

The particle therefore moves upon the inclined plane with an acceleration $g \sin \beta$ parallel to the line of greatest slope.

Hence the investigation of the motion is the same as that in Arts. 101—107, if we substitute "$g \sin \beta$" for

"g", and instead of "vertical distances" read "distances measured on the inclined plane parallel to the line of greatest slope."

EXAMPLES. XVIII.

1. A plane is inclined at 30° to the horizon; from its foot a particle is projected with a velocity of 600 feet per second in a direction inclined at an angle of 60° to the horizon; find the range on the inclined plane and the time of flight.

2. A particle is projected with velocity V, at an angle of 75° to the horizon, from the foot of a plane whose inclination is 30°. Find where it will strike the plane. Find also the maximum range of the particle on the inclined plane.

3. A particle is projected with velocity 64 feet per second at an angle of 45° with the horizon; find its range on a plane inclined at 30° to the horizontal and its time of flight. Find also its greatest range on the inclined plane with the given initial velocity.

4. A particle is projected with a velocity of 1280 feet per second at an angle of 45° with the horizontal; find its range on a plane inclined to the horizon at an angle $\sin^{-1}\frac{3}{5}$, when projected (i) up, (ii) down, the plane.

5. The velocity of projection of a rifle ball is 800 feet per second. Find its greatest range and the corresponding time of flight on planes inclined to the horizon at angles of

    (1) 45°,   (2) 60°,   (3) $\sin^{-1}\frac{1}{20}$,   (4) $\sin^{-1}\frac{5}{13}$.

6. The greatest range of a particle, projected with a certain velocity, on a horizontal plane is 5000 yards; find its greatest range on an inclined plane whose inclination is 45°.

Find also the greatest range when the particle is projected down the inclined plane.

7. The greatest range, with a given velocity of projection, on a horizontal plane is 1000 metres; shew that the greatest ranges up and down a plane inclined at 30° to the horizon are respectively $666\frac{2}{3}$ and 2000 metres.

8. From a point on a plane inclined at (1) 30°, (2) 60°, to the horizon a particle is projected at right angles to the plane with a velocity of 25 metres per second; find the range on the plane in the two cases.

*113.   *A particle is projected into the air with a given velocity and direction of projection; to shew that its path is a parabola.*

As in Art. 101, let u be the velocity and a the angle of projection, PP' the horizontal range, A the highest point and AM the perpendicular on PP'.   Then, by Art. 104,

$$AM = \frac{u^2 \sin^2 a}{2g} \quad \dots\dots\dots\dots\dots\dots\dots (1).$$

Also $PM =$ horizontal distance described in time $\dfrac{u \sin a}{g}$

$$= \frac{u^2 \sin a \cos a}{g} \quad \dots\dots\dots\dots\dots\dots\dots (2).$$

Let Q be any point on the path, and let QN and QL be the perpendiculars on AM and PP' respectively.   Let t be the time from P to Q.

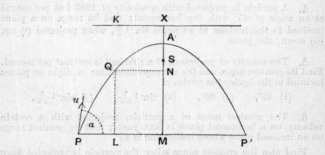

Then $QL =$ vertical distance described in time t

$$= u \sin a \cdot t - \tfrac{1}{2}gt^2 \quad \dots\dots\dots\dots\dots\dots\dots (3),$$

and $\qquad PL = u \cos a \cdot t \quad \dots\dots\dots\dots\dots\dots\dots\dots (4).$

Hence from (1) and (3),

$$AN = AM - NM = AM - QL$$

$$= \frac{u^2 \sin^2 a}{2g} - (u \sin a \cdot t - \tfrac{1}{2}gt^2) = \frac{g}{2}\left(\frac{u \sin a}{g} - t\right)^2.$$

Also, from (2) and (4),

$$QN = PM - PL = \frac{u^2 \sin a \cos a}{g} - u \cos a \cdot t$$

$$= u \cos a \left(\frac{u \sin a}{g} - t \right).$$

$$\therefore \ QN^2 = u^2 \cos^2 a \left(\frac{u \sin a}{g} - t \right)^2 = u^2 \cos^2 a \cdot \frac{2AN}{g}$$

$$= \frac{2u^2 \cos^2 a}{g} \cdot AN.$$

Measure AS vertically downwards and equal to $\dfrac{u^2 \cos^2 a}{2g}$.

$$\therefore \ QN^2 = 4AS \cdot AN.$$

But this is the fundamental property of the curve known as a parabola.

Hence Q lies on a parabola whose axis is vertical, whose vertex is at A, and whose latus rectum

$$= 4AS = \frac{2u^2 \cos^2 a}{g}.$$

Cor. I. It will be noted that the latus rectum, and therefore the *size*, of the parabola depends only on the initial horizontal velocity and is independent of the initial vertical velocity.

Cor. II. The height of the focus S above the horizontal line through $P = SM = AM - AS$

$$= \frac{u^2 \sin^2 a}{2g} - \frac{u^2 \cos^2 a}{2g} = -\frac{u^2}{2g} \cos 2a.$$

Hence, if a be less than $45°$, this distance is negative and the focus of the path is then situated *below* the horizontal line drawn through the point of projection.

*114. *To shew that the velocity at any point is equal in magnitude to that which would be acquired by a particle in falling freely through the height from the directrix to the point.*

In the figure of Art. 113, produce MA to X, making AX equal to AS, and draw XK horizontal. Then XK is the directrix.

If v be the velocity at Q, we have, by Art. 102,

$$v^2 = (u \sin a - gt)^2 + (u \cos a)^2$$
$$= u^2 - 2ug \sin a \cdot t + g^2 t^2$$
$$= 2g \left[\frac{u^2}{2g} - (u \sin a \cdot t - \tfrac{1}{2} gt^2) \right].$$

But $MX = MA + AX = \dfrac{u^2 \sin^2 a}{2g} + \dfrac{u^2 \cos^2 a}{2g} = \dfrac{u^2}{2g}$,

and

$$MN = QL = u \sin a \cdot t - \tfrac{1}{2} gt^2.$$

$$\therefore v^2 = 2g [MX - MN] = 2g \cdot NX.$$

Hence v is equal to the velocity that would be acquired in falling through the vertical distance from the directrix to the point Q.

115. Experimental Proof *that the path of a projectile is a parabola.*

Let AC be a curved board with a groove in it down which a small ball will run when released. Fix it firmly in front of a vertical black-board. Mark a point C on the groove, and let the ball always start from the same point C, and after running down the groove to A describe a path freely in the air just in front of the blackboard.

Fix to the board a number of small paper or cardboard hoops, so that the ball just passes through them; the hoops are adjusted by trial. After letting the ball run down the groove two or three times the position of the first hoop is ascertained; and then after similar experiments the positions of the rest of the hoops are found.

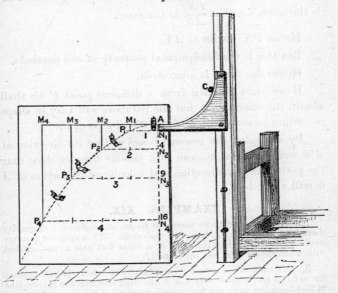

The ball must always be started very carefully from the same point C.

Draw a curve $AP_1P_2P_3\ldots$ passing through the centres of the hoops. This will be easily done by freehand drawing if a good many hoops are fixed in their proper positions.

Draw vertical lines P_1M_1, P_2M_2, $P_3M_3\ldots$ to meet in M_1, M_2, $\ldots$ the horizontal line through A.

Measure off the distances AM_1, AM_2, $\ldots$ and P_1M_1, P_2M_2, $\ldots$.

Then on taking the squares of AM_1, AM_2, AM_3, $\ldots$ and dividing them respectively by P_1M_1, P_2M_2, $\ldots$ we shall find that the results obtained are very approximately the same.

Hence for *any* point P on the curve we find that $\dfrac{AM^2}{PM}$ is the same, *i.e.* that $\dfrac{PN^2}{AN}$ is the same.

Hence PN^2 varies as AN.

But this is the fundamental property of the parabola.

Hence the curve is a parabola.

If we start the ball from a different point C we shall obtain the same result, but the parabola will vary in shape according to the position of the starting-point C.

By arranging the grooved board so that its direction at A is not horizontal, we can in a similar manner shew that the path with any direction and velocity of projection at A is still a parabola.

EXAMPLES. XIX.

1. On the moon there seems to be no atmosphere, and gravity there is about one-sixth of that on the earth. What space of country would be commanded by the guns of a lunar fort able to project shot with a velocity of 1600 feet per second?

2. A tennis-ball is served from a height of 8 feet; it just touches the net at a point where it is 3 ft. 3 ins. high and hits the service-line 21 feet from the net; the horizontal distance of the server from the foot of the net being 39 feet, shew that the horizontal velocity of the ball is about 171 feet per second and find the angle of projection.

3. A plane, of length 6 feet, is inclined at an angle of 30° to the horizon, and a particle is projected straight up the plane with a velocity of 16 feet per second; find the greatest height attained by the particle after leaving the plane, and the range on a horizontal plane passing through the foot of the inclined plane.

4. If a stone be hurled from a sling which has been swung in a horizontal circle of 3 feet radius, at a height of 6 feet from the ground, and at the steady rate of 21 revolutions in 2 seconds, find the range on the ground.

5. Two guns are pointed at each other, one upwards at the angle of elevation 30°, and the other downwards at the same angle of depression, the muzzles being 100 feet apart. If the charges leave the guns with velocities 1100 and 900 feet per second respectively, find when and where they will meet.

6. A projectile, aimed at a mark which is in the horizontal plane through the point of projection, falls a ft. short of it when the elevation is α, and goes b ft. too far when the elevation is β. Shew that, if the velocity of projection be the same in all cases, the proper elevation is

$$\frac{1}{2}\sin^{-1}\frac{a\sin 2\beta + b\sin 2\alpha}{a+b}.$$

7. A hill is inclined at an angle of 30° to the horizon; from a point on the hill one projectile is projected up the hill and another down, both starting with the same velocity; the angle of projection in each case is 45° with the horizon; shew that the range of one projectile is nearly $3\frac{3}{4}$ that of the other.

8. A particle is projected from a point on an inclined plane in a direction making an angle of 60° with the horizon; if the range on the plane be equal to the distance through which another particle would fall from rest during the time of flight of the first particle, find the inclination of the plane to the horizon.

9. From a point in a given inclined plane two bodies are projected with the same velocity in the same vertical plane at right angles to one another; shew that the difference of their ranges is constant.

10. The angular elevation of an enemy's position on a hill h feet high is β; shew that, in order to shell it, the initial velocity of the projectile must not be less than $\sqrt{gh\,(1+\operatorname{cosec}\beta)}$.

11. Shew that the greatest range on an inclined plane passing through the point of projection is equal to the distance through which the particle would fall freely during the corresponding time of flight.

12. A particle, projected with velocity u, strikes at right angles a plane through the point of projection inclined at an angle β to the horizon. Shew that the height of the point struck above the horizontal plane through the point of projection is $\dfrac{2u^2}{g}\dfrac{\sin^2\beta}{1+3\sin^2\beta}$, that the time of flight is $\dfrac{2u}{g\sqrt{1+3\sin^2\beta}}$, and that the range on a horizontal plane through the point of projection would be

$$\frac{u^2\sin 2\beta}{g}\frac{1+\sin^2\beta}{1+3\sin^2\beta}.$$

13. Shew that four times the square of the number of seconds in the time of flight in the range on a horizontal plane equals the height in feet of the highest point of the trajectory.

14. If the maximum height of a projectile above a horizontal plane passing through the point of projection be h, and α be the angle of projection, find the interval between the instants at which the height of the projectile is $h \sin^2 \alpha$.

15. Find the direction in which a rifle must be pointed so that the bullet may strike a body let fall from a balloon at the instant of firing; find also the point where the bullet meets the body, supposing the balloon to be 220 yards high, the angle of its elevation from the position of the rifleman to be 30°, and the velocity of projection of the bullet to be 1320 feet per second. [The balloon is at rest.]

16. Two particles are projected simultaneously, one with velocity V up a smooth plane inclined at an angle of 30° to the horizon, and the other with a velocity $\dfrac{2V}{\sqrt{3}}$ at an elevation of 60°. Shew that the particles will be relatively at rest at the end of $\dfrac{2V}{3g}$ seconds from the instant of projection.

17. The radii of the front and hind wheels of a carriage are a and b, and c is the distance between the axle-trees; a particle of dust driven from the highest point of the hind wheel is observed to alight on the highest point of the front wheel. Shew that the velocity of the carriage is

$$\sqrt{\frac{(c+b-a)\,(c+a-b)}{4\,(b-a)}}\,g.$$

18. Find the charge of powder required to send a 68 lb. shot, with an elevation of 15°, to a range of 3000 yards, given that the velocity communicated to the same shot by a charge of 10 lbs. is 1600 feet per second, and assuming that the kinetic energy of the shot is proportional to the magnitude of the charge.

19. A body, of mass 2 lbs., is projected with a velocity of 20 feet per second at an angle of 60° to the horizon; another body, of mass 3 lbs., is at the same time projected from the same point with a velocity of 40 feet per second at an angle of 30° to the horizon. Find to two places of decimals the height to which their common centre of gravity rises, and the distance of the point at which it meets the horizontal plane through the point of projection.

---

20. A train is travelling at the rate of 45 miles per hour, and a passenger throws up a ball vertically with an initial velocity of 12 feet per second; find the latus rectum of the path which it describes. If the ball be projected with the same velocity at 60° to the horizontal (1) in the same direction, (2) in the opposite direction, with the motion of the train, find the latus rectum in each case.

21. In a trajectory find the time that elapses before the particle is at the end of the latus rectum.

22. A particle is projected so as to enter in the direction of its length a small straight tube of small bore fixed at an angle of 45° to the horizon and to pass out at the other end of the tube; shew that the latera recta of the paths which the particle describes before entering and leaving the tube differ by $\sqrt{2}$ times the length of the tube.

23. A particle is projected horizontally from the top of a tower, 100 feet high, and the focus of the parabola which it describes is in the horizontal plane through the foot of the tower; find the velocity of projection.

24. A particle is projected with velocity $2\sqrt{ag}$ so that it just clears two walls, of equal height a, which are at a distance $2a$ from each other. Shew that the latus rectum of the path is $2a$, and that the time of passing between the walls is $2\sqrt{\dfrac{a}{g}}$.

25. Shew that the locus of the foci of all trajectories which pass through two given points is a hyperbola.

26. If t be the time in which a projectile reaches a point P of its path, and t' be the time from P till it strikes the horizontal plane through the point of projection, shew that the height of P above the plane is $\frac{1}{2}gtt'$.

27. If at any point of a parabolic path the velocity be u and the inclination to the horizon be θ, shew that the particle is moving at right angles to its former direction after a time $\dfrac{u}{g\sin\theta}$.

CHAPTER VIII.

COLLISION OF ELASTIC BODIES.

116. If a man allow a glass ball to drop from his hand upon a marble floor it rebounds to a considerable height, almost as high as his hand; if the same ball be allowed to fall upon a wooden floor, it rebounds through a much smaller distance.

If we allow an ivory billiard ball and a glass ball to drop from the same height, the distances through which they rebound will be different.

If again we drop a leaden ball upon the same floors, the distances through which it rebounds are much smaller than in either of the former cases.

Now the velocities of these bodies are the same on first touching the floor; but, since they rebound through different heights, their velocities on leaving the floor must be different.

The property of the bodies which causes these differences in their velocities after leaving the floor is called their **Elasticity.**

In the present chapter we shall consider some simple cases of the impact of elastic bodies. We can only discuss the cases of particles in collision with particles or planes, and of smooth homogeneous spheres in collision with smooth planes or smooth spheres.

117. Def. Two bodies are said to *impinge directly* when the direction of motion of each is along the common normal at the point at which they touch.

They are said to *impinge obliquely* when the direction of motion of either, or both, is not along the common normal at the point of contact.

The direction of this common normal is called the *line of impact*.

In the case of two spheres the common normal is the line joining their centres.

118. Newton's Experimental Law. Newton found, by experiment, that, if two bodies impinge directly, their relative velocity after impact is in a constant ratio to their relative velocity before impact, and is in the opposite direction. [The experiment is described in Art. 151.]

If the bodies impinge obliquely, their relative velocity resolved along their common normal after impact is in a constant ratio to their relative velocity before impact resolved in the same direction, and is of opposite sign.

This constant ratio depends on the substances of which the bodies are made, and is independent of the masses of the bodies. It is generally denoted by e and is called the Modulus or Coefficient of Elasticity, Restitution, or Resilience. Either of the two latter terms is better than the first.

If u and u' be the component velocities of two bodies before impact along their common normal (as in the figure of Art. 122), and v and v' the component velocities of the bodies *in the same direction* after impact, the law states that

$$v - v' = -e(u - u') \quad\ldots\ldots\ldots\ldots\ldots(1).$$

This experimental law may also be expressed in the form

Velocity of Separation $= e$ times the Velocity of Approach, these two velocities being measured in the direction of the common normal at the point of impact.

Thus in the case of Art. 122 the left-hand sphere caught up the right-hand sphere and the velocity of approach was $u - u'$; also after the impact the right-hand sphere must move away from the other, and the velocity of separation is $v' - v$; this second form of enunciation of the law therefore gives

$$v' - v = e(u - u'),$$

which is the same as (1).

The value of e has widely different values for different bodies; for two glass balls e is ·94; for two ivory ones it is ·81; for two of cork it is ·65; for two of cast-iron about ·66; whilst for two balls of lead it is about ·20, and for two balls, one of lead and the other of iron, the value is ·13.

Bodies for which the coefficient of restitution is zero are said to be "inelastic"; whilst "perfectly elastic" bodies are those for which the coefficient is unity. Probably there are no bodies in nature coming strictly under either of these headings; approximate examples of the former class are such bodies as putty or dough, whilst probably the nearest approach to the latter class is in the case of glass balls.

More careful experiments have shewn that the ratio of the relative velocities before and after impact is not absolutely constant, but that it decreases very slightly for very large velocities of approach of the bodies. In any case, however, the law is only an approximate one, and cannot be taken as rigorously true.

119. *Motion of two smooth bodies perpendicular to the line of impact.*

When two smooth bodies impinge, there is no tangential

action between them, so that the stress between them is entirely along their common normal, *i.e.* the line which is perpendicular to both surfaces at their point of contact. Hence there is no force perpendicular to this common normal, and therefore no change of velocity in that direction.

Hence the component velocity of each body in a direction perpendicular to the common normal is unaltered by the impact.

120. *Motion of two bodies along the line of impact.*

From Art. 86 it follows that, when two bodies impinge, the sum of their momenta along the line of impact is the same after impact as before.

The two principles enunciated in this and the previous article, together with Newton's experimental law, are sufficient to find the change in the motion of particles and smooth spheres produced by a collision.

We shall now proceed to the discussion of particular cases.

121. Impact on a fixed plane. *A smooth sphere, or particle, whose mass is m and whose coefficient of restitution is e, impinges obliquely on a fixed plane; to find the change in its motion.*

Let AB be the fixed plane, C the point at which the sphere impinges, and CN the normal to the plane at C so that CN passes through the centre, O, of the sphere.

Let DO and OE be the directions of motion of the centre of the sphere before and after impact, and let the angles NOD and NOE be a and θ. Let u and v be the velocities of the sphere before and after impact as indicated in the figure.

Since the plane is smooth, there is no force parallel to the plane; hence the velocity of the sphere resolved in a direction parallel to the plane is unaltered.

$$\therefore \ v \sin \theta = u \sin \alpha \ \dots \dots \dots \dots (1).$$

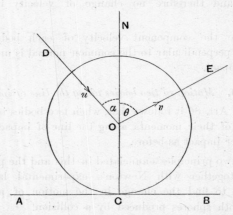

By Newton's experimental law, the normal velocity of separation is e times the normal velocity of approach.

Hence $v \cos \theta - 0 = e (u \cos \alpha - 0).$

$$\therefore \ v \cos \theta = eu \cos \alpha \dots \dots \dots \dots (2).$$

From (1) and (2), by squaring and adding, we have

$$v = u \sqrt{\sin^2 \alpha + e^2 \cos^2 \alpha},$$

and, by division, $\cot \theta = e \cot \alpha.$

These two equations give the velocity and direction of motion after impact.

The impulse of the force of impact on the plane is equal and opposite to the impulse of the force of impact on the sphere, and is therefore measured by the change of the momentum of the sphere perpendicular to the plane.

Hence the impulse of the blow $= mu \cos \alpha + mv \cos \theta$

$$= m (1 + e) u \cos \alpha.$$

Cor. 1. If the impact be direct, we have $a = 0$.

$$\therefore \ \theta = 0, \text{ and } v = eu.$$

Hence *The direction of motion of a sphere, which impinges directly on a smooth plane, is reversed and its velocity reduced in the ratio* $1 : e$.

Cor. 2. If the coefficient of restitution be unity, we have $\theta = a$, and $v = u$.

Hence *When the plane is perfectly elastic the angle of reflexion is equal to that of incidence, and the velocity is unaltered in magnitude.*

Cor. 3. If the coefficient of restitution be zero, we have $\theta = 90°$, and $v = u \sin a$.

Hence *A sphere after impact with an inelastic plane slides along the plane with its velocity parallel to the plane unaltered.*

Ex. *A ball, moving with a velocity of 10 feet per second, impinges on a smooth fixed plane at an angle of 45°; if the coefficient of restitution be* $\frac{4}{5}$, *find the velocity and direction of motion of the ball after the impact.*

Let its velocity after the impact be v at an angle θ with the fixed plane.

Its component velocities along and perpendicular to the plane, before impact, are each $10 \times \dfrac{1}{\sqrt{2}}$, *i.e.*, $5\sqrt{2}$. After impact its component velocities in the same two directions are $v \cos \theta$ and $v \sin \theta$.

Hence we have
$$v \cos \theta = 5\sqrt{2},$$
$$v \sin \theta = e \cdot 5\sqrt{2} = 4\sqrt{2}.$$

Therefore, by squaring and adding,
$$v^2 = 82, \text{ so that } v = \sqrt{82} = 9\cdot06.$$

Also, by division, $\tan \theta = \frac{4}{5}$, so that, by the table of natural tangents, $\theta = 38°40'$ nearly. Hence, after the impact, the ball moves with a velocity of $9\cdot06$ ft. per sec. at an angle of $38°40'$ with the plane.

EXAMPLES. XX.

1. A glass marble drops from a height of 9 feet upon a horizontal floor; if the coefficient of restitution be ·9, find the height to which it rises after the impact.

2. An ivory ball is dropped from a height of 25 feet upon a horizontal slab; if it rebound to a height of 16 feet, shew that the coefficient of restitution between the slab and the ball is ·8.

3. A heavy elastic ball drops from the ceiling of a room, and after rebounding twice from the floor reaches a height equal to one half that of the ceiling; shew that the coefficient of restitution is $\sqrt[4]{\frac{1}{2}}$.

4. From a point in one wall of a room a ball is projected along the smooth floor to hit the opposite wall and returns to the point from which it started; if the coefficient of restitution be $\frac{1}{2}$, shew that the ball takes twice as long in returning as it took in going.

5. From a point in the floor of a room a ball is projected vertically with velocity $32\sqrt{3}$ feet per second; if the height of the room be 16 feet, and the coefficients of restitution between the ball and the ceiling and the ball and the floor be each $\frac{1}{\sqrt{2}}$, shew that the ball, after rebounding from the ceiling and the floor, will again just reach the height of the ceiling.

6. A ball moving with a velocity of 8 ft. per sec. impinges at an angle of 30° on a smooth plane; find its velocity and direction of motion after the impact, the coefficient of restitution being $\frac{1}{2}$.

7. A sphere moving with a velocity of 5 ft. per sec. hits against a smooth plane, its direction of motion being inclined at an angle $\sin^{-1}\frac{3}{5}$ ($=36°52'$) to the plane; shew that after impact its velocity is $2\sqrt{5}$ ($=4·47$) ft. per sec. at an angle $\tan^{-1}\frac{1}{2}$ ($=26°34'$) with the plane, if the coefficient of restitution be $\frac{2}{3}$.

8. A ball falls from a height of 16 feet upon a plane inclined at (1) 30°, (2) 45°, and (3) 60°, to the horizon; find the velocity and direction of motion after the impact in the three cases, the coefficient of restitution being $\frac{3}{4}$.

122. Direct impact of two spheres. *A smooth sphere, of mass m, impinges directly with velocity u on another smooth sphere, of mass m', moving in the same direction with velocity u'. If the coefficient of restitution be e, to find their velocities after the impact.*

Let v and v' be the velocities of the two spheres after impact.

The velocity of approach is $u - u'$, and the velocity of separation is $v' - v$, so that by Newton's experimental law we have

$$v' - v = e\,(u - u') \quad \dots\dots\dots\dots(1).$$

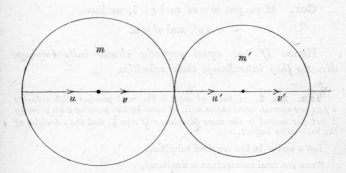

Again, the only force acting on the bodies during the impact is the blow along the line of centres. Hence, by Art. 120, the total momentum in that direction is unaltered.

$$\therefore \; mv + m'v' = mu + m'u' \quad \dots\dots\dots\dots(2).$$

Multiplying (1) by m', and subtracting from (2), we have

$$(m + m')\,v = (m - em')\,u + m'\,(1 + e)\,u'.$$

Again multiplying (1) by m, and adding to (2), we have

$$(m + m')\,v' = m\,(1 + e)\,u + (m' - em)\,u'.$$

These two equations give the velocities after impact.

If the second sphere be moving in a direction opposite to that of the first, we must change the sign of u'.

Also the impulse of the blow on the ball m

= the change produced in its momentum

$$= m\,(u - v) = \frac{mm'}{m+m'}\,(1 + e)\,(u - u').$$

The impulse of the blow on the other ball is equal and opposite to this.

Cor. If we put $m = m'$ and $e = 1$, we have

$$v = u', \text{ and } v' = u.$$

Hence *If two equal perfectly elastic balls impinge directly they interchange their velocities.*

123. Ex. 1. *A ball, of mass 8 lbs. and moving with velocity 4 feet per second, overtakes a ball, of mass 10 lbs. moving with velocity 2 feet per second in the same direction; if e be $\frac{1}{2}$, find the velocities of the balls after impact.*

Let v and v' be the required velocities.

Since the total momentum is unaltered,

$$\therefore\ 8v + 10v' = 8 \times 4 + 10 \times 2 = 52.$$

By Newton's Law,

$$v' - v = \tfrac{1}{2}\,(4 - 2) = 1.$$

Hence, by solving, $v = 2\tfrac{1}{3}$, and $v' = 3\tfrac{1}{3}$, feet per second.

Ex. 2. *If in the previous question, the second ball be moving in a direction opposite to the first, find the velocities.*

Here the equations are

$$8v + 10v' = 8 \times 4 - 10 \times 2 = 12,$$

and

$$v' - v = \tfrac{1}{2}\,(4 + 2) = 3,$$

since $v' - v$ is the velocity of separation and $4 + 2$ is the velocity of approach.

Hence, on solving, $v = -1$ and $v' = 2$ feet per second, so that each ball turns back after the impact, *since the velocities are reckoned positively in the direction in which the first was going before impact.*

124. Oblique impact of two spheres. *A smooth sphere, of mass m, impinges with a velocity u obliquely on a smooth sphere, of mass m′, moving with velocity u′. If the directions of motion before impact make angles α and β respectively with the line joining the centres of the spheres, and if the coefficient of restitution be e, to find the velocities and directions of motion after impact.*

Let the velocities of the spheres after impact be v and $v′$ in directions inclined at angles $θ$ and $φ$ respectively to the line of centres.

Since the spheres are smooth, there is no force perpendicular to the line joining the centres of the two balls, and therefore the velocities in that direction are unaltered.

Hence
$$v \sin θ = u \sin α \quad\quad\quad\quad\quad (1),$$
and
$$v′ \sin φ = u′ \sin β \quad\quad\quad\quad\quad (2).$$

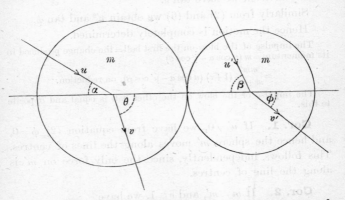

Since $u \cos α - u′ \cos β$ is the normal velocity of approach, and $v′ \cos φ - v \cos θ$ is the normal velocity of separation, we have, by Newton's Law,

$$v′ \cos φ - v \cos θ = e\,(u \cos α - u′ \cos β) \quad\quad (3).$$

Again, the only force acting on the spheres during the impact is the blow along the line of centres. Hence (Art. 120) the total momentum in that direction is unaltered.

$$\therefore mv \cos \theta + m'v' \cos \phi = mu \cos \alpha + m'u' \cos \beta \ldots (4).$$

The equations (1), (2), (3) and (4) determine the unknown quantities v, v', θ and ϕ.

Multiply (3) by m', subtract from (4), and we obtain

$$v \cos \theta = \frac{(m - em') u \cos \alpha + m' (1 + e) u' \cos \beta}{m + m'} \ldots \ldots (5).$$

So multiplying (3) by m, and adding to (4), we get

$$v' \cos \phi = \frac{m (1 + e) u \cos \alpha + (m' - em) u' \cos \beta}{m + m'} \ldots \ldots (6).$$

From (1) and (5) by squaring and adding we obtain v^2, and by division we have $\tan \theta$.

Similarly from (2) and (6) we obtain v'^2 and $\tan \phi$.

Hence the motion is completely determined.

The impulse of the blow on the first ball = the change produced in its momentum $= m (u \cos \alpha - v \cos \theta)$

$$= \frac{mm'}{m + m'} (1 + e) (u \cos \alpha - u' \cos \beta), \text{ on reduction.}$$

The impulse of the blow on the other ball is equal and opposite to this.

Cor. 1. If $u' = 0$, we have from equation (2) $\phi = 0$, and hence the sphere m' moves along the lines of centres. This follows independently, since the only force on m' is along the line of centres.

Cor. 2. If $m = m'$, and $e = 1$, we have

$$v \cos \theta = u' \cos \beta, \text{ and } v' \cos \phi = u \cos \alpha.$$

Hence *If two equal perfectly elastic spheres impinge they interchange their velocities in the direction of the line of centres.*

125. Ex. 1. *A ball, of mass 5 lbs. and moving with velocity 15 ft. per sec., impinges on a ball, of mass 10 lbs. and moving with velocity 5 ft. per sec.; if their velocities before impact be parallel and inclined at an angle of 30° to the line joining their centres at the instant of impact, find the resulting motion, the coefficient of restitution being $\frac{1}{2}$.*

Let the velocities after impact be v and v' at angles θ and ϕ to the line joining the centres.

Since the velocities perpendicular to the line of centres are unaltered, we have

$$v \sin \theta = 15 \sin 30° = \tfrac{15}{2} \quad\text{...............}(1),$$

and

$$v' \sin \phi = 5 \sin 30° = \tfrac{5}{2} \quad\text{...............}(2).$$

By Newton's Law,

$$v' \cos \phi - v \cos \theta = \tfrac{1}{2} \left[15 \cos 30° - 5 \cos 30° \right] = 5 \frac{\sqrt{3}}{2} \quad\text{......}(3).$$

Since the momentum along the line of impact is unaltered,

$$\therefore \ 5v \cos \theta + 10v' \cos \phi = 5 \cdot 15 \frac{\sqrt{3}}{2} + 10 \cdot 5 \frac{\sqrt{3}}{2}.$$

$$\therefore \ v \cos \theta + 2v' \cos \phi = 25 \frac{\sqrt{3}}{2} \quad\text{...............}(4).$$

Solving (3) and (4), we have

$$v \cos \theta = 5 \frac{\sqrt{3}}{2} \quad\text{...............}(5),$$

and

$$v' \cos \phi = 5\sqrt{3} \quad\text{...............}(6).$$

From (1) and (5), we have $v = 5\sqrt{3} = 8\cdot66$ ft. per sec. nearly, and $\theta = 60°$.

From (2) and (6), we have $v' = \frac{5}{2}\sqrt{13} = 9$ ft. per sec. nearly, and $\tan \phi = \frac{1}{2\sqrt{3}} = \frac{\sqrt{3}}{6}$, so that, by the table of natural tangents, $\phi = 16°6'$.

Ex. 2. *Two smooth balls, one of mass double that of the other, are moving with equal velocities in opposite parallel directions and impinge, their directions of motion at the instant of impact making angles of 30° with the line of centres. If the coefficient of restitution be $\frac{1}{2}$, find the velocities and directions of motion after the impact.*

Let the masses of the balls be $2m$ and m and let the velocities after impact be v and v' respectively at angles θ and ϕ to the line of centres.

Since the velocities perpendicular to the line of centres are unaltered,

$$\therefore \ v \sin \theta = u \sin 30° = \frac{u}{2} \quad\text{...............}(1),$$

and

$$v' \sin \phi = u \sin 30° = \frac{u}{2} \quad\text{...............}(2).$$

The normal velocity of approach is $u \cos 30° + u \cos 30°$, and the normal velocity of separation is $v' \cos \phi - v \cos \theta$, so that by Newton's Law, we have

$$v' \cos \phi - v \cos \theta = e \left[u \cos 30° + u \cos 30° \right] = u \frac{\sqrt{3}}{2} \ \ldots \ldots \ (3).$$

Since the momentum resolved parallel to the line of centres remains unaltered,

$$\therefore \ 2mv \cos \theta + mv' \cos \phi = 2mu \cos 30° - mu \cos 30°,$$

$$\therefore \ 2v \cos \theta + v' \cos \phi = u \frac{\sqrt{3}}{2} \ \ldots \ldots \ldots \ldots \ldots \ldots (4).$$

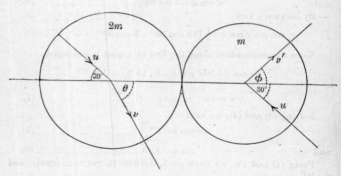

Solving (3) and (4), we have $v \cos \theta = 0$ and $v' \cos \phi = u \frac{\sqrt{3}}{2}$.

From these equations and (1) and (2), we obtain

$$\theta = 90°, \ v = \frac{u}{2}; \ \phi = 30°, \ v' = u.$$

Hence after impact the larger ball starts off in a direction perpendicular to the line of centres with half its former velocity, and the smaller ball moves as if it were a perfectly elastic ball impinging on a fixed plane.

EXAMPLES. XXI.

1. A sphere, of mass 4 lbs. and moving with velocity 5 ft. per sec., overtakes a sphere of mass 3 lbs. and moving with velocity 4 ft. per sec.; if the impact be direct and the coefficient of restitution be $\frac{1}{2}$, find the velocities of the spheres after impact.

2. A ball, of mass 10 lbs. and moving with velocity 6 ft. per sec., overtakes a sphere, of mass 8 lbs. and moving with velocity 3 ft. per sec.; if the impact be direct and the coefficient of restitution be $\frac{3}{4}$, find the velocities of the spheres after impact.

3. A sphere, moving with velocity 12 ft. per sec., meets an equal sphere moving in the same line with a velocity of 6 ft. per sec. in the opposite direction; if the coefficient of restitution be $\frac{1}{3}$, find their velocities after the impact.

4. If a ball overtake a ball of twice its own mass moving with one-seventh of its velocity, and if the coefficient of restitution between them be $\frac{3}{4}$, shew that the first ball will, after striking the second ball, remain at rest.

5. If the masses of two balls be as $2 : 1$, and their respective velocities before impact be as $1 : 2$ and in opposite directions, and e be $\frac{5}{6}$, shew that each ball will after direct impact move back with $\frac{5}{6}$ths of its original velocity.

6. A sphere impinges directly on an equal sphere at rest; if the coefficient of restitution be e, shew that their velocities after the impact are as
$$1 - e : 1 + e.$$

7. A ball, of mass m and moving with velocity u, impinges on a ball, of mass em and moving with velocity eu in the opposite direction; if the impact be direct and e be the coefficient of restitution, shew that the velocity of the second ball after impact is the same as that of the first ball before impact.

8. A ball, of mass 2 lbs., impinges directly on a ball, of mass 1 lb., which is at rest; find the coefficient of restitution if the velocity with which the larger ball impinges be equal to the velocity of the smaller ball after impact.

9. A ball of mass m impinges directly upon a ball of mass m_1 at rest; the velocity of m after impact is $\frac{3}{5}$ths of its velocity before impact and the coefficient of restitution is $\frac{3}{5}$; compare (i) the masses of the two balls, and (ii) the velocities of m and m_1 after impact.

10. Three spheres, whose masses are 2 lbs., 6 lbs., and 12 lbs., respectively, and whose velocities are 12, 4, and 2 feet per second respectively, are moving in a straight line in the above order. If the coefficient of restitution be unity, shew that the first two spheres will be brought to rest by the collisions which will take place.

11. A ball is let fall from a height of 64 feet, and at the same instant an equal ball is projected from the ground with a velocity of 128 feet per second to meet it in direct impact: if the coefficient of restitution be $\frac{1}{2}$, find the times that elapse after the impact before the balls reach the ground.

12. An inelastic sphere impinges obliquely on a second sphere at rest, whose mass is twice its own, in a direction making an angle of 30° with the line joining the centres of the spheres; shew that its direction of motion is turned through an angle of 30°.

13. Two equal balls moving with equal speeds impinge, their directions being inclined at 30° and 60° to the line joining their centres at the instant of impact; if the coefficient of restitution be unity, shew that after impact they are moving in parallel directions inclined at 45° to the line of centres.

14. Two equal balls, moving with equal velocities, impinge; if their directions of motion before impact make angles of 30° and 90° respectively with the line joining the centres at the instant of impact, and if the coefficient of restitution be $\frac{1}{3}$, shew that after impact the balls are moving in parallel directions, and that the velocity of one is double that of the other.

15. Two equal perfectly elastic balls impinge; if their directions of motion before impact be at right angles, shew that their directions of motion after impact are at right angles also.

16. A sphere, moving with velocity $u\sqrt{3}$, impinges on an equal sphere, moving with velocity u, their directions of motion before impact making angles of 30° and 60° with the line of centres; shew that, if the coefficient of restitution be unity, their directions of motion after impact make angles of 60° and 30° respectively with the line of centres.

17. A sphere, of mass $5m$ and moving with velocity $13u$, impinges on a sphere, of mass m and moving with velocity $5u$, their directions of motion being inclined at angles of $\sin^{-1}\frac{5}{13}$ and $\sin^{-1}\frac{3}{5}$ respectively to the line of centres; if the coefficient of restitution be $\frac{1}{2}$, find their velocities and directions of motion after the impact.

126. Action between two elastic bodies during their collision.

When two elastic bodies impinge, the time during which the impact lasts may be divided into two parts, during the first of which the bodies are compressing one another, and during the second of which they are recovering their shape.

That the bodies are compressed may be shewn experimentally by dropping a billiard ball upon a floor which has been covered with fine coloured powder. At the spot where the ball hits the floor, the powder will be found to be removed not from a geometrical point only, but from a small circle; this shews that at some instant during the compression the part of the ball in contact with the floor was a circle; it follows that the ball was then deformed and afterwards recovered its shape.

It is also found that the small circle is increased in size if the distance through which the ball is dropped be increased, in which case the velocity of the ball on hitting the floor is increased. Hence the greater the velocity at impact, the greater is the temporary deformation of the billiard ball.

The first portion of the impact lasts until the bodies are instantaneously moving with the same velocity; forces then come into play tending to make the bodies recover their shape. The mutual action between the bodies during the first portion of the impact is often called "the force of compression," and that during the second portion "the force of restitution."

We have no means of finding out what is the actual magnitude of the force between two bodies during an impact; we only know that it must vary very considerably, being zero at the commencement of the impact and zero at the end, and that it must be large at some instant during which the impact lasts. But, by Newton's Third Law, the force at *each instant* must be the same in magnitude for each body, but opposite in direction; hence the impulses of the forces acting on the two bodies must be equal, but in opposite directions.

127. It is easy to shew that the ratio of the impulses of the forces of restitution and compression is equal to the quantity e, which we have defined as the coefficient of restitution.

Consider the case of one sphere impinging directly on another, as in Art. 122, and use the same notation.

Let U be the common velocity of the bodies at the instant when the compression is finished. Then

$m (u - U)$ is the loss of momentum by the first ball,

and $m' (U - u')$ is the gain by the second ball.

Hence, if I be the impulse of the force of compression, we have
$$I = m (u - U) = m' (U - u'),$$
$$\therefore \frac{I}{m} + \frac{I}{m'} = u - U + U - u' = u - u' \dots\dots(1).$$

Again, the loss of momentum by the first ball during the period of restitution is $m (U - v)$, and the gain by the second ball is $m' (v' - U)$.

Hence, if I' be the impulse of the force of restitution,
$$I' = m (U - v) = m' (v' - U),$$
$$\therefore \frac{I'}{m} + \frac{I'}{m'} = U - v + v' - U = v' - v \dots\dots(2).$$

Hence, from (1) and (2), $\dfrac{I'}{I} = \dfrac{v' - v}{u - u'}$,

i.e. $\dfrac{\text{Impulse of the force of restitution}}{\text{Impulse of the force of compression}}$

$$= \frac{\text{Normal velocity of separation}}{\text{Normal velocity of approach}} = e.$$

$$\therefore I' = eI.$$

128. Loss of Kinetic Energy by Impact.
Two spheres of given masses moving with given velocities impinge; to shew that there is a loss of kinetic energy and to find the amount.

I. Let the collision be direct and the notation as in Art. 122.

Then we have

$$mv + m'v' = mu + m'u' \quad \ldots\ldots\ldots\ldots(1),$$

$$v' - v = e(u - u') \quad \ldots\ldots\ldots\ldots(2).$$

To the square of (1) add the square of (2) multiplied by mm'; we then have

$$(m^2 + mm')v^2 + (m'^2 + mm')v'^2 = (mu + m'u')^2 + e^2 mm'(u - u')^2,$$

i.e.
$$(m + m')(mv^2 + m'v'^2)$$

$$= (mu + m'u')^2 + mm'(u - u')^2 - (1 - e^2)mm'(u - u')^2$$

$$= (m + m')(mu^2 + m'u'^2) - (1 - e^2)mm'(u - u')^2.$$

$$\therefore \tfrac{1}{2}mv^2 + \tfrac{1}{2}m'v'^2 = \tfrac{1}{2}mu^2 + \tfrac{1}{2}m'u'^2 - \frac{1 - e^2}{2}\frac{mm'}{m + m'}(u - u')^2.$$

Hence the kinetic energy after impact

$$= \text{kinetic energy before impact} - \frac{1 - e^2}{2}\frac{mm'}{m + m'}(u - u')^2.$$

Hence the loss of kinetic energy is

$$\frac{1 - e^2}{2}\frac{mm'}{m + m'}(u - u')^2,$$

and this loss does not vanish unless $e = 1$, that is, unless the balls are perfectly elastic.

II. Let the collision be oblique and the notation as in Art. 124.

As in I., we have

$$\tfrac{1}{2}mv^2 \cos^2\theta + \tfrac{1}{2}m'v'^2 \cos^2\phi = \tfrac{1}{2}mu^2 \cos^2\alpha + \tfrac{1}{2}m'u'^2 \cos^2\beta$$

$$- \frac{1 - e^2}{2}\frac{mm'}{m + m'}(u \cos\alpha - u' \cos\beta)^2 \ldots(3).$$

Also, since $v \sin\theta = u \sin\alpha$, and $v' \sin\phi = u' \sin\beta$, we have

$$\tfrac{1}{2}mv^2 \sin^2\theta + \tfrac{1}{2}m'v'^2 \sin^2\phi = \tfrac{1}{2}mu^2 \sin^2\alpha$$

$$+ \tfrac{1}{2}m'u'^2 \sin^2\beta \ldots\ldots\ldots(4).$$

Adding (3) and (4), we have

The kinetic energy after impact = kinetic energy before impact $- \dfrac{1-e^2}{2}\dfrac{mm'}{m+m'}, (u\cos\alpha - u'\cos\beta)^2.$

Hence we see that in any impact, unless the coefficient of restitution be unity, some kinetic energy is lost, or, rather, is transformed.

This missing kinetic energy is converted into molecular energy and chiefly reappears in the shape of heat.

Cor. Suppose, as in the case of a nail hit by a hammer, that the object struck was at rest.

In this case $u'=0$ and $e=0$. Hence, by the result of I., the energy lost, or transformed,

$$= \tfrac{1}{2}\dfrac{mm'(1-e^2)}{m+m'} u^2.$$

$$\therefore \dfrac{\text{Mechanical energy lost by the blow}}{\text{Mechanical energy before the blow}}$$

$$= \tfrac{1}{2}\dfrac{mm'(1-e^2)}{m+m'} u^2 \div \tfrac{1}{2}mu^2 = \dfrac{m'}{m+m'}(1-e^2).$$

This latter expression is made smaller if the ratio of m to m' be made bigger, *i.e.*, the bigger the mass of the hammer compared with that of the nail, the smaller is the loss of mechanical energy at the impact.

129. Ex. 1. *A particle falls from a height h upon a fixed horizontal plane; if e be the coefficient of restitution, shew that the whole distance described by the particle before it has finished rebounding is* $\dfrac{1+e^2}{1-e^2}h$, *and that the time that elapses is* $\sqrt{\dfrac{2h}{g}}\dfrac{1+e}{1-e}.$

Let u be the velocity of the particle when it first hits the plane, so that $u^2 = 2gh.$

By Art. 121, Cor. 1, the particle rebounds with velocity eu.

The velocity when it again hits the plane is eu, and the velocity after the second rebound is e^2u.

Similarly the velocity after the third, fourth, ... rebounds is e^3u, e^4u, ...

The height to which the particle ascends after the first, second, ... rebounds are $\dfrac{e^2u^2}{2g}$, $\dfrac{(e^2u)^2}{2g}$, $\dfrac{(e^3u)^2}{2g}$ ... *i.e.*, e^2h, e^4h, e^6h,....

Hence the whole space described

$$= h + 2\,(e^2 h + e^4 h + e^6 h + \dots ad\ inf.)$$
$$= h + 2h\,\frac{e^2}{1 - e^2},$$

by summing the infinite geometric progression,

$$= h\,\frac{1 + e^2}{1 - e^2}.$$

Also the time of falling originally $= \sqrt{\dfrac{2h}{g}}$.

The times of ascending after the impacts are the times in which the velocities $eu,\ e^2 u,\ e^3 u,\ \dots$ are destroyed by gravity.

Hence these times are $\dfrac{eu}{g},\ \dfrac{e^2 u}{g},\ \dfrac{e^3 u}{g}\dots$ *i.e.*, $e\sqrt{\dfrac{2h}{g}},\ e^2\sqrt{\dfrac{2h}{g}},\ \dots$

Hence the whole time during which the particle is in motion

$$= \sqrt{\frac{2h}{g}} + 2\,.\,\sqrt{\frac{2h}{g}}\,[e + e^2 + e^3 + \dots ad\ inf.]$$
$$= \sqrt{\frac{2h}{g}}\left[1 + 2\,\frac{e}{1 - e}\right] = \sqrt{\frac{2h}{g}}\,\frac{1 + e}{1 - e}.$$

In theory therefore we have an infinite number of rebounds taking place in a finite time; in practice after a few rebounds the velocity of the ball becomes destroyed.

Since the height to which the particle rebounds after the first impact is $e^2 h$, *i.e.* e^2 times the height from which it fell,

$$\therefore\ e^2 = \frac{\text{height of rebound}}{\text{height of falling}}.$$

Hence the value of e for a given ball and a given floor may be easily found by experiment. For, if the ball be let fall from a given suitable height, it will be easy to find the height of rebound after a few trials, and then we easily have e^2.

Ex. 2. *From a point in a smooth horizontal plane a particle is projected with velocity u at an angle α to the horizon; if the coefficient of restitution between the particle and the plane be e, shew that the distance described along the plane before the particle ceases to rebound is $\dfrac{u^2}{g}\,\dfrac{\sin 2\alpha}{1 - e}$.*

The initial vertical velocity is $u \sin \alpha$.

The initial vertical velocities after the first, second,... rebounds are, as in the last example, $eu \sin \alpha,\ e^2 u \sin \alpha,\ e^3 u \sin \alpha,\dots$.

Hence the time between the first and second rebounds is, as in Art. 105, $2\,\dfrac{eu \sin \alpha}{g}$.

So the times in the other trajectories are $2\dfrac{e^2 u \sin a}{g}$, $2\dfrac{e^3 u \sin a}{g}$ ....

Hence the total time that elapses before the particle ceases to rebound

$$= \frac{2u \sin a}{g} + \frac{2eu \sin a}{g} + \frac{2e^2 u \sin a}{g} \dots ad \; inf.$$

$$= \frac{2u \sin a}{g}[1 + e + e^2 + \dots] = \frac{2u \sin a}{g} \cdot \frac{1}{1-e}.$$

During this time the horizontal velocity, being unaltered by the impacts, is always $u \cos a$.

Hence the horizontal distance described

$$= \frac{2u \sin a}{g} \cdot \frac{1}{1-e} \times u \cos a = \frac{u^2 \sin 2a}{g \, (1-e)}.$$

After the particle has ceased to rebound, it moves along the plane with constant velocity $u \cos a$.

EXAMPLES. XXII.

1. An elastic particle is projected so that it hits a vertical wall and returns after impact to the point from which it was projected, without hitting the ground. If the angle of projection be a, and the direction of the path of the particle when it again reaches the point of projection make an angle β with the horizontal, shew that $\tan a = e \tan \beta$, where e is the coefficient of restitution.

2. Shew that an elastic sphere let fall from a height of 16 feet above a fixed horizontal table will come to rest in 8 seconds, after describing 65 feet, supposing the coefficient of restitution to be $\frac{7}{9}$.

3. A ball falls from a height of 48 feet upon an elastic horizontal plane; if the coefficient of elasticity be $\frac{1}{3}$, find the total space described by the sphere before it finally comes to rest, and the time that elapses.

4. A particle is projected from a point in a horizontal plane with a velocity of 64 feet per second at an angle of 30° with the horizon; if the coefficient of restitution be $\frac{3}{4}$, find the distance described by it horizontally before it ceases to rebound, and the time that elapses.

5. A ball falls vertically for 2 seconds and hits a plane inclined at 30° to the horizon; if the coefficient of restitution be $\frac{3}{4}$, shew that the time that elapses before it again hits the plane is 3 seconds.

6. A perfectly elastic ball is dropped from the top of a tower of height h, and when it has fallen half-way to the ground it strikes a smooth rigid projecting stone inclined at 45° to the horizon; find where it will reach the ground.

7. A ball, at rest on a smooth horizontal plane at the distance of one yard from a wall, is impinged on directly by another equal ball moving at right angles to the wall with a velocity of a yard per second. If the coefficients of restitution between the balls, and the balls and wall, be each $\frac{1}{3}$, shew that they will impinge a second time at the end of 2·4 seconds, the radii of the balls being of inconsiderable magnitude.

8. Two equal marbles, A and B, lie in a smooth horizontal circular groove at opposite ends of a diameter; A is projected along the groove and at the end of time t impinges on B; shew that a second impact will occur at the end of time $\dfrac{2t}{e}$.

9. Two marbles, of equal diameter but of masses $10m$ and $11m$, are projected from the same point with velocities, equal in magnitude but opposite in direction, along a circular groove; where will the second impact take place if the coefficient of restitution be $\frac{3}{4}$?

10. A sphere, of mass m, impinges obliquely on a sphere, of mass M, which is at rest. Shew that, if $m = eM$, the directions of motion of the spheres after impact are at right angles.

11. A sphere impinges on a sphere of equal mass which is at rest; if the directions of motion after impact be inclined at angles of 30° to the original direction of motion of the impinging sphere, shew that the coefficient of restitution is $\frac{1}{3}$.

12. A ball impinges on another equal ball moving with the same speed in a direction perpendicular to its own, the line joining the centres of the balls at the instant of impact being perpendicular to the direction of motion of the second ball; if e be the coefficient of restitution, shew that the direction of motion of the second ball is turned through an angle $\tan^{-1}\dfrac{1+e}{2}$.

13. Two equal smooth elastic spheres, moving in opposite parallel directions with equal speeds, impinge on one another; if the inclination of their directions of motion to the line of centres be $\tan^{-1}\sqrt{e}$, where e is the coefficient of restitution, shew that their directions of motion will be turned through a right angle.

14. Two equal balls are in contact on a table; a third equal ball strikes them simultaneously and remains at rest after the impact; shew that the coefficient of restitution is $\frac{2}{3}$.

15. The masses of five balls at rest in a straight line form a geometrical progression whose ratio is 2, and their coefficients of restitution are each $\frac{2}{3}$. If the first ball be started towards the second with velocity u, shew that the velocity communicated to the fifth is $\left(\frac{5}{9}\right)^4 u$.

16. A ball of given elasticity slides from rest down a smooth inclined plane, of length l, which is inclined at an angle α to the horizon, and impinges on a fixed smooth horizontal plane at the foot of the former; find its range on the horizontal plane.

17. A heavy elastic ball falls from a height of n feet and meets a plane inclined at an angle of 60° to the horizon; find the distance between the first two points at which it strikes the plane.

18. An inelastic ball, of small radius, sliding along a smooth horizontal plane with a velocity of 16 feet per second, impinges on a smooth horizontal rail at right angles to its direction of motion; if the height of the rail above the plane be one half the radius of the ball, shew that the latus rectum of the parabola subsequently described is one foot in length.

19. A particle is projected along a smooth horizontal plane from a given point A in it, so that after impinging on an imperfectly elastic vertical plane it may pass through another given point B of the horizontal plane; give a geometrical construction for the direction of projection.

20. A smooth circular table is surrounded by a smooth rim whose interior surface is vertical. Shew that a ball, whose coefficient of restitution is e, projected along the table from a point in the rim in a direction making an angle $\tan^{-1}\sqrt{\dfrac{e^3}{1+e+e^2}}$ with the radius through the point, will return to the point of projection after two impacts on the rim. Prove also that when the ball returns to the point of projection its velocity is to its original velocity as $e^{\frac{3}{2}} : 1$.

If the angle that its direction of projection makes with the radius be $\tan^{-1} e^{\frac{3}{2}}$, shew that it will return to the point of projection after three rebounds.

21. Two elastic particles are projected simultaneously from a point in a smooth horizontal plane; shew that their centre of gravity will describe a number of arcs of the same parabola in different positions.

CHAPTER IX.

THE HODOGRAPH AND NORMAL ACCELERATIONS.

130. In the following chapter we shall consider the motion of a particle which moves in a curve. It will be convenient, as a preliminary, to explain how the velocity, direction of motion, and acceleration of a particle moving in any manner may be mapped out by means of another curve.

131. Hodograph. Def. *If a particle be moving in any path whatever, and if from any point O, fixed in space, we draw a straight line OQ parallel and proportional to the velocity at any point P of the path, the curve traced out by the end Q of this straight line is called the hodograph of the path of the particle.*

[The word Hodograph is derived from two Greek words ὅδος (pronounced Hodos) meaning "a path," and γράφειν (pronounced Graphein) meaning "to write."]

It is so called because it represents graphically to the eye the velocity and acceleration of the moving point.

132. Theorem. *If the hodograph of the path of a moving point P be drawn, then the velocity of the corresponding point Q in the hodograph represents, in magnitude and direction, the acceleration of the moving point P in its path.*

Let P and P' be two points on the path close to one another; draw OQ and OQ' parallel to the tangents at P and P' and proportional to the velocities there, so that Q and Q' are two points on the hodograph very close to one another.

Whilst the particle has moved from P to P' its velocity has changed from OQ to OQ', and therefore, as in Art. 27, the change of velocity is represented by QQ'.

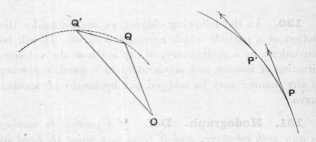

Now let P' be taken indefinitely close to P, so that QQ' becomes an indefinitely small portion of the arc of the hodograph.

If τ be the time of describing the arc PP', then, by Art. 28, the acceleration of $P = \dfrac{\text{change of velocity in time } \tau}{\tau}$

$= \dfrac{QQ'}{\tau} =$ velocity of Q in the hodograph.

Hence the velocity of Q in the hodograph represents, in magnitude and direction, the acceleration of P in the path.

133. Examples. 1. The hodograph of a point describing a circle with uniform speed is another circle which the corresponding point describes with uniform speed. For, in this case, since the magnitude of the velocity of P is constant, the line OQ is constant in length, and therefore Q always lies on a circle whose centre is O. Also, since the point P describes its circle uniformly, the tangent at P turns through equal angles in equal times, and therefore the line OQ turns through equal angles in equal times.

2. The hodograph of a point describing a straight line with constant acceleration is a straight line, which the corresponding point describes with constant velocity. For, in this case, the line OQ is always drawn in a fixed direction and the velocity of Q, being equal in magnitude to the constant acceleration of P, is also constant.

Normal Acceleration.

134. We have learnt from the First Law of Motion that every particle, once in motion and acted on by no forces, continues to move in a straight line with uniform velocity. Hence it will not describe a curved line unless acted upon by some external force. If it describe a curve with uniform speed, there can be no force in the direction of the tangent to its path, or otherwise its speed would be altered, and so the only force acting on it is normal (that is, perpendicular) to its path. If its speed be not constant, there must in addition be a tangential force.

In the following articles we shall investigate the simple case of the normal acceleration of a particle moving in a circle with constant speed.

135. Theorem. *If a particle describe a circle of radius r with uniform speed v, to shew that its acceleration is $\dfrac{v^2}{r}$ directed toward the centre of the circle.*

Let P and P' be two consecutive positions of the moving particle and Q and Q' the corresponding points on the hodograph. Since the speed of P is constant, the line $O'Q$ is of constant length, and therefore the point Q moves on a circle whose radius is v; also the angle $QO'Q'$ is equal to the angle between the tangents at P and P' and therefore is equal to the angle POP'.

Hence the arc QQ' : the arc PP' :: $O'Q : OP$ :: $v : r$.

Also the velocities of Q and P are proportional to the arcs QQ' and PP'.

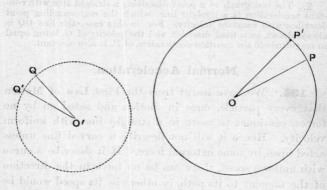

Hence the velocity of Q in the hodograph : v :: $v : r$.

$$\therefore \text{ velocity of } Q = \frac{v^2}{r}.$$

But the point Q is moving in a direction perpendicular to $O'Q$ and therefore parallel to PO; also the acceleration of the point P is equal to the velocity of Q (Art. 132).

Hence the acceleration of P is $\dfrac{v^2}{r}$ in the direction PO.

If the speed v be not constant but variable it can be shewn (*Elementary Dynamics*, Art. 157) that the normal acceleration is still $\dfrac{v^2}{r}$.

Cor. 1. If ω be the angular velocity of the particle about the centre O, we have $v = r\omega$, and the normal acceleration is therefore $\omega^2 r$.

Cor. 2. The force required to produce the normal acceleration is $m\,\dfrac{v^2}{r}$, where m is the mass of the particle.

136. Without the use of the hodograph, a proof of the very important theorem of the last article can be given as follows.

Let P' be a point on the circle very close to P. Draw the tangent $P'T$ at P' to meet the tangent, Px, at P in T.

Join P and P' to the centre, O, of the circle.

Since the angles at P and P' are right angles, a circle will go through the points O, P, T and P', and hence $\angle P'Tx$

$$= \text{supplement of } P'TP = POP' = \theta.$$

Let v be the speed in the circle, and let τ be the time of describing the arc PP'.

In time τ a velocity parallel to PO has been generated equal to $v \sin \theta$.

Hence the acceleration in the direction $PO = \dfrac{v \sin \theta}{\tau}$ (when τ, and therefore θ, is taken very small)

$$= \frac{v \cdot \theta}{\tau} = \frac{v}{\tau} \cdot \frac{\text{arc } PP'}{OP} = \frac{v}{r} \cdot \frac{\text{arc } PP'}{\tau}.$$

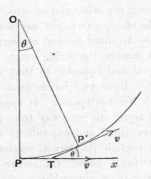

But, since v is the speed in the circle, therefore $\dfrac{\text{arc } PP'}{\tau} = v$.

Hence the required acceleration $= \dfrac{v^2}{r}$.

As in Art. 135, Cor. 1, this acceleration is equal to $r\omega^2$, where ω is the angular velocity.

Also the force towards the centre must be $m\dfrac{v^2}{r}$.

137. The force spoken of in the preceding articles, which is required to cause the normal acceleration of a body, may be produced in many ways.

For example, the body may be tethered by a string, extensible or inextensible, to a fixed point.

Again, the force may be caused by the pressure of a material curve by means of which the body is constrained to move in a curve; for example, a train may be made to describe the curved portion of a railway line by means of the pressure of the rails on the flanges of its wheels.

The force may also be of the nature of an attraction such as exists between the sun and earth, and which compels the earth to describe a curve about the sun.

138. When a man whirls in a circle a mass tied to one end of a string, the other end of which is in his hand, the tension of the string exerts the necessary force on the body to give it the required normal acceleration. But, by the third law of motion, the string exerts upon the man's hand a force equal and opposite to that which it exerts upon the particle; these two forces form the action and reaction of which Newton speaks. It *appears* to the man that the mass is trying to get away from his hand. For this reason a force, equal and opposite to the force necessary to give the particle its normal acceleration, is often called "its centrifugal force," *i.e.* centre-avoiding force. This may however be a somewhat misleading term; it seems to imply that the force *belongs* to the mass instead of being an external force acting on the mass. It also appears to imply that the particle wants to get away from the centre of the curve and is prevented from doing so; this is clearly not so; the particle would, if it were not prevented, move along the tangent to the curve, *i.e.* along the line Px of the figure of Art. 136; it has no wish, or tendency, to move in the direction OP.

A somewhat less misleading term is "centripetal force," *i.e.* centre-seeking force.

We shall avoid the use of either expression; the student who meets with them in the course of his reading will understand that the second of them means "the force which must act on the mass to give it the acceleration normal to the curve in which it moves," and that the first means a force equal and opposite to this.

This latter force (the so-called centrifugal force) is the force which acts on the body which causes the particle to describe its curved path, *e.g.* it is the force acting on the *rails* in the case of a railway train going round a curve, or on the *man's hand* in the case cited above.

139. Ex. 1. *A particle, of mass 3 lbs., moves on a smooth table with a velocity of 4 feet per second, being attached to a fixed point on the table by a string of length 5 feet; find the tension of the string.*

Here $v = 4$, and $r = 5$.

Therefore, by Art. 135, the acceleration toward the fixed point is

$$\frac{v^2}{5}, \quad i.e., \quad \frac{16}{5}.$$

Hence the tension of the string

$$= 3 \times \frac{16}{5} = \frac{48}{5} \text{ poundals} = \text{wt. of } \frac{48}{5 \times 32}, \quad i.e., \quad \frac{3}{10}, \text{ of a pound.}$$

Ex. 2. *A particle, of mass m, moves on a horizontal table and is connected by a string, of length l, with a fixed point on the table; if the greatest weight that the string can support be that of a mass of M pounds, find the greatest number of revolutions per second that the particle can make without breaking the string.*

Let n be the required number of revolutions, so that the velocity of the mass is $n \cdot 2\pi l$.

Therefore the tension of the string $= m \cdot \dfrac{4\pi^2 n^2 l^2}{l}$ poundals.

Hence $Mg = 4m\pi^2 n^2 l$, so that $n = \dfrac{1}{2\pi} \left(\dfrac{Mg}{ml} \right)^{\frac{1}{2}}$.

If the number of revolutions were greater than this number, the tension of the string would be greater than the string could exert, and it would break.

EXAMPLES. XXIII.

1. A string is 3 feet long, and has one end attached to a fixed point on a smooth horizontal table; if a mass of 5 lbs. tied at the other end of the string describe uniformly a horizontal circle with speed 6 feet per second, find the tension of the string.

2. A string is 4 feet long and can just support a weight of 9 lbs.; a mass of 8 lbs. is tied at its end and revolves uniformly on a horizontal table, the other end of the string being attached to a fixed point on the table; find the greatest number of revolutions per minute that can be made by the string without its breaking.

3. A string, 5 feet long, can just sustain a weight of 20 lbs.; if the revolving mass be 5 lbs., determine the greatest number of complete revolutions that can be made in one minute by the string without its breaking.

4. A string, $2\frac{1}{2}$ feet long, has a mass of one pound attached to one end and the other end is attached to a fixed point; if the mass be whirled round in a horizontal circle, whose centre is the fixed point, and if the resulting tension of the string be equal to the weight of 5 pounds, shew that the string is making about 76 revolutions per minute.

5. The tension of a string, one end of which is fixed and to the other end of which is attached a mass which revolves uniformly, is 9 times the weight of the revolving mass; find the velocity of the mass if the length of the string be 2 feet.

6. With what number of turns per minute must a mass of 10 grammes revolve horizontally at the end of a string, half a metre in length, to cause the same tension in the string as would be caused by a mass of one gramme hanging vertically?

7. A locomotive engine, of mass 10 tons, moves on a curve, of radius 600 feet, with a velocity of 30 miles per hour; what force tending toward the centre of the curve must be exerted by the rails so that this may be the case?

8. If, in the previous question, the mass of the engine be 12 tons, its velocity 60 miles per hour, and the radius of the curve 400 yards, what is the required force?

140. The Conical Pendulum. If a particle be tied by a string to a fixed point O, and move so that it describes a circle in a horizontal plane, the string describing a cone whose axis is the vertical line through O, then the string and particle together are called a conical pendulum.

When the motion is uniform, the relations between the velocity of the particle and the length and inclination of the string are easily found.

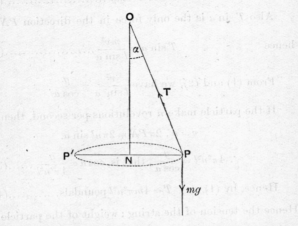

Let P be the particle tied by a string OP, of length l, to a fixed point O. Draw PN perpendicular to the vertical through O. Then P describes a horizontal circle with N as centre [*dotted in the figure*].

Let T be the tension of the string, a its inclination to the vertical, and v the velocity of the particle.

By Art. 135, the acceleration of P in the direction PN is $\dfrac{v^2}{PN}$, and hence the force in that direction must be

$$m \frac{v^2}{l \sin a}.$$

Now the only forces acting on the particle are the tension, T, of the string and the weight, mg, of the particle.

Since the particle has no acceleration in a vertical

direction, the forces acting upon it in that direction must balance, and hence we have

$$T \cos a = mg \quad \text{......................(1).}$$

Also $T \sin a$ is the only force in the direction PN, and

hence
$$T \sin a = \frac{mv^2}{l \sin a} \quad \text{...................(2).}$$

From (1) and (2), we have $\dfrac{v^2}{l \sin^2 a} = \dfrac{g}{\cos a}$.

If the particle make n revolutions per second, then

$$v = n \, . \, 2\pi PN = 2\pi nl \sin a.$$

$$\therefore \; 4\pi^2 n^2 l = \frac{g}{\cos a}, \; \text{that is, } \cos a = \frac{g}{4\pi^2 n^2 l} \; \text{......(3).}$$

Hence, by (1), $T = 4m\pi^2 n^2 l$ poundals............(4).

Hence the tension of the string : weight of the particle

$$:: 4\pi^2 n^2 l : g.$$

The equations (3) and (4) give a and T.

The time of revolution of the particle

$$= \frac{2\pi l \sin a}{v} = 2\pi \sqrt{\frac{l \cos a}{g}} = 2\pi \sqrt{\frac{ON}{g}},$$

and therefore varies as the square root of the depth of the particle below the fixed point.

141. Governors of steam engines. It is generally desirable that engines of the stationary kind should run at a constant speed. Their speed is therefore usually controlled by a Governor; this generally consists of two heavy revolving balls which are attached at the ends of light rods, the other ends of which are connected with a vertical shaft driven by the engine.

A simple form, known as Watt's Governor, is shewn in the figure.

When the shaft runs too fast the balls rise and lift the mechanism at c; by means of levers attached to it the valve regulating the supply of steam is partially closed and the speed is lessened; so when the shaft runs too slowly the balls fall and the supply of steam is increased. The governor thus automatically regulates the supply of steam, so that the engine runs at approximately a constant speed.

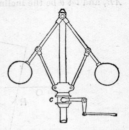

From the last result of Art. 140 it follows that, for a governor of a steam engine rotating 60 times per minute, the height is about 9·78 inches; for one making 100 revolutions per minute the height is 3·52 inches; this latter height is too small for practical purposes except for extremely small engines.

In order that governors may run at a high speed they are therefore usually loaded by means of a spring or weight so adjusted as to keep c lower than it would be in an unloaded governor.

142. Motion of bicycle rider on a circular path. When a man is riding a bicycle on a curved path he always inclines his body inwards towards the centre of his path. By this means the reaction of the ground becomes inclined to the vertical. The vertical component of this reaction balances his weight, and the horizontal component tends towards the centre of the path described by the centre of inertia of the man and his machine, and supplies the necessary normal acceleration.

143. Motion of a railway carriage on a curved portion of the railway line. When the rails are level, the force to give the carriage the necessary acceleration toward the centre of curvature of its path is given by the action of the rails on the flanges of the wheels with which the rails are in contact. In order, however, to avoid the large amount of friction that would be brought into play, and the consequent wearing away of the rails, the outer rail is generally raised so that the floor of the train is not horizontal. The necessary inclination of the floor, in order that there may be no action on the flanges, may be easily found as follows.

Let v be the velocity of the train, and r the radius of the circle described by its centre of inertia G.

Let the figure represent a section of the carriage in the vertical plane through the line joining its centre of inertia to the centre, O, of the circle which it is describing, and let the section meet the rails in the points A and B.

[*The wheels are omitted for the convenience of the figure.*]

Let R and S be the reactions of the rails perpendicular to the floor AB, and let θ be the inclination of the floor to the horizon.

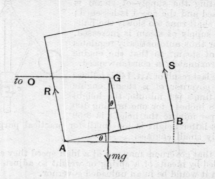

The resolved part, $(R+S)\sin\theta$, of the reactions in the direction GO supplies the force necessary to cause the acceleration towards the centre of the curve.

$$\therefore (R+S)\sin\theta = m\frac{v^2}{r} \quad\dots\dots\dots\dots\dots\dots(1).$$

Also the vertical components of the reactions balance the weight.

$$\therefore (R+S)\cos\theta = mg \quad\dots\dots\dots\dots\dots\dots(2).$$

From (1) and (2), $\qquad\qquad \tan\theta = \dfrac{v^2}{rg} \quad\dots\dots\dots\dots\dots\dots(3),$

giving the inclination of the floor.

If the width AB be given, we can now easily determine the height of the outer rail above the inner; for it is equal to $AB\sin\theta$.

It will be noted that the height through which the outer rail must be raised in order that there may be no horizontal thrust on the flanges depends on the velocity of the train. In practice the height is adjusted so that there is no thrust for trains moving with moderate velocities. For trains moving with higher velocities, the horizontal thrust of the rails on the flanges supplies the additional force required.

This thrust may be found as follows. Assuming that the height of the outer rail has been so adjusted that there is no side thrust for trains travelling with velocity v, let X be the side thrust, reckoned from B towards A, when the velocity of the train is V. Then instead of equations (1) and (2) we have, (if the above figure be used with the addition of a force X along BA),

$$(R+S)\sin\theta + X\cos\theta = m\frac{V^2}{r} \quad\dots\dots\dots\dots\dots(4),$$

and $\qquad (R+S)\cos\theta - X\sin\theta = mg \quad\dots\dots\dots\dots\dots(5).$

Hence we have

$$X = m \frac{V^2}{r} \cos \theta - mg \sin \theta$$

$$= m \cos \theta \left[\frac{V^2}{r} - g \tan \theta \right]$$

$$= m \cos \theta \left[\frac{V^2 - v^2}{r} \right], \text{ by equation (3)}.$$

If V exceed v, X is positive, and the side thrust is caused by the outer rail at B.

If V be less than v, X is negative and therefore acts from A to B, so that the side thrust is in this case caused by the inner rail at A.

144. Rotating sphere. *A smooth hollow sphere is rotating with uniform angular velocity ω about a vertical diameter; to shew that a heavy particle placed inside, and rotating with it, will only remain resting against the side of the sphere at one particular level, and that, if the angular velocity fall short of a certain limit, the particle will only rest at the lowest point of the sphere.*

Let AB be the axis of rotation of the sphere, A being the highest point, and let O be the centre; let P be the position of the particle when in relative equilibrium and PN the perpendicular on AB.

Now P describes a circle about N as centre with angular velocity ω, and therefore the force towards N must be $m\omega^2 \cdot PN$, or $m\omega^2 a \sin \theta$, where a is the radius of the sphere and θ the angle POB.

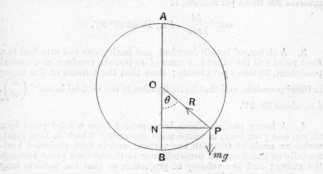

The horizontal component of the normal reaction, R, at P supplies this horizontal force, and the vertical component balances the weight of the particle.

Hence $\qquad\qquad R \sin \theta = m\omega^2 a \sin \theta$ ....(1),

and $\qquad\qquad R \cos \theta = mg$ ....(2).

From equation (1) we have, either $\sin \theta = 0$, or $R = m\omega^2 a$.

Substituting for R in (2), we have

$$\cos \theta = \frac{g}{\omega^2 a}\dots\dots\dots\dots\dots\dots(3).$$

Hence the particle is either at the lowest point, where $\sin \theta = 0$, or at a point determined by equation (3).

The value of θ given by (3) is impossible unless $g < \omega^2 a$, *i.e.*, unless the angular velocity ω is greater than $\left(\dfrac{g}{a}\right)^{\frac{1}{2}}$. If the angular velocity be less than this quantity, the only position of relative rest of the particle is at the lowest point of the sphere.

EXAMPLES. XXIV.

1. A mass of 4 pounds is tied at the end of a string, of length 3 feet, and revolves as a conical pendulum, the string being always inclined to the vertical at an angle of 45°; find the tension of the string and the velocity of the particle.

2. Shew that the inclination to the vertical of the string of a conical pendulum, when the string is 20 inches long and the pendulum revolves 200 times per minute, is

$$\cos^{-1}\frac{54}{125\pi^2}, \; i.e., \text{ about } 87° 30'.$$

3. A string, of length four feet, and having one end attached to a fixed point and the other to a mass of 40 pounds, revolves, as a conical pendulum, 30 times per minute; shew that the tension of the string is $160\pi^2$ poundals, and that its inclination to the vertical is $\cos^{-1}\left(\dfrac{8}{\pi^2}\right)$, *i.e.*, about 35° 51′.

4. A heavy particle which is suspended from a fixed point by a string, one yard long, is raised until the string, which is kept tight, makes an angle of 60° with the vertical, and is then projected horizontally in the direction perpendicular to the vertical plane through the string; find the velocity of projection so that the particle may move in a horizontal plane.

5. A railway carriage, of mass 2 tons, is moving at the rate of 60 miles per hour on a curve of 770 feet radius; if the outer rail be not raised above the inner, shew that the lateral thrust of the outer rail is equal to the weight of about 1408 pounds.

6. A train is travelling at the rate of 40 miles per hour on a curve, the radius of which is a quarter of a mile. If the distance between the rails be five feet, find how much the outer rail must be raised above the inner, so that there may be no lateral thrust on the rails.

7. A train is travelling at the rate of 30 miles per hour on a curve the radius of which is 400 yards. If the distance between the rails be five feet, find how much the outer rail must be raised above the inner so that there may be no lateral thrust on the rails.

8. A railway carriage moves on a circular curve; find to what height the outer rail must be raised above the inner so that there may be no lateral thrust on the rails if the radius of the curve be 1320 feet, the breadth between the rails 5 feet, and the carriage have a velocity of 45 miles per hour.

9. A mass is hung from the roof of a railway carriage by means of a string, six feet long; shew that, when the train is moving on a curve of radius 100 yards at the rate of 30 miles per hour, the mass will move from the vertical through a distance of 1 foot $2\frac{1}{4}$ inches approximately.

10. A bowl, 3 inches deep, is made from a spherical surface whose radius is 6 inches and rotates about its vertical axis. Find the greatest number of revolutions which it can make in a minute, if a particle can rest on its surface without being thrown out.

11. If 2θ be the vertical angle of a smooth hollow cone, whose axis is vertical and vertex downwards, shew that the distance from its axis of a body, moving in a circle on its surface and making n revolutions per second, is

$$\frac{g \cot \theta}{4\pi^2 n^2}.$$

12. The sails of a windmill are about 29 feet long, and revolve 10 times per minute; shew that a man clinging to the outer end of one of these sails would, at the highest point of his path, experience no reaction from the sail, and therefore could for a moment leave go without falling.

13. A heavy particle is connected by an inextensible string, 3 feet long, to a fixed point, and describes a circle in a vertical plane passing through the fixed point, making 600 revolutions per minute; neglecting the small variations in the speed of the particle, find the ratios of the tensions of the string in its two vertical positions and in its horizontal position.

14. Two particles, of the same mass, are fastened respectively to the middle point and one extremity of a weightless string, and are laid upon a smooth table, the other end of the string being fastened to a point in the table.

If the string be pulled tight, and the particles be so projected that they always remain in a straight line, shew that the tensions in the two portions of the string are as 3 : 2.

15. A train, moving in a straight line with velocity v, comes to a curve of radius r; shew that the mean slope of the surface of the water in a fixed tumbler carried by the train, or the mean deflection of a plummet attached by a short cord, will be

$$\tan^{-1}\frac{v^2}{gr}.$$

16. A particle, of mass m, is fastened by a string, of length l, to a point at a distance b above a smooth table; if the particle be made to revolve on the table n times per second, find the reaction of the table. What is the greatest value of n, so that the particle may remain in contact with the table?

17. A wet open umbrella is held with its handle upright and made to rotate about it at the rate of 14 revolutions in 33 seconds. If the rim of the umbrella be a circle of one yard in diameter, and its height above the ground be four feet, shew that the drops shaken off from the rim meet the ground in a circle of about five feet in diameter. If the mass of a drop be ·01 of an ounce, shew that the force necessary to keep it attached to the umbrella is about ·021 of a poundal and is inclined at an angle $\tan^{-1}\frac{1}{3}$ to the vertical.

18. A particle, of mass m, on a smooth table is fastened to one end of a fine string which passes through a small hole in the table and supports at its other end a particle of mass $2m$, the particle m being held at a distance c from the hole. Find the velocity with which m must be projected, so that it may describe a circle of radius c.

19. Two masses, m and m', are placed on a smooth table and connected by a light string passing through a small ring fixed to the table. If they be projected with velocities v and v' respectively at right angles to the portions of the string, which is initially tight, find the ratio in which the string must be divided at the ring, so that both particles may describe circles about the ring as centre.

20. Two masses, m and m', are connected by a string, of length c, which passes through a small ring; find how many revolutions per second the smaller mass, m', must make, as a conical pendulum, in order that the greater mass may hang at rest at a distance a from the ring.

21. A string, passing through a small hole in a smooth horizontal table, has a small sphere, of mass m, attached to each end of it; the upper sphere revolves in a circle on the table when suddenly it strikes an obstacle and loses half its velocity; find what diminution must be made in the mass of the lower sphere, so that the upper one may continue rotating in a circle.

22. A string PAQ passes through a hole A in a smooth table, the portion AP lying on the table, and AQ being at an angle of $45°$ to the vertical, and below the table, so that P and Q are in the same vertical line. If masses be attached at P and Q and, the strings being stretched, be each projected horizontally, find the ratio of the masses, so that the plane PAQ may always be vertical and the angle PAQ always $45°$. If the string be four feet in length, find the time of revolution.

23. A body, of mass m, moves on a horizontal table being attached to a fixed point on the table by an extensible string whose modulus of elasticity is λ; given the original length a of the string, find the velocity of the particle when it is describing a circle of radius r.

24. A particle is attached to a point A by an elastic string, whose modulus of elasticity is twice the weight of the particle and whose natural length is l, and whirled so that the string describes the surface of a cone whose axis is the vertical line through A. If the distance below A of the circular path during steady motion be l, shew that the velocity of the particle must be $\sqrt{3gl}$.

25. In Ex. 8 find the lateral thrust when the velocity is (1) 30, (2) 60 miles per hour, the mass of the carriage being 10 tons.

In each case state which rail causes the thrust.

CHAPTER X.

MOTION ON A SMOOTH CURVE UNDER THE ACTION OF GRAVITY.

145. THE general case of the motion of a particle, constrained to move on a given curve under any given forces, is beyond the scope of the present book; so also is the motion of a particle constrained to move under gravity on a given curve.

There is one proposition, however, relating to the motion of a particle under gravity which we can prove in an elementary manner, and which is very useful for determining many of the circumstances of the motion.

146. Theorem. *If a particle slide down an arc of any smooth curve in a vertical plane, and if u be its initial velocity and v its velocity after sliding through a vertical distance h, to shew that* $v^2 = u^2 + 2gh$.

Let A be the point of the curve from which the particle starts, and B the point whose distance from A, measured vertically, is h. Draw AM and BN horizontal to meet any vertical line in M and N.

Let P and Q be two points on the curve, very close to one another, and draw PR and QS perpendicular to MN. Then PQ is very approximately a small portion of a straight line. Draw QV vertical to meet PR in V.

The acceleration at P along PQ is $g \cos VQP$ and hence, if v_P and v_Q be the velocities at P and Q, we have

$$v_Q^2 = v_P^2 + 2g \cos VQP \,.\, PQ = v_P^2 + 2g \,.\, VQ.$$
$$\therefore \ v_Q^2 - v_P^2 = 2g \,.\, VQ,$$

i.e. the change in the square of the velocity is due to the vertical height between P and Q. Since this is true for every element of arc, it is true for the whole arc AB.

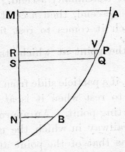

Hence the change in the square of the velocity in passing from A to B is that due to the vertical height h, so that

$$v^2 = u^2 + 2gh.$$

The theorem in the preceding article may be deduced directly from the Principle of the Conservation of Energy.

For, since the curve is smooth, the reaction of the arc is always perpendicular to the direction of motion of the particle. Hence, by *Statics*, Art. 196, no work is done on the body by the pressure of the curve. The only force that does work is the weight of the particle.

Hence, since the change of energy is equal to the work done, we have

$$\tfrac{1}{2}mv^2 - \tfrac{1}{2}mu^2 = \text{work done by the weight} = mgh.$$
$$\therefore \ v^2 = u^2 + 2gh.$$

147. If, instead of sliding *down* the smooth curve, the particle be started along it with velocity u, so that it moves *upwards*, the velocity v when its vertical distance from the starting point is h is, similarly, given by the equation

$$v^2 = u^2 - 2gh.$$

Hence the velocity of the particle will not vanish until it arrives at a point of the curve whose vertical height above the point of projection is $\dfrac{u^2}{2g}$.

It will be noticed that the height to which the particle will ascend is independent of the *shape* of the constraining curve, nor need it continually ascend. The particle may first ascend, then descend, then ascend again, and so on; the point at which it comes to rest finally will be at a height $\dfrac{u^2}{2g}$ above the point at which its velocity is u.

It follows that, if a particle slide from rest upon a smooth arc, it will come to rest when it is at the same vertical height as the starting point. An approximate example is the Switch-back railway in which the car almost rises to the same height as that of the point at which it started. The slight difference between theory and experiment is caused by the resistance of the air and the friction of the rails which, although small, are not quite negligible.

The heavier the car, the less will be found to be the difference between theory and experiment.

The expression for the velocity when the particle is at a vertical distance h from the starting point is the same, whether the particle be at that instant ascending or descending.

The theorem of the last article is true, not only of motion under gravity, but also in any case of the motion of a particle on a smooth curve under the action of a constant force in a constant direction, *e.g.* in the case of motion on a smooth inclined plane, if we substitute for "g" the acceleration caused by the forces.

It is also true if we substitute for the constraining curve an inextensible string fastened to a fixed point, or a weightless rod which is always normal to the path of the particle.

We cannot, in general, find the *time* of describing any given arc without the use of the Differential Calculus.

148. Galileo's Experiment. It is not easy to accurately perform experiments on a body sliding down a smooth curve; for it is practically impossible to get a smooth curve. We can however in the analogous case of a particle tied by a string verify experimentally the theorem of Art. 146.

Tie a heavy body, such as a lead sphere, to one end of a light flexible string the other end of which is attached to

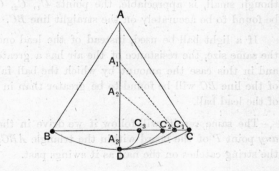

a fixed point A. Let the body swing about this point as centre in front of a blackboard.

Mark the point B on the blackboard from which the sphere is allowed to start and through it draw a horizontal line BA_3C. If the sphere be now allowed to swing about A, it will be found to come to rest at a point C which is very nearly on the straight line BA_3.

Now drive in a nail at a point A_1 vertically below A, the nail jutting out sufficiently to intercept the string. Start the sphere from the same point B as before; it will describe the arc BD and will then move on an arc DC_1 about A_1 as centre. The point C_1 at which it comes to rest will be found to be very nearly on the horizontal straight line. Reverse the operation, starting the sphere from C_1, and it will be found to describe the path C_1DB.

Repeat the experiment, driving in nails successively at A_2 and A_3. In each case the same result will be obtained, *viz.*, that if the sphere started from B it will come to rest at a point very nearly on the horizontal line through B.

If it were not for the resistance of the air, which, though small, is appreciable, the points C_1, C_2, C_3 would be found to be accurately on the straight line BC.

If a light ball be used, instead of the lead one, but of the same size, the resistance of the air has a greater effect, and in this case the amount by which the ball falls short of the line BC will be found to be greater than in the case of the lead ball.

The same results will follow if we drive in the nail at *any* point P of the board within the triangle ABC, so that the string catches on the nail as it swings past.

149. Motion on the outside of a vertical circle.

A particle slides from rest at the highest point down the outside of the arc of a smooth vertical circle; to shew that it will leave the curve when it has described vertically a distance equal to one third of the radius.

Let O be the centre, and A the highest point of the circle. Let v be the velocity of the particle when at a point P of the curve, R the pressure of the curve there, and r the radius of the circle. Draw PN perpendicular to the vertical radius OA, and let $AN = h$.

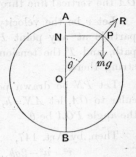

Then $v^2 = 2g \cdot AN = 2gh.$

The force along PO is

$$mg \cos \theta - R,$$

where θ is the angle POA.

But the force along PO must, by Art. 135, be $m \cdot \dfrac{v^2}{r}$.

$$\therefore \ m \frac{v^2}{r} = mg \cos \theta - R.$$

$$\therefore \ R = m \left[g \cos \theta - \frac{v^2}{r} \right] = m \left[g \frac{r-h}{r} - \frac{2gh}{r} \right]$$

$$= mg \frac{r - 3h}{r}.$$

Now R vanishes, and changes its sign, when $3h = r$, *i.e.*, when $h = \dfrac{r}{3}$. The particle will then leave the curve, and describe a parabola freely; for, to make it continue on the circle, the pressure R would have to become a tension; but this is impossible since the curve cannot *pull* the particle.

150. Motion in a vertical circle. *A particle, of mass m, is suspended by a string, of length r, from a fixed point and hangs vertically. It is then projected, with velocity u, so that it describes a vertical circle; to find the tension and velocity at any point of the subsequent motion, and to find also the condition that it may just make complete revolutions.*

Let O be the point to which the string is attached, and OA the vertical line through O.

Let v be the velocity of the particle at any point P of its path, and T the tension of the string there.

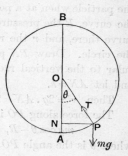

Let PN be drawn perpendicular to OA, let $AN = h$, and let the angle POA be θ.

Then, by Art. 147,

$$v^2 = u^2 - 2gh \dots \dots (1).$$

Also, by Art. 135, $m\dfrac{v^2}{r} =$ force at P along the normal, PO, to the path of the particle.

$$\therefore\ m\frac{v^2}{r} = T - mg\cos\theta = T - mg\,\frac{r-h}{r},$$

$$\therefore\ T = m\,\frac{v^2 + g(r-h)}{r} = m\,\frac{u^2 + g(r-3h)}{r} \dots \dots (2).$$

These two equations give the velocity of the particle, and the tension of the string, at any point of the path.

The particle will not reach the highest point B if the tension of the string become negative; for then, in order that the particle might continue revolving in a circle, the pull of the string would have to change into a push, and this is impossible in the case of a string.

Hence the particle will *just* make complete revolutions if the tension vanish at the highest point, where $h = 2r$.

This, from (2), is the case if

$$u^2 + g(r - 6r) = 0,$$

i.e., if

$$u^2 = 5gr.$$

Hence, for complete revolutions, u must not be less than $\sqrt{5gr}$.

When $u = \sqrt{5gr}$, the tension at the lowest point, by (2),

$$= m\frac{5gr + rg}{r} = 6mg \text{ poundals.}$$

Hence the string must, at the least, be able to bear a weight equal to six times the weight of the body.

*151. Newton's Experimental Law. By using the theorem of Art. 147, we can shew how Newton arrived at his law of impact as enunciated in Art. 118.

We suspend two spheres, of small dimensions, by parallel strings OA and $O'B$, whose lengths are so adjusted that when hanging freely the spheres are just in contact with their centres in a horizontal line.

One ball, A, is then drawn back, the string being kept tight, until its centre is at a height AM, $(= h)$, above its original position and is allowed to fall. Its velocity v on hitting the second ball B is $\sqrt{2gh}$.

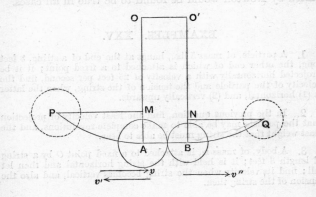

Let v' and v'' be the velocities of the spheres immediately after the impact, and h' and h'' the heights to which they rise before again coming to rest, so that

$$v' = \sqrt{2gh'}, \quad \text{and} \quad v'' = \sqrt{2gh''}.$$

The sphere A may either rebound, remain at rest, or follow after B.

Taking the former case the velocity of separation is

$$v' + v'', \quad i.e., \quad \sqrt{2g}\left(\sqrt{h'} + \sqrt{h''}\right).$$

Also the velocity of approach was $\sqrt{2g} \cdot \sqrt{h}$.

We should find that the ratio of $\left(\sqrt{h'} + \sqrt{h''}\right)$ to $\sqrt{h}$ would be the same whatever be the value of h and the ratio of the mass of A to that of B, and that it would depend simply on the substances of which the masses consist.

We have only considered one of the simpler cases. By carefully arranging the starting points and the instants of starting from rest, both spheres might be drawn aside and allowed to impinge so that at the instant of impact both were at the lowest points of their path. The law enunciated by Newton would be found to be true in all cases.

EXAMPLES. XXV.

1. A particle, of mass 5 lbs., hangs at the end of a string, 3 feet long, the other end of which is attached to a fixed point; if it be projected horizontally with a velocity of 25 feet per second, find the velocity of the particle and the tension of the string, when the latter is (1) horizontal, and (2) vertically upwards.

2. In the previous question, find the least velocity of projection that the particle may be able to make complete revolutions, and the least weight that the string must be able to bear.

3. A body, of mass m, is attached to a fixed point O by a string of length 3 feet; it is held with the string horizontal and then let fall; find its velocity when the string becomes vertical, and also the tension of the string then.

4. A smooth hoop, of diameter 9 feet, is placed in a vertical plane, and a bead slides on the hoop starting from rest at the highest point of the hoop; find its velocity,

(1) at the lowest point,

(2) at the end of a horizontal diameter,

(3) when it has described one-third of the vertical distance to the lowest point,

(4) when it has described one-third of the arcual distance to the lowest point.

5. A heavy particle is attached by a string, 10 feet long, to a fixed point, and swung round in a vertical circle. Find the tension and velocity at the lowest point of the circle, so that the particle may just make complete revolutions.

6. A cannon, of mass 12 cwt., rests horizontally, being supported by two vertical ropes, each of length 9 feet, and projects a ball of mass 36 lbs.; if the cannon be raised through 2·25 feet by the recoil, find the initial velocity of the ball, and the tension of the ropes at the instant of discharge and at the instant when the cannon first comes to rest.

7. A small heavy ring can slide upon a cord, 34 feet long, which has its ends attached to two fixed points, A and B, in the same horizontal line and 30 feet apart. The ring starts—the string being tight—from a point of the string distant 5 feet from A; shew that, when it has described a length of the cord equal to 3 feet, its velocity will be 10·12 feet per second nearly.

8. A particle slides down the arc of a vertical circle; shew that its velocity at the lowest point varies as the chord of the arc of descent.

9. A particle runs down the outside of a smooth vertical circle, starting from rest at its highest point; find the latus rectum of the parabola which it describes after leaving the surface.

10. A ball, of mass m, is just disturbed from the top of a smooth vertical circular tube, and runs down the interior of the tube impinging on a ball, of mass $2m$, which is at rest at the bottom of the tube; if the coefficient of restitution be $\frac{1}{3}$, find the height to which each ball will rise in the tube after the impact.

11. Two equal ivory balls are suspended by parallel threads, so that they are in contact, and so that the line joining their centres is horizontal, and two feet below the points of attachment of the threads. Determine the coefficient of restitution between the balls when it is found that, by allowing one ball to start from a position when its thread is inclined at 60° to the vertical, it causes the other ball after impact to rise through a vertical distance of $6\frac{3}{4}$ inches.

12. A circular arc, subtending 30° at its centre, is fixed in a vertical plane so that its highest point is in the same horizontal plane with its centre, and a smooth particle slides down this curve starting from rest at its highest point. Shew that the latus rectum of the parabola, which it describes after leaving the curve, is half the radius of the circular arc.

13. A weightless inextensible string, of length $2l$, is fastened at its extremities to two points A and B in the same horizontal line, at a distance l apart, and supports a body C of mass m, tied to its middle point. If C be projected perpendicular to the plane ACB with double the velocity requisite for it to describe a complete circle, find the greatest and least tension of the strings.

If one portion of the string be cut when C is halfway between its highest and lowest points, find the subsequent motion.

14. A smooth tube, in the form of 7 sides of a regular octagon each of whose sides is a, is placed so that one extreme side is lowest and horizontal and the other extreme side is vertical; an inelastic particle is just placed inside and connected by a string passing through the tube with an equal particle hanging vertically; find the velocity of the particles when the first leaves the tube.

15. Shew that the effect of the rotation of the earth is to lessen the apparent weight of a body at the equator by $\frac{1}{289}$ of itself, the earth being assumed to be a sphere of radius 4000 miles.

Shew also that the apparent weight of a train at the equator, which is travelling east at the rate of a mile per minute, is decreased by about ·004 of itself.

16. A particle slides down a smooth curve, through a vertical height h, and thus acquires sufficient velocity to run completely round the inside of a vertical circle of radius r (as in the centrifugal railway); prove that $2h$ must be greater than $5r$.

17. In the experiment of Art. 151 the spheres are of equal mass and the lengths of the strings attached to them are equal; the first descends through an arc whose chord is x, and the second ascends through an arc whose chord is y; shew that the coefficient of restitution is $\frac{2y - x}{x}$.

18. A small ball is tied to one end of an inelastic string the other end of which is attached to a fixed point O. It is held, with the string tight, at a point which is $1\frac{1}{2}$ feet above O and then let fall; if the length of the string be 3 feet, find its velocity immediately after the string again becomes tight and the height above O to which it subsequently rises.

19. A particle is projected along the inner surface of a smooth vertical circle of radius a, its velocity at the lowest point being $\frac{1}{5}\sqrt{95ga}$; shew that it will leave the circle at an angular distance $\cos^{-1}\frac{3}{5}$ from the highest point and that its velocity then is $\frac{1}{5}\sqrt{15ga}$.

20. A bullet of mass 200 grammes is moving with a horizontal velocity of 400 metres per second; it hits the centre of a face of a cube of wood, of mass 20 kilogrammes, which is suspended by a string, and becomes embedded in it. Through what height does the wood move before coming to rest?

21. A box of sand, of mass 2000 lb., is suspended by two equal vertical cords each 8 ft. long and a shot whose mass is 20 lbs. is fired into it in a horizontal direction passing through its centre of gravity and remains embedded; if the centre of gravity of the box recoils through a circular arc the length of whose chord is 6 feet, shew that the velocity of the shot was 1212 ft. per sec.

In general, if m and M be the masses of the bullet and box of sand, l be the length of each vertical cord, and k be the chord of recoil, the velocity of the shot is $\dfrac{M+m}{m}\,k\,.\,\sqrt{\dfrac{g}{l}}$.

[We can thus find the velocity of any bullet. We have only to determine experimentally the value of k.]

CHAPTER XI.

SIMPLE HARMONIC MOTION. PENDULUMS.

152. Theorem. *If a point Q describe a circle with uniform angular velocity, and if P be always the foot of the perpendicular drawn from Q upon a fixed diameter AOA' of the circle, to shew that the acceleration of P is directed towards the centre, O, of the circle and varies as the distance of P from O, and to find the velocity of P and its time of describing any space.*

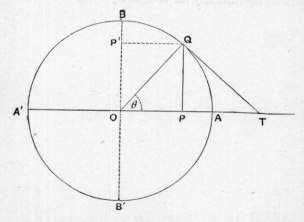

Let a be the radius of the circle, and let the angle QOA be θ. Draw QT the tangent at Q to meet OA in T.

Let ω be the constant angular velocity with which the point Q describes the circle.

Since P is always at the foot of the perpendicular to AA' drawn from Q, its velocity and acceleration are the same as the resolved parts, parallel to AO, of the velocity and acceleration of Q.

By Art. 135, Cor. I., the acceleration of Q is $a\omega^2$ towards O.

Hence the acceleration of P along $PO = a\omega^2 \cos\theta = \omega^2 . OP$, and therefore varies as the distance of P from the centre of the circle.

Also the velocity of P

$$= a\omega \cos QTO = a\omega \sin \theta = \omega . PQ = \omega \sqrt{a^2 - x^2} \ldots\ldots(1),$$

where OP is x.

This velocity is zero at A and A', and greatest at O.

Also the acceleration vanishes, and changes its sign, as the point P passes through O.

The point P therefore moves from rest at A, has its greatest velocity at O, comes to rest again at A', and then retraces its path to A.

Also the time in which P describes any distance AP

$$= \text{time in which } Q \text{ describes the arc } AQ$$

$$= \frac{\theta}{\omega} = \frac{1}{\omega} \cos^{-1}\left(\frac{x}{a}\right) \ldots\ldots\ldots\ldots\ldots\ldots\ldots\ldots(2).$$

Hence the time from A to $A' = \frac{1}{\omega} \cos^{-1}(-1) = \frac{\pi}{\omega}$.

Also the time from A to A' and back again to A

$$= \frac{2\pi}{\omega} \ldots\ldots\ldots\ldots\ldots\ldots\ldots(3).$$

153. Simple Harmonic Motion. Def. *If a point move in a straight line so that its acceleration is always directed towards, and varies as its distance from, a fixed point in the straight line, the point is said to move with simple harmonic motion.*

The point P in the previous article moves with simple harmonic motion.

From the results (1), (2) and (3) of the previous article we see, by equating ω^2 to μ, that if a point move with simple harmonic motion, starting from rest at a distance a from the fixed centre O, and moving with acceleration $\mu \cdot OP$, then

(1) its velocity when at a distance x from O is

$$\sqrt{\mu\,(a^2 - x^2)},$$

(2) the time that has elapsed when the point is at a distance x from O is $\dfrac{1}{\sqrt{\mu}} \cos^{-1} \dfrac{x}{a}$,

and (3) the time that elapses before it is again in its initial position is $\dfrac{2\pi}{\sqrt{\mu}}$.

The range, OA or OA', of the moving point on either side of the centre O is called the **Amplitude** of the motion.

The time that elapses from any instant till the instant in which the moving point is again moving through the same position with the same velocity and direction is called the **Periodic Time** of the motion.

It will be noted that **the periodic time, $\dfrac{2\pi}{\sqrt{\mu}}$, is independent of the amplitude of the motion.**

154. From the result (2) of the previous article, it follows that, if t be the time the moving point takes to describe the distance from rest at a to the distance x, then

$$x = a \cos\left(\sqrt{\mu}\,t\right).$$

From (1) it then follows that the velocity v

$$= \sqrt{\mu\left[a^2 - a^2 \cos^2\left(\sqrt{\mu}\,t\right)\right]}$$
$$= a\sqrt{\mu}\sin\left(\sqrt{\mu}\,t\right).$$

155. Examples of Simple Harmonic Motion.

This motion is of frequent occurrence in Physical and Mechanical problems.

It is the motion of a point of a tuning fork, and of a point in a violin string when the string is plucked sideways. The motion of a pendulum (Art. 158) is simple harmonic when the angle through which it moves is small; so also is that of a mass tied to an elastic string or a spring and allowed to oscillate up and down in a vertical line. The motion of the revolving mass of a Conical Pendulum (Art. 140) as seen from a distant point in its plane is simple harmonic; and also that of Jupiter's satellites when observed from a distant point in their plane.

Generally the motion of all elastic bodies, in which the force brought into play is proportional to the displacement, follows the same law.

The expression Simple Harmonic Motion is often shortened into S.H.M.

156. Ex. 1. *A point moves with simple harmonic motion whose period is 4 seconds; if it start from rest at a distance 4 feet from the centre of its path, find the time that elapses before it has described 2 feet and the velocity it has then acquired.*

If the acceleration be μ times the distance, we have $\dfrac{2\pi}{\sqrt{\mu}} = 4$.

$$\therefore \quad \mu = \left(\frac{\pi}{2}\right)^2.$$

When the point has described 2 feet it is then at a distance of 2 feet from the centre of its motion.

Hence, by Art. 153 (2), the time that has elapsed

$$= \frac{1}{\sqrt{\mu}} \cos^{-1} \frac{x}{a} = \frac{1}{\frac{\pi}{2}} \cos^{-1} \left(\frac{2}{4} \right) = \frac{2}{\pi} \times \frac{\pi}{3} = \frac{2}{3} \text{ second.}$$

Also, by Art. 153 (1), the velocity it has acquired

$$= \sqrt{\mu (a^2 - x^2)} = \sqrt{\left(\frac{\pi}{2} \right)^2 (4^2 - 2^2)} = \pi \sqrt{3} \text{ feet per second.}$$

Ex. 2. *A point starts from rest at a distance of 16 feet from the centre of its path and moves with simple harmonic motion; if in its initial position the acceleration be 4 ft.-sec. units, find* (1) *its velocity when at a distance of 8 feet from the centre and when passing through the centre, and* (2) *its periodic time.*

(1) Let the acceleration be μ times the distance.

Then $\mu \times 16 = 4$, *i.e* $\mu = \frac{1}{4}$.

Hence, by Art. 153 (1), its velocity when at a distance of 8 feet from the centre $= \sqrt{\frac{1}{4} (16^2 - 8^2)} = \sqrt{48} = 4 \sqrt{3}$ feet per second.

Also its velocity when passing through the centre

$$= \sqrt{\frac{1}{4} \cdot 16^2} = 8 \text{ feet per second.}$$

(2) Its periodic time $= \frac{2\pi}{\sqrt{\mu}} = 4\pi =$ about $12\frac{4}{7}$ seconds.

Ex. 3. *A light spiral spring, whose unstretched length is l cms. and whose modulus of elasticity is the weight of n grammes, is suspended by one end and has a mass of m grammes attached to the other; shew that the time of a vertical oscillation of the mass is*

$$2\pi \sqrt{\frac{m}{n} \cdot \frac{l}{g}}.$$

Let O be the fixed end of the spring, OA its position when unstretched. When the particle is at P, where $OP = x$, let T be the tension of the spring. Then, by Hooke's Law,

$$T = \lambda \frac{x - l}{l} = ng \frac{x - l}{l}.$$

Hence the resultant upward force on $P = T - mg$

$$= ng \frac{x - l}{l} - mg = \frac{ng}{l} \left[x - \frac{m + n}{n} l \right].$$

Let O' be a point on the vertical through O such that

$$OO' = \frac{m + n}{n} l.$$

Hence the resultant upward force on P

$$= \frac{ng}{l}[OP - OO'] = \frac{ng}{l} \cdot O'P.$$

Hence the upward acceleration of $P = \frac{n}{m} \frac{g}{l} O'P$, *i.e.*, its motion is simple harmonic about O' as centre, and its time of oscillation, by Art. 153,

$$= 2\pi \div \sqrt{\frac{n}{m} \frac{g}{l}} = 2\pi \sqrt{\frac{ml}{ng}}.$$

It will be noted that O' is the point where the mass would hang at rest. For, if it were placed at rest at P, the upward tension would

$$= ng \frac{OO' - l}{l} = ng \left[\frac{\frac{m+n}{n} l - l}{l} \right] = mg,$$

and would therefore just balance its weight.

EXAMPLES. XXVI.

1. A particle moves in a straight line with simple harmonic motion; find the time of an oscillation from rest to rest when

   (1) the acceleration at a distance 2 feet is 4 ft.-sec. units;

   (2) the acceleration at a distance 3 inches is 9 ft.-sec. units;

   (3) the acceleration at a distance one foot is π^2 ft.-sec. units.

2. In each of the cases in the previous example, find the velocity when the point is passing through the centre of its path, the amplitudes of the motions being respectively 2 feet, 3 inches, and one foot.

3. A particle moves in a straight line with simple harmonic motion, and its periods of oscillation are (1) 2, (2) $\frac{1}{10}$, and (3) π seconds, respectively; the amplitude of its motion in each case is one foot; find the velocity of the particle when moving through the centre of its path.

4. A point, moving with s.h.m., has a velocity of 4 feet per second when passing through the centre of its path, and its period is π seconds; what is its velocity when it has described one foot from the position in which its velocity is zero?

5. A point moves with s.h.m.; if, when at distances of 3 and 4 feet from the centre of its path, its velocities are 8 and 6 feet per second respectively, find its period and its acceleration when at its greatest distance from the centre.

6. A mass of one gramme vibrates through a millimetre on each side of the middle point of its path 256 times per second; assuming its motion to be simple harmonic, shew that the maximum force upon the particle is $\frac{1}{10}(512\pi)^2$ dynes.

7. A horizontal shelf moves vertically with s.h.m., whose complete period is one second; find the greatest amplitude in centimetres that it can have, so that objects resting on the shelf may always remain in contact with it.

8. A mass of 12 lbs. is hanging by a light spiral spring which stretches one inch for each pound-weight of tension. If the upper end of the spring be instantaneously raised four inches and then held fast, find the amplitude and period of the subsequent motion of the mass.

9. A weight is attached to the lower end of a light spiral spring whose upper end is fixed and is released. If it oscillate in a vertical line through a space of six inches, what is the period of its oscillation?

10. An elastic string, to the middle point of which a particle is attached, is stretched to twice its natural length and placed on a smooth horizontal table, and its ends are then fixed. The particle is then displaced in the direction of the string; find the period of oscillation.

11. A rod AB is in motion so that the end B moves with uniform speed u in a circle whose centre is C, whilst the end A moves in a straight line passing through C. If $AB=BC=a$, and $AC=x$, shew that the velocity of A is $u\dfrac{\sqrt{4a^2-x^2}}{a}$, and that it moves with simple harmonic motion.

[Hence we have a method of obtaining practically a simple harmonic motion. Let CB be a revolving crank and BA a connecting rod, of length equal to CB, attached to a point A, which, as in the case of the piston of a steam engine, is compelled to move in a straight line CA. Then the motion of A is simple harmonic.]

157.   *Extension to motion in a curve.*

Suppose that a moving point P is describing a portion, AOA', of a curve of any shape, starting from rest at A and moving so that its tangential acceleration is always along the arc towards O and equal to μ. arc OP, then the propositions of Art. 153 are true with slight modifications.

For let $O'B$ be a straight line equal in length to the

arc OA, and let P' be a point describing it with acceleration $\mu \cdot O'P'$; also let $O'P' = \text{arc } OP$.

Since the acceleration of P' in its path is always the same as that of P, the velocities acquired in the same time are the same, and the times of describing the same distances are the same.

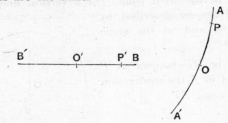

Hence

(1) The velocity of P = the velocity of P'
$$= \sqrt{\mu \left(O'B^2 - O'P'^2\right)} = \sqrt{\mu \left\{(\text{arc } OA)^2 - (\text{arc } OP)^2\right\}},$$

(2) The time from A to P = time from B to P'
$$= \frac{1}{\sqrt{\mu}} \cos^{-1}\left(\frac{O'P'}{O'B}\right) = \frac{1}{\sqrt{\mu}} \cos^{-1}\left(\frac{\text{arc } OP}{\text{arc } OA}\right),$$

and (3) The time from A to A' and back again $= \dfrac{2\pi}{\sqrt{\mu}}$.

PENDULUMS.

158. Simple pendulum. A particle tied to one end of a string, the other end of which is fixed, and which oscillates in a vertical circle having the fixed point as centre, is called a simple pendulum.

The time of oscillation depends on the angle through which the string swings on each side of the vertical.

If however this angle of oscillation be small, we shall shew in the next article that the time of oscillation of the pendulum is approximately constant.

159. Theorem. *If a particle be tied by a string to a fixed point, and allowed to oscillate through a* **small** *angle about the vertical position, to shew that the time of a complete oscillation is* $2\pi \sqrt{\dfrac{l}{g}}$, *where l is the length of the string.*

Let O be the fixed point, OA a vertical line, AP a portion of the arc described by the particle, and let the angle AOP be θ.

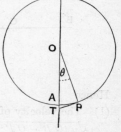

If PT be the tangent at P meeting OA in T, the acceleration of the bob along PT

$= g \sin \theta$

$= g\theta$, approximately, if θ be small

$= \dfrac{g}{l} \times$ arc AP.

The acceleration along the tangent to the path therefore varies as the arcual distance from the lowest point.

It follows that the motion is harmonic and hence, by Art. 157 (3), the time of a complete oscillation is independent of the extent of the oscillation, and equals

$$\frac{2\pi}{\sqrt{\dfrac{g}{l}}}, \ i.e. \ 2\pi \sqrt{\frac{l}{g}}.$$

The first discovery of this principle of the time of swinging of a pendulum is said to have been made by Galileo about the year 1582; he observed that the great bronze lamp which hangs from the roof of the cathedral at Pisa seemed to have a uniform time of swing, whatever be the arc through which it moved, and he verified the fact by counting the beats of his pulse.

Ex. *Find the length of a pendulum which will oscillate 56 times in 55 seconds.*

The time of oscillation is $\dfrac{55}{56}$ seconds. Hence, if l be the length of the pendulum, we have

$$\frac{55}{56} = \pi \sqrt{\frac{l}{g}} = \frac{22}{7} \sqrt{\frac{l}{32}};$$

$$\therefore \sqrt{\frac{l}{32}} = \frac{5}{16}.$$

$$\therefore l = 32 \times \frac{25}{256} = \frac{25}{8} \text{ feet} = 37\tfrac{1}{2} \text{ inches.}$$

160. Experimental Verification. The important result of the previous article may be easily verified to a fair degree of accuracy. We cannot actually make use of the "particle" and the "massless string" of the mathematical demonstration; but a small sphere, made of brass or other metal, with a hook firmly fastened to it and a light strong silk thread will make a very good approximation.

First, *to shew that the time varies as the square root of the length.*

Take several such spheres, and to them attach threads the other ends of which are attached to fixed points; for example by passing the threads through eyes screwed into a fixed horizontal bar, and then tieing their other ends to some convenient support. Adjust the lengths so that the distances measured from the centre of the spheres to the points from which the strings swing are in the ratios of 1, 4, 9, 16.... [For example, let the lengths be 6 ins., 2 ft., 4 ft. 6 ins., 8 ft....] Start the balls all swinging, through small angles, at the same instant. Their times of oscillation will be found to be as 1, 2, 3, 4,... *i.e.* as the square roots of their lengths. This will be best seen if the observer sets only two swinging at a time. For example the first will be found to swing in half the time of the second, and hence will be found to complete every second complete swing at the same time as the second pendulum completes its swing.

So the first pendulum will be found to oscillate three times for each oscillation of the third pendulum, and hence every third oscillation of the first pendulum will be found to end simultaneously with successive swings of the third pendulum.

Similarly for any other case.

Secondly, *to shew that the time of oscillation is independent, approximately, of the material of which the bob is made.*

Take spheres, of the same size approximately, but made of different materials, provided that these materials are not made of very light substances such as cork. As in the first experiment attach them by strings of the same length and set them all swinging together. This may be done by pushing the spheres all side-ways to the same extent by means of a board, and then sharply withdrawing the board. The pendulums will then be found to swing in the same time for a large number of oscillations provided the lengths of the strings have been carefully adjusted so as to be equal. After some time the spheres, made of the lighter material, will be found to lag behind the others; this is because the resistance of the air has more effect on the lighter than on the heavier spheres.

Thirdly, *to find the value of g by means of a simple pendulum.*

Take one of the spheres and adjust the length of its string to a convenient distance, say about two feet. Carefully measure the distance from the point of suspension of the silk thread to the centre of the sphere. Set the sphere swinging and find the time T of a complete oscillation. This is best done by observing the time of (say) 40 observations and dividing the result by 40. [An ordinary watch with a seconds hand will give sufficiently accurate results.]

Then in the formula

$$T = 2\pi \sqrt{\frac{l}{g}},$$

of Art. 159, we now know both l and T, so that the value of g

$$= 4\pi^2 \frac{l}{T^2}.$$

By the use of a logarithm Table, or by ordinary calculation, we now easily obtain the value of g correct to the second place of decimals in foot-second units.

Similarly, if we measure l in centimetres, we shall get the value of g in the C.G.S. system.

161. Seconds Pendulum. A seconds pendulum is one which vibrates from rest to rest (*i.e.* makes half a *complete* oscillation) in one second.

Hence, if l be its length, we have

$$1 = \pi \sqrt{\frac{l}{g}}.$$

$$\therefore l = \frac{g}{\pi^2} \text{ feet.}$$

Since g varies at different points of the earth's surface, we see that the length of the seconds pendulum is not the same at all points of the earth.

For an approximate value, putting $g = 32 \cdot 2$ and $\pi = \frac{2\,2}{7}$, we have

$$l = 3 \cdot 26 \text{ feet} = 39 \cdot 12 \text{ inches.}$$

If we use the centimetre-second system we have, by putting $g = 981$, $l = 99 \cdot 3$ centimetres.

For the latitude of London more accurate values are $39 \cdot 13929\ldots$ inches and $99 \cdot 413\ldots$ centimetres.

EXAMPLES. XXVII.

[*In the following examples, π may be taken to be $\frac{22}{7}$.*]

1. If $g = 32 \cdot 2$, what is the length of a pendulum vibrating in $2 \cdot 5$ seconds?

2. The time of a complete vibration at a given place of a pendulum 64 metres long is 16 seconds; shew that the corresponding value of g is 987 cm.-sec. units.

3. A pendulum, 3 feet long, is observed to make 700 oscillations in 671 seconds; find approximately the value of g.

4. Given that the length of a seconds pendulum is $39 \cdot 12$ inches, find the lengths of the pendulums which will vibrate in (1) half a second, (2) one quarter of a second, (3) 2 seconds.

5. How many oscillations will a pendulum, of length $53 \cdot 41$ centimetres, make in 242 seconds at a place where g is 981?

6. Shew that a pendulum, one mile in length, would oscillate in 40 seconds nearly.

7. A pendulum, of length $37 \cdot 8$ inches, makes 183 beats in three minutes at a certain place; find the acceleration due to gravity there.

8. How many oscillations will a pendulum, of length 4 feet, make in one day?

9. A pendulum, 450 feet long, has been suspended in the Eiffel tower; prove that it makes a complete oscillation in about $23\frac{4}{7}$ seconds.

162. The result of Art. 159, although not mathematically accurate, is very approximately so. If the angle a through which the pendulum swings on each side of the vertical be $5°$, the result is within one two-thousandth part of the accurate result, so that a pendulum which beats seconds for very small oscillations would lose about 40 seconds per day, if made to vibrate through $5°$ on each side of the vertical.

163. The simple pendulum of which we have spoken is idealistic. In practice, a pendulum consists of a wire whose mass, although small, is not zero and a bob at the end which is not a particle. Whatever be the shape of the pendulum, the simple pendulum which oscillates in the same time as itself is called its **simple equivalent pendulum.**

The discussion of the connection between a rigid body and its simple equivalent pendulum is not within the range of this book. We may, however, mention that a uniform rod, of small section, swings about one end in the same time as a simple pendulum of two-thirds its length.

164. *Acceleration due to gravity.* Newton discovered, as a fundamental law of nature, that every particle attracts every other particle with a force which varies directly as the product of the masses and inversely as the square of the distance between them.

From this fact it can be shewn, as in any treatise dealing with Attractions, that a sphere attracts any particle *outside* itself just as if the whole mass of the sphere were collected at its centre, and hence that the acceleration caused by its attraction varies inversely as the square of the distance of the particle from the centre.

Similarly the attraction on a particle *inside* the earth can be shewn to vary directly as its distance from the centre of the earth.

Hence, if g_1 be the value of gravity at a height h above the earth's surface, g the value at the surface, and r the earth's radius, then $g_1 : g :: \dfrac{1}{(r+h)^2} : \dfrac{1}{r^2}$,

so that
$$g_1 = g \left(\frac{r}{r+h} \right)^2 .$$

So, if g_2 be the value at the bottom of a mine of depth d, we have $g_2 = g \dfrac{r-d}{r}$. The value of g is therefore greater at the earth's surface than either outside or inside the earth.

165. We shall now investigate the effect on the time of oscillation of a simple pendulum due to a *small* change in the value of g, and also the effect due to a *small* change in its length.

If a pendulum, of length l, make n complete oscillations in a given time, to shew that

(1) *If g be changed to g + G, the number of oscillations gained is* $\dfrac{n}{2} \cdot \dfrac{G}{g}$,

(2) *If the pendulum be taken to a height h above the earth's surface, the number of oscillations lost is* $n\dfrac{h}{r}$, *where r is the radius of the earth,*

(3) *If it be taken to the bottom of a mine of depth d, the number lost is* $\dfrac{n}{2}\dfrac{d}{r}$,

(4) *If its length be changed to l + L, the number lost is* $\dfrac{n}{2}\dfrac{L}{l}$.

Let T be the original time of oscillation, T' the new time of oscillation, and n' the new number of oscillations in the given time, so that

$$nT = n'T'.$$

(1) In this case $T = 2\pi\sqrt{\dfrac{l}{g}}$ and $T' = 2\pi\sqrt{\dfrac{l}{g+G}}$.

Hence $\dfrac{n'}{n} = \dfrac{T}{T'} = \sqrt{1 + \dfrac{G}{g}} = 1 + \dfrac{1}{2}\dfrac{G}{g}$, approximately,

$\left(\text{by Binomial Theorem, squares of } \dfrac{G}{g} \text{ being neglected}\right)$.

Hence the number of oscillations gained $= n' - n = \dfrac{n}{2}\dfrac{G}{g}$.

So, if g become $g - G$, the number lost is $\dfrac{n}{2}\dfrac{G}{g}$.

(2) If $g - G$ be the value of gravity at a height h, we have
$$\frac{g-G}{g} = \frac{r^2}{(r+h)^2} = \left(1 + \frac{h}{r}\right)^{-2} = 1 - \frac{2h}{r} \text{ approximately.}$$

Therefore $G = g\dfrac{2h}{r}$, and hence, as in (1), the number of oscillations lost is $n\dfrac{h}{r}$.

(3) If $g - G$ be the value at a depth d, we have $g - G : g :: r - d : r$, so that the number of oscillations lost $= \dfrac{n}{2}\dfrac{G}{g} = \dfrac{n}{2}\dfrac{d}{r}$.

(4) When the length l of the pendulum is changed to $l + L$, we have

$$T = 2\pi\sqrt{\frac{l}{g}} \text{ and } T' = 2\pi\sqrt{\frac{l+L}{g}}.$$

$$\therefore \frac{n'}{n} = \frac{T}{T'} = \left(1 + \frac{L}{l}\right)^{-\frac{1}{2}} = 1 - \frac{1}{2}\frac{L}{l} \text{ approximately.}$$

Hence the number of oscillations lost $= n - n' = \frac{n}{2}\frac{L}{l}$.

From this article it follows that the height of a mountain, or the depth of a mine, could be found by finding the number of oscillations lost by a pendulum which beats seconds on the surface of the earth.

166. Ex. 1. *A pendulum, which beats seconds at the surface of the earth, is carried to the top of a mountain 5 miles high; find the number of seconds it will lose in a day, assuming the radius of the earth to be 4000 miles.*

Let g and g_1 be the accelerations due to gravity at the sea-level and the top of the mountain respectively.

Then

$$g : g_1 :: \frac{1}{4000^2} : \frac{1}{4005^2}.$$

$$\therefore \frac{g}{g_1} = \left(\frac{4005}{4000}\right)^2 = \left(\frac{801}{800}\right)^2.$$

Since the pendulum beats seconds at the earth's surface, we have

$$1 = \pi \sqrt{\frac{l}{g}} \quad \dots\dots\dots\dots\dots\dots\dots\dots(1).$$

Also, if T be the time of oscillation at the top of the mountain, we have

$$T = \pi \sqrt{\frac{l}{g_1}} \quad \dots\dots\dots\dots\dots\dots\dots\dots(2).$$

Dividing (2) by (1), we have

$$T = \sqrt{\frac{g}{g_1}} = \frac{801}{800}.$$

Hence the number of beats in a day at the top of the mountain

$$= \frac{86400}{T} = 86400 \times \frac{800}{801}$$

$$= 86400 \times \frac{1}{1 + \frac{1}{800}} = 86400\left(1 + \frac{1}{800}\right)^{-1}$$

$$= 86400\left(1 - \frac{1}{800}\right) \text{ approximately}$$

$$= 86400 - 108.$$

Therefore the number of beats lost is 108.

Ex. 2. *A faulty seconds pendulum loses 20 seconds per day; find the required alteration in its length, so that it may keep correct time.*

The pendulum beats 86380 times in 86400 seconds, so that its time of oscillation is $\dfrac{8640}{8638}$ seconds. Hence, if l be its length,

$$\frac{8640}{8638} = \pi \sqrt{\frac{l}{g}} \quad \dots\dots\dots\dots\dots\dots(1)$$

Let $l + x$ be the true length of the seconds pendulum at the place. Then

$$1 = \pi \sqrt{\frac{l+x}{g}} \quad \dots\dots\dots\dots\dots\dots(2).$$

Subtracting the square of (1) from the square of (2), we have

$$1 - \left(\frac{8640}{8638}\right)^2 = \pi^2 \cdot \frac{x}{g};$$

$$\therefore x = -\frac{g}{\pi^2}\left[\left(\frac{8640}{8638}\right)^2 - 1\right]$$

$$= -\frac{g}{\pi^2}\left[\left(1 - \frac{2}{8640}\right)^{-2} - 1\right] = -\frac{32 \times 7^2}{22^2}\left[1 + \frac{4}{8640} - 1\right] \text{ approximately}$$

$$= -\frac{32 \times 49}{484} \cdot \frac{4}{8640} = -\frac{49}{121 \times 270} \text{ feet} = -\cdot018 \text{ inch.}$$

Hence the pendulum must be *shortened* by ·018 inch.

167. *Verification of the law of gravity by means of the moon's motion.* We may shew roughly the truth of the law of gravitation, by finding the time that the moon would take to travel round the earth, on the assumption that it is kept in its orbit by means of the earth's attraction.

Let f be the acceleration of the moon due to the earth's attraction; then, since the distance between the centres of the two bodies is roughly 60 times the earth's radius, we have $f : g :: \dfrac{1}{(60r)^2} : \dfrac{1}{r^2}$, so that $f = \dfrac{g}{3600}$.

Let v be the velocity of the moon round the earth, so that, by Art. 135,

$$\frac{v^2}{60r} = f = \frac{g}{3600}.$$

$$\therefore v^2 = \frac{gr}{60}.$$

Hence the periodic time of the moon

$$= 2\pi \times 60r \div v = 2\pi \cdot 60 \times \sqrt{\frac{60r}{g}} \text{ seconds.}$$

Taking the radius of the earth to be 4000 miles, and g as $32\cdot2$, this time is $27\cdot4$ days, and this is approximately the observed time of revolution.

EXAMPLES. XXVIII.

1. A pendulum which beats seconds at Greenwich, where $g = 32\cdot2$, is taken to another place where it loses 20 seconds per day; find the value of g at the latter place.

2. A seconds pendulum, which gains 10 seconds per day at one place, loses 10 seconds per day at another; compare the accelerations due to gravity at the two places.

3. Assuming the values of g in foot-second units at the equator and the north pole to be $32\cdot09$ and $32\cdot25$ respectively, find how many seconds per day would be gained at the north pole by a pendulum which would beat seconds at the equator.

4. A clock with a seconds pendulum loses 9 seconds per day; find roughly the required alteration in the length of the pendulum.

5. A clock gains five seconds per day; shew how it may be made to keep correct time.

6. If a pendulum oscillating seconds be lengthened by its hundredth part, find the number of oscillations it will lose in a day.

7. A simple seconds pendulum is lengthened by $\frac{1}{20}$th inch; find the number of seconds it will lose in 24 hours.

8. A simple pendulum performs 21 complete vibrations in 44 seconds; on shortening its length by $47\cdot6875$ centimetres it performs 21 complete vibrations in 33 seconds; find the value of g.

9. A simple seconds pendulum consists of a heavy ball suspended by a long and very fine iron wire; if the pendulum be correct at a temperature $0°$ C., find how many seconds it will gain, or lose, in 24 hours at a temperature of $20°$ C., given that the iron expands by $\cdot000233$ of its length owing to this rise of temperature.

10. If a seconds pendulum lose 10 seconds per day at the bottom of a mine, find the depth of the mine and the number of seconds that the pendulum would lose when halfway down the mine.

11. A clock, which at the surface of the earth gains 10 seconds a day, loses 10 seconds a day when taken down a mine; compare the accelerations due to gravity at the top and bottom of the mine and find its depth.

12. If a seconds pendulum be carried to the top of a mountain half a mile high, how many seconds will it lose per day, assuming the earth's centre to be 4000 miles from the foot of the mountain, and by how much must it be shortened so that it may beat seconds at the summit of the mountain?

13. Shew that the height of a hill at the summit of which a seconds pendulum loses n beats in 24 hours is approximately $245 \cdot n$ feet.

---

14. A balloon ascends with a constant acceleration and reaches a height of 900 feet in one minute. Shew that a pendulum clock, which has a seconds pendulum and is carried in the balloon, will gain at the rate of about 28 seconds per hour.

15. A cage-lift is descending with unit acceleration; shew that a pendulum clock, which has a seconds pendulum and is carried with it, will lose at the rate of about 56 seconds per hour.

16. Shew that a seconds pendulum would, if carried to the moon, oscillate in $2\frac{1}{4}$ seconds, assuming the mass of the earth to be 81 times that of the moon, and that the radius of the earth is 4 times that of the moon.

17. A railway train is moving uniformly in a circular curve at the rate of 60 miles per hour, and in one of the carriages a seconds pendulum is observed to beat 121 times in 2 minutes. Shew that the radius of the curve is about 1317 feet.

18. A particle would take a time t to move down a straight tube from the surface of the earth (supposed to be a homogeneous sphere) to its centre; if gravity were to remain constant from the surface to the centre, it would take a time t'; shew that

$$t : t' :: \pi : 2\sqrt{2}.$$

19. A simple pendulum swings under gravity in such a manner that, when the string is vertical, the force which it exerts on the bob is twice its weight; shew that the greatest inclination of the string to the vertical is $\dfrac{\pi}{3}$.

20. A mass is hung on the end of a string 8 feet long and swings to and fro through a distance of 3 inches. Find approximately the periodic time of the swing, the accelerations at the ends of the swing, and the velocity at the middle.

CHAPTER XII.

UNITS AND DIMENSIONS.

168. WHEN we wish to state the magnitude of any concrete quantity we express it in terms of some unit of the same kind as itself, and we have to state,

(1) what is the unit we are employing, and

(2) what is the ratio of the quantity we are considering to that unit.

This latter ratio is called the *measure* of the quantity in terms of the unit. Thus, if we wish to express the height of a man, we may say that it is six feet. Here a foot is the unit and six is the measure. We might as well have said that he is 2 yards, or 72 inches high.

The measure will vary according to the unit we employ. The measure of any quantity multiplied into the unit employed is always the same (*e.g.*, 2 yards = 6 feet = 72 inches).

Hence, if k and k' be the measures of a physical quantity when the units used are denoted by $[K]$ and $[K']$, we have

$$k\,[K] = k'\,[K'],$$

and hence

$$[K] : [K'] :: \frac{1}{k} : \frac{1}{k'},$$

so that, by the definition of variation, we have $[K] \propto \dfrac{1}{k}$, *i.e.*, *the unit in terms of which any quantity is measured varies inversely as the measure and conversely.*

169. A straight line possesses length only, and no breadth or thickness, and hence is said to be of one dimension in length.

An area possesses both length and breadth, but no thickness, and is said to be of two dimensions in length. The unit of area usually employed is that whose length and breadth are respectively equal to the unit of length. Hence if we have two different units of length in the ratio $\lambda : 1$, the two corresponding units of area are in the ratio $\lambda^2 : 1$, so that, if $[A]$ denote the unit of area and $[L]$ the unit of length, then

$$[A] \propto [L]^2.$$

For example, 12 inches make 1 foot, but 144 (*i.e.*, 12²) square inches make one square foot.

A volume possesses length, breadth, and thickness, and is said to be of three dimensions in length. The unit is that volume whose length, breadth, and thickness are each equal to the unit of length. As in the case of areas, it follows that, if $[V]$ denote the unit of volume, then

$$[V] \propto [L]^3.$$

Since the units of area and volume depend on that of length, they are said to be **derived units**, whilst the unit of length is called a fundamental unit.

Another fundamental unit is the unit of time, usually denoted by $[T]$. A period of time is of one dimension in time.

The third fundamental unit is the unit of mass, denoted by $[M]$. Any mass is said to be of one dimension in mass.

These are the three fundamental units; all other units depend on these three, and are therefore called derived units.

170. In Art. 9 we defined the unit of velocity to be the velocity of a point which describes the unit of length in the unit of time. Hence if the unit of length, or the unit of time, or both, be altered, the unit of velocity will, in general, be altered.

For example, let the units of length and time be changed from a foot and a second to 2 feet and 3 seconds. The new unit of velocity is the velocity of a point which describes 2 feet in 3 seconds, *i.e.*, which describes $\frac{2}{3}$ foot in one second, *i.e.*, is equal to $\frac{2}{3}$rds of the original unit of velocity.

Similarly, since a body is moving with unit acceleration when the change in its velocity per unit of time is equal to the unit of velocity, it follows that the unit of acceleration depends on the units of velocity and time, *i.e.*, it depends ultimately upon the units of length and time.

Again, the unit of force is, by Art. 61, that force which in the unit of mass produces the unit of acceleration. Hence the unit of force is altered when either the unit of mass, or the unit of acceleration, or both, are altered. Hence the unit of force depends ultimately upon the units of length, time, and mass.

171. Theorem. *To shew that the unit of velocity varies directly as the unit of length, and inversely as the unit of time.*

In one system let the units of length, time, and velocity be denoted by $[L]$, $[T]$, and $[V]$, and in a second system by $[L']$, $[T']$, and $[V']$; also let

$$[L'] = m\,[L], \text{ and } [T'] = n\,[T].$$

Then a body is said to be moving

with the original unit of velocity

when it describes a length $[L]$ in time $[T]$;

therefore with velocity $m[V]$

when it describes a length $m[L]$ in time $[T]$;

therefore with velocity $\dfrac{m}{n}[V]$

when it describes a length $m[L]$ in time $n[T]$;

therefore with velocity $\dfrac{m}{n}[V]$

when it describes a length $[L']$ in time $[T']$.

But it is moving with velocity $[V']$ when it describes a length $[L']$ in time $[T']$.

$$\therefore \ [V'] = \frac{m}{n}[V].$$

$$\therefore \ [V'] : [V] :: m : n$$

$$:: \frac{[L']}{[L]} : \frac{[T']}{[T]}$$

$$:: \frac{[L']}{[T']} : \frac{[L]}{[T]};$$

hence, by the definition of variation,

$$[V] \propto \frac{[L]}{[T]}, \ i.e., \propto [L][T]^{-1}.$$

172. Theorem. *To shew that the unit of acceleration varies directly as the unit of length, and inversely as the square of the unit of time.*

Take the units of length and time as before, and let $[F]$ and $[F']$ denote the corresponding units of acceleration.

Then a body is said to be moving

with the original unit of acceleration

when a vel. of $[L]$ per $[T]$ is added on per $[T]$;

therefore with acceleration $m\,[F]$

when a vel. of $m\,[L]$ per $[T]$ is added on per $[T]$;

therefore with acceleration $\dfrac{m}{n}\,[F]$

when a vel. of $m\,[L]$ per $n\,[T]$ is added on per $[T]$;

therefore with acceleration $\dfrac{m}{n^2}\,[F]$

when a vel. of $m\,[L]$ per $n\,[T]$ is added on per $n\,[T]$;

therefore with acceleration $\dfrac{m}{n^2}\,[F]$

when a vel. of $[L']$ per $[T'']$ is added on per $[T'']$.

But now the body is moving with the new unit of acceleration $[F']$;

$$\therefore\ [F'] = \frac{m}{n^2}[F].$$

$$\therefore\ [F'] : [F] :: m : n^2$$
$$:: \frac{[L']}{[L]} : \frac{[T']^2}{[T]^2}$$
$$:: \frac{[L']}{[T']^2} : \frac{[L]}{[T]^2}.$$

Hence, by the definition of variation,

$$[F] \propto \frac{[L]}{[T]^2},\ i.e.,\ \propto [L][T]^{-2}.$$

173. Ex. 1. *If the units of length and time be changed from a foot and a second to 100 feet and 50 seconds respectively, find in what ratio the units of velocity and acceleration are changed.*

The new unit of velocity is a velocity of 100 feet per 50 seconds, *i.e.*, a velocity of 2 feet per second. Hence the new unit of velocity is twice the original unit of velocity.

Again a body is moving with the new unit of acceleration

when a velocity of 100 feet per 50 seconds is added on per 50 secs.,

i.e.,...........................2 feet per 1 sec.......................per 50 secs.,

i.e.,........................ $\frac{1}{2\,5}$ feet per second.....................per sec.

Hence the new unit of acceleration is $\frac{1}{2\,5}$th of the original unit of acceleration.

Otherwise thus; Taking the same notation as in Arts. 171 and 172, we have

$$[L'] = 100\,[L], \quad \text{and} \quad [T'] = 50\,[T].$$

$$\therefore \frac{[V']}{[V]} = \frac{[L'][T']^{-1}}{[L][T]^{-1}} = 100 \times [50]^{-1} = \frac{100}{50} = 2,$$

and

$$\frac{[F']}{[F]} = \frac{[L'][T']^{-2}}{[L][T]^{-2}} = 100 \times (50)^{-2} = \frac{100}{2500} = \frac{1}{25},$$

so that the new units of velocity and acceleration are respectively double and one twenty-fifth of the original units.

Ex. 2. *Find the measure of the acceleration due to gravity in the yard-minute system, assuming its value in the foot-second system to be* 32·2.

In a falling body a velocity of 32·2 ft. per sec. is added on per sec.,

∴ .... $60 \times 32 \cdot 2$ ft. per. minute is added on
per sec.,

∴ .... $60^2 \times 32 \cdot 2$ ft. per minute is added on
per min.,

∴ .... $\dfrac{60^2}{3} \times 32 \cdot 2$ yds. per minute is added

on per minute.

$$\therefore \text{ the required measure} = \frac{60^2 \times 32 \cdot 2}{3} = 38640.$$

This may be more concisely put as follows:

Let x be the new measure; then

$$x \times [F'] = 32 \cdot 2 \times [F],$$

$$\therefore x = 32 \cdot 2 \times \frac{[F]}{[F']} = 32 \cdot 2 \times \frac{[L][T]^{-2}}{[L'][T']^{-2}} = 32 \cdot 2 \times \frac{1}{3 \times (60)^{-2}}$$

$$= 32 \cdot 2 \times \frac{60^2}{3} = 38640, \text{ as before.}$$

Ex. 3. *If the acceleration of a falling body be taken as the unit of acceleration, and the velocity generated in a falling body in one minute as the unit of velocity, find the units of length and time.*

Using the same notation as in Arts. 171 and 172, the same acceleration is in the two systems represented by

$$32\,.[F] \quad \text{and} \quad 1\,.[F'].$$

$$\therefore 1\,.[F'] = 32\,[F].$$

$$\therefore [L'][T']^{-2} = 32\,.[L][T]^{-2} \quad\quad\quad\ldots\ldots\ldots\ldots\ldots(1).$$

In ft.-sec. units the velocity generated in one minute $= 60 \times 32$.

Hence $60 \times 32\,.[V]$ and $1\,.[V']$ represent the same velocity. Hence

$$1\,.[L'][T']^{-1} = 60 \times 32\,[L][T]^{-1} \quad\quad\ldots\ldots\ldots\ldots(2).$$

Dividing the square of equation (2) by (1), we have

$$[L'] = \frac{60^2 \cdot 32^2}{32}[L] = 60^2 \times 32 \text{ feet.}$$

Hence, from (2),

$$\frac{[T']}{[T]} = \frac{1}{60 \times 32}\left[\frac{L'}{L}\right] = \frac{1}{60 \times 32} \times 60^2 \times 32.$$

$$\therefore \ [T'] = 60\,[T] = 60 \text{ seconds} = \text{one minute.}$$

EXAMPLES. XXIX.

1. If the unit of length be one mile, and the unit of time one minute, find the units of velocity and acceleration.

2. If the unit of length be one mile, and the unit of time 4 seconds, find the units of velocity and acceleration.

3. If the unit of velocity be a velocity of 30 miles per hour, and the unit of time be one minute, find the units of length and acceleration.

4. If the unit of acceleration be that of a freely falling body, and the unit of time be 5 seconds, shew that the unit of velocity is a velocity of 160 ft. per sec.

5. What must be the unit of length, if the acceleration due to gravity be represented by 14, and the unit of time be five seconds?

6. If the unit of velocity be a velocity of 3 miles per hour, and the unit of time one minute, find the unit of length.

7. If the acceleration of a falling body be the unit of acceleration, and the velocity acquired by it in 5 seconds be the unit of velocity, shew that the units of length and time are 800 feet and 5 seconds respectively.

8. What is the measure of the acceleration due to gravity,

(1) when a foot and half a second are the units of length and time,

(2) when the units are a mile and eleven seconds,

(3) when the units are 10 yards and 10 minutes respectively?

9. Find the measure in the centimetre-minute system of the acceleration due to gravity, assuming a metre to be 39·37 inches.

10. The acceleration produced by gravity being 32 in ft.-sec. units, find its measure when the units are $\frac{1}{10000}$ of an hour and a centimetre, given 1 centimetre = ·0328 ft.

11. If the area of a ten acre field be represented by 100, and the acceleration of a heavy falling particle by $58\frac{2}{3}$, find the unit of time.

174. Dimensions. Def. *When we say that the dimensions of a physical quantity are* α, β, *and* γ *in length, time, and mass respectively, we mean that the unit in terms of which the quantity is measured varies as*

$$[L]^{\alpha}[T]^{\beta}[M]^{\gamma}.$$

Thus the results of Arts. 171 and 172 are expressed by saying that the dimensions of the unit of velocity are 1 in length and − 1 in time; while those of the unit of acceleration are 1 in length and − 2 in time.

The cases in Arts. 171 and 172 have been fully written out, but the results may be obtained more simply as in the following article.

175. (1) **Velocity.** Let v denote the numerical measure of the velocity of a point which undergoes a displacement whose numerical measure is s, in a time whose numerical measure is t, so that

$$s = vt.$$

If $[L]$, $[T]$, and $[V]$ denote the units of length, time, and velocity respectively, we have, as in Art. 168,

$$s \propto \frac{1}{[L]}, \ t \propto \frac{1}{[T]}, \ \text{and} \ v \propto \frac{1}{[V]}.$$

$$\therefore \ \frac{1}{[L]} \propto \frac{1}{[V]} \frac{1}{[T]}.$$

Hence
$$[V] \propto [L][T]^{-1}.$$

(2) **Acceleration.** Let v denote the velocity acquired by a particle moving with acceleration f for time t, so that

$$v = ft.$$

If $[F]$ denote the unit of acceleration, we have

$$f \propto \frac{1}{[F]}.$$

$$\therefore \quad \frac{1}{[V]} \propto \frac{1}{[F]} \frac{1}{[T]}.$$

Hence $\quad [F] \propto [V][T]^{-1} \propto [L][T]^{-2}.$

(3) **Density.** Let d be the density of a body whose mass is m and volume u, so that $m = du$.

If $[D]$ and $[U]$ denote the units of density and volume, we have

$$d \propto \frac{1}{[D]}; \quad u \propto \frac{1}{[U]}.$$

$$\therefore \quad \frac{1}{[M]} \propto \frac{1}{[D][U]}.$$

$$\therefore \quad [D] \propto [M][U]^{-1} \propto [M][L]^{-3}.$$

If the body be very thin, so that it may be considered as a surface only, we see similarly that the unit of surface density

$$\propto [M][L]^{-2}.$$

So, if the body be such that its breadth and thickness may be neglected, (so that it is a material line only), we have

unit of linear density $\propto [M][L]^{-1}.$

(4) **Force.** If p be the force that would produce acceleration f in mass m, we have $p = mf$.
Hence, if $[P]$ denote the unit of force, we have

$$[P] \propto [M][F] \propto [M][L][T]^{-2}.$$

(5) **Momentum.** If k be the momentum of a mass m moving with velocity v, we have

$$k = mv.$$

Hence, if $[K]$ denote the unit of momentum,

$$[K] \propto [M][V] \propto [M][L][T]^{-1}.$$

(6) **Impulse.** If i be the impulse of a force p acting for time t, we have

$$i = pt.$$

Hence, if $[I]$ denote the unit of impulse,

$$[I] \propto [P][T] \propto [M][L][T]^{-1},$$

so that an impulse is of the same dimensions as a momentum.

(7) **Kinetic Energy.** If e be the kinetic energy of a mass m moving with velocity v, we have

$$e = \tfrac{1}{2}mv^2.$$

Hence, if $[E]$ denote the unit of kinetic energy,

$$[E] \propto [M][V]^2 \propto [M][L]^2[T]^{-2}.$$

(8) **Work.** If w be the work done when a force p moves its point of application through a distance s, then

$$w = ps.$$

Hence, if $[W]$ denote the unit of work,

$$[W] \propto [P][L] \propto [M][L]^2[T]^{-2}.$$

Hence work and kinetic energy are of the same dimensions.

(9) **Power** or Rate of work. If h be the power at which work w is done in time t, then

$$h = \frac{w}{t} = wt^{-1}.$$

Hence, if $[H]$ denote the unit of power,

$$[H] \propto [W][T]^{-1} \propto [M][L]^2[T]^{-3}.$$

(10) **Angular velocity.** If ω be the angular velocity of a point which moves with velocity v in a circle of radius r, we have

$$\omega = \frac{v}{r} = vr^{-1}. \quad \text{(Art. 26.)}$$

Hence, if $[\Omega]$ denote the unit of angular velocity, then

$$[\Omega] = [V][L]^{-1} = [T]^{-1}.$$

176. Ex. 1. *If the unit of mass be 112 lbs., the unit of length one mile, and the unit of time one minute, find the unit of force.*

The unit of force is (Art. 61) the force which in unit mass produces unit acceleration,

i.e., which in 112 lbs. produces an acceleration of 1 mile per min.
$$\text{per min.,}$$

i.e., in 112 lbs. .... $\dfrac{1}{60}$ mile per sec. per
$$\text{min.,}$$

i.e., in 112 lbs. .... $\dfrac{1}{60^2}$ mile per sec. per
$$\text{sec.,}$$

i.e., in 112 lbs. .... $\dfrac{1760 \times 3}{60^2}$ ft. per sec.
$$\text{per sec.,}$$

i.e., in 1 lb. .... $\dfrac{1760 \times 3 \times 112}{60^2}$ ft. per
$$\text{sec. per sec.}$$

Hence the new unit of force $= \dfrac{1760 \times 3 \times 112}{60^2}$ poundals

$$= 164\tfrac{4}{15} \text{ poundals} = \text{wt. of about } 5\tfrac{2}{15} \text{ lbs.}$$

Otherwise thus: By Art. 175 (4), we have

$$\frac{[P']}{[P]} = \frac{[M'][L'][T']^{-2}}{[M][L][T]^{-2}} = 112 \times 1760 \cdot 3 \times (60)^{-2}$$

$$= \frac{112 \times 1760 \cdot 3}{60^2} = 164\tfrac{4}{15}, \text{ as before.}$$

Ex. 2. *The kinetic energy of a body expressed in the foot-pound-second system is 1000; find its value in the metre-gramme-minute system, having given 1 foot = 30·5 cms., and 1 lb. = 450 grammes, approximately.*

Let x be the measure in the new system, so that

$$x[E'] = 1000[E],$$

i.e., $x[M'][L']^2[T']^{-2} = 1000[M][L]^2[T]^{-2}.$

But $[M] = 450[M'],$ $[L] = \cdot 305[L'],$ and $[T] = \tfrac{1}{60}[T'].$

$$\therefore \quad x = 1000 \times 450 \times [\cdot 305]^2 \times 60^2$$

$$= 150{,}700{,}500.$$

Ex. 3. *If the unit of velocity be* 12 *feet per second, the unit of acceleration* 24 *foot-second units, and the unit of force* 20 *poundals, what are the units of mass, length, and time?*

Find also the corresponding unit of work.

The unit of velocity $[V']$ is equal to $12[V]$.

$$[L'][T']^{-1} = 12[L][T]^{-1} \quad \text{..........................(1)}.$$

The unit of acceleration $[F']$ is equal to $24[F]$.

$$\therefore \ [L'][T']^{-2} = 24[L][T]^{-2} \quad \text{....................(2)}.$$

The unit of force $[P']$ is equal to $20[P]$.

$$\therefore \ [M'][L'][T']^{-2} = 20[M][L][T]^{-2} \quad \text{...............(3)}.$$

Dividing (2) by (1), we have

$$[T']^{-1} = 2[T]^{-1}.$$

$$\therefore \ [T'] = \tfrac{1}{2}[T] = \cdot 5 \text{ second.}$$

Dividing the square of (1) by (2), we have

$$[L'] = \frac{12^2}{24}[L] = 6[L] = 6 \text{ feet.}$$

Dividing (3) by (2), we have

$$[M'] = \tfrac{20}{24}[M] = \tfrac{5}{6} \text{ lb.}$$

Hence the required units of mass, length, and time, are

$$\tfrac{5}{6} \text{ lb.}, \quad 6 \text{ feet}, \quad \text{and} \quad \tfrac{1}{2} \text{ sec.}$$

Also, by Art. 175 (8), we have

$$\frac{[W']}{[W]} = \frac{[M'][L']^2[T']^{-2}}{[M][L]^2[T]^{-2}} = \frac{5}{6} \times (6)^2 \times \left(\frac{1}{2}\right)^{-2}.$$

$$\therefore \ [W'] = \frac{5 \cdot 6^2 \cdot 2^2}{6}[W] = 120 \text{ foot-poundals.}$$

EXAMPLES. XXX.

1. If 39 inches be the unit of length, 3 seconds the unit of time, and 1 cwt. the unit of mass, find the unit of force.

2. If the units of mass, length, and time be 10 lbs., 10 feet, and 10 seconds respectively, find the units of force and work.

3. If the unit of length be 2 feet, what must be the unit of time in order that one pound-weight may be the unit of force, the unit of mass being one pound?

4. If the unit of mass be 1 cwt., the unit of force the weight of one ton, and the unit of length one mile, shew that the unit of time is $\frac{1}{2}\sqrt{33}$ seconds.

5. If the unit of velocity be a velocity of one mile per minute, the unit of acceleration be the acceleration with which this velocity would be acquired in 5 minutes, and the unit of force be equal to the weight of half a ton, find the units of length, time, and mass.

6. If a hundredweight be the unit of mass, a minute the unit of time, and the unit of force the weight of a pound, find the unit of length.

7. If the unit of force be equal to the weight of 5 ounces, the unit of time be one minute, and a velocity of 60 feet per second be denoted by 9, find the units of length and mass.

8. If $5\frac{1}{2}$ yards be the unit of length, a velocity of one yard per second the unit of velocity, and 6 poundals the unit of force, what is the unit of mass?

9. Taking as a rough approximation 1 foot = 30·5 cms., 1 lb. = 453 grammes, and the acceleration of a falling body = 32 ft.-sec. units, shew that

      (i)   1 Poundal = 13816 Dynes,

      (ii) 1 Foot-Poundal = 421403 Ergs,

     (iii) 1 Erg = $7\cdot416 \times 10^{-8}$ Foot-Pounds,

     (iv) 1 Horse-Power = $7\cdot416 \times 10^{9}$ Ergs per sec.

10. In two different systems of units an acceleration is represented by the same number, whilst a velocity is represented by numbers in the ratio 1 : 3; compare the units of length and time.

If further the momentum of a body be represented by numbers in the ratio 5 : 2, compare the units of mass.

11. If the units of length, velocity, and force be each doubled, shew that the units of time and mass will be unaltered, and that of energy increased in the ratio 1 : 4.

12. If the unit of time be one hour, and the units of mass and force be the mass of one hundredweight and the weight of a pound respectively, find the units of work and momentum in absolute units.

13. Find a system of units such that the momentum and kinetic energy of a mass of 4 lbs., moving with a velocity of 5 feet per second, may each be numerically equal to unity, and such that the unit of force may be the weight of one pound.

14. If the unit of acceleration be that of a body falling freely, the unit of velocity the velocity acquired by the body in 5 seconds from rest, and the unit of momentum that of one pound after falling for 10 seconds, find the units of length, time, and mass.

15. If the unit of work be that done in lifting one hundredweight through three yards, the unit of momentum that of a mass of one pound which has fallen vertically 4 feet under gravity, and the unit of acceleration three times that produced by gravity, find the units of length, time, and mass.

16. Find the units of length, time, and mass supposing that when a force equal to the weight of a gramme acts on the mass of 16 grammes the acceleration produced is the unit of acceleration, that the work done in the first four seconds is the unit of work, and that the force is doing work at unit rate when the body is moving at the rate of 90 cms. per second.

17. The velocity of a train running at the rate of 60 miles per hour is denoted by 8, the resistance the train experiences and which is equal to the weight of 1600 lbs. is denoted by 10, and the number of units of work done by the engine per mile by 10. Find the units of length, time, and mass.

18. In a certain system of absolute units the acceleration produced by gravity in a body falling freely is denoted by 3, the kinetic energy of a 600 pound shot moving with velocity 1600 feet per second is denoted by 100, and its momentum by 10; find the units of length, time, and mass.

19. If the kinetic energy of a train, whose mass is 100 tons and whose velocity is 45 miles per hour, be denoted by 11, whilst the impulse of the force required to bring it to rest is denoted by 5, and 40 horse-power by 15, find the units of length, time, and mass, and shew that the acceleration due to gravity is denoted by 2016, assuming its measure in foot-second units to be 32.

20. If the unit of force be the weight of one pound, what must be the unit of mass so that the equation $P = mf$ may still be true?

Verification of formulae by means of counting the dimensions.

177. Many formulae and results may be tested by means of the dimensions of the quantities involved. Suppose we have an equation between any number of physical quantities. Then the sum of the dimensions in each term of one side of the equation in length, time, and mass respectively must be equal to the corresponding sums on the other side of the equation. For suppose that the dimensions in length of one side of the equation differed from the corresponding dimensions on the other side of the equation ; then, on altering the unit of length, the two members of the equation would be altered in different ratios and would be no longer equal ; this however would be clearly absurd ; for two quantities which are equal must have the same measures whatever (the same) unit is used. For example, if two sums of money are the same, their measures must be the same whether we express the amounts in pounds, shillings, or pence.

Again, suppose an equation gives us as a result that 3 feet = 10 seconds ; this would be clearly incorrect.

So such an equation as

$$3v^2 = 5mu^2 + 2fs,$$

must be incorrect; for two of the terms are of no dimensions in mass, and the third term, $5mu^2$, is of one dimension in mass. This latter term is therefore the one that is probably incorrect.

Consider again the possibility of the equation

$$Pvs^2 + 8mf^2s - 10v^3f = 0,$$

where the symbols have the meanings we have used throughout this book.

Let us set down the dimensions only ; they are, for the several terms,

$$[M]\frac{[L]}{[T]^2}\cdot\frac{[L]}{[T]}\cdot[L]^2, \quad [M]\cdot\left\{\frac{L}{[T]^2}\right\}^2[L], \quad \left\{\frac{[L]}{[T]}\right\}^3\frac{[L]}{[T]^2},$$

i.e.
$$[M]\frac{[L]^4}{[T]^3}, \quad [M]\frac{[L]^3}{[T]^4}, \quad \frac{[L]^4}{[T]^5}.$$

The equation is thus hopelessly incorrect; for the terms have neither the same dimensions in mass, nor in length, nor in time.

So again if, in solving a question where we want the work done, we get an answer of the form

$$\text{Work} = MPv + 3Mvf,$$

15—2

this is clearly incorrect. For, by Art. 175, the dimensions of a Work are

$$[M]\frac{[L]^2}{[T]^2}.$$

Also the dimensions of MPv are

$$[M].\frac{[M][L]}{[T]^2}.\frac{[L]}{[T]}, \quad i.e. \quad [M]^2\frac{[L]^2}{[T]^3},$$

which is of wrong dimensions in both mass and time.

Also, the dimensions of $3Mvf$ are

$$[M].\frac{[L]}{[T]}.\frac{[L]}{[T]^2}, \quad i.e. \quad \frac{M[L]^2}{[T]^3},$$

which is of the wrong dimensions in time.

178. Much information may be often easily obtained by considering the dimensions of the quantities involved. Thus the time of oscillation of a simple pendulum (which consists of a mass m tied by means of a light string of length l to a fixed point) may be easily shewn to vary as $\sqrt{\dfrac{l}{g}}$. For, assuming the time of oscillation to be independent of the arc of oscillation, the only quantities that can appear in the answer are m, l, and g. Let us assume the time of oscillation to vary as $m^\alpha l^\beta g^\gamma$.

The dimensions of this quantity expressed in the usual way are

$$[M]^\alpha [L]^\beta \left\{\frac{[L]}{[T]^2}\right\}^\gamma,$$

or

$$[M]^\alpha [L]^{\beta+\gamma} [T]^{-2\gamma}.$$

Now the answer is necessarily of one dimension in time, and of none in mass, or length. Hence we have

$$\alpha = 0, \quad \beta + \gamma = 0, \quad \text{and} \quad -2\gamma = 1.$$
$$\therefore \gamma = -\tfrac{1}{2} \text{ and } \beta = \tfrac{1}{2},$$

and the time of oscillation therefore $\propto \sqrt{\dfrac{l}{g}}$. [Art. 159.]

Table of Dimensions and Values of Fundamental Quantities.

		Dimensions in	
Physical Quantity	*Mass*	*Length*	*Time*
Volume density	1	−3	
Surface density	1	−2	
Line density	1	−1	
Velocity		1	−1
Acceleration		1	−2
Force	1	1	−2
Momentum	1	1	−1
Impulse	1	1	−1
Kinetic energy	1	2	−2
Power or Rate of work	1	2	−3
Angular velocity			−1

Values of "g."

Place	*Ft.-sec. units*	*Cm.-sec. units*
The equator	32·091	978·10
Latitude 45°	32·17	980·61
Paris	32·183	980·94
London	32·191	981·17
North Pole	32·252	983·11

Length of the seconds pendulum at London

$$= 39 \cdot 139 \text{ inches} = 99 \cdot 413 \text{ centimetres.}$$

1 centimetre	$= \cdot 39370$ inches $= \cdot 032809$ feet.
1 foot	$= 30 \cdot 4797$ centimetres.
1 gramme	$= 15 \cdot 432$ grains $= \cdot 0022046$ lb.
1 lb.	$= 453 \cdot 59$ grammes.
1 dyne	$=$ weight of $\frac{1}{981}$ gramme approx.
1 poundal	$= 13825$ dynes.
1 foot-poundal	$= 421390$ ergs.

MISCELLANEOUS EXAMPLES.

1. A particle falls freely from the top of a tower, and during the last second of its motion it falls $\frac{5}{9}$ths of the whole height; what is the height of the tower?

2. A man ascends the Eiffel Tower to a certain height and drops a stone. He then ascends another 100 feet and drops another stone. The latter takes half a second longer than the former to reach the ground. Neglecting the resistance of the air, find the elevation of the man when he dropped the first stone and the time it took to drop.

3. A bullet moving with a velocity of 1200 ft. per sec. has this velocity reduced to one-half after penetrating one inch into a target. Assuming the resistance to be uniform, how far will it penetrate before its velocity is destroyed?

4. Two scale-pans, each of mass 7 ozs., are connected by a light inextensible string which passes over a smooth pulley. If a mass of 5 ozs. be placed in one pan and one of 8 ozs. in the other, find the pressures of the masses on the scale-pans.

5. Two equal masses, attached by an inextensible weightless thread which passes over a light pulley, hang in equilibrium. Shew that the tension of the thread is unaltered when $\frac{1}{n}$th of its mass is added to one, and $\frac{1}{n+2}$th of its mass removed from the other.

6. A weightless string, of length a, with masses m and $3m$ attached to its ends is placed on a smooth horizontal table perpendicular to an edge with the mass m just over the edge. If the height of the table above the inelastic floor be also a, shew that the mass $3m$ will strike the floor at a distance a from the mass m.

7. A particle falling under gravity describes 100 feet in a certain second; how long will it take to describe the next 100 feet, the resistance of the air being neglected?

If owing to resistance it takes ·9 sec., find the ratio of the resistance (assumed to be constant) to the weight of the particle.

8. The bob of a simple pendulum is held so that the string is horizontal and stretched, and is then let go. Shew that during the subsequent motion the tension of the string varies as the vertical distance of the bob below its initial position.

9. A particle hanging vertically from a fixed point by means of a string of length r is projected horizontally with velocity $\sqrt{6gr}$. Shew that the tension of the string when the particle is at the end of a horizontal diameter is to its tension when the particle is at the highest point as $4:1$.

10. A locomotive engine draws a load of m lbs. up an incline of inclination α to the horizon, the coefficient of friction being μ. If, starting from rest and moving with uniform acceleration, it acquires a velocity v in t seconds, shew that the average horse-power at which the engine has worked is $\dfrac{mv}{1100}\left[\dfrac{v}{gt}+\mu\cos\alpha+\sin\alpha\right]$.

11. A body is thrown up in a lift with a velocity u relative to the lift and the time of flight is found to be t. Shew that the lift is moving up with an acceleration $\dfrac{2u-tg}{t}$.

12. The smoke from a steamer which is sailing due north extends in the direction E.S.E., whilst that from another sailing with the same velocity due south extends in the direction N.N.E.; shew that the wind blows in the direction N.E. with a velocity equal to that of the steamer.

13. A horse gallops round a circus, whose radius is 60 feet, with a velocity of 15 miles per hour; shew that the least value of the coefficient of friction between his hoofs and the ground is about $\frac{1}{4}$.

14. A slip-carriage was detached from a train and brought to rest in n minutes during which time it described a distance of s feet. Assuming the retardation to be uniform, find the velocity with which the train was moving when the carriage was slipped.

15. A ship sailing south-east sees another ship, which is steaming at the same rate as itself, and which always appears to be in a direction due east and to be always coming nearer. Find the direction of the motion of the second vessel.

16. A perfectly elastic particle is projected with velocity v at an elevation θ. A smooth plane passes through the point of projection and is inclined at an angle α to the horizon. Shew that the particle will return to the point of projection provided $\cot\alpha\cot(\theta-\alpha)$ is an integer.

17. A particle moves from rest in a straight line with alternate acceleration and retardation of magnitudes f and f' during equal intervals of time t; at the end of $2n$ such intervals prove that the space it has described is $\dfrac{nt^2}{2}[(2n+1)f - (2n-1)f']$.

18. A particle is placed upon a rough horizontal plate (coefficient of friction μ) at a distance a from a vertical axis about which the plate can rotate; find the greatest number of revolutions per minute which the plate can make without the particle moving relatively to the plate.

19. A cannon ball has a range R on a horizontal plane. If h and h' are the greatest heights in the two paths for which this is possible, prove that $R=4\sqrt{hh'}$.

20. Find the greatest angle through which a person can oscillate on a swing, the ropes of which can just support twice the person's weight when at rest.

21. Two masses, m and m', are connected by a string of given length passing through a small smooth ring which turns freely about a vertical axis. The particle m' is made to rotate with angular velocity ω in a horizontal circle, so that the particle m remains at rest hanging freely from the ring. Shew that the distance of m' from the ring is $\dfrac{mg}{m'\omega^2}$.

22. Two inelastic balls of equal size, but of masses m and m', lie in contact on a smooth table. The former receives a blow in a direction through its centre making an angle α with the line of centres. Shew that the kinetic energy of the balls is

$$\frac{m'(m+m'\sin^2\alpha)}{m(m'+m\sin^2\alpha)}$$

of what it would have been if the balls had been interchanged and m' had received the blow.

23. A heavy particle projected with velocity u strikes at an angle of $45°$ an inclined plane of angle β which passes through the point of projection. Shew that the vertical height of the point struck above the point of projection is $\dfrac{u^2}{g}\dfrac{1+\cot\beta}{2+2\cot\beta+\cot^2\beta}$.

24. An elastic body is projected from a given point with a given velocity V and after hitting a vertical wall returns to the point from which it started. Shew that the distance of the point from the wall must be less than $\dfrac{e}{1+e}\dfrac{V^2}{g}$, where e is the coefficient of restitution.

25. Two particles, of masses m and m', are moving in parallel straight lines at a distance a apart with given velocities v and v'; the particles are connected by a string of such a length that at the instant when it becomes taut it is inclined at an angle a to the two parallel straight lines; assuming that $v > v'$, shew that the impulsive tension on the string at the instant it tightens is $\dfrac{mm'}{m+m'}(v-v')\cos a$.

26. A smooth wedge, of mass M, is placed on a horizontal plane and a particle, of mass m, slides down its slant face which is inclined at an angle a to the horizon. Shew that the acceleration of m relative to the plane face is $\dfrac{M+m}{M+m\sin^2 a} \cdot g \sin a$.

27. A particle is placed on the face of a smooth wedge which can slide on a horizontal table; find how the wedge must be moved in order that the particle may neither ascend nor descend. Also find the pressure between the particle and the wedge.

28. A particle, of mass m_1, is fastened to one end of a string, and one of mass m_2 to the middle point, the other end of the string being fastened to a fixed point on a smooth horizontal table. The particles are then projected so that the two portions of the string are always in the same straight line and so that the particles describe horizontal circles; shew that the tensions of the two portions of the string are as

$$2m_1 + m_2 : 2m_1.$$

29. At one end of a light string passing over a small fixed pulley a weight of 3 lbs. is suspended and a light pulley is suspended at the other end. Over this pulley another light string passes with weights of 2 lbs. and 1 lb. suspended at its ends. The whole system is let go from a position of rest; find the pressure on the fixed pulley while the system is moving and also the acceleration of the greatest weight.

30. In a system of three movable weightless pulleys in which all the strings are attached to a beam, the highest string after passing over a fixed pulley has a mass of 3 lbs. attached to it, and the lowest pulley has a mass of 28 lbs. hung on to it. Shew that the larger mass will descend with an acceleration of $\dfrac{g}{55}$.

31. Two straight railways converge to a level crossing at an angle a, and two trains are moving towards the crossing with velocities u and v. If a and b are the initial distances of the trains from the crossing, shew that their least distance apart will be

$$\frac{(av - bu)\sin a}{\sqrt{u^2 + v^2 - 2uv\cos a}}.$$

32. If the distance between two moving points at any time be a, if V be their relative velocity, and if u and v be the components of V respectively in and perpendicular to the direction of a, shew that their distance when they are nearest to one another is $\dfrac{av}{V}$, and that the time that elapses before they arrive at their nearest distance is $\dfrac{au}{V^2}$.

33. Two particles, of masses M and $M+m$, are connected by a light string and placed near one another on a smooth table; on the string slides a light smooth pulley, supporting a mass M, which is placed just over the edge of the table; find the resulting acceleration of the pulley.

34. In the system of pulleys where each string is attached to the bar which supports the weight, if there be two movable pulleys of negligible mass and the power be quadrupled, shew that the weight will ascend with acceleration $\dfrac{3g}{29}$.

35. A string, one end of which is fixed, has slung on it a mass of 3 lbs. and then passes over a smooth pulley and has a mass of 1 lb. attached to its other end; shew that the larger mass descends with acceleration $\dfrac{g}{7}$ and that the tension of the string is $1\frac{2}{7}$ lbs. wt.

36. A cyclist, riding at a speed V, overtakes a pedestrian who can move at a speed not greater than v, the two travelling along parallel tracks at a distance d apart. Shew that if the cyclist rings his bell when at a distance less than $\dfrac{V}{v}d$, he may safely maintain his speed and keep to his course regardless of the behaviour of the pedestrian.

37. A boy throws a stone into the air with velocity V at an elevation α; after an interval of time $\dfrac{2VV'\sin(\alpha-\alpha')}{g[V\cos\alpha + V'\cos\alpha']}$ he throws another with velocity V' at an elevation α'; shew that the second stone will strike the first.

38. A shot, of mass m, penetrates a thickness t of a fixed plate of mass M; if M be free to move, and the resistance be supposed uniform, shew that the thickness penetrated is $\dfrac{M}{M+m}t$.

39. A string sustains a mass P at one end, then passes over a fixed pulley, then under a movable pulley to which a mass R is attached, and then over a fixed pulley and is attached to a mass Q at its other end. Assuming the masses of the string and pulleys to be negligible, and that the parts of the string not in contact with the pulleys are vertical, find the acceleration of R and the tension of the string.

40. A wedge of mass M can slide on a smooth horizontal plane, and the wedge has a face inclined at an angle a to the horizontal. Initially the wedge is at rest and a particle of mass m is projected directly up the inclined face. If the particle rise to a height h above the point of projection, shew that the velocity of projection is

$$\left\{ 2gh \; \frac{M+m}{M+m\sin^2 a} \right\}^{\frac{1}{2}}.$$

41. A particle is at rest on a rough plane (coefficient of friction μ) inclined to the horizon at an angle a. The plane is moved horizontally with a constant acceleration f in a direction away from the particle; prove that the particle will remain at rest relative to the plane if $f < \dfrac{\mu g \cos a - g \sin a}{\cos a + \mu \sin a}$.

42. A regular hexagon stands with one side on the ground and a particle is projected so as just to graze its four upper vertices. Shew that the velocity of the particle on reaching the ground is to its least velocity as $\sqrt{31}$ to $\sqrt{3}$.

43. In order to raise a weight which is half as much again as his own a man fastens a rope to it and passes the rope over a smooth pulley; he then climbs up the rope with an acceleration relative to the rope of $\dfrac{6g}{7}$. Shew that the weight rises with acceleration $\dfrac{g}{7}$, and find the tension of the rope.

44. A wedge of mass M and angle a can move freely on a smooth horizontal plane; a smooth sphere of mass m strikes it in a direction perpendicular to its inclined face and rebounds. Shew that the ratio of the velocities of the sphere just before and just after the impact is

$$M + m \sin^2 a : eM - m \sin^2 a,$$

where e is the coefficient of restitution.

45. Over a smooth light pulley is passed a string supporting at one end a weight of mass 4 lbs. and at the other a pulley of mass 1 lb. A string with masses 2 lbs. and 3 lbs. attached to its ends passes over the second pulley; shew that the acceleration of the 4 lbs. mass is $\dfrac{9g}{49}$.

46. A string, of natural length a, is stretched on a smooth table between two fixed points at a distance na apart and a particle of mass m is attached to the middle point of the string; the particle is then displaced towards one of the fixed points through a distance not exceeding $\dfrac{n-1}{2} a$ and then liberated; shew that it will perform oscillations in a period which is independent of n and of the distance through which it is displaced.

47. If the unit of kinetic energy be that of 5 lbs. which has fallen 50 feet from rest, the unit of momentum the momentum thus generated, and the unit of length the distance through which the particle has fallen, find the unit of time.

48. A particle P moves in a circle, of which OA is a diameter, and OY is drawn perpendicular to the tangent at P. Shew that the velocity of Y relative to P is equal to the velocity of P.

49. Two men, of masses M and $M+m$, start simultaneously from the ground and climb with uniform vertical accelerations up the free ends of a weightless inextensible rope which passes over a smooth pulley at a height h from the ground. If the lighter of the two men reach the pulley in t secs., shew that the heavier cannot get nearer to it than $\dfrac{m}{M+m}\left[\dfrac{gt^2}{2}+h\right]$.

50. A train, of mass M, is travelling with uniform velocity on a level line; the last carriage, whose mass is m, becomes uncoupled and the driver discovers it after travelling a distance l and shuts off steam. Shew that when both parts come to rest the distance between them is $\dfrac{M}{M-m}\,l$, if the resistance to motion be uniform and proportional to the weight, and the pull of the engine be constant.

51. A small smooth pulley of mass M is lying on a smooth table; a light string passes round the pulley and has masses m and m' attached to its ends, the two portions of the string being perpendicular to the edge of the table and passing over it so that the masses hang vertically; shew that the acceleration of the pulley is

$$\frac{4mm'}{M\left(m+m'\right)+4mm'}\,g.$$

52. Shew that, if the effect of a horizontal wind on a projectile be an acceleration f in the direction of the wind and the effect of the resistance of the air be neglected, the latus-rectum of the path of a particle projected with velocity v at an angle a to the horizon in the same vertical plane as the direction of the wind is

$$\frac{2v^2\,(g\cos a+f\sin a)^2}{(f^2+g^2)^{\frac{3}{2}}}.$$

53. A particle lies on a smooth horizontal table at the foot of a smooth wedge of angle a and height h, and the wedge is made to move along the table with constant acceleration f. If $f>g\tan a$, prove that the particle will ascend the plane. Shew also that if the wedge moves in this way for time t, and then moves with constant velocity equal to that gained, the particle will just reach the top if

$$t^2=\frac{2gh\sec a}{f\,(f\cos a-g\sin a)}.$$

54. Weights of 10 and 2 lbs. hanging by vertical strings balance on a wheel and axle. If a mass of 1 lb. be added to the smaller weight, find the acceleration with which it will begin to descend, and the tension of each rope, neglecting the mass of the wheel and axle.

55. In the differential wheel-and-axle c is the radius of the wheel, and a and b the radii of the two parts of the axle. A weight P attached to the wheel-rope just keeps the system in equilibrium; if P be doubled, prove that it descends with acceleration

$$g \times \frac{2c}{a - b + 4c},$$

the mass of the wheel and axle being neglected.

56. A perfectly elastic particle is projected with a velocity v in a vertical plane through a line of greatest slope of an inclined plane of elevation α; if after striking the plane it rebounds vertically, shew that it will return to the point of projection at the end of time

$$\frac{6v}{g\left[1 + 8\sin^2\alpha\right]^{\frac{1}{2}}}.$$

57. Two pulleys, each of mass m, are connected by a string hanging over a smooth fixed pulley; a string with masses $2m$ and $3m$ at its ends is hung over one pulley, and one with masses m and $4m$ over the other. If the system is free to move, shew that the acceleration of either pulley is $\frac{4g}{25}$.

58. A rough vertical circle, carrying a bead, turns in its own plane about its centre with uniform angular velocity greater than

$$\sqrt{\frac{g}{a}}\left[1 + \frac{1}{\mu^2}\right]^{\frac{1}{4}},$$

where a is the radius and μ is the coefficient of friction. Shew that the bead will never slip.

59. A particle is projected along the inside of a vertical hoop from its lowest point with such a velocity that it leaves the hoop and returns to the point of projection again. Find the velocity of projection and determine where the particle leaves the hoop.

60. A particle which hangs from a fixed point by a string of length a is projected horizontally from the position of equilibrium with a velocity due to a height $a + b$. If $2b < 3a$, shew that the string will be loose for a time t given by the equation

$$27ga^2t^2 = 32b\left(9a^2 - 4b^2\right).$$

61. A heavy particle is attached to one end of an elastic string, the other end of which is fixed. The modulus of elasticity of the string is equal to the weight of the particle. The string is drawn vertically down till it is four times its natural length, and then is let go. Shew that the particle will return to this point in time

$$\sqrt{\frac{a}{g}} \left[2\sqrt{3} + \frac{4\pi}{3} \right],$$

where a is the unstretched length of the string.

62. Two men, A and B, each of mass m, sit in loops at the ends of a light flexible rope passing over a smooth pulley, A being h feet higher than B. In B's hands is placed a ball, of mass $\frac{m}{10}$, which he instantly throws up to A, so that it just reaches him. Prove that by the time A has caught the ball he has moved up through the distance $\frac{2}{19}h$, and that he will cease ascending when he has ascended a total height of $\frac{59}{361}h$.

63. A smooth ring, of mass M, is threaded on a string whose ends are then placed over two smooth fixed pulleys with masses m and m' tied on to them respectively, the various portions of the string being vertical. The system being free to move, shew that the ring will remain at rest if

$$\frac{4}{M} = \frac{1}{m} + \frac{1}{m'}.$$

64. A particle, of mass m, is placed on the face of a smooth wedge, of mass M, which moves along a smooth horizontal table being pulled horizontally by a string which, after passing over a smooth pulley carries a mass M' hanging vertically, the motions being all in a vertical plane passing through a line of greatest slope. Shew that the acceleration of m relative to the wedge is

$$\frac{(M + M' + m)\sin\alpha + M'\cos\alpha}{M + M' + m\sin^2\alpha}\, g,$$

where α is the inclination of the face. Find also the pressure of m on the wedge.

65. A smooth wedge is free to move on a horizontal plane in the direction of the projection of the lines of greatest slope and is held whilst a particle is projected up its face in a direction inclined to the lines of greatest slope, and is then immediately released. Shew that the track of the particle on the plane is a parabola.

66. A perfectly elastic ball is thrown from the foot of a plane inclined at an angle α to the horizon. If after striking the plane at a distance l from the point of projection it rebounds and retraces its former path, shew that the velocity of projection is

$$\sqrt{\frac{gl\,(1 + 3\sin^2\alpha)}{2\sin\alpha}}.$$

67. A heavy mass M, which can slide along a straight horizontal bar is attached to a fixed point at a distance c from the bar by a spiral spring of natural length a less than c such that a mass m hung on to it will stretch it by a length e; shew that the time of a small oscillation of M along the bar, when it is slightly disturbed, will be

$$2\pi \left\{ \frac{Mec}{mg\,(c-a)} \right\}^{\frac{1}{2}}.$$

68. A railway carriage is travelling on a curve of radius r with velocity v; if h be the height of the centre of inertia of the carriage above the rails (which are at the same horizontal level) and $2a$ be the distance between them, shew that the carriage will upset if

$$v > \sqrt{\frac{gra}{h}}.$$

69. A wedge of mass M rests with a rough face in contact with a horizontal table and with another face which is smooth inclined at an angle a to the table. The angle of friction between the wedge and the table is ϵ. A particle of mass m slides down the smooth face. Find the condition that the wedge may move; and prove that, if it move, its acceleration is

$$\frac{m \cos a \sin\,(a - \epsilon) - M \sin \epsilon}{M \cos \epsilon + m \sin a \sin\,(a - \epsilon)}\, g.$$

70. A window is supported by two cords passing over pulleys in the frame-work of the window (which it loosely fits), the other ends of the cords being attached to weights each equal to half the weight of the window. One cord breaks and the window descends with acceleration f. Shew that $f = g\, \dfrac{a - b\mu}{3a + b\mu}$, where μ is the coefficient of friction, and a is the height and b the breadth of the window.

71. A weight of 300 lbs. is lifted by a vertical force which varies continually as the weight is raised according to the following table;

Height in feet above the ground;	0,	1,	2,	3,	4,	5,	6,
Lifting force in lbs. wt.;	450,	320,	270,	410,	480,	610,	900.

Find at the time when it is 5·5 feet from the ground (i) the potential energy stored in the mass, (ii) the kinetic energy of the mass, (iii) the work done by the force.

72. A mass of 10 lbs. is attached to the ground by a spring which requires a pull of 10 lbs. weight to stretch it one inch. The mass is lifted by a force which continually varies with the height as in the following table;

x in inches;	0,	1,	2,	3,	4,	5,	6,
Force in lbs. wt.;	22,	36·2,	44·5,	49,	52,	51·8,	48.

Estimate the kinetic and potential energies of the mass when it has been lifted 2 inches and 4 inches respectively and estimate the velocity when it has been lifted 6 inches.

73. An engine pumps water through a hose, and the water leaves the hose with a velocity v; shew that the rate at which the engine is working varies as v^3.

74. The weight supported by the driving wheels of a locomotive engine is 24 tons and the coefficient of friction between the wheels and the rails is $\frac{1}{6}$; if the engine be of 700 H.P., shew that the maximum velocity which the train can have, so that the wheels do not slip, is about 30 miles per hour.

75. A railway train, of mass M, goes from rest at one station to rest at a second station, a distance l, in t seconds; the friction of the rails, etc. causes a resistance of R lbs. wt., and for a portion of the distance the engine exerts a constant pull equal to P lbs. wt. Shew that

$$P = \frac{R^2 g t^2}{R g t^2 - 2Ml},$$

and that P acts for a time

$$t - \frac{2Ml}{Rgt}.$$

76. A cyclist and his machine together are of mass M lbs.; if he ride, without pedalling, down an incline of 1 in m with a uniform speed of v ft. per sec., shew that to go up an incline of 1 in n at the same rate he must work at a rate equal to

$$M\left[\frac{1}{m} + \frac{1}{n}\right]\frac{v}{550} \text{ H.P.}$$

77. A cyclist rides at the rate of 12 miles per hour on the level and 5 miles per hour up an incline of 1 in 40. The resistance to his motion other than that due to the incline being supposed constant, find this resistance, and also his greatest velocity down an incline of 1 in 100, if the weight of the rider and his machine be 180 lbs., and if he always works at a constant H.P.

78. Find the velocity acquired by a block of wood, of mass M lbs., which is free to recoil when it is struck by a bullet of mass m lbs., moving with velocity v in a direction passing through its centre of gravity.

If the bullet be embedded a feet, shew that the resistance of the wood to the bullet supposed uniform is

$$\frac{Mm}{M+m}\frac{v^2}{2ga} \text{ lbs. wt.,}$$

and that the time of penetration is $\frac{2a}{v}$ secs. during which time the block will move $\frac{m}{M+m}a$ feet.

ANSWERS TO THE EXAMPLES.

I. (Pages 13—16.)

4. 100 feet.   **5.** 120°.

7. At an angle $\cos^{-1}\left(-\frac{3}{5}\right)$, *i.e.* 126° 52′ with the current; perpendicular to the current so that his resultant direction makes an angle $\tan^{-1}\frac{5}{3}$, *i.e.* 59° 2′, with the current.

8. $4\sqrt{3}$ miles per hour; 12 miles per hour.

9. At an angle of 150° with AB produced; it will strike X at right angles at the end of fifteen minutes.

10. At an angle of $\cos^{-1}\left(-\frac{11}{15}\right)$ with the direction of the car's motion.

11. $\sqrt{29}$ at an angle of elevation of $\tan^{-1}\frac{2}{5}$ with a horizontal line which is inclined at $\tan^{-1}\frac{4}{3}$ north of east.

12. $(\sqrt{3}-1)\,u$; $(\sqrt{6}-\sqrt{2})\dfrac{u}{2}$.   **13.** 60°.

14. 14 at an angle $\cos^{-1}\frac{13}{14}$ with the greatest velocity.

II. (Pages 21—24.)

1. 55 ft. per sec. at an angle $\tan^{-1}\left(-\frac{3}{4}\right)$ with the direction of the train's motion.

2. 20 miles per hour at an angle $\tan^{-1}\frac{3}{4}$ west of north.

3. 15 miles per hour north-east.

4. 10 miles per hour towards the south-east.

5. 39 miles per hour in a direction $\cos^{-1}\frac{5}{13}$ north of east.

6. $32\frac{8}{11}$ miles per hour.

7. $2\sqrt{2}$ miles per hour at 45° to the vertical.

8.　$7\sqrt{5-2\sqrt{2}}$ miles per hour. Draw OA (=14) towards the east and OB (= 7) towards the south-east and complete the parallelogram $OABC$. Then OC is the required direction.

10.　$5\frac{5}{11}$ secs.　　　　　　　　13.　24 minutes; 6 miles.

14.　$2\frac{1}{12}$ ft. per sec. at $\tan^{-1}\frac{3}{4}$ with BA; 3 feet at the end of $1\frac{23}{25}$ seconds.

16.　$4\sqrt{2}$ miles per hour towards the south-east.

17.　Towards the east.　　　　　18.　$3v$ and v.

III.　(Pages 26—28.)

1.　$\dfrac{20\pi}{3}$ radians per sec.

2.　8π radians per sec.; $50\frac{2}{7}$ ft. per sec.

3.　$\dfrac{\pi}{300}$ ft. per sec.; $\dfrac{\pi}{1800}$ radians per sec.

4.　1 : 20 : 360.　　　　　5.　$2\frac{1}{4}$ miles per hour.

6.　$\dfrac{D-d}{D}V$.　　　　　　8.　$\dfrac{3a\pi}{u}$.

10.　$60\sqrt{3}$ (= 103·9) miles per hour at $\pm 30°$ to the horizon.

11.　$\frac{88}{3}$ radians per sec.; 30 miles per hour.

12.　22 radians per sec.; 30 miles per hour.

13.　20 miles per hour; 10 miles per hour at $\pm 60°$ to the horizon; $10\sqrt{3}$ miles per hour at $\pm 30°$ to the horizon.

IV.　(Page 30.)

2.　5 miles per hour in a direction $\tan^{-1}\frac{4}{3}$ north of west.

3.　5 ft. per sec. at $120°$ with its original velocity.

4.　$20\sqrt{2}-\sqrt{2}$ ft. per sec. towards N.N.W.

5.　12 ft. per sec. at $120°$ with its original direction.

V. (Pages 39—41.)

1. (1) 17 ft. per sec.; $47\frac{1}{2}$ feet. (2) 0; $24\frac{1}{2}$ feet.
   (3) $-\frac{55}{18}$; $1\frac{7}{11}$ secs. (4) 3 ft. per sec.; 6 secs.

2. 40 ft. per sec.; 400 feet. 3. 40 secs.

4. 20 ft.-sec. units. 5. 10 secs.; 150 cms.

6. In 50 secs.; 25 metres. 7. 18 ft.-sec. units.

8. 10 ft. per sec.; $-\frac{1}{5}$ ft.-sec. unit.

9. 19 ft. per sec.; 3 ft.-sec. units; $60\frac{1}{6}$ ft.

10. 5 secs.; $12\frac{1}{2}$ ft. 11. 16 ft.-sec. units; 30 ft. per sec.

12. 30 ft. per sec.; -2 ft.-sec. units. 13. 30 ft.

14. $\dfrac{1}{3}$, $\dfrac{\sqrt{2}-1}{3}$, and $\dfrac{\sqrt{3}-\sqrt{2}}{3}$ secs. respectively.

15. In 2 secs. at 16 ft. from O. 16. Yes.

17. Its displacement is $\sqrt{61+42\sqrt{2}}$ ft. at an angle $\tan^{-1}\dfrac{2+\sqrt{2}}{3}$ north of east.

18. 10 secs. or 30 secs. 20. $36\frac{1}{4}$ miles per hour.

21. 323·5 feet; in the 4th sec.; 24 ft.-sec. units.

22. 372·5 feet; $\frac{3}{5}$ ft.-sec. units.

VI. (Pages 46—48.)

1. 25 ft.; $\frac{1}{4}$ sec. and $2\frac{1}{4}$ secs.

2. (i) In $\frac{15}{32}$ sec.; (ii) in $1\frac{1}{4}$ secs.

3. In $1\frac{1}{4}$ and $2\frac{1}{2}$ secs.; 50 ft.

4. (1) 1600 ft.; (2) $\frac{1}{4}\sqrt{10}$ sec.; (3) 60 ft. per sec. upwards.

5. 432 ft. 6. 44 secs. 7. 2 secs. or $5\frac{1}{2}$ secs.

8. 545 cms. per sec.; $\frac{4}{9}$ sec. 9. 10·2 secs.

10. 218 metres; $6\frac{2}{3}$ secs.   11. 32·18.

12. 900 ft.; $7\frac{1}{2}$ secs.   13. 100 ft.

14. 400 ft.   15. 144 ft.

16. 256 ft. per sec.; 1024 ft.

17. $t = 5$; 64 ft. per sec.   18. 784 ft.

19. 1120 ft. per sec.   20. 150 ft.

VII. (Pages 50.)

1. 200 ft.; 5 secs.   2. $16\sqrt{3}$ ft. per sec.; $\frac{5}{8}\sqrt{3}$ secs.

3. 30°.   4. 1 : 4.

5. (1) $-89\frac{3}{5}$ ft.; $-60\frac{4}{5}$ ft. per sec.

    (2) $217\frac{3}{5}$ ft.; $92\frac{4}{5}$ ft. per sec.

6. 30°.   7. $\cos^{-1}\frac{1}{4}$, *i.e.*, 75° 31′.

VIII. (Pages 54—57.)

1. 4080 ft.   2. 1 sec.; $1\frac{1}{2}$ secs.

3. 96 ft. per sec.; zero.

4. The first will have fallen through one-quarter of the height of the tower.

5. $\dfrac{3h}{8}$.

6. $\sqrt{gh}$, $\sqrt{gh}$, and 0, where h is the height of the plane.

7. At the end of time $\dfrac{1}{g}(u + \frac{1}{2}gt)$ from the starting of the first particle and at a height of $\dfrac{1}{2g}(u^2 - \frac{1}{4}g^2t^2)$.

8. 15 secs.   9. 96 ft.   10. 196 ft.; 112 ft. per sec.

11. The parts are 32, 96, and 160 feet; 3 secs.

19. $\sqrt{\dfrac{2h}{g}}\cosec\alpha\sec\beta$.   20. $\sqrt{fs\left(3 - \dfrac{1}{n}\right)}$.

24. $\frac{22}{45}$ ft.-sec. units; $\frac{44}{45}$ ft.-sec. units; 40 miles per hour.

25. 60 miles per hour; 44 secs.; 1936 ft.; 8 secs.

28. $\frac{32}{23}$ ft.-sec. units; 40 ft. per sec.

29. $\frac{11}{45}$ ft.-sec. units; $\frac{55}{54}$ ft.-sec. units; 2 hrs. $3\frac{1}{10}$ mins.

IX. (Pages 66—68.)

4. (1) $\frac{1}{2}$, (2) $\frac{g}{2}$, (3) $\frac{g}{448}$ ft.-sec. units.

5. (1) 200 poundals; (2) $6\frac{1}{4}$ lbs. wt.

6. 15 lbs. wt. **7.** $15\frac{2}{5}$ lbs. wt.

8. 48 ft.-sec. units; 720 ft.

9. 14 : 981; 140 cms. per sec.

10. $7\frac{1}{2}$ secs.; $13\frac{1}{3}$ ft. per sec. **11.** 2 min. 56 secs

12. 14 secs. **14.** 180 feet.

15. $363\frac{1}{3}$ cms. per sec.; $181\frac{2}{3}$ cms.; 21800 cms.

16. 49·05 kilogrammes. **17.** 144 lbs.

18. 12 lbs. **19.** $7\frac{11}{16}$ lbs. wt.; $237\frac{3}{8}$ lbs. wt.

20. They are equal. **21.** 110 lbs. wt.

24. $133\frac{1}{3}$ ft. per sec.

X. (Pages 81, 82.)

1. $\frac{g}{5}$; $7\frac{1}{5}$ lbs. wt.

2. (1) 4 ft.-sec. units; (2) $7\frac{7}{8}$ lbs. wt.; (3) 20 ft. per sec.; (4) 50 ft.

3. (1) $10\frac{2}{3}$ ft. per sec.; (2) $21\frac{1}{3}$ ft.; (3) 640 and -512 ft. respectively.

4. 4·41...metres; 495 grammes' wt. **6.** By 2 lbs. wt

7. $\frac{2P}{3}$. **8.** $\frac{m}{2}$. **9.** 16 ft.

10. (1) $\dfrac{g}{10}$; (2) $\sqrt{5}$ secs.; (3) $\dfrac{16}{5}\sqrt{5}$ ft. per sec.

11. 2 secs.

12. (1) 2 ft.-sec. units; (2) $2\frac{13}{16}$ lbs. wt.; (3) 6 ft. per sec.; (4) 9 ft.

13. $\dfrac{3-2\sqrt{2}}{7}g$; $\frac{7}{4}(\sqrt{2}+1)$ sec. **14.** 40 ft.

15. 24 lbs. 10 ozs. **16.** 5 ozs. **17.** In ratio 19 : 13.

18. $2\frac{1}{2}$ and $3\frac{1}{3}$ lbs. wt.; $\dfrac{g}{6}$. **19.** 29 ft. 9 ins. nearly.

XI. (Pages 86—88.)

1. $\frac{11}{26}g$; ·3. **2.** 40·6 ft. per sec.; 96 feet.

3. ·1. **4.** $\dfrac{\sqrt{2}}{2}$ sec.; $8\sqrt{2}$ ft. per sec.

5. $\frac{1}{2}\sqrt{5}$ secs.; $\frac{16}{5}\sqrt{5}$ ft. per sec.

6. $16\sqrt{5}$ ft. per sec.; 80 ft. per sec.

8. The larger mass descends with acceleration
$$\dfrac{2\sqrt{3}-3}{9}g.$$

9. The particles do not move. **10.** $2117\frac{1}{2}$ ft.

11. 605 : 18. **12.** (i) 5 min. 8 secs.; (ii) 6776 feet.

13. 1 min. $42\frac{2}{3}$ secs.; $2258\frac{2}{3}$ feet.

14. $5\frac{20}{27}$ tons' wt. **15.** 1 mile 1408 yds.

16. $1224\frac{2}{3}$ yds. **17.** $411\frac{61}{125}$ feet.

18. $5\frac{21}{80}$ tons' wt.; 1 in 77 about; 1 in 50.

XII. (Pages 93—97.)

1. Zero. **2.** (i) 20 lbs. wt.; (ii) $20\frac{5}{8}$ lbs. wt.

3. 154 lbs. wt.; 70 lbs. wt. **4.** $\dfrac{g}{8}$.

5. $2057\frac{1}{7}$ ft.

6. 297 grammes' wt.; 270 and 264 grammes' wt.

7. $3\frac{3}{4}$ ozs. wt. ; $\dfrac{g}{4}$; $2\frac{1}{2}$ ozs. wt. ; 3 ozs. wt.

8. ·938 ton's wt.   9. 39·4 lbs. wt. nearly.

10. 7521 lbs. wt. nearly.   13. 10 hang vertically.

14. 3 : 5.   16. 80 feet.   18. $6\frac{7}{8}$ tons.

21. 2 : 1.   22. 1·9...secs.   23. $\dfrac{3WP}{W+4P}$.

24. m goes up with acc. $\dfrac{3g}{13}$; M goes down with acc. $\dfrac{g}{13}$.

26. $M = \dfrac{4mm'}{m+m'}$; the acc. is $\dfrac{m-m'}{m+m'}g$.

27. $\frac{8}{23}$ ft.-sec. units.   28. $\frac{8}{55}g$.

29. 320 feet ; 28 miles per hour.

XIII. (Page 102.)

1. $4\frac{2}{27}$ ft. per sec.   4. $6\frac{1}{4}$ ft. per sec.

5. $17\frac{6}{7}$ ft. per sec.   6. 6·8...ft.

7. $9\frac{209}{324}$ tons' wt.   8. 1431 ft. per sec. nearly.

XIV. (Page 105.)

1. 160.   2. $213\frac{1}{3}$.   3. 119·4$\dot{6}$.

4. 14·685 lbs. wt.   5. $21\frac{3}{5}$.   6. $68\frac{68}{135}$.

7. 7,392,000 ft. lbs. ; 7·4$\dot{6}$ H.-P.   8. 152 ft. lbs.

9. 209·2...tons' wt.

XV. (Pages 111, 112.)

1. (i) 5120, (ii) 1280, (iii) 0, units of kinetic energy.

2. 15625.   3. 125×10^9.

4. 625×10^{10} ; 3125×10^8.   5. $3160\frac{40}{81}$ ft. lbs.

6. 1 : 2 ; 15 : 1 ; 300 and 600 poundals ; 600 and 20 feet.

XVI. (Pages 114—117.)

3. 896000 units of impulse ; 4 ft.

4. $\frac{5}{7}$ ft. ; $\frac{1}{14}\sqrt{10}$ ($= \cdot 226\ldots$) secs. ; $\frac{3}{4}$.

5. 7·997 cms. per sec. ; 40775 grammes' wt. nearly.

6. Wt. of 104 cwt.

7. The masses move with a velocity of 24 ft. per sec.

8. $\frac{8}{3}\sqrt{6}$ ft. per sec. ; $\frac{4}{3}\sqrt{30}$ ft. per sec.

11. $\dfrac{u}{g}$, where u is the common velocity.

12. $\dfrac{m}{M + m}$.   13.   7 ft. ; $26\frac{1}{4}$ secs.

14. The velocities become ultimately equal.

16. $\cdot 16\dot{9}$: 1.   17. $20\sqrt{2}$ ft. per sec. ; 560,000 ft.-lbs.

18. $11\frac{31}{54}$ tons' wt. ; 28, 233, $333\frac{1}{3}$ ft.-lbs.

19. $11\frac{63}{137}$ tons.   21.   3520 ft.-lbs.

22. $10\frac{10}{39}$.   23. $\dfrac{88Rn}{E}$.

24. 3 lbs. wt. ; $24\frac{4}{9}$ lbs. wt.

26. $33\frac{1}{3}$ units ; $1\frac{1}{24}$ lbs. wt. ; $\frac{5}{528}$ H.-P.

27. 69·12 lbs. wt.

XVII. (Pages 127, 128.)

1. (1) 16 ft. ; 2 secs. ; 110·9 ft. ; (2) 75 ft. ; 4·33 secs. ; 173·2 ft. ; (3) 134·4 ft. ; 5·795 secs. ; 144 ft. ; (4) 225 ft. ; $7\frac{1}{2}$ secs. ; 1200 ft.

2. 72 ft. ; $112\frac{1}{2}$ ft. ; $312\frac{1}{2}$ ft.

3. 2609·58…metres ; 652·39…metres.

4. 4·04 secs. ; 20 metres.

6. $13333\frac{1}{3}$ ft. per sec.   7. $2h$; $2\sqrt{gh}$.

8. 50·1 at $\tan^{-1}\frac{6}{11}$ (= 28° 36′) to the horizon.

9. (1) $16\sqrt{17}$ (= 65·97) ft. per sec. at $\tan^{-1}4$ (= 75° 58′) with the horizon.

(2) $16\sqrt{37}$ (= 97·32) ft. per sec. at $\tan^{-1}6$ (= 80° 32′) with the horizon.

10. 5543 yards nearly.   **11.**   13 secs. ; 3328 ft.

13. $40\sqrt{6}$ (= 97·98) ft. per sec. at 45° to the horizon.

14. $80\sqrt{110}$ (= 839·04) ft. per sec. ; $48\sqrt{110}$ (= 503·4) ft. per sec.

15. 1 : $\sqrt{3}$; 1 : 1.   **17.**   (1) 45° ; (2) 30°.

18. 15° or 75°.

XVIII.   (Page 133.)

1. 2500 yards ; 21·7 secs.

2. At a distance $\dfrac{V^2}{48}(\sqrt{3}-1)$; $\dfrac{V^2}{48}$.

3. 62·5 ft. nearly ; $\frac{2}{3}(3\sqrt{2}-\sqrt{6})$, *i.e.*, 1·2 secs. nearly ; $85\frac{1}{3}$ ft.

4. (1) 16000 ft. ; (2) 112000 ft.

5. 11716 ft. and 27 secs. nearly ; 10718 ft. and 25·9 secs. nearly ; 19048 ft. and 34·4 secs. nearly ; $14444\frac{4}{9}$ ft. and nearly 30 secs.

6. 2929 yards nearly ; 17071 yards nearly.

8. 84·95 metres ; 441·4 metres.

XIX.   (Page 138—141.)

1. A circle of about 91 miles radius.

2. About $\tan^{-1}\frac{1}{10}$ (*i.e.* 5° 43′) to the horizon.

3. $3\frac{1}{4}$ ft. ; 9·185… ft.   **4.**   About 121 ft.

5. In $\frac{1}{20}$th sec. at a point whose horizontal and vertical distances from the first gun are 47·63… and 27·46 ft.

8.   30°.   14. $2\sqrt{\dfrac{2h}{g}}\cos\alpha.$

15.   The rifle must be pointed at the balloon; the bullet will strike the body when it has fallen 16 ft.

18. $2\frac{1}{4}$ lbs.   19.   5·6 ft.; 29·32 ft.

20. $272\frac{1}{4}$ ft.; 324 ft.; 225 ft.

21. $\dfrac{u}{g}(\sin\alpha \pm \cos\alpha)$ secs., where u is the velocity, and α the angle, of projection.

23.   80 ft. per sec.

XX.   (Page 148.)

1.   7·29 ft.

6. $2\sqrt{13}\,(=7\cdot2)$ ft. per sec. at $\tan^{-1}\dfrac{\sqrt{3}}{6}\,(=16°\,6')$ with the plane.

8.   (1) $4\sqrt{43}\,(=26\cdot2)$ ft. per sec. at $\tan^{-1}\dfrac{3\sqrt{3}}{4}\,(=52°25')$ with the plane;

(2) $20\sqrt{2}\,(=28\cdot3)$ ft. per sec. at $\tan^{-1}\frac{3}{4}\,(=36°\,52')$ with the plane;

(3) $4\sqrt{57}\,(=30\cdot2)$ ft. per sec. at $\tan^{-1}\dfrac{\sqrt{3}}{4}\,(=23°\,25')$ with the plane.

XXI.   (Pages 154—156.)

1. $4\frac{5}{14}$ and $4\frac{6}{7}$ ft. per sec.   2. $3\frac{2}{3}$ and $5\frac{11}{12}$ ft. per sec.

3.   The first remains at rest; the second turns back with a velocity of 6 ft. per sec.   8. $\frac{1}{2}$.

9.   (1) The masses are as 3 : 1; (2) the velocities are as 1 : 2.

11.   5·66... and 2·5 secs.

17. $5\sqrt{5}u\,(=u\times11\cdot180...)$ at $\tan^{-1}\frac{1}{2}\,(=26°\,34')$, and

$\sqrt{205}u\,(=u\times14\cdot318...)$ at $\tan^{-1}\frac{3}{14}\,(=12°\,6')$ with the line of centres.

XXII. (Pages 162—164.)

3. 60 ft.; 3·464 secs.   **4.** 8 secs.; 443·4 ft.

6. At a distance h from the foot of the tower.

9. At a point distant $\frac{1}{18}$th of the circumference from the starting point.

16. $4el \sin^2 a \cos a$.   **17.** $2\sqrt{3}\,ne\,(1 + e)$ ft.

19. Draw BN perpendicular to the vertical plane, and produce to C so that $BN = e \cdot CN$; the required direction is then AC.

XXIII. (Page 172.)

1. 60 poundals.   **2.** 28·6.   **3.** 48·3.

5. 24 ft. per sec.   **6.** About 13·4.

7. $1\frac{1}{120}$ tons' wt.   **8.** 2·42 tons' wt.

XXIV. (Pages 178—181.)

1. About 5·66 lbs. wt.; about 8·24 ft. per sec.

4. 12 ft. per sec.   **6.** 4·9 inches.

7. 3·02 inches.   **8.** 6·18 inches.

10. $60\sqrt{\dfrac{g}{\pi^2}} =$ about 108.   **13.** 371 : 369 : 370.

16. $m\,(g - 4\pi^2 n^2 b)$ poundals; $\dfrac{1}{2\pi}\sqrt{\dfrac{g}{b}}$.   **18.** $\sqrt{2gc}$.

19. $mv^2 : m'v'^2$.   **20.** $\dfrac{1}{2\pi}\sqrt{\dfrac{mg}{m'\,(c - a)}}$.

21. It must be reduced to one quarter of its original value.

22. $1 : \sqrt{2}$; $\dfrac{\pi}{2}\sqrt{2\sqrt{2} - 2}$ secs.   **23.** $\sqrt{\dfrac{\lambda}{m}\dfrac{r\,(r - a)}{a}}$.

25. (1) ·57 ton's wt. on the inner rail approx.; (2) ·80 ton's wt. on the outer rail approx.

XXV. (Pages 190—193.)

1. (1) 20·8 ft. per sec.; 22·6 lbs. wt.; (2) 15·5 ft. per sec.; 7·6 lbs. wt.

2. 21·9 ft. per sec.; 30 lbs. wt.

3. $8\sqrt{3}$ ft. per sec.; $3mg$.

4. (1) 24 ft. per sec.; (2) $12\sqrt{2}$ ft. per sec.; (3) $8\sqrt{3}$ ft. per sec.; 12 ft. per sec.

5. 6 times the wt. of the particle; 40 ft. per sec.

6. 448 ft. per sec.; wt. of 9 cwt.; wt. of $4\frac{1}{2}$ cwt.

9. $\frac{16}{27}$ of the radius of the circle.

10. $\dfrac{d}{81}$ and $\dfrac{16d}{81}$, where d is the diameter of the circle.

11. $e = \frac{1}{2}$.   **13.** $7\sqrt{3m}$ lbs. wt.; $5\sqrt{3m}$ lbs. wt.

14. $\frac{1}{8}\sqrt{ga(187 + 11\sqrt{2})}$.   **18.** 12 ft. per sec.; 9 ins.

20. 80 cms. nearly.

XXVI. (Pages 199, 200.)

1. (1) $\frac{1}{2}\pi\sqrt{2}$ secs.; (2) $\dfrac{\pi}{6}$ secs.; (3) 1 sec.

2. $2\sqrt{2}$, $1\frac{1}{2}$, and π ft. per sec.

3. (1) π, (2) 32π, and (3) 2 ft. per sec.

4. 3·46 ft. per sec.   **5.** π secs.; 20 ft.-sec. units.

7. 25 centimetres nearly.   **8.** 4 ins.; 1·11 secs.

9. $\dfrac{\pi}{8}\sqrt{2}$ secs. = ·56 sec.

10. $\pi\sqrt{\dfrac{am}{\lambda}}$, where a is the unstretched length of the string, λ its modulus of elasticity, and m the mass of the particle.

XXVII. (Page 206.)

1. 20·4 ft.   **3.** 32·249.

4. (1) 9·78 ins.; (2) 2·445 ins.; (3) 156·48 ins.

5. 330.   **7.** 32·16...   **8.** 77756 nearly.

XXVIII. (Pages 211, 212.)

1. 32·185.   2. 1·00046 : 1.   3. About 215.
4. It must be shortened by ·008 inch.
5. It must be lengthened by ·0045 inch.
6. 432.   7. 55.   8. 981.
9. It loses about 10 secs.   10. 1630 yards; 5 secs.
11. 1·0005 : 1; 1·852 miles.
12. 10·8 secs.; about ·01 inch.

20. π secs.; $\dfrac{g}{64}$; 3 ins. per sec.

XXIX. (Page 219.)

1. 88 ft. per sec.; $\frac{22}{15}$ ft.-sec. units.
2. 1320 ft. per sec.; 330 ft.-sec. units.
3. 880 yards; $\frac{11}{15}$ ft.-sec. units.
5. $57\frac{1}{7}$ feet.   6. 88 yds.
8. (1) 8, (2) $\frac{11}{15}$, (3) 384000.   9. 3511303.
10. $126\frac{18}{41}$.   11. 11 secs.

XXX. (Pages 224—226.)

1. $40\frac{4}{9}$ poundals.   2. 1 poundal; 10 foot-poundals.
3. $\frac{1}{4}$ sec.   5. 8800 yards; 300 secs.; $54\frac{6}{11}$ tons.
6. $342\frac{6}{7}$ yards.   7. 400 ft.; 90 lbs.
8. 11 lbs.   10. 1 : 9; 1 : 3; 2 : 15.
12. $\frac{4}{7} \times 120^{4}$; 115200.   13. $1\frac{9}{16}$ ft.; $\frac{5}{8}$ sec.; 8 lbs.
14. 800 ft.; 5 secs.; 2 lbs.
15. 14112 yards; 21 secs.; $\frac{1}{126}$ lb.
16. 18·21... metres; 5·45 secs.; 4·30... grammes.
17. 1 mile; 8 minutes; $99\frac{57}{77}$ tons.
18. 600 ft.; $7\frac{1}{2}$ secs.; 1200 lbs.
19. $2\frac{241}{352}$ miles; $15\frac{3}{4}$ minutes; 88 tons.   20. g lbs.

MISCELLANEOUS EXAMPLES.
[Pages 231—240.]

1. 144 feet.

2. 576 feet; 6 secs.

3. $1\frac{1}{3}$ inchs.

4. $7\frac{1}{9}$ oz. wt.; $5\frac{5}{9}$ oz. wt.

7. ·77...sec.; 217 : 162.

14. $\dfrac{s}{30n}$.

15. South-west.

18. $\dfrac{30}{\pi}\sqrt{\dfrac{\mu g}{a}}$.

20. 60° on each side of the vertical.

27. With an acceleration $g \tan a$ toward the side on which the particle is; $\sec a$ times the weight of the particle.

29. $5\frac{11}{17}$ lbs. wt.; $\dfrac{g}{17}$.

33. $\dfrac{2M+m}{6M+5m}g$.

39. $g\left(\dfrac{1}{P} + \dfrac{1}{Q} - \dfrac{4}{R}\right) \div \left(\dfrac{1}{P} + \dfrac{1}{Q} + \dfrac{4}{R}\right)$; $4g \div \left(\dfrac{1}{P} + \dfrac{1}{Q} + \dfrac{4}{R}\right)$.

43. $\frac{12}{7}$ times the weight of the man.

47. $\frac{5}{4}\sqrt{2}$ secs.

54. $\dfrac{5g}{17}$; $2\frac{2}{17}$ lbs. wt.; $10\frac{10}{17}$ lbs. wt.

59. $\sqrt{\dfrac{7ag}{2}}$; at a point where the radius makes an angle of 30° with the horizon.

64. $mg \cos a \dfrac{M + M' - M' \tan a}{M + M' + m \sin^2 a}$.

69. The coefficient of friction must be $< \dfrac{m \cos a \sin a}{M + m \cos^2 a}$.

71. 1650 ft. lbs.; 737·5 ft. lbs.; 2387·5 ft. lbs.

72. 2·45... and $3\frac{1}{3}$ ft. lbs.; 3·89... and 10 ft. lbs.; 3·9 ft. per sec.

77. $3\frac{3}{14}$ lbs. wt.; $27\frac{3}{11}$ miles per hour.

CAMBRIDGE: PRINTED BY J. B. PEACE, M.A., AT THE UNIVERSITY PRESS.

$$u^2 \sin^2 \lambda - 2g s' = u^2 \sin^2 \lambda - g s$$

C. K. Cautaufermale

B. M. Davies.